C0-AUU-191

American Musicological Society
Music Library Association Reprint Series

Dover Publications, Inc., New York, in cooperation with the American Musicological Society and the Music Library Association, has undertaken to bring back into print a select list of scholarly musical works long unavailable to the researcher, student, and performer. A distinguished Committee representing both these professional organizations has been appointed to plan and supervise the series, which will include facsimile editions of indispensable historical, theoretical and bibliographical studies as well as important collections of music and translations of basic texts. To make the reprints more useful and to bring them up to date, new introductions, supplementary indexes and bibliographies, etc., will be prepared by qualified specialists.

Sir John Hawkins, *A General History of the Science and Practice of Music*
W. H., A. F., and A. E. Hill, *Antonio Stradivari, His Life and Work*
Curt Sachs, *Real-Lexikon der Musikinstrumente,* new revised, enlarged edition
The Complete Works of Franz Schubert (19 volumes), the Breitkopf & Härtel Critical Edition of 1884-1897 *(Franz Schubert's Werke. Kritisch durchgesehene Gesammtausgabe.)*
Charles Read Baskervill, *The Elizabethan Jig and Related Song Drama*
George Ashdown Audsley, *The Art of Organ-Building,* corrected edition
Emanuel Winternitz, *Musical Autographs from Monteverdi to Hindemith,* corrected edition
William Chappell, *Popular Music of the Olden Time,* 1859 edition
F. T. Arnold, *The Art of Accompaniment from a Thorough-Bass as Practised in the 17th and 18th Centuries*
The Breitkopf Thematic Catalogue, 1762-1787, with new introduction and indexes by B. S. Brook
Otto Kinkeldey, *Orgel und Klavier in der Musik des 16. Jahrhunderts*
Andreas Ornithoparcus, *Musice active micrologus,* together with John Dowland's translation, *A. O. his Micrologus, or Introduction, Containing the Art of Singing*
O. G. T. Sonneck, *Early Concert-life in America (1731-1800)*
Giambattista Mancini, *Practical Reflections on the Figurative Art of Singing* (translated by Pietro Buzzi)
Denis Stevens, *Thomas Tomkins, 1572-1656*
Thoinot Arbeau, *Orchesography* (translated by Mary Stewart Evans)
Edmond vander Straeten, *La Musique aux Pays-Bas avant le XIXe siècle*
Frits Noske, *La Mélodie française de Berlioz à Duparc* (translated by Rita Benton)
Board of Music Trade, *Complete Catalogue of Sheet Music and Musical Works* (1870)

THE BREITKOPF THEMATIC CATALOGUE

The Six Parts and Sixteen Supplements 1762-1787

Edited and with an Introduction and Indexes by
BARRY S. BROOK

DOVER PUBLICATIONS, INC., NEW YORK

To David Stimer
1914—1966

Published in Canada by General Publishing Company, Ltd.,
30 Lesmill Road, Don Mills, Toronto, Ontario.
Published in the United Kingdom by Constable and Company, Ltd.
10 Orange Street, London W.C.2.

This Dover edition, first published in 1966, is an unabridged and unaltered republication of all six parts and all sixteen supplements of the Thematic Catalogue (*Catalogo delle Sinfonie*, etc.) issued by the firm of Breitkopf in Leipzig between 1762 and 1787 (see Outline of Contents, p. xvii, for exact original titles and publication dates of the individual parts).

A new Introduction, Outline of Contents, Index of First Lines and General Index have been prepared by Barry S. Brook specially for this edition.

The publisher is grateful to the Library of Congress and the Sibley Library of the Eastman School of Music for their cooperation in the reproduction of those parts of the Catalogue in their respective collections (see Introduction, p. vii, for further details).

The title page frame is from the original publication of the opera *Talestri, Regina delle Amazzoni* by E.T.P.A. (Maria Antonia Walpurgis), published by B. C. Breitkopf and Son, Leipzig, 1765 (see page 286 of the Thematic Catalogue).

Library of Congress Catalog Card Number: 65-26977
Manufactured in the United States of America

Dover Publications, Inc., 180 Varick Street, New York, N.Y. 10014

CONTENTS

INTRODUCTION TO THE DOVER EDITION

Preamble

The Breitkopf Catalogue was originally published in six parts and sixteen supplements over a period of a quarter of a century, from 1762 to 1787. There were altogether twenty-two individual volumes containing a total of 888 pages, but no table of contents or index of any kind.[1]

The Breitkopf Catalogue was the first printed thematic catalogue of music. It remains the largest and most valuable of its kind. It reflects the panorama of musical life in its time in all its opulence. It offers eloquent testimony regarding musical taste and sociology. It provides invaluable information on the production and dissemination of both manuscripts and prints. It is an indispensable bibliographical tool for the identification and dating of a vast quantity of music of all genres, vocal and instrumental, secular and religious. In short, it is a fascinating document and one of the most important contemporary reference sources on music of the eighteenth century.

Its 888 pages contain almost 15,000 incipits, averaging sixteen per page, each providing the following information: genre, composer, title and instrumentation, plus text underlay for some 1300 vocal works. On occasion, the composer's official position and place of work are also given. When a composition is *not* in manuscript, the place and method of publication (print or engraving) are often supplied. A total of over 1000 different composers are represented.

In the monographs of many eighteenth-century specialists the term "Breitkopf Catalogue" is common bibliographical currency. To give but a few examples, H. C. Robbins Landon begins his monumental study of *The Symphonies of Joseph Haydn* with a page-length quotation from the illuminating *Nacherinnerung* appended to Parte I^ma^ (see pp. 29–32 below for complete original and pp. xiii–xiv for translation). Jens Peter Larsen still uses his set of photostats made decades ago of the *Catalogo delle Sinfonie* to document his current studies. In Bathia Churgin's recent dissertation, *The Symphonies of G. B. Sammartini* (Harvard University, 1963), the Breitkopf Catalogue is the source for a substantial percentage of the datings. In our musical lexicons the hand of Breitkopf is often present anonymously. As Kathi Meyer has pointed out in her pioneering article, "Early Breitkopf and Härtel Thematic Catalogues of Manuscript Music,"[2] when Gerber gives a list of works without quoting his sources, it is often identical to Breitkopf's (e.g., in the case of Sammartini). Later lexicographers often copied Gerber verbatim. Today we still must go back to Breitkopf for documentation on major composers as well as on hundreds of *illustres inconnus* about whom little other information exists. The Breitkopf Catalogue often provides the only evidence of the existence of lost works, and for extant compositions it is frequently the only source of chronology.

Complete copies of the Breitkopf Catalogue are *rarissimi*. None appears to have been listed in antiquarian catalogues during this century, although the sixteen supplements were once available at a price of 180 marks (No. 290 in Leo Lippmannsohn's Katalog 233, *Musikbibliographie und Notation*). This scarcity was initially caused by the fact that Breitkopf "sacrificed profit for love of accuracy" and "printed only a small number of copies of this first effort" (see below, p. xiii). Most of these copies disappeared during the nineteenth century, an era which placed little value upon most eighteenth-century music and even less upon its thematic catalogues. It was not until the advent of modern musicology in the twentieth century and the work of such great scholars as Otto Erich Deutsch, that the significance of the Thematic Catalogue was fully established.

[1] To avoid confusion the word *catalogue* will be used here for eighteenth-century publications and the word *index* for the two union indexes of names and of first lines that have been especially prepared for this edition (see pp. xxix–lxxxi at the end of this volume).

[2] *Musical Quarterly,* XXX (1944), pp. 163–173. The title of this important study is misleading on three counts, all of which remain unclarified in the body of the article. Härtel was not part of the firm when the thematic catalogues were published—his name does not appear on any imprint; secondly, many of the catalogues listed in the article are *not* thematic; finally, the Thematic Catalogue itself includes incipits of many engraved and printed items marked "intagliati e stampati" and is *not* limited to works in manuscript; this latter misconception exists in several other more recent sources as well.

There are about eight or nine full sets of the Breitkopf Thematic Catalogue extant; the files of the Répertoire International des Sources Musicales (RISM) have brought to light an equal number of incomplete sets and a handful of individual volumes. The following libraries possess full copies: Ascona, Hoboken Collection; Berlin, Staatsbibliothek; Brussels, Bibliothèque Royale de Belgique (Fétis Collection No. 5197); Brussels, Conservatoire Royale de Musique; The Hague, Gemeente Museum; London, British Museum, Hirsch Collection; Vienna, Gesellschaft der Musikfreunde.

No complete copy exists in the United States. Incomplete sets are found in the Library Company of Philadelphia, the Library of Congress at Washington and the Sibley Library of the Eastman School of Music at Rochester. Complete copies in photostat may be found at the Library of Congress, the New York Public Library, Harvard University, etc. The present edition has been prepared photolithographically from holdings in two different institutions: the Library of Congress (the six parts) and the Sibley Library of the Eastman School (the sixteen supplements).

Johann Gottlob Immanuel Breitkopf (1719–1794)

The early history of the famous Leipzig firm known as Breitkopf, and after 1795 as Breitkopf & Härtel, dates back to 1542.[3]

It was in 1719 that the business passed into the hands of the Breitkopf family through the marriage of Bernhard Cristoph Breitkopf (1695–1777). Under Bernhard Cristoph, the printing operations expanded rapidly and soon included a book publishing department, numbering the most eminent poets, scholars and philosophers of Germany among its authors. The first publication bearing the Breitkopf name, a periodical entitled *Acta Eruditorum*, appeared in 1719. Prophetically this was also the year of birth of Johann Gottlob Immanuel Breitkopf, compiler of the *Catalogo*; his fame was to eclipse that of his distinguished father.

Johann Gottlob Immanuel Breitkopf was a man of extraordinary imagination, intellect and energy. Although inscribed in the Book Printers Guild at seventeen, he had, at first, little interest in his father's business and an idealistic distaste for "trade" in general. After three stimulating years at the University of Leipzig (1737–1740) and a year of travel in Germany, he agreed to try to combine his scientific and humanistic interests with his father's dynastic ambitions and entered the family firm. Characteristically, he plunged into a thorough historical and mathematical investigation of the arts of calligraphy, engraving and printing. This study was to occupy him throughout his life and was soon to make him one of the leading authorities on the art of printing. He saw his role as the restorer of good taste and beauty in German typography through knowledge, inventiveness and practical experimentation. When he was twenty-six, his father put the entire printing establishment into his hands and he was to make it "the most complete in the world." It was not long before the "Golden Bear" was an international symbol.

Breitkopf maintained contact with the leading minds of Germany, such as Gottsched (with whom he had studied at the University), Cramer, Lessing, Winckelmann and Goethe.[4] He built a personal library of almost 20,000 volumes, astonishing for his time. His interests and activities included the development of a method of printing maps and charts typographically, the designing of a set of Chinese letters for printing purposes, the reproduction of portrait drawings using typographical characters, the printing of playing cards of many different kinds, the manufacture of colored papers for various decorative and utilitarian uses, such as wallpaper, book paper, drawing paper, etc.

On Breitkopf's personality and philosophy, Hase has written, "He deserves praise for breaking with the brutal hazing practices taken over from the University. He did not torture his apprentices with horned skullcaps, jawbreakers, wooden spoons, etc." Despite the initial irritation of fellow guildsmen, his example was followed throughout Germany "and the instruments of torture and folk humor disappeared into the attic."[5]

Breitkopf also fought successfully for freedom of the press: "He must have been very pleased," wrote Hase, "when he could announce in the first copy of his new periodical, *Magazin des Buch- und Kunst- Handels*, July 1780: 'His Highness the Elector of Saxony has lifted the very strict oath which the censorship required until now from the book printers in Leipzig, Wittenberg and the whole country, and has transformed this into a mere

[3] The most complete history of the firm, whence most of the facts in this section are drawn, may be found in Oskar von Hase's *Breitkopf & Härtel Gedenkschrift und Arbeitsbericht,* 4. Auflage, Leipzig, Breitkopf & Härtel, 1917.

[4] See Goethe's *Dichtung und Wahrheit,* Book Eight, for a description of a visit to the Breitkopf home. Goethe's earliest poems were set to music by J. G. Immanuel's oldest son, Bernhard Theodor, and printed with Immanuel's music type characters.

[5] Hase, *op. cit.,* p. 97.

declaration under oath; he has instructed the censors not to alter or strike anything in the works submitted to them, but instead, in matters of doubt, to return the manuscript.'"[6]

Breitkopf summed up his philosophy as a printer in the speech he customarily read to his own apprentices: "The art of the book printer preserves all the other arts from decay; it instructs in the basic principles of religion and morals, and preserves for eternity the noble actions of good men of all classes. So this art does a lot of good, and the fruits it produces prove its inestimable value. But it does this only in the hands of honest men, while in the hand of an evil person it is just as capable of doing evil."

Breitkopf and Music

The old ledgers of the Breitkopf firm show many transactions between J. S. Bach and Bernhard Christoph Breitkopf. Breitkopf senior published Bach's music in the *Musikalisches Gesangbuch*, edited by Schemelli (1736), as well as the texts to several of his cantatas. But it was not until the time of Johann Gottlob Immanuel Breitkopf that the firm really became a music house. Soon after taking over the printing department, J. G. Immanuel, who had an excellent musical background and played clavier tolerably well, applied his inventive brain to the problem of the printing of music. By 1754, after careful study, computation and experimentation, he produced a set of type characters for music that were movable and divisible in a multitude of ways. He believed he had far surpassed Petrucci, Attaingnant, and other predecessors by finding a versatile solution to the age-old problem of publishing music that avoided the difficulties and expense of engraving and music copying. His first important publication employing the new characters was a luxurious opera score with the following title and imprint: *Il trionfo della fedeltà. Dramma per musica di E.T.P.A.* [the pseudonym—in full, "Ermelinda Talia Pastorella Arcada"—of the future Electress Maria Antonia Walpurgis of Saxony]. *Stampato in Lipsia nella stamperia di Giov. Gottlob Immanuel Breitkopf inventore di questa nuova maniera di stampar la musica con carratteri separabili e mutabili é questo dramma pastorale la prima opera stampata di questa nuova guisa; comminciata nel mese di luglio 1755, e terminata nel mese d'aprile 1756.* Breitkopf tells us further, in a statement published in 1755 accompanying a sonnet by J. F. Graefe with music also by E.T.P.A.:

> The previously used music type has come into disuse somewhat, as it does not have the external elegance which is demanded nowadays, nor does it sufficiently meet the needs of today's perfected tonal art. The book printers themselves have not been very satisfied with it, because . . . it cannot be used by the setter without much patching up and artifice. The multiplicity of old characters, which amounted to several hundred, has been reduced to less than half, yet with this amount everything in contemporary music can be represented, including even all the newer French piano styles; the procedure is so simple and uniform that one will only need one hundredweight of the new type per page compared to the previously needed three to four and one-half hundredweight; and yet with this much smaller quantity much more can be achieved, and with greater ease.

Breitkopf began publishing music in a steady stream. Within a few years there appeared the *Berlinische Oden und Lieder*, a *Recueil d'Airs à Danser*, as well as compositions and theoretical works by Rutini, d'Alembert, C. H. Graun, Galuppi, Löwe and Sarti. He printed some works for distribution by his own house, some at the expense of individual composers[7] and some on orders from other publishers. The following composers, listed by Hase, entered into close relations with the Breitkopf firm during these years, and with some of them the association lasted for life: Johann Mattheson, Georg Philipp Telemann, Johann Joachim Quantz, Johann Gottlieb and Carl Heinrich Graun (1760, *The Death of Jesus*), Gottfried August Homilius, Carl Philipp Emanuel Bach, Johann Christoph Friedrich Bach, Johann Heinrich Rolle, Leopold Mozart, Johann Friedrich Agricola, Johann Lorenz Albrecht, Ernst Wilhelm Wolf, Karl Ditters von Dittersdorf, Friedrich Wilhelm Rust, Johann Gottlieb Naumann, Karl Stamitz, Johann Abraham Peter Schulz, Christian Gottlob Neefe, Johann Nikolaus Forkel, Johann Friedrich Reichardt, Federigo Fiorillo, Johann Gottfried Schicht, Christian Kalkbrenner, Johann Rudolf Zumsteeg, Karl Cannabich, etc. It must be understood, however, that in most instances Breitkopf made and sold *manuscript* copies of these composers' works rather than printing them. This points up the irony of the story: Breitkopf's hopes for his music type were never realized. According to Gerber, writing in 1790,

[6] Hase, *op. cit.*, p. 99.

[7] For example: *Sechs Sonaten für das Klavier von Nathanael Gottfried Gruner in Gera. Leipzig, auf Kosten des Autors, und in Commission bey Johann Gottlob Immanuel Breitkopf, 1781* (copy in the Universitätsbibliothek, Halle).

the Breitkopf music presses printed relatively few works.[8] The excellence of his results was more in his mind's eye than on paper, as a glance at the pages of the Thematic Catalogue which follow will prove. The inevitable hairline spaces between the tiny segments of staff (and between most other particles of type) are not conducive to elegance or continuity of line. Furthermore, no matter how much of an advance his method was over older music printing procedures, it could not compete with the improved engraving processes which in the 1770's and 1780's, and until the invention of lithography, came to rule the reproduction of music. Several other printers in this period tried their hand at creating music type characters with equal or far greater lack of success.[9] This was to be expected when not even Breitkopf's experience and enthusiasm for movable type printing could succeed in overcoming the economic impracticality and the aesthetic limitation of its application to music.

The history of the production and distribution of manuscript and printed music in the second half of the eighteenth century is fascinating and little known; it reflected profound social changes in an increasingly music-hungry Europe. Recent researches by H. C. Robbins Landon, Jan LaRue, Cari Johansson, Cecil Hopkinson, Claudio Sartori and Alexander Weinmann, among others, have illuminated many of its aspects. In the earlier eighteenth century, the principal method of music dissemination was the manuscript copy prepared on direct order by the professional copyist. Printing from type or engraving by tin or copper plate was less common and more expensive. With the rise of the bourgeoisie and the development of public concert life, an enormous demand for music arose from *Kenner und Liebhaber* as well as from beginners of all ages. Germany, Austria-Hungary and Italy clung longest to the copying procedure, while in such cities as Amsterdam, London and especially Paris the engraver began gradually to replace the copyist. In Leipzig, Breitkopf played a doubly conservative role. Not only did he try to further his own music printing method at the expense of the engraving process, but, as will be seen below, he maintained one of the greatest copying establishments in Europe.

In this period Leipzig was a major German cultural crossroads. Arnold Schering, writing about the period after 1780, states:

> There was no shortage of connoisseurs with a thorough knowledge of music, who played well, and knew how to distinguish good from bad. These connoisseurs were found in various strata of upper middle class society: merchants, higher officials, book and art dealers, literati, professors, doctors, lawyers and others who had enjoyed a higher education.
>
> In these circles the better type of *Hauswerk* was often performed. The female members of the family especially began to sing and play at an early age. Books about art were read, merits of composers and virtuosi argued, and doors opened wide and willingly to artists with letters of recommendation. It was felt that the enjoyment [of the arts] conferred a certain obligation upon recipients thereof. Singers, composers, performers loved to visit [Leipzig].[10]

The Non-Thematic Catalogues

Leipzig in the eighteenth century was the center of the German publishing industry. Its Book Fairs were the largest in the country. The trade catalogues (*Messkataloge*) prepared for these fairs often included music publications and provide the background for the later specialized music catalogues.[11] Indeed, Breitkopf's first music catalogues closely resembled the regular book lists; they were non-thematic and were issued in conjunction with the Book Fairs. He continued to publish these more conventional *Verzeichnisse* throughout and after the twenty-five-year period in which the twenty-two volumes of the Thematic Catalogue appeared. They are prototypes of many put out by German music publishers and commission merchants in the last third of the century. Unlike French and English publishers, who added a one or two-page tightly spaced catalogue to their engraved scores and parts, the German music printers and dealers, more closely allied to the book trade, issued their music catalogues separately as pamphlets or books, some with hundreds of pages.[12] These catalogues, which never have been adequately investigated, are the direct forerunners of the Meysel-Whistling-Hofmeister *Handbuch der Musikalischen Literatur* series begun in 1817.

[8] *Historisch-Biographisches Lexicon,* Leipzig, 1790, Vol. I, Column 202.

[9] E.g., Enschedé in Holland and Loiseau in France; see C. Enschedé, *Fonderies de caractères,* Haarlem, 1908, and B. Brook, *La Symphonie Française,* Paris, 1962.

[10] Arnold Schering, *Musikgeschichte Leipzig's,* Dritter Band (1723–1800), Kistner & Siegel, Leipzig, 1941, p. 596.

[11] The early history of *Messkataloge* as related to music has been documented by Albert Göhler, *Verzeichnis der in den Frankfurter und Leipziger Messkatalogen der Jahre 1564 bis 1759 angezeigten Musikalien,* Leipzig, 1902.

[12] E.g., Westphal (Hamburg, 1782, 287 pp.), Traeg (Vienna, 1799, 233 pp.), Unser (Königsberg, 1809, 202 pp.), Werckmeister (Berlin, 1809, 172 pp.).

The Breitkopf non-thematic *Verzeichnisse* are particularly significant for us because they are closely related to their thematic counterparts and often furnish more detailed information than do the *Cataloghi* about individual composers or works. To give but a single obvious example, on page 8 of our Thematic Catalogue, Parte I^ma^, 1762, one reads, "VI. Sinfonie del Georg. Gebel, Maestr. di Cap. di Pr. di Schw. Rs," followed by the six incipits. On page 46 of the *Erste Ausgabe* of the non-thematic *Verzeichniss Musicalischer Werke* (see below), published one year *earlier*, in 1761, name and title are given in full and price is added: "Gebel, Georgio, Maestro di Capella di Princ. di Schwarzburg-Rudolst. VI Sinfonie à 4, 6 & 8 Voci. à 5 thl. 8 gl."

Breitkopf published over two dozen non-thematic catalogues before 1800. They fall into four groups of which the first three (1760–1780) roughly parallel in time and content the Thematic Catalogue (1762–1787):

Group I. *Catalogue of* [*Printed*] *Music Books concerning both Theory and Practice*. . ., published in six parts, 1760–1780.

Group II. *Catalogue of* [*Manuscript*] *Musical Works for Practical Performance*. . ., published in four parts, 1761–1780.

Group III. *Catalogue of Latin and Italian Church Music* [*in Manuscript*]. . ., published in one volume in 1769.

Group IV. A series of some fifteen smaller catalogues published between 1792 and 1801.

It should be added that these important works are as difficult to find as the Thematic Catalogue. Their full German titles read:[13]

[Group I]

Verzeichniss musikalischer Bücher, sowohl zur Theorie als Praxis, und für alle Instrumente, in ihre gehörigen Classen ordentlich eingetheilet; welche bei Johann Gottlob Immanuel Breitkopf [Parts three and four read "*Bernh. Christoph Breitkopf & Sohn*"] *in Leipzig um beystehende Preise in Louis d'or à 5 Thlr zu bekommen sind.*

Erste Ausgabe, Leipzig, in der Neujahr-Messe 1760 [pp. 1–33]. [Title pages for Ausgaben II to VI identical except where noted.]

Zweyte Ausgabe, Leipzig, in der Oster-Messe 1761 [pp. 33–56].

Dritte Ausgabe, Leipzig, nach der Ostermesse 1763 [pp. 57–88].

Vierte Ausgabe, Leipzig, in der Oster-Messe 1770 [pp. 89–116].

Fünfte Ausgabe, Leipzig, nach der Oster-Messe 1777 [pp. 117–148; add after the word *Instrumente: "davon die Anfänge in dem V. VI. VII. VIII. IX. und Xten Supplemente zu finden sind"*].

Sechste Ausgabe, Leipzig, nach der Ostermesse 1780 [pp. 149–172; add after the word *Instrumente: "davon die Anfänge in dem XI. XII. und XIII. Supplemente zu finden sind"*].

[Group II]

Verzeichniss Musicalischer Werke, allein zur Praxis, sowohl zum Singen, als für alle Instrumente, welche nicht durch den Druck bekannt gemacht worden, in ihre gehörige Classen ordentlich eingetheilet; welche in richtigen Abschriften bey Joh. Gottlob Immanuel Breitkopf [Part three reads "*Bernh. Christoph Breitkopf & Sohn*"] *in Leipzig, um beystehende Preisse zu bekommen sind in Louis d'ors à 5 Thlr.*

Erste Ausgabe, Leipzig, in der Michaelmesse 1761 [64 pp.].

Zweyte Ausgabe, Leipzig, in der Neujahrmesse 1764 [54 pp.].

Dritte Ausgabe, Leipzig, nach der Michaelmesse 1770 [45 pp.].

Vierte Ausgabe, Leipzig, nach der Ostermesse 1780 [32 pp.].

[Group III]

Verzeichniss lateinischer und italiänischer Kirchen-Musiken, an Motetten, Hymnen und Liedern, Psalmen, Magnificat, Sanctus, Kyrie, Missen und Passions-Oratorien sowohl in Partitur als in Stimmen, alle in Manuscript; desgleichen an Präambulis, Fugen, Fugetten, Versetten und Interludiis nach den gewöhnlichen Kirchentönen, Sonatinen, Sonaten und Concerten vor die Orgel, gedruckt und in Kupfer gestochen; welche bey Bernh. Christoph Breitkopf und Sohn in Leipzig um beystehende Preisse in Louis d'ors à 5 Thlr. zu bekommen sind. Leipziger Ostermesse, 1769 [24 pp.].

[Group IV*a*]

Verzeichniss neuer Musicalien welche in der Breitkopfischen Buchhandlung in Leipzig zu bekommen sind [in thirteen parts].

[1] Ostermesse, 1792.

[2] Ostermesse, 1793.

[3] Michaelis-Messe, 1793.

[4] Ostermesse, 1794.

[13] In Kathi Meyer's aforementioned article (see footnote 2) these titles contain some unfortunate errors. In the first group, for example, the Fünfte and Sechste Ausgaben have been omitted and the word *Anfänge* is given as *Anhänge*, confusing the relationship to the incipits in the Thematic Catalogue.

[5] Michaelis-Messe, 1794.
[6] Ostermesse, 1795.
[7] Michaelis-Messe, 1795.
[8] Ostermesse, 1796.
[9] Michaelis-Messe, 1796.
[10] Michaelis-Messe, 1797.
[11] Jubilate-Messe, 1798.
[12] Jubilate-Messe, 1800.
[13] Jubilate-Messe, 1801.

[Group IV*b*]
Verzeichniss von Wiener Musikalien, welche in der Breitkopfischen Buchhandlung in Leipzig zu bekommen sind [ca. 1800].

[Group IV*c*]
Verzeichniss Musikalischer Schriften welche von der Breitkopfischen Buchhandlung am alten Neumarkte in Leipzig verlegt, oder doch in mehrerer Anzahl bey ihr zu bekommen sind [in two parts].
[1] 1792 [20 pp.]
[2] 1794 [22 pp.]

A complete concordance of the entries in the above non-thematic *Verzeichnisse* with those of the thematic *Cataloghi* would be a worthwhile undertaking, perhaps only feasible with digital computer assistance. It is worth noting that the non-thematic catalogues all employ German title pages and headings, while the thematic *Cataloghi*, perhaps because they contain actual notes, are in Italian.

The Thematic Catalogue

The imaginative accomplishment represented by the Breitkopf Thematic Catalogue has not been fully appreciated in its time nor in ours. For one thing, Breitkopf seems to have been the first to use the word *theme* to represent the introductory bars of a piece.[14] He opens his *Nacherinnerung* in Parte Ima by speaking of works "*die ich durch die* Themata [Breitkopf prints this word in boldface] . . . *kenntlich zu machen . . . gesucht habe.*"

The good Dr. Burney, that perceptive foreign correspondent, did grasp the significance of the Catalogue on his visit to Leipzig in 1772:

> . . . M. Breitkopf, the most considerable vendor of musical compositions in Europe, whom I visited immediately on my arrival in this city; but I found him rather taciturn than communicative. . . . he seems . . . to have been the first who gave to his catalogues an index *in notes*, containing the *subjects* or two or three first bars, of the several pieces in each musical work; by which a reader is enabled to discover not only whether he is in possession of an entire book but of any part of its contents.
>
> Besides *printed* copies of works of the most celebrated composers of all nations, he sells, in manuscript, at a reasonable price, single pieces of any work already printed, as well as of innumerable others which have never been published.[15]

A perusal of the entire Catalogue reveals a musical culture of an extraordinary, and to most of us an unsuspected, breadth and diversity. One is struck by the fact that only about three or four per cent of its contents represents works written by Haydn and Mozart. One may be surprised to learn that a number of names (Benda, Dittersdorf, Graun, Hasse, Vaňhal and Ernst Wilhelm Wolf [!]) are followed by lists of works equal to or larger than that for Haydn (Mozart is way down in this popularity poll and J. S. Bach—of Leipzig—is represented by only four works).

Some of the very earliest compositions of Mozart, Haydn and Beethoven are included, e.g., Köchel Nos. 1, 7, 8 and 9, Op. I and II, listed as "*intagliate in Parigi,*" 1767 (p. 287), or Haydn's *Divertimento in A* (p. 120) or the "*Variations da Louis van BETTHOVEN* [*sic*]*, age de dix ans. Mannheim*" (p. 808).

Further perusal of the Catalogue reveals the presence of such fascinating instruments as: Flauto d'Amore, Sampogne, Trommel, Zinche e Tromboni, Violino discordato. The lute is honored with an eight-page, specially numbered section of its own (pp. 369–376) listing sixty-six *Partite,* including a group by Sylvius Leopold Weiss in a sequence of twelve different keys; the incipits are given in Breitkopf's specially designed type characters for lute tablature.

In 1766, a Sign. Romano offers a sinfonia with no fewer than sixteen parts (p. 218)! Some rather uncommon genre headings catch one's eye: Madrigali, Cosac, Ricercare, Concertini, etc. Specific titles worth noting include: *Sinf*[*onia*] *Hypochondr*[*iaca*] by Schmittbauer (p. 762); *Sinfonia Nazionale* by Dittersdorf (p. 302); *Sinfonia Pantomima* by Vaňhal (p. 471);

[14] This did not escape the unerring attention of Prof. Deutsch; see his article, "Thematische Kataloge," in *Fontes Artis Musicae,* 1958/2, pp. 73–79.

[15] Charles Burney, *The Present State of Music in Germany, the Netherlands and United Provinces,* 2nd ed., London, 1775 (2 vol.), Vol. 2, pp. 73–74.

Sinf[onia] Russa by dall'Oglio (p. 216); *Das Kosackenlager oder der verunglückte Stutzer* (The Cossack Camp, or The Unlucky Dandy) by Mašek (p. 863).

The twenty-five-year period spanned by the Catalogue, so valuable for dating purposes, also permits us to observe changes in fashion and taste, such as the vagaries of genre and composer popularity, the rapid increase in woodwind concertos in the 1780's, the rise of music engraving, etc.

Breitkopf's "Nacherinnerung"

Breitkopf tells us a great deal about himself, his times and his Catalogue in the *Nacherinnerung* (Afterword) to Parte I^{ma} (see pp. 29–32), herewith translated in full:

> I present herewith the first of the promised *musical catalogues* of all *practical works* by *various authors* which may be found in my offices; I have tried to make them recognizable by their *themes* in so far as space will allow, and to differentiate one from another as one differentiates books by their titles. Fair judges will realize that it is sufficiently troublesome just to assemble a rather considerable stock of such items, or to wrest them, so to speak, from the hands of certain musicians; but that it is even more troublesome, and is a rather difficult task, to arrange them into some kind of order. How many conflicts does one not have to resolve, how many concealed obstacles does one not have to surmount if one desires to give each composer his due and if one seeks to ascribe pieces appearing under *various names* to their true authors! And when inquiries do not bring clarification in such doubtful cases, which I came upon quite often, how easy it is for one's judgment to lead one astray just as often as in the proper direction!
>
> I must therefore ask forgiveness of connoisseurs and amateurs of music, and even of a few of the composers themselves whose names appear in this catalogue, or will appear in the future, for certain unavoidable errors. At the same time I beseech them, if some of their own pieces or those of others have been incorrectly set down, to let me have a note to that effect so that, in case there is a new edition of this *Catalogue*, old errors may be rectified and new ones avoided. For this reason I have printed only a small number of copies of this first effort, and have gladly sacrificed profit for love of accuracy.
>
> If famous composers would themselves not mind compiling a catalogue of their practical works in a free hour and would be kind enough to send it to me, I would not only acknowledge this with many thanks, but would also continue my endeavors all the more encouraged in proportion to the possibility of my relying on the accuracy of such communications. It does not matter that I would not yet possess the items which appear in such a catalogue, because I would take steps to acquire these at once, should there be any demand for them among music lovers.
>
> It is not only the incorrectness of names, however, which may have occasionally led me into error, but also the *instruments* and the *number of voices* which I have indicated above each and every theme. Who does not know of the liberties this or that musician takes in a piece by now omitting, now adding voices, or by transcribing pieces intended for this or that instrument for another one? I have myself found sufficient traces of such arbitrary alterations; and how many may I not have discovered, all of which account for so many errors in my Catalogue?
>
> I must, therefore, in this connection have recourse again to the kindness of those who are more precisely informed. The pleasure they would give me with reliable communications (suppositions are of little use to me except when they concern matters about which complete certainty is impossible) is at the same time a kindness rendered to the whole of music; bibliography [*Bücherkenntniss*] has often been the concern of many learned men, and some prolific authors have themselves compiled a complete catalogue of their works and writings to protect the world from errors, so that today *Historia litteraria*, that immense subject, has been brought into such an excellent state of order that we can only hope for the same in music at this time. Should the worshippers of this noble art, for some of whom music is their chief concern, be less zealous in contributing their share toward casting a light upon music literature that they lacked until now?
>
> In this first section of my Catalogue I have had to keep within the limits of my own stock, and I have decided to continue in this way until I am in a position, through communications from others, to furnish more complete and correct catalogues. Proceeding along the lines of my previously published *Catalogues of Musical Printed Books and Unprinted Works*, and following the order used in them, I will continue to submit to the musical world with their *themes* the practical works that were listed in the previous catalogues by title only. This first attempt includes the symphonies that were listed by the names of their composers *from the 45th to the 49th page of the Catalogue of Musical Works That Have Not Been Made Known Through Printing*. Next in line will be *trios* for *violins* and *flutes*. *Piano pieces*, *solos*, *duets*, *quartets*, *concertos* on *various instruments* will follow in their turn. The quite considerable stock that I have of sacred and secular *vocal items*, and especially of *operas*, will likewise be listed aria by aria. From time to time one will find that the number of symphonies with themes will be greater or smaller than the number given in the [non-thematic] Title Catalogues. When the number is greater, it is because in the time which has passed

between the publication of that catalogue and this one I have received from many authors more than I then had, and I did not wish to leave any blank lines [staves], having decided that the arrangement [of the incipits] should be by half-dozens; when the number is smaller, it is because I have discovered some incorrect statements for which substitutions could not immediately be found. The difference in the price which must arise from this, will be easily grasped if one considers that I have fixed the price at 4 gl. per sheet, and that I charge for a full sheet for each main voice, such as violin, viola, bass viol, oboe, but only for half a sheet for horns and other reinforcing voices; so that everyone will be able to find the costs of his choices easily, since I will maintain these prices as long as the [stability of the] currency permits.

Everyone who is not a stranger to these matters will easily see how much trouble, time and expenditure are involved here and how much I need to be encouraged by the reasonable approval and kind support of sensible men. But if there be those who would indulge in censure and ridicule at my expense because they consider themselves better qualified and more experienced in this field, I will then take the liberty likewise to cast ridicule and censure because no one before me came upon an idea which so redounds to the honor and profit of music and of famous composers, which in execution is as difficult as it is troublesome, and which has all the more claim to a kindly judgment since there was no foundation upon which to build, but it was necessary to break the ice and struggle through a multitude of doubts and uncertainties.

Leipzig, New Year's Fair, 1762
Joh. Gottlob Immanuel Breitkopf.

Accuracy of Chronology and Attribution

Breitkopf himself has just given us fair warning! Nowhere is scholarly caution more necessary than when using the Breitkopf Catalogue! There are errors and pitfalls galore, some due to the compiler's own carelessness, others the fault of documents received from composers (e.g., wrong notes, incorrect instrumentation). Often the times themselves were responsible (consistency in spelling was unknown). Once all this has been said, one may appropriately add that it is astonishing that there are not many *more* mistakes than do actually exist. The percentage of errors is in fact low.

How dependable is the Breitkopf Catalogue for establishing chronology?

To answer this difficult question one must recall the circumstances surrounding its publication over a quarter of a century and add equal parts of conjecture and common-sense analysis of the available evidence. The Catalogue's six initial parts, each covering a different genre, appeared between 1762 and 1765. Most of the items named therein were already in stock when the Catalogue was begun. Indeed, many had already been listed in the 1761 non-thematic catalogue entitled *Verzeichniss Musicalischer Werke*. Some of the composers represented were long dead. Thus the time lag between the creation of a work and its appearance in the first six volumes of the Catalogue varies from about two to a dozen or more years.

The first ten supplements appeared yearly between 1766 and 1775. In the first supplement there could in some instances be an enforced delay of five years or more; symphonies, for example, had not been listed in Parts II to VI. They had been accumulating since the appearance of Parte I^ma^ in 1762. For the second through the tenth supplement the delay may be said to have stabilized to around one to two years (with the usual exceptions). Supplements XI to XVI were published from one to three years apart; thus the basic time lag could vary between one and four years. Even the oft-stated and apparently obvious point that the Breitkopf chronology represents the latest possible dating for a work needs examination. It was quite possible for a composer to send in incipits of works still in progress or hardly begun, especially since Breitkopf liked to list themes by the half-dozen. Confusion also arises when an incipit appears two or more times in different sections of the Catalogue; usually this represents different editions or manuscripts of the work.

Robbins Landon has stated that after the autographs and dated authentic parts, the Breitkopf Catalogue is scarcely of less importance than the Entwurf Katalog as the primary source for the dating of Haydn's work. "The catalogue remains invaluable for chronology," he writes, "even if . . . its worth is negative in that it is able to provide only the latest possible date."[16] Finally let us not forget that in many instances Breitkopf's is the *only* date available.

How dependable is the Breitkopf Catalogue with respect to attributions?

Johann Gottlob Immanuel himself provides the best clue to the answer in the *Nacherinnerung* to Parte I^{ma} (pp. 29–32) translated above and in the *Nachricht* to Supplemento IX (p. 560), herewith translated in full:

> The publication of Supplement IX was delayed this long contrary to expectation; we wished to avoid the reproach that we were mingling old works with the new or listing others under the wrong names, and therefore proceeded all the more carefully. This reproach has always been made about *manuscript works*, but those amateurs who think they are thus safer

[16] H. C. Robbins Landon, *The Symphonies of Joseph Haydn*, London, Rockliff, 1955, p. 69.

with *engraved and printed music* are invited to examine pages 11, 16, 24, 35 of this Supplement [equals pp. 531, 536, 544 and 555, containing internally conflicting attributions] in order to decide the question; since Herr Cammerm[usicus] Eichner of Berlin assures us that the two clavier concertos on the last-indicated page [35, equals 555] are not his. In any case we assure the public that we do not perpetrate this kind of inexactitude intentionally and indeed that we earnestly endeavor to uncover such errors rather than to profit therefrom.

Leipzig, July 25, 1775 B.C.B. and S[on]

There is a sizable number of misattributions and internal conflicts in the Catalogue, sometimes within a few pages of one another.[17] Originally the feasibility of indicating errors in the body of the Catalogue was considered. However, since correcting all or even most of the mistakes was clearly an impossibility at this time, it was decided not to attempt a partial job, but to leave the original intact. A number of clarifications and identifications have been incorporated into the General Index (see below). The obvious need for a "corrected" Breitkopf will be met by a Corrigenda Supplement scheduled to appear ca. 1970. The ready availability of the present volume combined with the upsurge of eighteenth-century research now going on will, it is hoped, greatly facilitate this undertaking. Scholars are hereby invited to send in corrigenda in all categories, identification of anonymi, conflicting parentage solutions, etc. Furthermore, the contents of the Breitkopf Catalogues are ideally suited to analysis by automatic data processing equipment. This would make possible automatic transposition and conflict detection of the entire corpus of incipits as well as all manner of tabulation, concordance and manipulation of non-thematic information. Perhaps the results of such a computer-aided study, if undertaken, could be included in the projected Supplement.

[17] As an example, Jan LaRue had kindly provided the following list of such conflicts as regards incipits of symphonies from his invaluable *Union Catalogue of 18th Century Symphonies* (conflicts in other genres are similarly coming to light in Prof. LaRue's concerto and chamber music files):

Rugietz (p. 593) equals Sonnleithner (524)
Martino (21) equals Pergolesi (216)
Luchesi (486) equals Spiller (594)
Baisiello (702) equals Galuppi (442)
Querfurth (217) equals Graaf (445)
Schmidtbauer (564) equals Sterkel (762)
Reluzzi (23) equals Gluck (9)
Hofmann (483) equals Ordonez (262)
Kunz (20) equals Querfurth (217)
Hennig (338) equals Houpfeld (447)
Ardina (590) equals Brodsky (522)
Rutini (264) equals G. A. Graun (12)
Polazzi (217) equals Martino (22)

On Indexes and Pagination

For reasons stated above, Breitkopf's original Catalogue has been left intact except for the addition to each page of the number and date of the supplement or part in which it appears and a new consecutive pagination for all of the volumes. *Each page will thus show both an internal and an overall pagination plus date and a part or supplement number.* (Each page of this volume contains two facing pages of the original Catalogue.)

The Catalogue contains, as already indicated, a total of 888 pages, with almost 15,000 musical incipits and 1300 first lines representing over one thousand composers. As an aid to organizing and using this information, three indexing tools have been prepared for this edition:

(1) An *Outline of Contents*, appearing just *before* the Catalogue itself (pp. xvii–xxvii) and indicating all the major and minor headings of its twenty-two parts and supplements;

(2) An *Index of First Lines* appearing just *after* the Catalogue (pp. xxix–xlviii) and giving text underlays for all vocal incipits;

(3) A *General Index* of names and titles (pp. xlix–lxxxi).

At the risk of belaboring the obvious, it may be pointed out that the Outline of Contents gives a much needed survey of the entire Catalogue and permits consultation of specific sections in each part or supplement on the basis of instrument or genre. The Index of First Lines has already been of help in the identification of anonymous vocal works. The General Index is worthy of special comment since it contains identifications and clarifications that go beyond the Catalogue itself. A vague title or an incomplete composer's name appearing with an incipit can often be clarified by checking the entry for that incipit in the General Index. For example: Which Bach is the composer of the incipit on p. 252 given as "Trio del Sigr. Bach."? If it has been properly identified, the incipit is indexed under the composer's full name, in this instance Carl Philipp Emanuel. If it had *not* been identified, the incipit would appear under "Bach" without indication of first name.

On the next page, 253, a composer's name is given as "Sig[no]ra Agnesi." The Index will provide the full name thus: "Agnesi [-Pinottini, Maria Teresa]." Or take the name "Iust" (p. 799) in the Catalogue, which could refer to either of two composers, Just or Yost. Although the letters "J" and "I" are often interchanged, this is not the case here and the Index will identify "Iust" properly as "Yost" on the basis of external evidence. Another example may be seen on page 285, where an incipit is indicated thus: "Sinf. di Hasse, Nell' Opera Clelia." The word "Clelia" in the Index refers one to "Trionfo di Clelia, Il," where one finds four page entries; two of these pages contain the incipits of twenty arias in the opera.

Acknowledgments

The notion of reprinting the Breitkopf Thematic Catalogue had its birth during conversations with Albert Vander Linden at the Brussels Conservatoire a decade ago. We speculated about the unlikelihood of finding a publisher at all and the improbability of doing so in time for the bicentenary of the publication of the Catalogue's Parte I^{ma}, 1962. Mr. Vander Linden not only helped foster the idea but generously made available for microfilming the Brussels Conservatoire copy of the Catalogue, as well as Alfred Wotquenne's old handwritten index thereof. The present indexes have been completely redone and owe much to the scrupulous care of the late David Stimer, who, between concert engagements, found working on them relaxing. Jan LaRue checked the entire General Index and made a number of invaluable suggestions. Gustave Reese kindly read through the Introduction and made many constructive comments. Wolfgang Matthäus graciously provided information from his as yet unpublished research on Frankfurt and Leipzig printers. Harold Spivacke, Chief, Music Division, Library of Congress, and Ruth Watanabe, Music Librarian, Sibley Library, Eastman School of Music, kindly made their holdings of the parts and supplements of the Breitkopf Thematic Catalogue available for photographic reproduction for this edition. Finally, thanks are due to the President and superb staff of Dover Publications, who accepted without blinking the AMS-MLA Reprint Committee's recommendation to publish this rather esoteric work, and who, whenever production problems arose, always managed to surmount the insurmountable.

Barry S. Brook

Queens College,
City University of New York,
Flushing, N.Y.
June 1966

OUTLINE OF CONTENTS OF CATALOGUE

CATALOGO

DELLE

SINFONIE,

CHE SI TROVANO

IN MANUSCRITTO

NELLA OFFICINA MUSICA

DI

GIOVANNO GOTTLOB IMMANUEL BREITKOPF,

IN LIPSIA.

PARTE Ima.

1762.

VI. Sinfonie del Giov. AGRELL, Maest. di Capella in Norimberga.
I a 6 Voci. 2 Corni.
IV. a 6 Voci.
II. a 4 Voci.
V. a 4 Voci.
III. a 6 Voci. 2 Corni.
VI. a 4 Voci.
VI. Sinfonie del Giov. ADAM, Compos. di Ball. di Ré di Polon.
V. a 10 Voc. 2 Corni. 2 Flaut. 2 Oboi.
IV. a 6 Voci. 2 Corni.
II. a 6 Voci.
VI. a 4 Voci. 2 Corni.
III. a 6 Voci. 2 Oboi.
VI. a 6 Voci.
VI. Sinfonie del C. F. E. BACH, Musico di Camera di Ré di Pruss.
I. a 4 Voci.
IV. a 6 Voci. 2 Corni.
II. a 4 Voci.
V. a 4 Voci.
III. a 4 Voci.
VI. a 4 Voci.
tr

VI. Sinfonie del G. BENDA, Maest. di Cap. di Duca di Gotha.
I. a 4 Voci.
tr
IV. a 6 Voc. 2 Corni.
II. a 6 Voci. 2 Corni.
V. a 6 Voci. 2 Corni.
III. a 6 Voci. 2 Corni.
VI. a 8 Voci. 2 Corni. 2 Fl.
VI. Sinfonie del Fr. BENDA, Mus. di Cam. di Ré di Pruss.
I. a 4 Voci.
IV. a 4 Voci.
II. a 4 Voci.
V. a 4 Voci.
III. a 4 Voci.
VI. a 4 Voci.
VI. Sinfonie del BERNASCONI. Raccolta I.
I. a 4 Voci.
IV. a 4 Voci.
II. a 4 Voci.
V. a 4 Voci.
III. a 4 Voci.
VI. a 4 Voci.

4 SINFONIE.
VI. Sinfonie del BERNASCONI. Raccolta II.
I. a 6 Voci. 2 Corni.
IV. a 6 Voci. 2 Corni.
II. a 6 Voci. 2 Corni.
V. a 6 Voci. 2 Corni.
III. a 6 Voci. 2 Corni.
VI. a 8 Voci. 2 Corni. 2 Fl. 2 Ob.
IV. Sinfonie del Wenceslao Raimondo BIRCK, in Vienna.
I. a 4 Voci.
III. a 4 Voci.
II. a 4 Voci.
IV. a 6 Voci. 2 Oboi.
VI. Sinfonie del BRIOSCHI. Raccolta I.
I a 6 Voci.
IV. a 4 Voci.
II. a 4 Voci.
V. a 4 Voci.
III. a 4 Voci.
VI. a 4 Voci.

SINFONIE. 5
VI. Sinfonie del BRIOSCHI. Raccolta II.
I. a 4 Voci.
IV. a 4 Voci.
II. a 4 Voci.
V. a 4 Voci.
III. a 4 Voci.
VI. a 4 Voci.
VI. Sinfonie del BRIOSCHI. Raccolta III.
I. a 4 Voci.
IV. a 4 Voci.
II. a 4 Voci.
V. a 4 Voci.
III. a 4 Voci.
VI. a 4 Voci.
VI. Sinfonie del CAMMERLOHER, Musico di Cam. d'Elett. di Bavaria. Raccolta I.
I. a 4 Voci.
IV. a 4 Voci.
II. a 4 Voci.
V. a 4 Voci.
III. a 4 Voci.
VI. a 4 Voci.

6 SINFONIE.

VI. Sinfonie del CAMMERLOHER, *Musico di Cam. d'Elect. di Bavaria. Raccolta I.*

I. a 4 Voci. IV. a 4 Voci.

II. a 4 Voci. V. a 4 Voci.

III. a 4 Voci. VI. a 4 Vc.

VI. Sinfonie del CAMMERLOHER, *Musico di Cam. d'Elect. di Bavaria. Raccolta II.*

I. a 4 Voci. IV. a 4 Voci.

II. a 4 Voci. V. a 4 Voci.

III. a 4 Voci. VI. a 4 Voci.

VI. Sinfonie del CAMMERLOHER, *Musico di Cam. d'Elect. di Bavaria. Raccolta III.*

I. a 4 Voci. IV. a 4 Voci.

II. a 4 Voci. V. a 4 Voci.

III. a 4 Voci. VI. a 4 Voci.

Clamor Asinorum.

SINFONIE. 7

VI. Sinfonie del Pietro CONTI. *Raccolta I.*

I. a 4 Vocl. IV. a 4 Voci.

II. a 4 Voci. V. a 4 Voci.

III. a 4 Voci. VI. a 4 Voci.

VI. Sinfonie del Christof. FOERSTER, *Maestr. di Capell. di Pr. di Schwarzb. Rudolst. Raccolta I.*

I. a 4 Voci. IV. a 4 Voci.

II. a 4 Voci. V. a 6 Voci. *2 Corni.*

III. a 4 Voci. VI. a 4 Voci.

VI. Sinfonie del Christ. FOERSTER, *Maestr. di Cap. di Pr. di Schw. Rud. Raccolta II.*

I. a 6 Voci. *2 Corni.* II. a 8 Voci. *2 Tromb. 2 Oboi.*

II. a 6 Voci. *2 Corni.* V. a 8 Voci. *2 Corni. 2 Oboi.*

III. a 6 Voci. *2 Corni.* VI. a 10 Voc. *1 Tromb. 3 Ob. 2 Fag. oblig.*

8 SINFONIE.
VI. Sinfonie del Balth. GALUPPI, Muſ. in Venezia. Raccolta I.
I. a 4 Voci.
III. a 6. Voci. 2 Oboi.
II. a 4 Voci.
V. a 6 Voci. 2 Corni.
III. a 4 Voci.
VI. a 6 Voci. 2 Corni.
VI. Sinfonie del Balth. GALUPPI, Muſ. in Venez. Racc. II.
I. a 8 Voci. 2 Corni. 2 Oboi.
IV. a Voci.
II. a 8 Voc.
V. a 6 Voci.
III. a 10 Voci. 2 Tromb. 2 Corn. 2 Oboi.
VI. a 6 Voci. 2 Corni.
VI. Sinfonie del Georg. GEBEL, Maeſtr. di Cap. di Pr di Schw. Rud.
I. a 4 Voci.
IV. a 6 Voc. 2 Corn.
II. a 4 Voci.
V. a 8 Voci. 2 Corni. 2 Oboi.
III. a 4 Voci.
VI. a 4 Voci.

SINFONIE. 9
VI. Sinfonie del Cheval. GLUCK, in Vienna.
I. a 4 Voci.
IV. a 6 Voci. 2 Corni.
II. a 4 Voci.
V. a 6 Voci. 2 Corni.
III. a 6 Voci. 2 Corni.
VI. a 10 Voci. 2 Ob. Fl. Fag. 2 Cor.
VI. Sinfonie del C. E. GRAUN, Maeſtr. di Cap. di Ré di Pruſſ. Racc. I.
I. nel Opera Rodelinda a 8 V. Cor. Ob.
IV. nel Op. Catone. Ouv. 8 V. Cor. Ob.
II. nel Op. Cleop. Ouvert. a 8 V. Cor. Ob.
V. nel Op. Aleſſandro a 8 Vo. Corn. Ob.
III. nel Op. Artaferſe. a 6 Voc. 2 Cor.
VI. nel Op. Lucio. Papirio. Ouv. 8 V. C. O.
VI. Sinfonie del C. E. GRAUN, Maeſtro di Cap. di Ré di Pruſſ. Racc. II.
VII. nel Op. Adriano. a 8 Voc. Cor. Ob.
X. nel Opera le Feſte galante. 6 Vo. Cor.
VIII. nel Op. Demofonte a 6 Voc. Cor.
XI. nel Opera Cinna, a 6 Voc. 2 Corn.
IX. nel Opera Cajo Fabricio. a 6 V. Cor.
XII. nel Op. l'Europa gal. a 8 V. Cor. Ob.

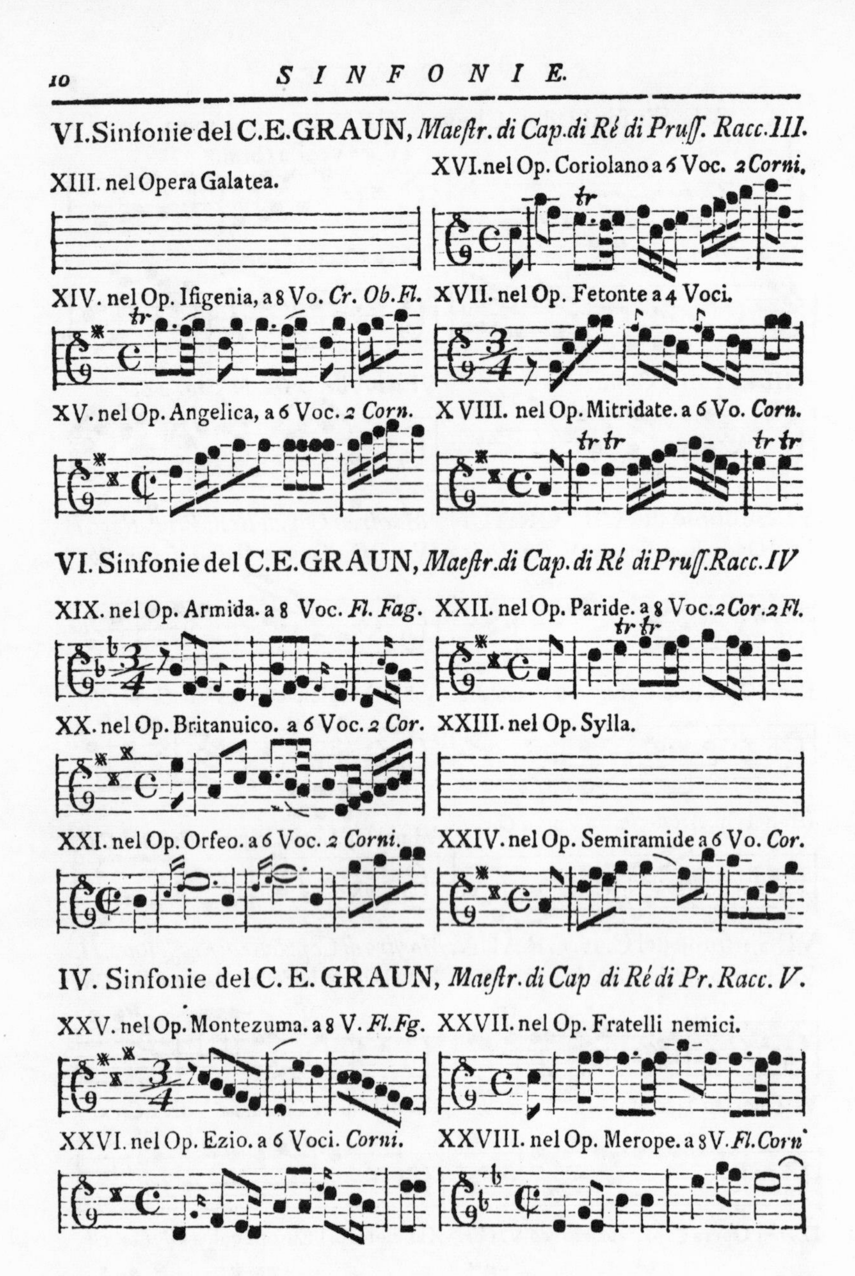
10 SINFONIE.
VI. Sinfonie del C.E. GRAUN, Maestr. di Cap. di Ré di Pruss. Racc. III.
XIII. nel Opera Galatea.
XVI. nel Op. Coriolano a 6 Voc. 2 Corni.
tr
XIV. nel Op. Ifigenia, a 8 Vo. Cr. Ob. Fl.
tr
XVII. nel Op. Fetonte a 4 Voci.
XV. nel Op. Angelica, a 6 Voc. 2 Corn.
XVIII. nel Op. Mitridate. a 6 Vo. Corn.
tr tr
tr tr
VI. Sinfonie del C.E. GRAUN, Maestr. di Cap. di Ré di Pruss. Racc. IV
XIX. nel Op. Armida. a 8 Voc. Fl. Fag.
XXII. nel Op. Paride. a 8 Voc. 2 Cor. 2 Fl.
tr tr
XX. nel Op. Britanuico. a 6 Voc. 2 Cor.
XXIII. nel Op. Sylla.
XXI. nel Op. Orfeo. a 6 Voc. 2 Corni.
XXIV. nel Op. Semiramide a 6 Vo. Cor.
IV. Sinfonie del C. E. GRAUN, Maestr. di Cap di Ré di Pr. Racc. V.
XXV. nel Op. Montezuma. a 8 V. Fl. Fg.
XXVII. nel Op. Fratelli nemici.
XXVI. nel Op. Ezio. a 6 Voci. Corni.
XXVIII. nel Op. Merope. a 8 V. Fl. Corn.

SINFONIE. 11
VI. Sinfonie del Giov. Amad. GRAUN, Maestro di Concerto di Ré di Prussia. Raccolt. I.
I. a 4 Voci.
tr
IV. a 4 Voci.
II. a 4 Voci.
V. a 4 Voci.
III. a 4 Voci.
VI. a 4 Voci.
VI. Sinfonie del Giov. Amad. GRAUN, Maestro di Concerto di Ré di Pruss. Raccolta II.
I. a 6 Voci. 2 Corni.
IV. a 6 Voci. 2 Corni.
II. a 6 Voci. 2 Corni.
V. a 6 Voci. 2 Corni.
III. a 6 Voci. 2 Corni.
VI. a 6 Voci. 2 Corni.
VI. Sinfonie del Giov. Amad. GRAUN, Maestro di Concerto di Ré di Pruss. Racc. III.
I. a 6 Voci. 2 Corni.
tr
IV. a 6 V. 2 Corni.
tr
II. a 6 Voci. 2 Oboi. o Flaut.
V. a 6 Voci. 2 Corni.
III. a 6 Voci. 2 Oboi o Flaut.
VI. a 6 Voci. 2 Corni.

12 SINFONIE.
VI. Sinfonie del Giov. Amad. GRAUN, Maestro di Concerto di Ré di Pruss. Raccolta IV.
I. a 8 Voci. 2 Corni. 2 Oboi.
IV. a 8 Voci. 2 Corni. 2 Fl.
II. a 8 Voci. 2 Corni. 2 Oboi.
V. a 8 Voci. 2 Corni. 2 Fl.
III. a 8 Voci. 2 Corni. 2 Ob.
VI. a 8 Voci. 2 Corni. 2 Fl.
VI. Sinfonie del Giov. Amad. GRAUN, Raccolta V.
I. a 10 Voci. 2 Corni. 2 Fl. 2 Ob.
IV. a 12 Voci. 2 Corn. 2 Fl. 2 Ob. 2 Fag.
tr
II. a 10 Voci. 2 Corn. 2 Fl. 2 Ob.
V. a 12 Voci. 2 Corn. 2 Fl. 2 Ob. 2 Fag.
III. a 10 Voci. 2 Corn. 2 Fl. 2 Ob.
VI. a 12 Voci. 2 Corn. 2 Fl. 2 Ob. 2 Fag.
tr
VI. Sinfonie del G. A. GRAUN, Maest. di Conc. di Ré di Pr. Racc. VI.
I. a 4 Voci.
IV. a 6 Voci. 2 Corni.
II. a 4 Voci.
V. a 6 Voci. 2 Corni.
III. a 4 Voci.
VI. a 9 Voci. 2 Corn. 2 Ob. 1 Fag.

SINFONIE. 13
VI. Sinfonie del Sign. GIULINI.
I. a 4 Voci.
IV. a 6 Voci. 2 Oboi.
II. a 4 Voci.
V. a 6 Vc. 2 Corni.
III. a 6 Voci.
VI. Sinfonie del G. HARRER, Direttore della Musica in Lipsia. Raccolta I.
I. a 6 Voci. 2 Corni.
IV. a 6 Voci. 2 Oboi.
II. a 6 Voci. 2 Corni.
V. a 6 Voci. 2 Oboi.
III. a 6 Voci. 2 Corni.
VI. a 6 Voci. 2 Oboi.
VI. Sinfonie del G. HARRER, Direttore della Musica in Lipsia.
I. a 4 Voci.
IV. a 8 Voci. 2 Corni. 2 Ob.
II. a 4 Voci.
V. a 8 Voci. 2 Corni. 2 Oboi.
III. a 8 Voci. 2 Corni. 2 Oboi.
VI. a 8 Voci. 2 Corni. 2 Oboi.

14 SINFONIE.

VI. Sinfonie del G. A. HASSE, *Primo Maestro di Capella di S. M. il Ré di Polon. Elett. di Sassonia. Raccolta I.*

I. nel Opera Cleofide. a 8 Voc. 2 *Cr.* 2 *Ob.*

IV. nel Op. Asteria a 8 Voc. 2 *Cor.* 2 *Ob.*

II. nel Op. Fabricio, a 6 Voci. 2 *Corni.*

V. nel Op. Atalanta. a 10 Voc. 2 *C.* 2 *Ob.* 2 *Fl.*

III. nel Opera Senocrita.

VI. Op. la Clem. di Tito. a 9 V. 2 *O.* 2 *F.* 1 *F.*

VI. Sinfonie del G. A. HASSE. *Raccolta II.*

VII. nel Op. Irene. *Ouv.* 10 Vc. 2 *C.* 2 *O.* 2 *Fl.*

X. nel Op. Artaserse a 6 Voci. 2 *Corn.*

VIII. nel Op. Alfonso a 10 Vc. 2 *C.* 2 *O.* 2 *F.*

XI. nel Op. Numa. a 8 Voci.

IX. nel Op. Demetrio a 10 V. 2 *C.* 2 *O.* 2 *F.*

XII. nel Op. Luc. Papirio 12 Voc. 2 *C.* 2 *Ob.* 2 *Fl.* 2 *Fag.*

VI. Sinfonie del G. A. HASSE. *Raccolta III.*

XIII. nel Opera Didone aband. a 9 Voci 2 *Corn.* 2 *Ob.* 1 *Fag.*

XVI. nel Opera Arminio a 6 Voc. 2 *Cor.*

XIV. nel Op. Asilo d'amore a 6 V. 2 *Cr.*

XVII. nel Opera Semiramide a 10 Voci. 2 *Corni.* 2 *Ob.* 2 *Fl.*

XV. nel Opera Antigono, a 8 Voci. 2 *Corn.* 2 *Flauti.*

XVIII. nel Opera la Spartana a 10 Voci, 2 *Corni.* 2 *Oboi.* 2 *Flaut.*

SINFONIE. 15

VI. Sinfonie del G. A. HASSE. *Raccoltaa IV.*

XIX. nel Op. Leucippo, a 8 V. 2 *Cor.* 2 *Ob.*

XXII. nel Op. Attilio Regolo. a 6 Voci. 2 *Corni.*

XX. nel Op. Demofonte, a 6 Voc. 2 *Cor.*

XXIII. nel Opera Ciro ricon. a 9 Voci, 2 *Corni.* 2 *Oboi.* 1 *Fag.*

XXI. nel Op. Il Natal. di Giove a 8 Voci. 2 *Corni.* 2 *Oboi.*

XXIV. nel Opera Ipermestra, a 9 Voci. 2 *Corni.* 2 *Oboi.* 1 *Fagott.*

IV. Sinfonie del G. A. HASSE. *Raccolta V.*

XXV. nel Opera Adriano, a 10 Voci. 2 *Corni.* 2 *Oboi.* 2 *Flauti.*

XXVII. nel Op. l'Eroe Cinese, a 6 Voci. 2 *Corni.*

XXVI. nel Opera Solimanno, a 6 Voci. 2 *Oboi.*

XXVIII. nel Opera Artemisia, a 10 Voc. 2 *Corn.* 2 *Ob.* 2 *Fl.*

IV. Sinfonie del G. A. HASSE. *Raccolta VI.*

XXIX. nel Op. Ezio. a 10 Voc. 2 *Corni.* 2 *Oboi.* 2 *Flauti.*

XXXI. nel Opera Olimpiade *Ouverture* a 10 Voci. 2 *Corni.* 2 *Ob.* 2 *Fl.*

XXX. nel Opera il Ré Pastore a 11 Voci. 2 *Corni.* 2 *Ob.* 2 *Fl.* 1 *Fagotto.*

XXXIII. nel Opera Alcide al Bivio, Ouverture.

16
SINFONIE.
VI. Sinfonie del G. A. HASSE, P. M. di Cap. di S. M. il Ré di P. E. di S. Raccolta VII.
I. a 8 Voci. 2 Corni. 2 Oboi.
IV. a 4 Voci.
II. a 4 Voci.
V. a 6 Voci. 2 Corni.
III. a 4 Voci.
VI. a 8 Voci. 2 Corni. 2 Oboi.
V. Sinfonie del I. A. HILLER, in Lipſia.
I. a 6 Voci. 2 Corni.
IV. a 6 Voci. 2 Corni.
II. a 6 Voci. 2 Flauti.
V. a 4 Voci.
III. a 4 Voci.
VI. Sinfonie del Carl HOECKH, Maeſtro di Concerto di Principe d'Anhalt-Zerbſt.
I. a 6 Voci. 2 Corni.
IV. a 6 Voci. 2 Flauti.
II. a 4 Voci.
V. a 4 Voci. 2 Oboi.
III. a 6 Voci. 2 Oboi.
VI. a 8 Voci. 2 Corni. 2 Oboi.

SINFONIE.
17
VI. Sinfonie del Mich. HOFFMANN, Muſico in Bresla.
I. a 4 Voci.
IV. a 4 Voci.
II. a 4 Voci.
V. a 4 Voci.
III. a 4 Voci.
VI. a 4 Voci.
V. Sinfonie del Leop. HOFFMANN, Muſico in Vienna.
I. a 4 Voci.
IV. a 4 Voci.
II. a 4 Voci.
V. a 4 Voci.
III. a 6 Voci. 2 Oboi.
VI. Sinfonie del HOLZBAUER, Maeſt. di Cap. d'El. Pal. Racc. I.
I. a 4 Voci.
IV. a 4 Voci.
II. a 4 Voci.
V. a 4 Voci.
III. a 4 Voci.
VI. a 6 Voci. 2 Corni.

18 SINFONIE.
VI. Sinfonie del HOLZBAUER, Maestr. di Cap. d'El. Pal. Racc. II.
I. a 6 Voci. 2 Corni.
IV. a 8 Voci. 2 Corni. 2 Oboi.
II. a 7 Voci. 2 Corni. Violoncello Oblig.
V. a 8 Voci. 2 Corni. 2 Oboi.
III. a 8 Voci.
VI. a 11 Voc. 2 Clar. Tymp. 2 Cor. 2 Ob. 2 Fl.
VI. Sinfonie del HORN, Direttore della Musica di S. E. il Comte di Brühl in Dresda.
I. a 4 Voci.
IV. a 6 Voci. 2 Corni.
II. a 5 Voci. 1 Flauto.
V. a 8 Voci. 2 Corni. 2 Oboi.
III. a 6 Voci. 2 Corni.
VI. a 8 Voci. 2 Corni.
VI. Sinfonie del Giov. Amad. JANITZSCH, Mus. di Cam. di Ré di Pruss. Raccolta I.
I. a 4 Voci.
IV. a 4 Voci.
II. a 4 Voci.
V. a 4 Voci.
III. a 4 Voci.
VI. a 4 Voci.
SINFONIE. 19
VI. Sinfonie del Giov. Amad. JANITZSCH, Musico di Camera di Ré di Pruss. Raccolta. II.
I. a 4 Voci.
IV. a 4 Voci.
II. a 4 Voci.
V. a 6 Voci. 2 Corni.
III. a 4 Voci.
VI. a 6 Voci.
III. Sinfonie di Nic. JOMELLI, Primo Maest. di Cap. di Duca di Wurtenberg.
I. a 6 Voci. 2 Corni.
II. a 6 Voci. 2 Corni.
III. a 6 Voci. 2 Corni.
IV. Sinfonie del JULINI.
I. a 5 Voci. 2 Corni.
III. a 6 Voci. 2 Corni.
II. a 6 Voci. 2 Oboi.
IV. a 6 Voci. 2 Corni.

20
SINFONIE.
IV. Sinfonie del KRAUSE, Organista in Zittau.
I. a 4 Voci.
III a 6 Voci. 2 Oboi.
tr
II. a 6 Voci. 2 Oboi.
IV. a 8 Voci. 2 Corni. 2 Ob.
III. Sinfonie del KUNZ, Direttore della Musica in Lubeck.
I. a 4 Voci.
II. a 6 Voci.
III. a 9 Voci. 2 Tromb. Tymp. 2 Oboi.
VI. Sinfonie del LAMPUGNANI.
I. a 4 Voci.
IV. a 6 Voci. 2 Corni.
II. a 6 Voci. 2 Corni.
V. a 8 Voci. 2 Tromb. o Corni. 2 Oboi.
III. a 6 Voci. 2 Oboi.
VI. a 6 Voci. 2 Corni.

SINFONIE.
21
IV. Sinfonie del Pietro LOCATELLI, da Bergamo.
I. a 4 Voci.
III. a 4 Voci.
II. a 4 Voci.
IV. a 4 Voci.
VI. Sinfonie del Joh. Batt. MARTINO, in Milano. Racc. I.
I. a 4 Voci.
IV. a 4 Voci.
II. a 4 Voci.
V. a 4 Voci.
III. a 4 Voci.
VI. a 4 Voci.
VI. Sinfonie del Joh. Batt. MARTINO, in Milano.
Raccolta II.
I. a 6 Voci. 2 Corni.
IV. a 6 Voci. 2 Corni.
II. a 6 Voci. 2 Corni.
V. a 6 Voci. 2 Corni.
III. a 6 Voci. 2 Corni.
VI a 6 Voci. 2 Corni.

VI. Sinfonie 2. del J. B. MARTINO, & 4. del MARTINI. Raccolta III.
I. a 8 Voci. 2 Tromb. 2 Oboi. Martino.
IV. a 4 Voci.
II. a 8 Voci. 2 Corni. 2 Oboi.
V. a 4 Voci.
III. a 4 Voci. Martini.
VI. a 3 Voci.
tr
VI. Sinfonie del L. MOZART, Muſ. di Cam. d' Arciveſc. di Salzburg.
I. a 4 Voci.
IV. a 4 Voci.
II. a 4 Voci.
tr
V. a 4 Voci.
III. a 4 Voci.
VI. a 6 Voci. 2 Corni.
VI. Sinfonie del Georg. NERUDA, Muſico di Cam. di S. M. il Ré di Pol. Elett di Saſſ.
I. a 4 Voci.
IV. a 6 Voci. 2 Corni.
II. a 4 Voci.
V. a 6 Voci. 2 Corni.
III. a VI. Voci. 2 Oboi.
VI. a 6 Voci. 2 Corni.
VI. Sinfonie del RELUZZI, Muſico in Praga. Raccolta I.
I. a 6 Voci. Corni.
IV. a 6 Voci. 2 Corni.
tr tr
II. a 6 Voci. Corni.
V. a 6 Voci. 2 Corni.
III. a 6 Voci. 2 Corni.
VI a 6 Voci.
VI. Sinfonie del RELUZZI, Muſico in Praga. Raccolta II.
I. a 4 Voci.
IV. a 6 Voci. 2 Corni.
II. a 6 Voci. 2 Corni.
V. a 8 Voci. 2 Corni. 2 Flaut.
III. a 6 Voci. 2 Corni.
VI. a 8 Voci. 2 Corni. 2 Fl.
VI. Sinfonie del F. X. RICHTER, Muſico di Camera d' Elettor. Palat.
I. a 4 Voci.
IV. a 4 Voci.
II. a 4 Voci.
V. a 6 Voci. 2 Corni.
III. a 4 Voci.
VI. a 6 Voci. 2 Corni.

24 SINFONIE.
VI. Sinfonie del ROELLIG, Musico in Dresda. Raccolta I.
I. a 4 Voci.
IV. a 4 Voci.
II. a 4 Voci.
V. a 4 Voci.
III. a 4 Voci.
VI. a 4 Voci.
VI. Sinfonie del ROELLIG, Musico in Dresda. Raccolta II.
I. a 6 Voci. 2 Corni.
IV. a 8 Voci. 2 Corni. 2 Oboi.
II. a 6 Voci. 2 Corni.
V. a 8 Voci. 2 Corni. 2 Oboi.
III. a 4 Voci.
VI. a 8 Voci. 2 Corni. 2 Oboi.
VI. Sinfonie del Giov. Enr. ROLLE, Dirett, della Musica in Magdeburg.
I. a 4 Voci.
IV. a 6 Voci. 2 Corni.
II. a 6 Voci. 2 Corni.
V. a 8 Voci. 2 Corni. 2 Obvi.
III. a 6 Voci. 2 Corni.
VI. a 8 Voci. 2 Corni. 2 Ob.

SINFONIE. 25
VI. Sinfonie del SCALABRINI.
IV. a 4 Voci.
I. a 4 Voci.
II. a 4 Voci.
V. a 4 Voci.
III. a 2 Voci.
V. a 4 Voci.
IV. Sinfonie del Giuseppe SCARLATTI.
I. a 8 Voci. 2 Corni. 2 Oboi.
III. a 4 Voc. nel Opera Gran Madre.
II. a 4 Voci. nel Opera: de gustibus.
IV. a 8 Voc.
tr
IV. Sinfonie del Ioh. STAMITZ, Maest. di Conc. d'Elett. Palat.
I. a 4 Voci.
III. a 8 Voci. 2 Corni. 2 Fl.
II. a 8 Voci. 2 Oboi. 2 Corni.
IV. a 6 Voci.

26 SINFONIE.
VI. Sinfonie del STEINMETZ, Musico in Dresda.
I. a 4 Voci.
IV. a 6 Voci. 2 Corni.
II. a 6 Voci. 2 Corni.
V. a 8 Voci. 2 Corni. 2 Oboi.
III. a 6 Voci. 2 Corni.
VI. a 8 Voci.
VI. Sinfonie del Giuf. UMSTADT, Musico in Dresda.
I. a 4 Voci.
IV. a 6 Voci. 2 Oboi.
II. a 4 Voci.
V. a 6 Voci. 2 Oboi.
III. a 4 Voci.
VI. a 6 Voci. 2 Corni.
V. Sinfonie del D. Anton. VIVALDI.
I. a 4 Voci.
IV. a 4 Voci.
II. a 4 Voci.
V. a 4 Voci.
III. a 4 Voci.

SINFONIE. 27
VI. Sinfonie del Christof. WAGENSEIL, Comp. della Cam. d. S. M. Imp. Raccolta.
I. a 4 Voci.
IV. a 8 Voci. 2 Corni. 2 Ob.
II. a 4 Voci.
V. a 8 Voci. 2 Corni. 2 Oboi.
III. a 5 Voci.
VI. a 8 Voci. 2 Corni. 2 Oboi.
VI. Sinfonie del Christ. WAGENSEIL, Comp. della Cam. d. S. M. Imp. Raccolta II.
I. a 6 Voci. 2 Oboi.
IV. a 6 Voci. 2 Oboi.
III. a 6 Voci. 2 Oboi.
V. a 6 Voci. 2 Oboi.
III. a 6 Voci. 2 Oboi.
VI. a 6 Voci.
VI. Sinfonie del Christ. WAGENSEIL, Comp. della Cam. di S. M. Imp. Racc. III.
I. a 6 Voci. 2 Corni. 2 Flauti.
IV. a 6 Voci. 2 Corni.
II. a Voci.
V. a 6 Voci.
III. a 6 Voci. 2 Oboi.
VI. a 6 Voci.

F I N E.

Nacherinnerung.

Ich mache hier den Anfang mit den versprochenen **musicalischen Verzeichnisse** aller **practischen Werke** der **verschiedenen Autoren**, die sich in meiner Officin befinden, und die ich durch die **Themata**, so viel der Raum verstatten will, kenntlich zu machen, und von einander zu unterscheiden gesucht habe, so wie man die Bücher nach ihren Titeln unterscheidet. Billige Beurtheiler werden von selbst einsehen, daß es Mühe genung koste, einen in etwas beträchtlichen Vorrath von dergleichen Sachen zusammen zu bringen, oder, so zu sagen, gewissen Musikern aus den Händen zu winden: daß es aber noch mehr Mühe koste, und eine ziemlich beschwerliche Arbeit sey, sie in eine gewisse Ordnung zu bringen. Wie manchen Streit hat man nicht auszumachen, und wie manchen geheimen Kampf zu überwinden, wenn man einem jeden Verfasser das Seinige geben, und die unter **verschiedenen Nahmen** vorkommenden Stücke ihren wahren Meistern zueignen will? Und wenn man in so zweifelhaften Fällen, dergleichen mir gar oft vorgekommen sind, durch Nachfragen nicht viel heraus bringt, wie leicht wird man alsdann von seiner Beurtheilungskraft eben so oft irre geführt als sicher geleitet?

Ich muß daher bey Kennern und Liebhabern der Musik, ja bey einigen Componisten selbst, deren Nahmen in diesem Verzeichnisse vorkommen, oder künftig vorkommen werden, wegen gewisser unvermeidlicher Fehler um Vergebung bitten, und sie zugleich ersuchen, daß, wenn einige ihrer Stücke selbst, oder auch anderer Verfasser, unrichtig angegeben worden, sie mir darüber mit einer kleinen Nachricht zu statten kommen, da-

damit bey einer etwan zu wiederholenden Auflage dieses Catalogs die alten Fehler verbessert, und neue vermieden werden mögen. Ich habe deswegen nur eine kleine Anzahl Exemplarien von diesem ersten Versuche gedruckt, und den Nutzen der Liebe zur Richtigkeit gern aufgeopfert.

Wollten berühmte Componisten sichs gefallen lassen, bey einer müßigen Stunde, ein Verzeichniß ihrer practischen Werke selbst aufzusetzen, und mir es freundschaftlich mitzutheilen: so würde ich es nicht allein mit allem Dank erkennen, sondern auch in meiner Bemühung um so viel muthiger fortfahren, je sicherer ich mich auf solche Nachrichten verlassen könnte. Es hindert nichts, daß ich alsdann die Sachen noch nicht haben würde, die in einem solchen Verzeichnisse stünden, weil ich mich auf den Fuße setzen würde, mir dieselben sogleich anzuschaffen, wenn sich einige Nachfrage unter den Musikliebhabern dazu finden sollte.

Doch die Unrichtigkeit des Nahmens ist es nicht allein, die mich bisweilen zu Fehlern verleitet haben wird, sondern auch die **Instrumente**, und die **Anzahl der Stimen**, die ich über jedwedem Themate angegeben habe. Wer weiß nicht, welche Freyheit sich dieser oder jener Musiker nimmt, bey einem Stücke bald Stimmen hinweg zu lassen, bald zuzusetzen; bald Stücke, die auf dieses oder jenes Instrument gesetzt sind, auf ein anderes über zu tragen? Auch von dergleichen willkührlichen Veränderungen habe ich Spuren genung gefunden; und wie viele können mir unentdeckt geblieben seyn, die alsdann in meinem Verzeichnisse eben so viele Fehler ausmachen?

Ich muß daher in diesem Stücke meine Zuflucht wiederum zu der Gütigkeit derer nehmen, die genauer davon unterrichtet sind. Das Vergnügen, das sie mir durch ihre aufrichtigen Nachrichten (denn mit Vermuthungen ist mir nicht viel gedient, sie müßten denn Dinge betreffen, die man zu keiner völligen Gewißheit bringen könnte,) erweisen, ist zugleich eine Gefälligkeit die sie der ganzen Musik erzeigen: Die Bücherkenntniß ist so oft die Beschäftigung vieler gelehrten Männer gewesen, und einige fruchtbare Autoren haben selbst, um die Welt vor Irrthümern zu bewahren, ein vollständiges Verzeichniß ihrer Werke und Schriften gemacht, so daß heut zu Tage die Historia litteraria, dieses unübersehliche Feld, dennoch in eine so vortreffliche Ordnung gebracht ist, die wir der Musik zur Zeit nur noch wünschen können. Sollten nun die Verehrer dieser edlen Kunst, und die zum Theil dieselbe ihr Hauptgeschäfte seyn lassen, weniger eifrig seyn, das ihrige beyzutragen, um der musikalischen Litteratur ein Licht anzuzünden, dessen sie bisher noch entbehren müssen?

Ich habe mich mit dieser ersten Abtheilung meines Catalogs in den Grenzen meines Vorraths halten müssen, und habe beschlossen in denselben so lange fortzufahren, bis ich durch auswärtige Nachrichten in den Stand gesetzt werde, vollständigere und richtigere Verzeichnisse zu liefern. Ich werde nach Maaßgebung meiner bisher bekannt gemachten **Verzeichnisse musikalischer gedruckter Bücher und ungedruckter Werke**, und der darinnen beliebten Ordnung fortfahren, die daselbst nur dem Nahmen nach verzeichneten practischen Arbeiten mit den **Thematen** der musikalischen Welt vorzulegen. Dieser erste Versuch begreift die Sinfonien, welche, nach dem Namen ihrer Verfasser, **auf der 45. bis 49sten Seite des Verzeichnisses der musikalischen Werke, welche nicht durch den Druck bekannt gemacht worden,** stehen. Die Reihe wird zuerst an die **Trios**, auf **Violinen** und **Flöten** kommen. **Claviersachen; Solos, Duetten, Quadros, Concerte,** auf **allerley Instrumente** sollen alle zu ihrer Zeit nachfolgen. Der ziemliche Vorrath, den ich von geistlichen und weltlichen **Singesachen**, beson-

besonders von **Opern** habe, soll auf gleiche Weise, Arie vor Arie in ein Verzeichniß gebracht werden. Hin und wieder wird man finden, daß etliche Sinfonien in Noten mehr oder weniger stehen, als in dem Nahmen Verzeichnisse angegeben worden. Erstes rührt daher, daß ich in der Zeit, welche zwischen der Ausgabe jenes und dieses Catalogs verstrichen ist, von manchem Autor mehrere bekommen, als ich dazumal hatte, und nicht gern leere Zeilen lassen wollte, da ich die Einrichtung einmal zu halben Dutzenden gemacht hatte; das letzte aber kömmt von der Entdeckung einiger falschen Angaben, deren Stelle ich nicht sogleich ersetzen konnte. Der Unterschied des Preises, welcher daher entstehen muß, wird leicht zu heben seyn, wenn man zum Grunde setzt, daß ich jeden Bogen zu 4 gl. bestimme, und zu jeder Hauptstimme, als Violine, Viole, Baß, Oboe, einen Bogen, zu den Hörnern, und andern Ausfüllstimmen aber, nur halbe Bogen rechne; so daß ein jeder die Kosten des Verlangten leicht finden wird, da ich bey solchen Preise so lange, als es nur die Münze gestattet, bleiben werde.

Jedweder, der in diesen Sachen kein Fremdling ist, wird leicht einsehen, wie viel Mühe, Zeit und Kosten darzu erfodert werde, und wie sehr ich nöthig habe, durch einen vernünftigen Beyfall und eine gütige Unterstützung verständiger Männer ermuntert zu werden. Will man sich aber, auf meine Unkosten, mit Tadeln und Spotten etwas zu gute thun, weil man sich zu so einer Arbeit für geschickter und erfahrner hält: so werde ich mir die Freyheit nehmen, ebenfalls darüber zu spotten und zu tadeln, daß man nicht lange vor mir auf einem Einfall gerathen ist, der der Musik und berühmten Componisten so sehr zur Ehre und Nutzen gereicht, der in der Ausführung eben so schwer als verdrüßlich ist, und der ein so viel größeres Recht zu einer gütigen Beurtheilung hat, weil man nichts vorgearbeitet gefuuden, sondern das Eis selbst brechen, und sich durch mancherley Zweifel und Ungewißheiten hindurch winden müssen.

Leipziger Neujahrsmesse, 1762.

Joh. Gottlob Immanuel Breitkopf.

CATALOGO
DEI
SOLI, DUETTI, TRII
E
CONCERTI
PER
IL VIOLINO,

IL VIOLINO PICCOLO, E DISCORDATO,
VIOLA DI BRACCIO, VIOLA D'AMORE,
VIOLONCELLO PICCOLO E VIOLONCELLO,
E VIOLA DI GAMBA.

CHI

SI TROVANO IN MANUSCRITTO
NELLA OFFICINA MUSICA DI BREITKOPF
IN LIPSIA.

PARTE IIda.

1762.

SOLI ò SONATE

A VIOLINO SOLO

COL BASSO.

VI. Sonate, a Violino Solo con Baſſo, di Joh. AGRELL.
Direttore della Muſica in Norimberga.

VI. Sonate a Violino Solo con Baſſo, di Fr. BENDA.
Muſ. di Camera di Ré di Pruſſia. Racc. I.

VI. Sonate a Violino Solo con Baſſo, di Fr. BENDA.
Muſ. di Cam. di Ré di Pruſſ. Racc. II.

VI. Sonate a Violino Solo con Baſſo, di Fr. BENDA.
Muſ. di Cam. di Ré di Pruſſ. Racc. III.

VI. Sonate a Violino Solo con Baſſo, di Fr. BENDA.
Muſ. di Cam. di Ré di Pruſſ. Racc. IV.

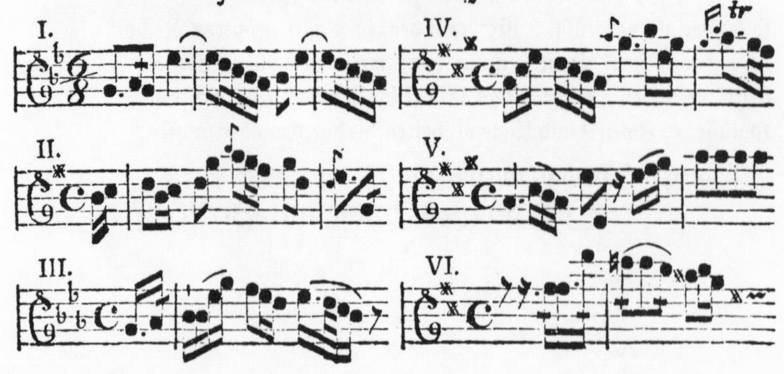

VI. Sonate a Violino Solo con Baſſo, di Fr. BENDA.
Muſ. di Cam. di Ré di Pruſſ. Racc. V.

VI. Sonate a Violino Solo con Baſſo, di Fr. BENDA.
Muſ. di Cam. di Ré di Pruſſ. Racc. VI.

VI. Sonate a Violino Solo con Baſſo, di Fr. BENDA.
Muſ. di Cam. di Ré di Pruſſ. Racc. VII.

VI. Sonate a Violino Solo con Baſſo, di Fr. BENDA.
Muſ. di Cam. di Ré di Pruſſ. Racc. VIII.

XVI. Capricetti a Violino Solo, del Sign. Fr. BENDA.

VI. Sonate a Violino Solo con Baſſo, di Giuſeppi CASELLI.

VIII. Sonate a Violino Solo con Baſſo, del Sign. GIOVANINI.

VI. Sonate a Violino Solo con Baſſo, di Giov. Amad. GRAUN. *Maeſtr. di Conc. di Ré di Pruſſ. Racc. I.*

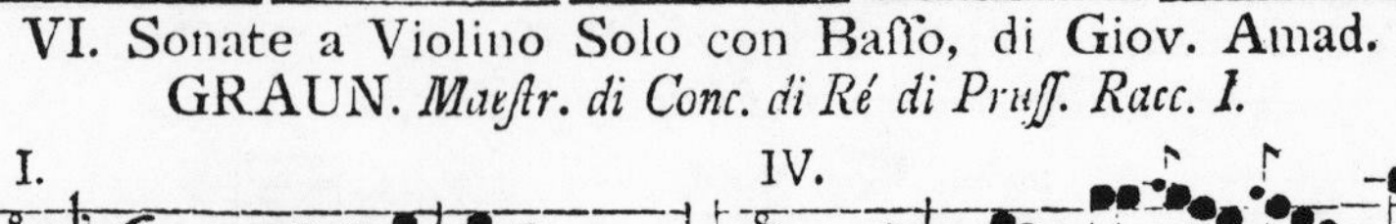

VI. Sonate a Violino Solo con Baſſo, di Giov. Amad. GRAUN. *Maeſt. di Conc. di Ré di Pruſſ. Racc.-II.*

VI. Sonate a Violino Solo con Baſſo, di Diſma HATASCH, *Muſico di Cam. di S. Maeſt. il Duca di Gotha. Racc. I.*

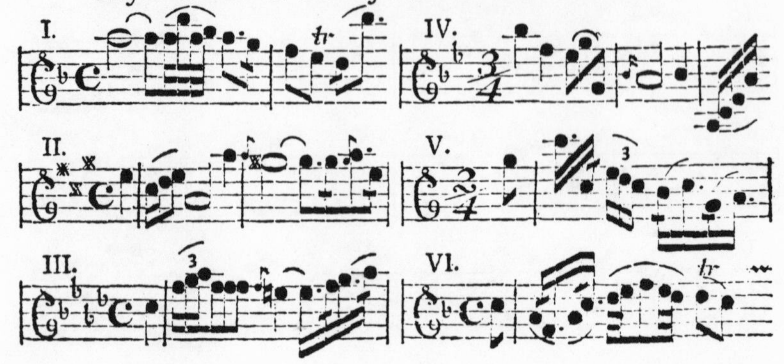

8 SOLI a VIOLINO.
VI. Sonate a Violino Solo con Basso, di Carl HOECKH.
Maestro di Conc. di S. A. S. il Princ. d' Anhalt Zerbst. Racc. I.
I. Ad. ausgef.
IV.
tr
II. Adag. ausgef.
V.
III. Adag. ausgesetzt.
VI.
VI. Sonate a Violino Solo con Basso, di C. HOECKH.
M. d. Con. d. S. A. S. il P. d. A. Z. Racc. II.
I.
IV.
II.
V.
III.
VI.

VI. Sonate a Violino Solo con Basso, di Giov. Giorg.
NERUDA. Mus. di Cam. di Ré di Pol. Racc. I.
I.
IV.
II.
V.
III.
VI.

SOLI a VIOLINO. 9
VI. Sonate a Violino Solo con Basso, del Sign.
SUCCARI, o ZUCCARI.
I.
IV.
II.
V.
III.
II. Sonate, di ORSLER
Musico in Vienna.
III. Sonate, da diversi
Maestri. Racc. I.
I.
I. di Færster.
II.
II. di Pfeiffer.
III. di Teleman.

VI. Sonate a Violino Solo con Basso, da diversi
Maestri. Raccolta. II.
I. di Krebs.
IV. di Scheibe.
II.
V.
III.
VI.

DUETTI.

VI. Sonate a due Violini ſenza Baſſo, del Sign. Antonio MOSELLE.

IV. Sonate a due Violini ſenza Baſſo.

TRII.

VI. Sonate a due Violini et Baſſo, del Sign.
G. BENDA.

VII. Sonate a due Violini et Baſſo, del Sign.
BRIOSCHI.

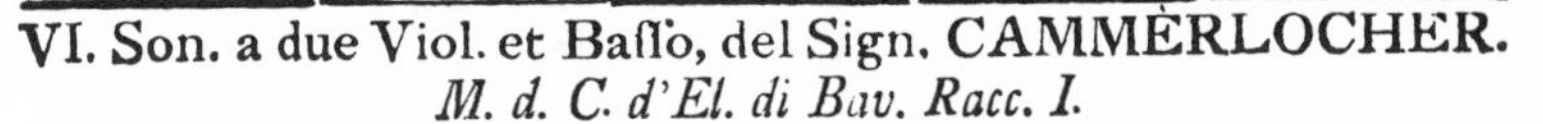

VI. Son. a due Viol. et Baſſo, del Sign. CAMMERLOCHER.
M. d. C. d'El. di Bav. Racc. I.

VI. Sonate a due Violini et Baſſo, del Sign.
CAMMERLOCHER. *Racc. II.*

VI. Sonate a due Violini et Baſſo, del Sign.
CAMMERLOCHER. *Racc. III.*

VI. Sonate a due Violini et Baſſo, del Sign. CAMMERLOCHER. *Racc. IV.*

VI. Sonate a due Violini et Baſſo, del Sign. FASCH.
M. d. Conc. di Princ. d'Anh. Zerbſt.

VI. Sonate a due Violini et Baſſo, di Adelb. FAUNER. *in Vienna.*

IV. Sonate a due Violini et Baſſo, di Georg. GEBEL.
Maeſtr. di Cap. di Princ. di Schwarzb.

VI. Sonate a due Violini et Baſſo, di G. A. GRAUN.
Maeſtro di Concerto di Ré di Pruſſia. Racc. I.

VI. Sonate a due Violini et Baſſo, di G. A. GRAUN.
M. di Conc. di Ré di Pr. Racc. II.

VI. Sonate a due Violini et Baſſo, di G. A. GRAUN.
M. di Con. di Ré di Pr. Racc. III.

VI. Sonate a due Violini et Baſſo, di G. A. GRAUN.
M. di Con. di Ré di Pr. Racc. IV.

VI. Sonate a due Violini et Baſſo, di GRAVINA.
M. di Cam. di Duca di Wurtenberg.

VI. Divertimenti a due Violini et Baſſo, del Sign. HELMANN.

VII. Partite a due Violini et Baſſo, di Carl. HOECKH.
Maeſt. di Cap. di Pr. d' Anh. Zerbſt.

IV. Sonate a due Violini et Baſſo, di KOHAUT.
Muſica in Vienna.

III. Sonate a due Violini et Baſſo, di
KRAUSE.

VI. Sonate a due Violini et Baſſo, di
MARTINO. *Racc. I.*

VI. Sonate a due Violini et Baſſo, di
MARTINO. *Racc. II.*

VI. Sonate a due Violini et Baſſo, di
MARTINO. *Racc. III.*

VI. Sonate a due Violini et Baſſo, di
MARTINO. *Racc. IV.*

VI. Sonate a due Violini et Baſſo, di
MARTINO. *Racc. V.*

VI. Sonate a due Violini et Baſſo, del Sign. Antonio MOSELLE.

VI. Sonate a due Violini et Baſſo, di Joh. Georg. NERUDA. *Muſico di Cam. di Ré di Polon. Racc. I.*

VI. Sonate a due Violini et Baſſo, di Joh. Georg. NERUDA. *Muſ. di Cam. di Ré di Pol. Racc. II.*

VI. Sonate a due Violini et Baſſo, *con Fuge*, di Joh. Georg. NERUDA. *Muſ. di Cam. di Ré di Pol. Racc. III.*

III. Sonate a due Violini et Baſſo, *con Variazioni*, di J. G. NERUDA. *Muſ. di Cam. di Ré di Pol. Racc. IV.*

VI. Sonate a due Violini et Baſſo, di Joh. Georg. ORSLER. *Raccolta I.*

VI. Sonate a due Violini et Baſſo, di Joh. Georg.
ORSLER. *Racc. II.*

VI. Sonate a due Violini et Baſſo, di Joh. Georg.
ORSLER. *Racc. III.*

IV. Sonate a due Violini et Baſſo, di Joh. Georg.
ORSLER. *Racc. IV.*

VI. Sonate a due Violini et Baſſo, di PICHLER.
in Vienna.

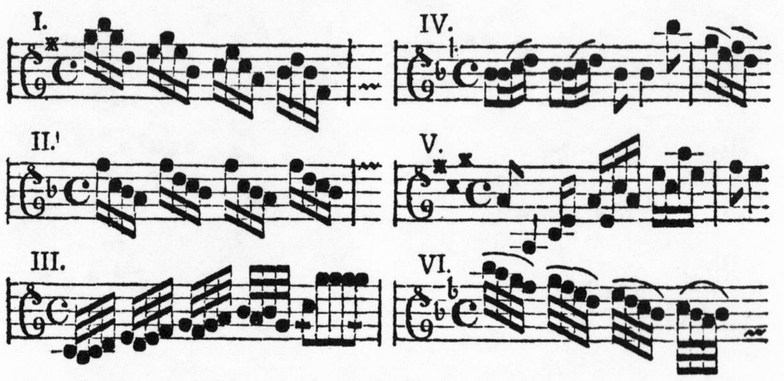

VI. Sonate a due Violini et Baſſo, del Sign.
RELUZZI. *Racc. I.*

III. Sonate a due Violini et Baſſo, del Sign.
RELUZZI. *Racc. II.*

VI. Sonate a due Violini et Baſſo, di Chriſtoph WAGENSEIL.
Comp. di Cam. di S. M. Imper. Racc. I.

VI. Sonate a due Violini et Baſſo, di Chriſt. WAGENSEIL.
Comp. di Cam. di S. M. Imper. Racc. II.

IV. Sonate a due Violini et Baſſo, di Chriſt. WAGENSEIL.
Comp. di Cam. di S. M. Imper. Racc. III.

VI. Sonate a due Violini et Baſſo, di Chriſt. WAGENSEIL.
Comp. di Cam. di S. M. Imp. Racc. IV.

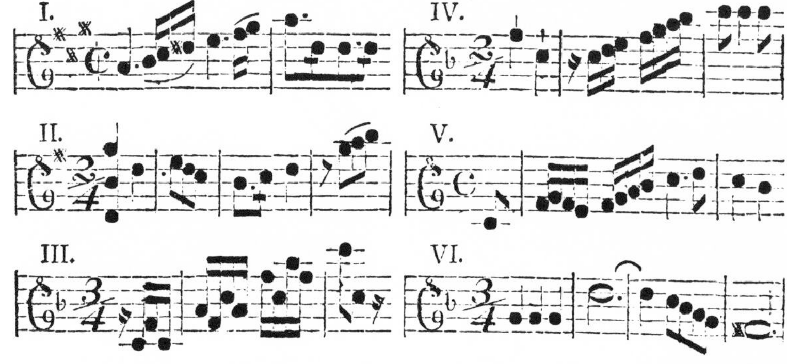

V. Sonate a due Violini et Baſſo, di Chriſt. WAGENSEIL.
Comp. di Cam. di S. M. Imper. Racc. V.

VI. Sonate a due Violini et Baſſo, da diverſi Autori. *Racc. I.*

26
TRII a VIOLINO.
VI. Sonate a due Violini et Baſſo, da diverſi Autori. Racc. II.
I. di Birck.
IV. di Clari.
II. di Birck.
tr
V. di Giraneck.
III. di Clari.
VI. di Giraneck.
VI. Sonate a due Violini et Baſſo, da diverſi Autori. Racc. III.
I di Harrer.
tr
IV. di Holtzbauer.
II. di Harrer.
V. di Perez.
III. di Holtzbauer.
VI. di Perez.
VI. Sonate a due Violini et Baſſo, da diverſi Autori. Racc. IV.
I. di J. S. Bach.
tr
IV. di Janitſh.
II. di F. W. Bach.
V. di Mozart.
tr
tr
III. di Hendel.
VI. di Tzart.

TRII a VIOLINO.
27
VI. Sonate a due Violini et Baſſo, da diverſi Autori. Racc. V.
I. di Enderlein.
IV. di Scheibe.
II. di Paganelli.
V. di Torelli.
III di Reuter.
VI. di Turno.
VI. Sonate a due Violini et Baſſo, da diverſi Autori. Racc. VI.
I. di Allai.
Conc. noturno.
IV. di Collabrat.
II. di Bernaſconi.
V. di Gaſparini.
III. di Biancolini.
3
3
VI. di Porpora.

CONCERTI.

II. Conc. di G. AGRELL.

I. *a Viol. Conc. 2 Viol. V. B.*

II.

III. Conc. di Fr. BENDA. *R. I.*

I. *a Viol. Conc. 2 Viol. V. B.*

II.

III.

III. Conc. di Fr. BENDA. *R. II.*

I. *a Viol. C. 2 Viol. V. B.*

II.

III.

III. Con. di Fr. BENDA. *R. III.*

I. *a Viol Conc. 2 Viol. V. B.*

II.

III.

IV. Concerti di Fr. BENDA. *Racc. IV.*

I. *a Viol. Conc. 2 Viol. V. B.*

II.

III.

IV.

IV. Conc. di Georg. BENDA. *Racc. I.*

I. *a Viol. Conc. 2 Viol. V. B.*

III.

II.

IV.

III. Conc. di G. BENDA. *R. II.*

I. *a Viol. Conc. 2 Viol. V. B.*

II.

III.

III. Conc. di G. BENDA. *R. III.*

I. *a Viol. Conc. 2 Viol. V. B.*

II.

III.

III. Conc. di Giov. BENDA.

I. *a Viol. Conc. 2 Viol. V. B.*

II.

III.

III. Concerti di CATANEO.

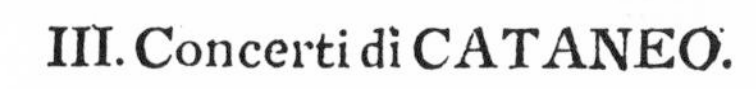

I. *a Viol. Conc. 2 Viol. V. B.*

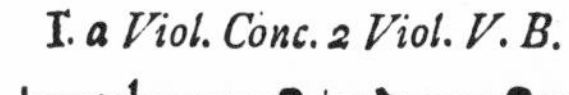

II.

III.

30
CONCERTI a VIOLINO.
III. Con. di FOERSTER. R. I.
I. a Viol. Conc. 2 Viol. V. B.
II.
III.
III. Con. di FOERSTER. R. II.
I. a Viol. Conc. 2 Viol. V. B.
II.
III.
III. C. di FOERSTER. R. III.
I. a Viol. Conc. 2 Viol. V. B.
II.
tr
III.
III. C. di FOERSTER. R. IV.
I. a Viol. C. Fl. Trav. Obl. 2 Viol. V. B.
II. a Viol. C. Fl. Tr. Obl. 2 Viol. V. B.
III. Viol. picc. C. Oboe Obl. 2 Viol. V. B.
III. Con. di FOERSTER. R. V.
I. 2 Viol. Conc. 2 Viol. rip. V. B.
II. a Viol. Conc. 2 Corni. 2 Viol. V. B.
III. a Viol. C. 2 Corn. 2 Oboi 2 Viol. V. B.
II. Concerti, di GALLO.
I. a Viol. Conc. 2 Viol. V. B.
II.

CONCERTI a VIOLINO.
31
III. Conc. di GRAUN. R. I.
I. a Viol. Conc. 2 Viol. V. B.
II.
III.
III. Conc. di GRAUN. R. II.
I. a Viol. Conc. 2 Viol. V. B.
II.
III.
III. Conc. di GRAUN. R. III.
I. a Viol. Conc. 2 Viol. V. B.
II.
III.
III. Conc. di GRAUN. R. IV.
I. a Viol. Conc. 2 Viol. V. B.
II.
III.
III. Conc. di GRAUN. R. V.
I. a Viol. Conc. 2 Viol. V. B.
II.
III.
III. Conc. di GRAUN. R. VI.
I. a Viol. Conc. 2 Viol. V. B.
II.
III.

32 CONCERTI a VIOLINO.
III. Conc. di GRAUN. R. VII.
I. a Viol. Conc. 2 Viol. V. B.
II.
III.
III. Conc. di GRAUN. R. VIII.
I. a Viol. Conc. 2 Viol. V. B.
II.
III.
III. Conc. di GRAUN. R. IX.
I. 2 Viol. Conc. 2 Viol. rip. 2 Corn. V. B.
II.
II.
III. Conc. di GIRANECK. R. I.
I. a Viol. Conc. 2 Viol. V. B.
II.
III.
III. Con. di GIRANECK. R. II.
I. a Viol. Conc. 2 Viol. V. B.
II.
III.
III. Con. di GIRANECK. R. III.
I. a Viol. Conc. 2 Viol. V. B.
II.
III.

CONCERTI a VIOLINO. 33
III. Con. di GIRANECK. R. IV.
I. a Viol. C. 2 Viol. V. B.
II.
III.
III. Con. di GIRANECK. R. V.
I. a Viol. Conc. 2 Viol. V. B.
II.
III.
II. Conc. di GIRANEK. R. VI.
I. a Viol. Conc. 2 Viol. V. B.
II.
II. Conc. di HERTEL.
I. a Viol. Conc. 2 Viol. V. B.
II.
III. Conc. di HOECKH. R. I.
I. a Viol. Conc. 2 Viol. V. B.
II.
III.
III. Conc. di HOECKH. R. II.
I. a Viol. Conc. 2 Viol. V. B.
II.
III.

34 CONCERTI a VIOLINO.
III. Conc. di HOECKH. R. III.
I. a Viol. Conc. 2 Viol. V. B. e Voci rip.
II.
III.
III. Conc. di HOECKH. R. IV.
I. a Viol. Conc. 2 Viol. V. B. e Voci rip.
II.
III.
III. Conc. di HOECKH. R. V.
I. a Viol. Conc. 2 Viol. V. B.
tr.
II.
III.
III. Conc. di HOECKH. R. VI.
I. a Viol. Conc. 2 Viol. V. B, 2 Corni.
II.

IV. Concerti di HORN.
I. a Viol. Conc. 2 Viol. V. B.
II.
III.
IV.

II. Concerti di KUBASCH.
I. a Viol. Conc. 2 Viol. V. B.
II.

CONCERTI a VIOLINO. 35
III. Conc. di MARTINO. R. I.
I. a Viol. Conc. 2 Viol. V. B.
II.
III.
III. Conc. di MARTINO. R. II.
I. a Viol. Conc. 2 Viol. V. B.
II.
III. 2 Viol. oblig. 2 rip. 2 Oboi oblig. 2 Corni. V. B.
II. Concerti di MARCELLO.
I. a Viol. Conc. 2 Viol. V. B.
II.
II. Concerti di MOSELLE.
I. a Viol. C. 2 Corn. 2 Viol. 2 V. rip. V. B.
II. 2 Viol. C. 2 Viol. 2 Viol. rip. V. B.
III. Conc. di NERUDA.
I. a Viol. C. 2 Viol. 2 Viol. rip. V. B.
II.
III.
II. Conc. di NOFERI.
I. a Viol. Conc. 2 Viol. V. B.
II.

36 CONCERTI a VIOLINO.
III. Conc. di PFEIFFER. R. I.
I. a Viol. Conc. 2 Viol. V. B.
III. Conc. di PFEIFFER. R. II.
I. a Viol. Conc. 2 Viol. V. B.
III. Con. di PFEIFFER. R. III.
I. a Viol. Conc. 2 Viol. V. B.
III. Con. di PFEIFFER. R. IV.
I. a Viol. Conc. 2 Viol. V. B.
III. C. gr. di PIANTANIDA.
I. 2 Viol. C. 2 Viol. rip. V. C. V. rip. B. C.
III. C. gr. di PIANTANIDA.
I. 2 Viol. C. 2 Viol. rip. V. C. et rip. B. C.

CONCERTI a VIOLINO. 37
II. Concerti di REZEL.
I. a Viol. Conc. 2 Viol. V. B.
II. C. di SCHWANENBERG.
I. a Viol. Conc. 2 Viol. V. B.
III. Concerti di SCACCIA.
I. a Viol. Conc. 2 Viol. V. B.
III. Conc. di STAMITZ. R. I.
I. a Viol. Conc. 2 Viol. V. B.
III. Conc. di STAMITZ. R. II.
I. a Viol. Conc. 2 Viol. V. B.
III. Conc. di STAMITZ. R. III.
I. a Viol. Conc. 2 Viol. V. B.

38 CONCERTI a VIOLINO.
III. Conc. di STAMITZ. R. IV.
I. a Viol. Conc. 2 Viol. V. B.
II. 2 Corni.
III.
II. Conc. di WODIZKA.
I. a Viol. Conc. 2 Viol. V. B.
II.
IV. Concerti di ZUCCARI.
I. a Viol. Conc. 2 Viol. V. B.
II.
III.
IV.
V.

39
VIOLINO PICCOLO.
IV. Sonate a Violino piccolo, con più Stromenti.
I. di Janitsch. a 4 V. Viol. picc. Ob. V. B.
III. di Rosetti. a 4 V. Viol. picc. 2 Ob. V. B.
II. di Krause. a 4 V. Viol. picc. 2 Viol. B.
IV. di Doles. a 3 V. Viol. picc. Viol. B.
I. Partie di Harrer. a 5 V. Viol. picc. C. 2 Viol. V. B.
I. Concerto di Foerster. a Viol. picc. C. Ob. d'Amor. 2 Viol. V. B.
VI. Concerti di PFEIFFER. a Violino piccolo Concertato.
I. a Viol. picc. Conc. 2 Viol. V. B.
IV.
II.
V.
III.
VI.
VIOLINO DISCORDATO.
I. Sonate di Koenig, a Viol. discord. Flauto e Basso.

V I O L A.

IV. Sonate a Viola Sola coll Cembalo, da diversi Autori. *R. I.*

IV. Sonate a Viola Sola con Basso, da diversi Autori. *R. II.*

VI. Sonate a Viola. *con più Stromenti.*

IV. Sonate del Sgr. JANITZSCH, a 4: Viola *con altri Stromenti.*

V. Concerti à Viola *Concertato.*

VIOLA D'AMORE.

III. Partite à Viola d'Amore Solo col Basso.

42 CONCERTI a VIOLA D'AMORE.

IV. Sonate a Viola d'Amore e Baſſo.

I. del Sgr. Harrer. III. del Sgr. Krumlowsky.

II. del Sgr. Harrer. IV. del Sgr. Krumlowsky.

IV. Partite a Viola d'Amore, *con altri Stromenti.*

I. del Sg. Harrer, *a 1 C. 1 Fl. V. d. A. e B.* III. del S. Wentzel, *a V. d. A. 2 V. e B.*

II. del Sr. Krumlowsky, *a V. d. A. 2 V. c. B.* IV. del S. Wentzel, *a V. d. A. 2 V. e B.*

V. Concerti del Sgr. HOFFMANN.

I. *a Viola d'Amor. 2 Ob. d'Amor, Viola con Cemb.* IV. *a 2 Viol. d'Amor. 2 Fagot. 6 Flaut. Baſſ. e Cemb.*

II. *a 2 Viole d'Amor. 2 Oboi d'Amor. Viola e Cemb.* V. Intrada, *a 2 V. d. A. 2 C. Ingl. 1 Ob. Violon. o Fag.*

III. *a 2 Viole d'Amor. 2 Ob. d'Amor. Viola con Cemb.*

II. Conc. del Sgr. WENTZEL, a Viola d'Amore *con Stromenti.*

I. *a Viol. d'Am. Flaut. Violin. c. B.* II. *a V. d'Am. Liuto, Fl. 2 C. 2 V. V. e B.*

Aria, del Sgr. J. S. BACH, a Viol. d'Amore *con Stromenti.*

I. *a Viola d'Amore, Violin. Conc. 2 Violin. Sopr. Viola et Baſſo.*

VIOLONCELLO.

V. Sonate a Violoncello Solo coll Baſſo da diverſi Autori.

III. Sonate a 2 Violoncelli del ANONYMO italiano.

V. Sonate a 2 Violoncelli e Baſſo del ANONYMO.

II. Sonate a Violoncello con altri Stromenti dell' ANONYMO.

IV. Concerti del Sgr. RETZEL, *a Violoncello conc. 2 Violini. Viola e Basso.*

VIOLONCELLO PICCOLO,

ò

VIOLONCELLO DA BRACCIA.

IV. Sonate del ANONYMO, a Violoncello piccolo Solo c. Basso. *Racc. I.*

V. Sonate del ANONYMO, a Violoncello piccolo Solo c. Basso. *Raccolta II.*

V. Sonate da diversi Autori a Violoncello piccolo Solo col Basso.

II. Trio da diversi Autori a Violonc. Piccol. con altri Stromenti.

III. Quadri da diversi Autori a Violonc. picc. c. altri Strom.

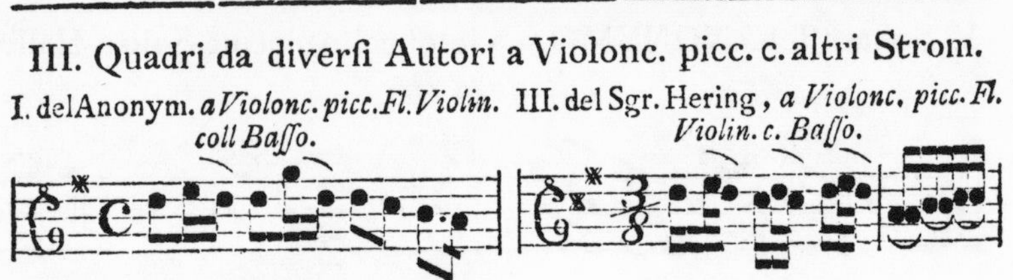

I. del Anonym. *a Violonc. picc. Fl. Violin. coll Basso.*

III. del Sgr. Hering, *a Violonc. picc. Fl. Violin. c. Basso.*

II. del Anonymo, *2 Violon. picc. Flaut. Violin. coll Basso.*

Concerti a Violoncello picc. concertato con altri Stromenti.

III. Conc. da diversi Autori, *a Violonc. pic. conc. 2 Viol. V. c. B. Racc. I.*

I. del Sgr. Fœrster.

II. del Sgr. Gœrner.

III. del Sgr. Graun.

II. Conc. da diversi Autori, *a Violonc picc. conc. Racc. II. 2 Viol. V. c. B.*

I. del Sgr. Riedel.

II. del Sgr. Riedel.

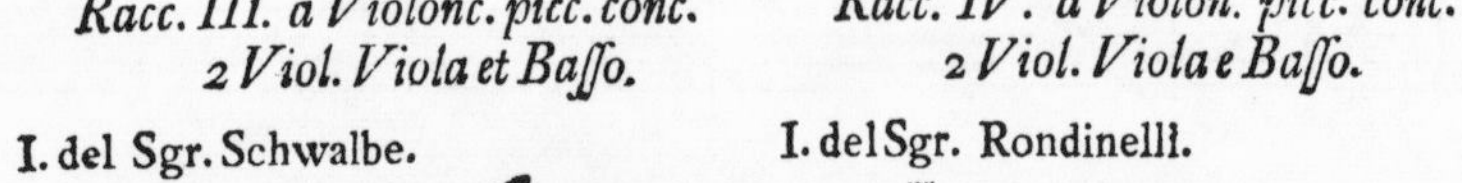

III. Concerti da divers. Autori. *Racc. III. a Violonc. picc. conc. 2 Viol. Viola et Basso.*

I. del Sgr. Schwalbe.

II. del Sgr. Schwalhe.

III. del Sgr. Schwalbe.

III. Concerti da divers. Autori, *Racc. IV. a Violon. picc. conc. 2 Viol. Viola e Basso.*

I. del Sgr. Rondinelli.

II. del Sgr. Wiedner.

III. del Sgr. Wiedner.

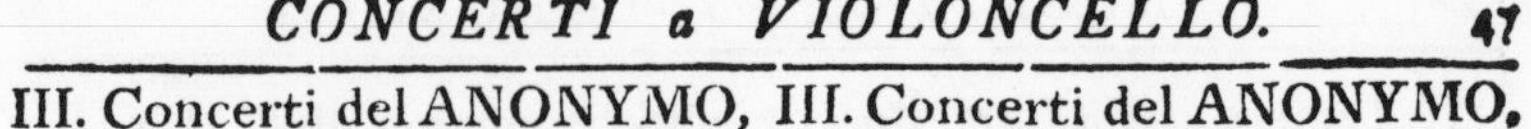

III. Concerti del ANONYMO, *Racc. V. a Violonc. piccolo conc. Violini, Viol. e Basso.*

I.

II.

III.

III. Concerti del ANONYMO, *Racc. VI. a Violonc. piccolo conc. 2 Violini, Viola e Basso.*

I.

II.

III.

III. Concerti dell'ANONYMO *Racc. VII. a Violoncello picc. conc. 2 Violini Viola e Basso.*

I.

II.

III.

II. Concerti dell'ANONYMO, *Racc. VIII. picc. conc. 2 Violini Viola e Basso.*

I.

II.

VIOLA DA GAMBA.

VI. Sonate del Sgr. MENTE, a Viola da Gamba Sola c. Basso.

I. II. III. IV. V. VI.

III. Suites del Sgr. MENTE, a Viola da Gamba Sola coll Basso.

IV. Trio a Viola da Gamba con div. Stromenti.

I. del Sgr. Gebel, a V. d. . Ott. Ob. e B. III. del Sgr. Pepusch, *a Viol. d. G. Fl. e B.*

II. del Sg. Hendel, *a Cemb. obl. e V. d. G.* IV. del Sgr. Pfeiffer, *a Cemb. obl. e V. d. G.*

VI. Sonate del Sgr. REICHENHAUER, a Viola da Gamba, *c. altri Stromenti.*

I. *a 2 Viole da Gamba, c. Cemb.* IV. *a 1 V. d. G. Violonc. picc. c. Cembalo.*

II. *a 2 Viole da Gamb. c. Cemb.* V. *a 1 V. d. G. 1 Violonc. picc. e Cembalo.*

III. *a 1 V. d. G. 1 Violonc. picc. c. Cemb.* VI. *a 1 V. d. G. 1 Violone. picc. e Cemb.*

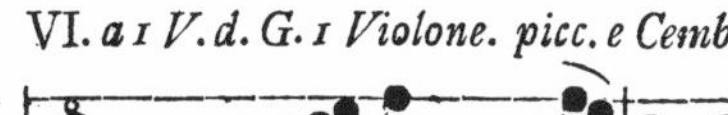

II. Quadri, a Viola da Gamba, *con altri Stromenti.*

I. del Sg. Gebel, *a V. d. G. picc. Flauti Violin. e Basso.* II. del Sg. Janitzsch, *a Viola da Gamb. Ob. Viola c. Basso.*

I. Partita del Sgr. HARRER. I. Conc. del Sg. STOLTZE.

I. *a V. d. G. Ottav. Fl. Ob. Violin. c. B.* I. *a V. d. G. conc. 2 Viol. Viola c. B.*

IL FINE.

CATALOGO DE' SOLI, DUETTI, TRII E CONCERTI

PER

IL FLAUTO TRAVERSO,

FLAUTO PICCOLO, FLAUTO D'AMORE, FLAUTO DOLCE, FLAUTO-BASSO, OBOE, OBOE-D'AMORE, FAGOTTO, SAMPOGNE, CORNO DI CACCIA, TROMBA, ZINCHE E TROMBONI.

CHE

SI TROVANO IN MANOSCRITTO NELLA OFFICINA MUSICA DI BREITKOPF IN LIPSIA.

PARTE IIIza.

1763.

SOLI ò SONATE
a
FLAUTO TRAVERSO SOLO
COLL BASSO.

VIII. Sonate a Flauto Solo coll Baſſo, del Sgr. ABEL,
Muſic. de la Chamb. du Roy de Polon.

III. Sonate a Flauto Solo coll Baſſo, del Sgr. W. F. BACH.

IV. Sonate a Flauto Solo coll Baſſo, del Sgr. QUANTZ.

II. Sonate, a Flauto Solo coll Baſſo, del Sgr. RIEDT.

II. Sonate a Flauto Solo coll Baſſo, del TROMLITZ.

II. Sonate a Flauto Solo coll Baſſo, di ſua Maeſtà il Re di Pruſſia. *(come ſi dice)*

III. Sonate, *a Fl. Solo coll Baſſo.* III. Sonate, *a Fl. Solo coll Baſſo.*

VI. Sonate a Flauto Traverſo Solo coll Baſſo del ANONYMI diverſ.

DUETTI a FLAUTO TRAVERSO.

III. Duetti del Sgr. BOEHME.

VI. Duetti del Sgr. GRAUN, *Maeſtro di Cap. di Re di Pruſſia.*
ô del Sgr. SUSS, *Muſico in Caſſel.*

VII. Duetti del Sgr. QUANTZ. *(come ſi dice.)*

III. Duetti del Sgr. SCHIRER.

VI. Duetti del Sgr. SCHRAMM, Muſico in Dreſda.

Raccolta 1.

VI. Duetti del Sgr. SCHRAMM, Muſico in Dresda. *Raccolta II.*

VI. Duetti del Sgr. SCHRAMM, Muſico in Dresda. *Raccolta III.*

VI. Duetti del Sgr. TROMLITZ. *Raccolta I.*

VI. Duetti del Sgr. TROMLITZ. *Raccolta II.*

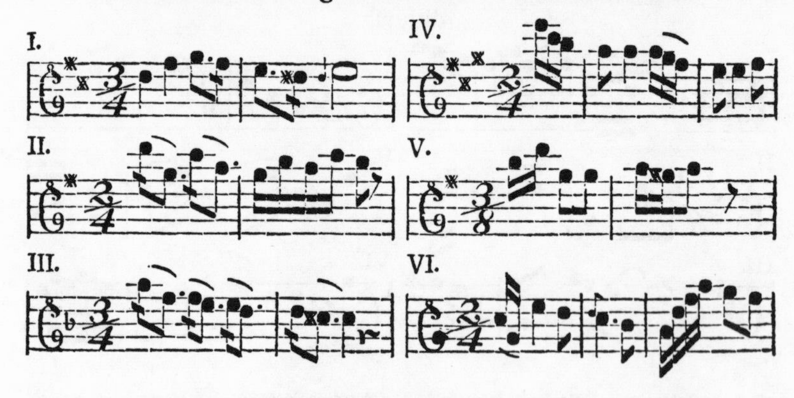

VI. Duetti del Sign. TROMLITZ, *Raccolta III.*

II. Duetti del Sgr. HOLZBAUER et TROMLITZ.

TRII o SONATE a 2. FLAUTI TRAVERSI e BASSO.

VI. Sonate a 2 Flaut. Trav. et Baſſo del C.H. ABEL, Muſ. di Cam. di Ré di Polonia.

III. Sonate a 2 Flaut. Trav. et Baſſo del J. A. HASSE, Primo Maeſtro di Cap. di Ré di Polonia.

III. Sonate a 2 Flaut. Tr. et Baſſo del G.F. KLEINKNECHT Muſ. di Cam. di Marg. di Brand. Culmb.

VI. Sonate a 2 Flaut. Trav. e Baſſo, di G. Giac. QUANTZ, Muſico di Cam. di Ré di Pruſſia. *Racc. I.*

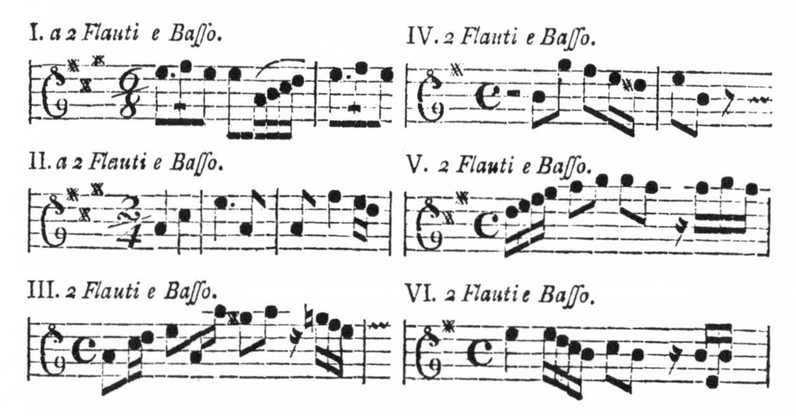

III. Sonate a 2. Flaut. Trav. e Baſſo, di G. G. QUANTZ, Muſ. di Cam. di Ré di Pruſſia. *Racc. II.*

III. Sonate a 2. Flaut. Trav. e Baſſo di F. W. RIEDT, Muſ. di Camera di Ré di Pruſſia.

10 TRII a FLAUTO TRAVERSO e BASSO.
VI. Sonate a 2. Flaut. Trav. e Basso di SCHAFFRATH, Mus. di S. A. la Pr. Am. di Pruss.
I. 2 Flauti e Basso.
IV. 2 Flauti e Basso.
II. 2 Flauti e Basso.
V. 2 Flauti e Basso.
III. 2 Flauti e Basso.
VI. 2 Flauti e Basso.
VI. Sonate a 2. Flauti coll Basso di SORGE.
I. 2 Flauti e Basso.
IV. Flauto piccolo, Viol. ó Ob. et Basso.
II. 2 Flauti e Basso.
V. 2 Flauti e Basso.
III. 2 Flauti e Basso.
VI. Flauto, Violino Basso.
VII. Sonate a 2. Flauti coll Basso di Telemann.
I. 2 Flauti e Basso.
V. 2 Flauti e Basso.
II. 2 Flauti e Basso.
VI. 2 Flauti e Basso.
III. 2 Flauti e Basso.
VII. 2 Flauti e Basso.
IV. 2 Flauti e Basso.

TRII a FLAUTO TRAVERSO. 11
VI. Sonate a 2. Flauti coll Basso. (da diversi Autori) Racc. I.
I. di Bonagetti, a 2 Flauti coll Basso.
IV. di Heinichen, a 2 Flauti coll Basso.
II. di Chelleri, a 2 Flauti coll Basso.
V. di Heinichen, a 2 Flauti coll Basso.
III. di Ferrai, a 2 Flauti coll Basso.
VI. di Hendel, a 2 Flauti c. Basso.
VI. Sonate, a 2 Flauti coll Basso, (da diversi Autori.) Racc. II.
I. di Hendel, a 2 Flauti e Basso.
IV. di Neruda, a 2 Flauti coll Basso.
II. di Janitzsch, a 2 Flauti coll Basso.
V. di Neruda, a 2 Flauti coll Basso.
III. di Janitzsch, a 2 Flauti coll Basso.
VI. di Nichelmann, a 2 Flaut. c. Basso.
IV. Sonate a 2 Flauti coll Basso, (da diversi Autori) Racc. III.
I. di Ruge, a 2 Flauti coll Basso.
III. di Schultz, a 2 Flauti coll Basso.
II. di Ruge, a 2 Flauti coll Basso.
IV. di Wagenseil, a 2 Flauti coll Basso.

TRII o SONATE
a
FLAUTO TRAVERSO, VIOLINO
e
BASSO.

VI. Sonate a Flauto, Violino et Baſſo, del C. F. E. BACH, Muſ. di Cam. di Ré di Pruſſia.

V. Sonate a Flauto Violino et Baſſo, di FR. GIORG et GIOV. BENDA.

III. Sonate, a Flauto Viol. coll Baſſo, di Giov. A. HASSE,
Primo Maeſtro di Cap. di Ré di Polon.

IV. Sonate a Flauto Violino, coll Baſſo di PICHLER,
Muſico in Vienna.

VI. Sonate a Flauto Violino coll Baſſo, di ROELLIG,
Muſico in Dresda.

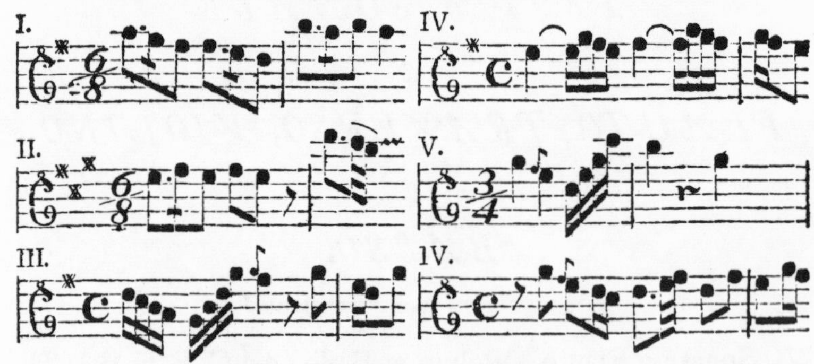

VI. Sonate, a Flauto Violino coll Baſſo, da diverſi Autori.
Raccolta I.

VI. Sonate, Flauto Violino, coll Baſſo, da diverſi Autori.
Raccolta II.

CONCERTI a FLAUTO TRAVERSO CONCERTATO 2. VIOLINI VIOLA e BASSO.

III. Concerti, di C. F. ABEL, *Raccolta I.* III. Concerti di C. F. ABEL, *Raccolta II.*

I. *Flaut. Trav. concert. 2 Viol. Viola e B.* I. *Flaut. Trav. conc. 2 Viol. Viola e B.*

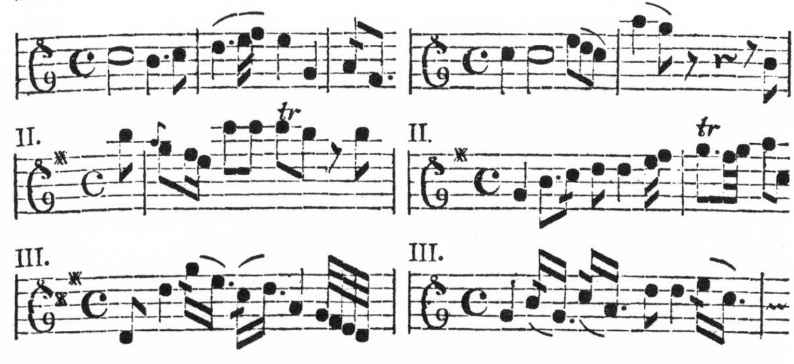

III. Concerti di Fr. BENDA. III. Conc. di C. FOERSTER.

I. *Flaut. Trav. conc. 2 Viol. Viola c. B.* I. *Fl. Trav. conc. 2 Viol. Viola c. Basso.*

III. *Flaut. Trav. conc. Oboe conc. 2 Viol. Viola c. B.*

II. Concerti di GIRANECK, *Flauto conc. 2 Viol. Viola c. Basso.*

III. Conc. di C. H. GRAUN. *Raccolta I.* III. Conc. di C. H. GRAUN. *Raccolta II.*

I. *a Flauto conc. 2 Viol. Viola col Basso.* I. *Flauto conc. 2 Viol. Viola col Basso.*

IV. Concerti di HARTWIG, *a Flauto Trav. Conc. 2. Violino, Viola col Basso.*

III. Concerti di G. A. HASSE. *Raccolta I.* III. Concerti di G. A. HASSE. *Raccolta II.*

I. *a Flaut. Concert. 2 Viol. Viola c. Basso.* I. *Flaut. Trav. Conc. 2 Violini c. Basso.*

III. Concerti di G. A. HASSE. *Raccolta III.*

III. Concerti di KRAUSE.

IV. Concerti di HORN, *a Flauto Conc. 2. Violini col Baſſo.*

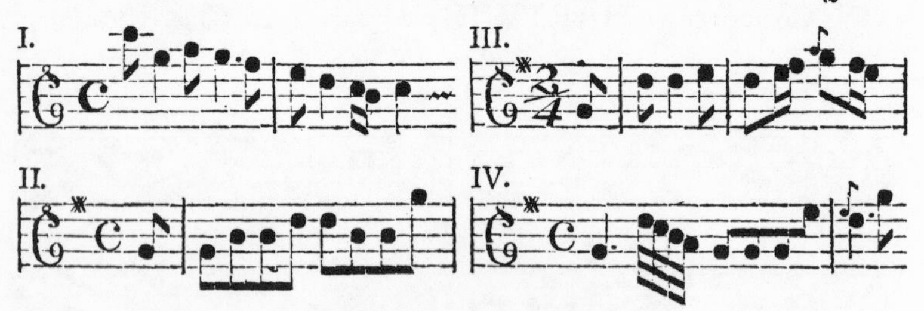

III. Concerti d'Adamo MAHAUT, *a Flaut. Trav. Conc. 2. Violini, Viola col Baſſo.*

II. Concerti di Giov. PFEIFFER, *a Flaut. Trav. conc. 2 Violini Viola col Baſſo.*

IV. Concerti di Giov. Gioach. QUANTZ, *Flaut. Trav. Conc. 2 Violini, Viola col Baſſo.*

III. Concerti di ROELLIG, *a Flauto Traverſo Conc. 2 Violini, Viola coll Baſſo.*

II. Concerti d'Adamo SCHURER.

IV. Concerti di STAMITZ.

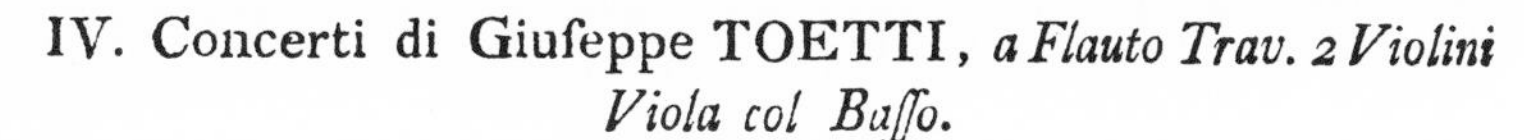

IV. Concerti di Giuseppe TOETTI, *a Flauto Trav. 2 Violini Viola col Basso.*

II. Concerti da diversi Autori. *Raccolta I.*

III. Concerti da diversi Autori. *Raccolta II.*

III. Concerti da diversi Autori. *Raccolta III.*

III. Concerti da diversi Autori. *Raccolta IV.*

FLAUTO PICCOLO.

III. Concerti a Flauto piccolo.

FLUTE DOUCE.

VI. Duetti di HARRER, *a due Flauti dolci. Racc. I.*

VI. Duetti di HARRER, *a due Flauti dolci. Racc. II.*

VI. Duetti di HARRER, *a 2. Flauti dolci. Racc. III.*

VI. Duetti di HARRER, *a 2. Flauti dolci. Racc. IV.*

VI. Duetti di HARRER, *a 2. Flauti dolci. Racc. V.*

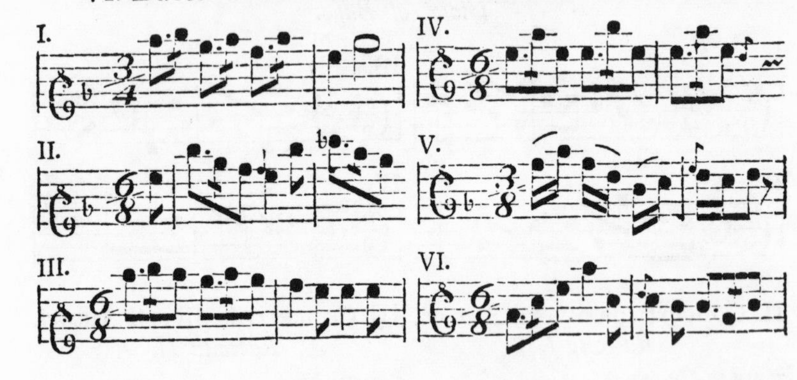

VI. Duetti di HARRER, *a 2. Flauti dolci. Raccolta VI.*

VI. Duetti di HARRER, *a 2. Flauti dolci. Racc. VII.*

VI. Duetti di HARRER, *a 2. Flauti dolci.* *Raccolta VIII.*

III. Duetti di HARRER, *a 2. Flauti dolci.*

I. Trio di TELEMANN, *a Flauto dolce, Oboe col Basso.*

I. Concerto a Flauto Traverso d'Amore, *2 Violini Viola col Basso.*

I. Trio di S. BACH, a Flauto Basso, *Fagotto c. Violone.*

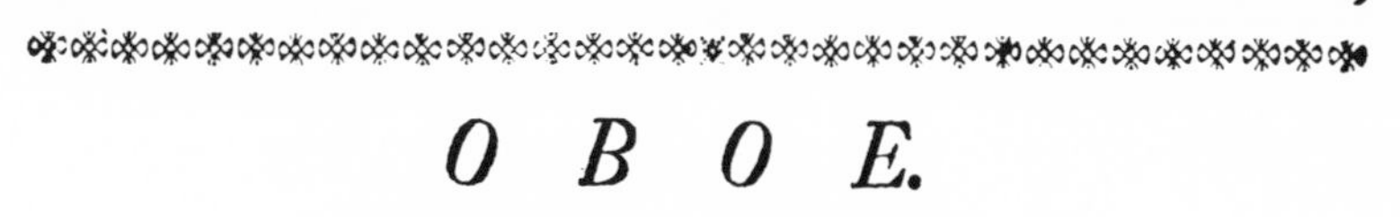

OBOE.

SOLI.

VI. Sonate a Oboe Solo col Basso.

TRII.

III. Sonate di HARRER, *a Oboe, Violino col Basso.*

I. *a Oboe Viol. col Basso.*

II. *a Oboe Violino col Basso.*

III. *a 2 Oboi e Fagotto.*

III. Sonate da diversi, a Oboe con alt. Str. *Racc. I.*

II. di Janitzsch, *a Oboe 2 Viol. c. Basso.*

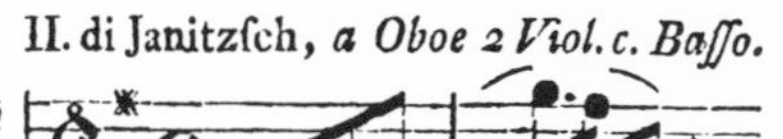

III. di Kœnig, *a Oboe Violini c. Basso.*

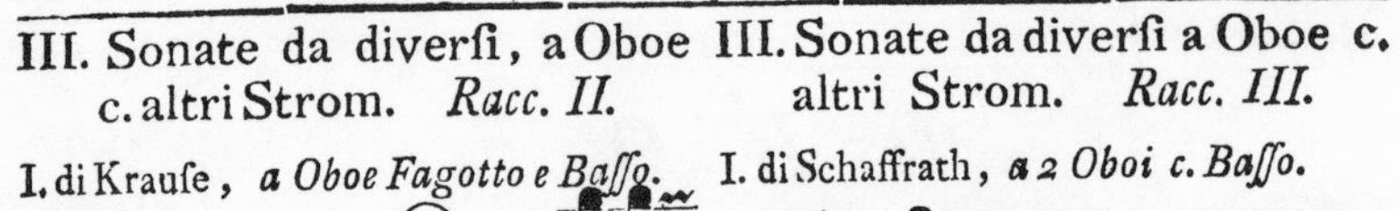

III. Sonate da diverſi, a Oboe c. altri Strom. *Racc. II.*

I. di Krauſe, *a Oboe Fagotto e Baſſo.*

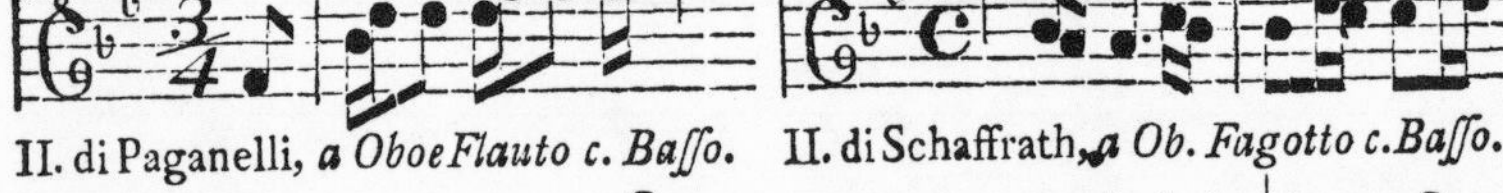

II. di Paganelli, *a Oboe Flauto c. Baſſo.*

III. di Stœltzel, *a Oboe Violino Cembalo.*

III. Sonate da diverſi a Oboe c. altri Strom. *Racc. III.*

I. di Schaffrath, *a 2 Oboi c. Baſſo.*

II. di Schaffrath, *a Ob. Fagotto c. Baſſo.*

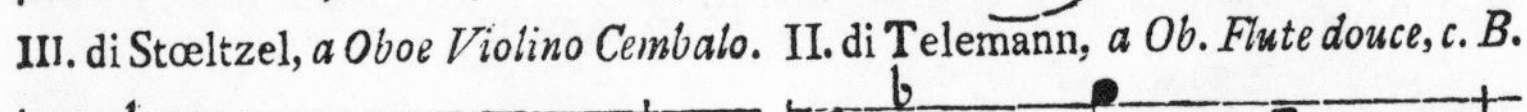

II. di Telemann, *a Ob. Flute douce, c. B.*

QUADRI.

III. Quadri, da diverſi a Oboe c. altri Strom. *Racc. I.*

I. di Haſſe, *a Oboe, Viol. Fag. Violonc.*

III. di Telemann, *a Oboe. Violino, Viola coll Baſſo.*

III. di Krauſe, *a Oboe 2 Violini c. Baſſo.*

III. Quadri, da diverſi, a Oboe c. altri Strom. *Racc. II.*

I. di Krauſe, *a 2 Oboi, Fagotto c. Baſſo.*

II. di Roſetti, *a 2 Ob. Violino picc. Baſſo.*

III. di Scheibe, *a Oboe, 2 Violini c. Baſſo.*

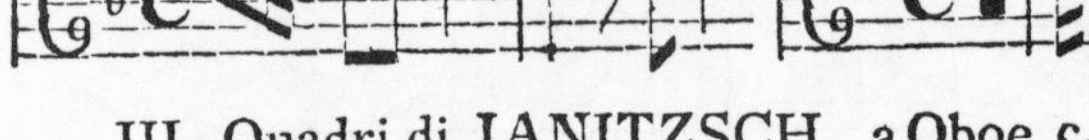

III. Quadri di JANITZSCH, a Oboe c. altri Strom.

I. *a Ob. Violi. picc. Viola ò Viol. da Gamba c. Baſſo.*

II. *a Oboe, Violino, Violetta c. Fondamento.*

III. *a Oboe, 2 Violino col Baſſo.*

II. Quadri di JANITZSCH et TELEMANN.

I. di Janitzſch, *a Oboe Flauto, Violino col Baſſo.*

II. di Janitzſch, *a Oboe, Violetta, o Viola di Braccio, col Baſſo.*

CONCERTI.

III. Concerti di ADAM, a Oboe Conc. 2 Viol. V. c. B. *Racc. I.*

I.

II.

III.

II. Concerti di ADAM, a Oboe Conc. 2 Viol. V. B. *Racc. II.*

I.

II.

III. Concerti di DOMINICO, a Oboe Conc. 2 Viol. V. B.

I.

II.

III.

III. Conc. di FASCH, a Oboe Conc. 2 Violini V. B. *R. I.*

I.

II.

III. *a Ob. Conc. 1 Fl. Viol. Viola, Baſſono oblig. Violonc.*

Muſique de Table.

III. Concerti di FASCH, a 2 Ob. Conc. con altri Strom. *R. II.*

I. *a 2 Oboi oblig. 2 Clar. 2 Corn. 2 Viol. 1 Fag. Viola c. Basso.*

II. *a 2 Ob. 2 Fl. 2 Viol. Fag. Viola c. B.*

III. *2 Ob. 2 Fl. 2 Viol. 2 Fag. Viola c. B.*

II. Concerti di FEHRE, a Oboe Conc. 2 Viol. V. B.

I.

II.

III. Concerti di FOERSTER, a Ob. Conc. 2 Viol. Viola c. B. *Raccolta I.*

I.

II.

III.

III. Concerti di FOERSTER, a Oboe Conc. 2 Viol. Viola c. B. *Raccolta II.*

I.

II.

III.

II. Concerti di FOERSTER, a Oboe Conc. 2 Viol. Viola c. B. *Raccolta III.*

I.

II.

II. Concerti di HARTWIG, a Oboe Conc. 2 Violini, Viola c. Basso.

I.

II.

II. Concerti di ROELLIG, a Oboe Conc. 2 Viol. V. c. B.

I.

II.

III. Concerti di SUHL, a Oboe Conc. 2 Violini, Viol. c. B.

II.

II.

III.

III. Conc. a Oboe Conc. 2 Viol. V. B. *Racc. I.*

I. di Briochi, *a 2 Oboi oblig.*

II. di Mozart, *a Oboe Concert. 2 Corni.*

III. di Retzel.

III. Conc. a Oboe Conc. 2 Viol. V. c. B. *Racc. II.*

I. di Schaffrath.

II. di Wiedner.

OBOE D'AMORE.

PARTITE e SONATE.

II. Partite a 2 Oboi d' Amore, *con più Stromenti.*

I. di Hofmann, *a 2. Oboi d' Amore, 2 Corni c. Basso.*

II. di Pfeiffer, *a 2 Oboe d'Amore, 2 Cor. 2 Viol. Viola c. Basso.*

II. Sonate di TELEMANN, a 2 Oboi d'Amore. &c. &c.

I. *a 2 Oboi d'Amore, 2 Viole c. Violono.* II. *a 2 Oboi d'Amore, 2 Violini, c. Viol.*

T R I I.

III. Sonate a Oboe d'Amore, Violino col Basso.

I. di Anonymo. III. di Graun.

II. di Fasch.

C O N C E R T I.

III. Concerti, a Oboe d'Amore c. altri Strom. *Racc. I.*

III. Concerti a Oboe d'Amore, c. altri Strom. *Raccolta II.*

I. di Graun, *a Oboe d'Amore Conc. Violini, Viola c. Basso.*

I. di Heinrici, *a 2 Oboe d'Amore, Conc. 2 Viol. 2 Corni, c. Basso.*

II. di Graun, *a Oboe d'Amore Conc. 2 Viol. Viola c. Basso.*

II. di Lotti, *a Oboe d'Amore, Conc. 2 Violini, Viola c. Basso.*

III. di Hofmann, *a 2 Oboe d'Amore, 2 Flauti, 2 Viol. Viola c. Bassono Cemb.*

III di Quantz, *a Oboe Conc. 2 Violini Viola c. Basso.*

BASSONO ô FAGOTTO.

S O L I.

IV. Sonate a Fagotto Solo con Cembalo.

I. di Anonymo. III. di Benda.

II. di Benda. IV. di Benda.

T R I I.

III. Sonate di SCHAFFRATH, a Fagotto oblig.

I. *a Fagotto, Flauto col Basso.* III. *a Fagotto, Violino c. Basso.*

II. *a Fagotto, Oboe c. Basso.*

IV. Sonate da diversi a Fagotto obligato.

I. di Bach, *a Fag. oblig. Flauto Basso, Cembalo.*

III. di Graun, *a Fagotto oblig. Violino c. Cembalo.*

II. di Graun, *a Fagotto oblig. Violino col Basso.*

IV. di Krause, *a Fagotto Oboe col Basso.*

QUADRI.

VI. Quadri di REINICKE, a Fagotto, 2 Violini e Baſſo.

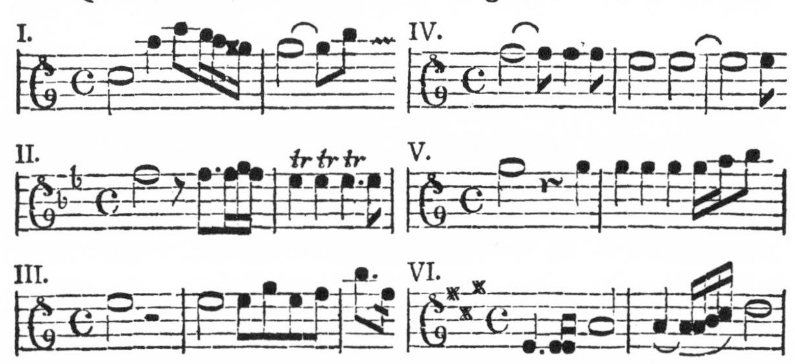

IV. Quadri da diverſi a Fagotto obligato.

I. di Hartwig, *a Fagotto 2 Flauti, col Cembalo.* III. di Hendel, *a Fagotto, 2 Oboi col Baſſo.*

II. di Haſſe, *a Fagotto, Oboe, Violino, Violoncello.* IV. di Krauſe, *a Fagotto, 2 Oboi, col Baſſo.*

CONCERTI.

III. Concerti da diverſi a Fagotto oblig.

I. di Mengis, *a Fagotto oblig. 2 Violino Viola c. Baſſo.* III. di Rœllig, *a Fagotto oblig. 2 Violini, Viola c. Baſſo.*

II. di Mengis, *a Fagotto oblig. 2 Oboi c. Baſſo.*

II. Concerti di SCHAFFRATH, a Fagotto Conc.

I. *Fagotto, 2 Violini, Viola c. Baſſo.* II. *Fagotto, 2 Violini, Viola c. Baſſo.*

SAMPOGNE.

I. Concerto del TELEMANN, *a 2 Sampogoni, Violini Uniſoni c. Baſſo.*

CORNO DA CACCIA.

VI. Duetti, del ANONYMO, *2 Corni da Caccia.*

VI. Duetti, del ANONYMO, *2 Corni da Caccia.*

III. Concerti a Corno Concertato.

I. di Graun, *a Corno Conc. Oboe Violini col Basso.*

III. di Quantz, *a Corno Conc. 2 Violini Viola c. Basso.*

II. di Vogler, *a Corno Conc. Oboe Solo 2 Violini, Viola c. B.*

TROMBA.

I. Trio di PEPUSCH, a Tromba, *Violino col Basso.*

II. Concerti, a Tromba obligata, *2 Violini, Viola c. Basso.*

I. di Hartwich.

II. di Schencke.

ZINCHE e TROMBONI.

II. Ricercari del Luigi BATTIFERI.

a 5. Soggetti.

a 6. Soggetti.

FINE.

CATALOGO
DE'
SOLI, DUETTI, TRII, TERZETTI, QVARTETTI E CONCERTI
PER
IL CEMBALO E L'HARPA.

CHE
SI TROVANO IN MANOSCRITTO
NELLA OFFICINA MUSICA DI BREITKOPF
IN LIPSIA.

PARTE IVta.

1763.

SOLI ô SONATE
A
CEMBALO SOLO.

III. Partite di C.P.E.BACH, per il Cembalo Solo.
Raccolta I.

VI. Sonate di C.P.E. BACH, per il Cemb. Solo. *Racc. II.*

VI. Sonate di C. P. E. BACH, per il Cemb. Solo. *Racc. III.*

VI. Sonate di Ch. Sigm. BINDER, per il Cembalo Solo. *Raccolta I.*

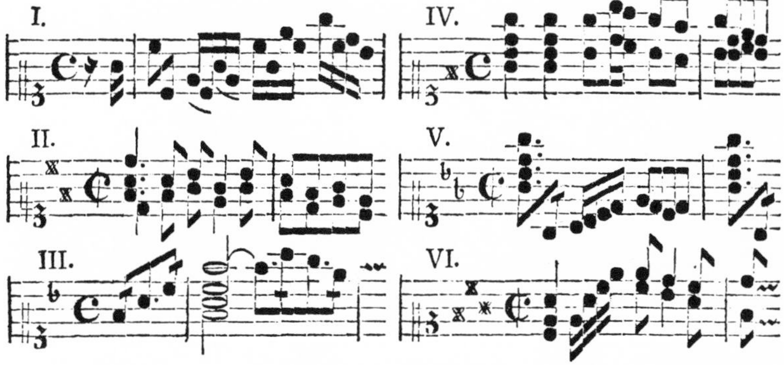

VI, Sonate di Ch. Sigm. BINDER, per il Cembalo Solo. *Racc. II.*

VI. Sonate di Ch. Sigm. BINDER, per il Cembalo Solo. *Racc. III.*

VI. Sonate di Chr, Sigm. BINDER, per il Cembalo Solo. *Racc. IV.*

VI. Sonate di Fortun. CHELLERY, per il Cembalo Solo. *Racc. I.*

II. Sonate di Balth. GALUPPI, per il Cembalo Solo.

III. Partite di J.C. GERSTENBERGER, per il Cemb. S.

III. Sonate di G. HARRER, per il Cemb. Solo.

IV. Sonate di J. A. HASSE. per il Cemb. Solo, fatte per S. A. R. la Delphina di Fr. *Racc. I.*

IV. Sonate di J. A. HASSE, per il Cembalo Solo, *Racc. II.*

II. Sonate et I. Partita di HENDEL, per il Cemb. Solo.

Divertimento di Giuf. HAYDEN, per il Cemb. Solo.

IV. Sonate di J. L. KREBS, per il Cembalo Solo.

II. Sonate di MARCELLO, per il Cembalo Solo.

II. Sonate di NICHELMANN, per il Cembalo Solo.

II. Sonate di Frid. Chr. MOHRHEIM, per il Cembalo Solo.

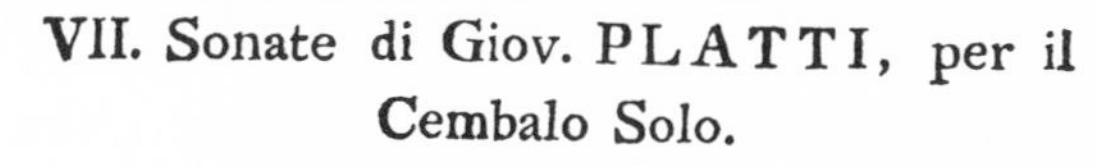

VII. Sonate di Giov. PLATTI, per il Cembalo Solo.

VII. Suites di J. H. ROLLE, per il Cembalo Solo.

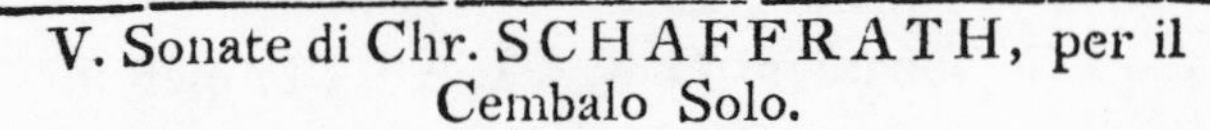

V. Sonate di Chr. SCHAFFRATH, per il Cembalo Solo.

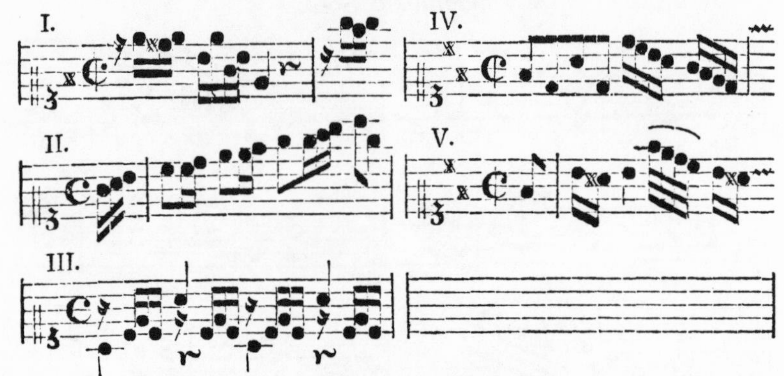

VII. Pieces di J. A. SCHEIBE, per il Cembalo Solo.

IV. Sonate di Jos. UMSTADT, per il Cembalo Solo.

III. Sonate di TRANSCHEL, per il Cembalo Solo,

I. Sinfonia di SCHEINPFLUG, per il Cemb. S.

I. Sonata di SCHOBERTH, per il Cembalo Solo.

VI. Suites di WAGENSEIL, ô vero Divertimenti per il Cembalo Solo. *Raccolta I.*

VI. Suites de WAGENSEIL, à Clavessin seul. *Recueil II.*

VI. Suites de WAGENSEIL, pour le Clavesſin ſeul.
Raccolta III.

VI. Suites de WAGENSEIL, pour le Clavesſin ſeul.
Raccolta IV.

III. Suites de WAGENSEIL, pour le Clavesſin ſeul.
Raccolta V.

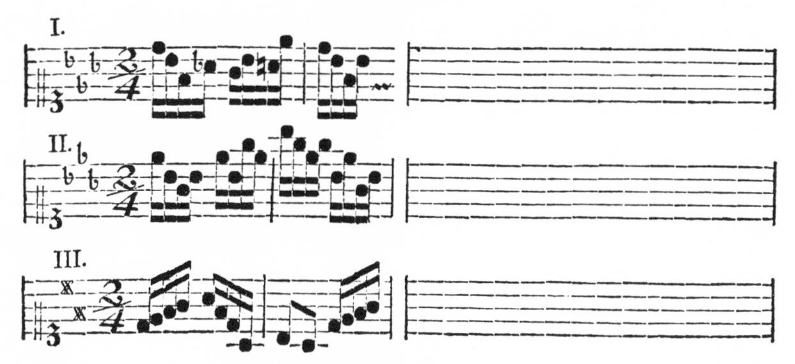

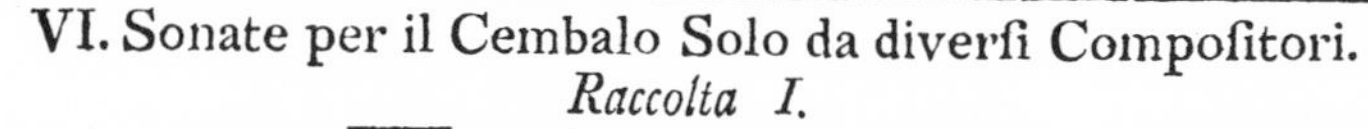

VI. Sonate per il Cembalo Solo da diverſi Compoſitori.
Raccolta I.

VI. Sonate per il Cembalo Solo da diverſi Compoſitori.
Raccolta II.

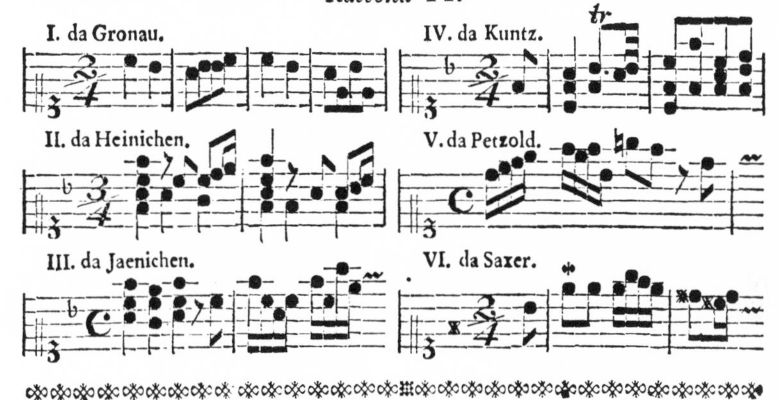

DUETTI

A DUE

CLAVICEMBALI CONCERTATI.

I. Concerto di F. W. BACH, a due Clavicembali Concertati.

T R I I
a Clavicembalo obligato con Flauto ô Violino.

I. Sonata del Sigr. C. P. E. BACH, *a Cl. ob. c. V.*

I. Sonata del Sigr. G. BENDA, *a Cl. ob. c. Fl.*

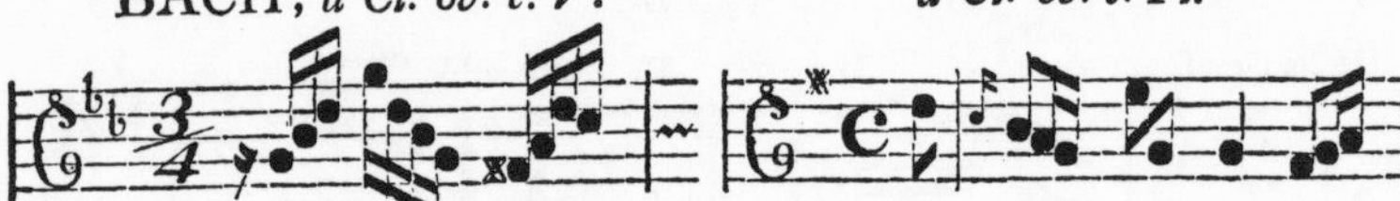

VI. Sonate del Sigr. BINDER, *a Cl. ob. c. V.*

I. Sonata del Sigr. ELTERLEIN, *a Cl. ob. c. V.*

III. Sonate del S. FRITSCH, *a Cl. ob. c. Fl.*

I. Sonata del Sigr. EYSEL, *a Cl. ob. c. V.*

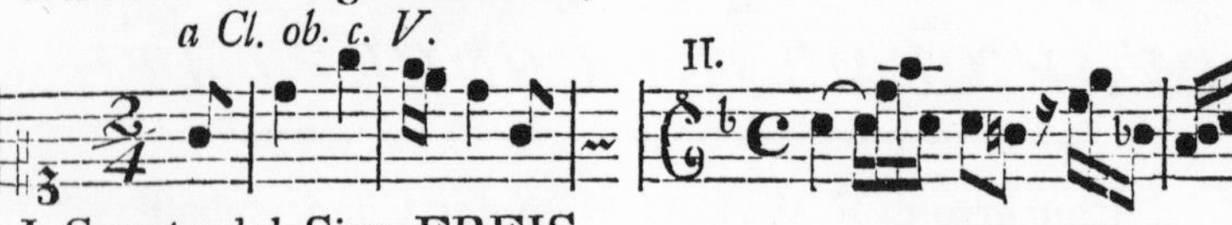

I. Sonata del Sigr. FREISLICH, *a Cl. ob. c. V.*

I. Sonata del Sigr. HENDEL, *a Cl. obl. con Viola ô Gamba.*

I. Sonata del Sigr. KUIHL, *a Cl. ob. c. V.*

II. Sonate del Sigr. LEFFLOTH, *a Cl. ob. c. V.*

I. Sonata del Sigr. MAHAUT, *a Cl. ob. c. V.*

IV. Sonate del Sigr. PFEIFFER, *a Cl. obl.*

I. *c. Viol. ô Oboe.*

II. Sonate del Sigr. PICKEL, *a Cl. ob. c. V.*

II. *c. Gamba ô Viola.*

III. *c. Violino.*

I. Sonata del Sigr. RIEPEL, *a Cl. ob. c. V.*

IV. *c. Viol. ô Oboe.*

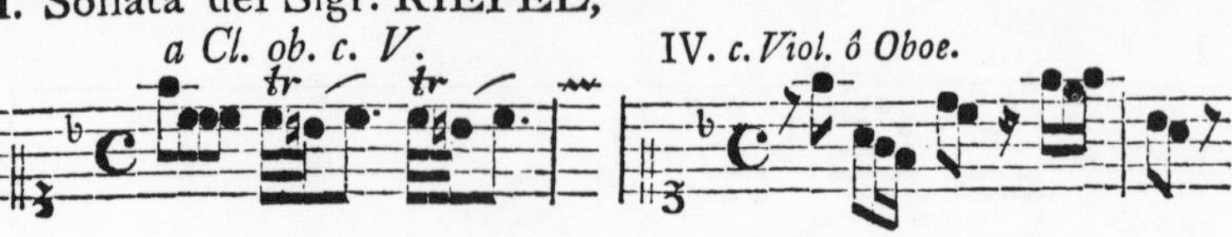

II. Sonate del Sigr. QUANTZ, *a Cl. obl. con Flauto Trav.*

VI. Divertimenti del Sigr. ROELLIG, a Cemb. obl. c. Flauto o Violino.
I.
II.
III.
IV.
V.
VI.

VI. Partite del Sigr. ROELLIG, a Cemb. obl. c. Flauto Trav.
I.
II.
III.
IV.
V.
VI.

VI. Sonate del Sigr. ROLLE, a Cemb. obl con Violino.
I.
II.
III.
IV.
V.
VI.

I. Sonata del Sigr. ROTH, a Cl. obl. c. V.
I. Sonata del Sigr. SCHALE, a Cl. obl. c. V.
VII. Sonate del Sigr. SCHEIBE, a Cl. obl. c. V.
I.
II.
III.
IV.
V.
VI.
VII.
I. Sonata del Sigr. STAINMETZ, a Cl. obl. c. V.
I. Sonata del Sigr. SCHMIDT, a Cl. obl. c. V.
I. Sonata del Sigr. SEYFFERT, a Cl. obl. c. V.
I. Sonata del Sigr. WAGENSEIL, a Cl. obl. c. V.
III. Sonate del Sigr. WIEDNER, a Cl. obl. c. V.
I.
II.
III.
II. Sonate del Sigr. WEINER, a Cl. obl. c. V.
I.
II.

TERZETTI

a Cembalo obligato con altri Stromenti obligati.

III. Partite del Sigr. REICHERT, *a Cl. obl. c. Flauto. e Violino.*

III. Terzetti del Sigr. WAGENSEIL, *a Cl. obl. c. Violino e Viola.*

II. Partite del Sigr. ROELLIG, *a Cemb. obl. c. Violino e Violoncello.*

QUARTETTO

a Cembalo obligato con altri Stromenti obligati.

I. Quart. del Sigr. L. HOFFMANN, *a Cemb. obl. con Violino, Violoncello obl. et Basso.*

CONCERTI

a Cembalo obligato con altri Stromenti obligati.

I. Concerto di J. ADAM, *a Cembalo obligato con 2 Violini, Viola e Basso.*

III. Concerti di J. AGRELL, *a Cl. ob. c. 2 Viol. V. B. Racc. I.*

III. Concerti di J. AGRELL, *a Cl. ob. c. 2 Viol. V. B. Racc. II.*

III. Concerti di J. AGRELL, *a Cl. ob. c. 2 Viol. V. B. Racc. III.*

III. Concerti di J. AGRELL, *a Cl. ob. c. 2 Viol. V. B. Racc. IV.*

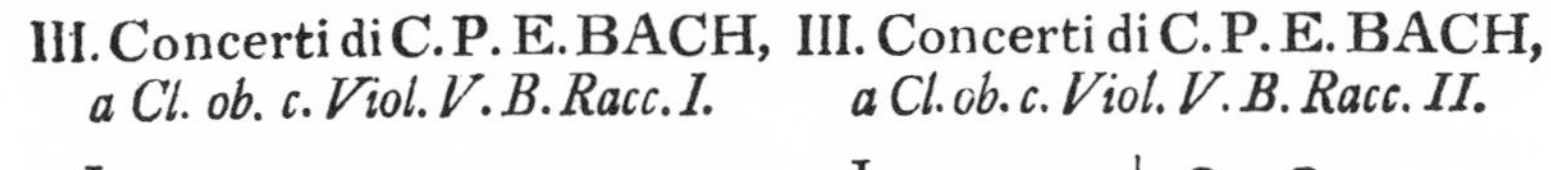

III. Concerti di C.P.E.BACH, *a Cl. ob. c. Viol. V. B. Racc. I.*

III. Concerti di C.P.E.BACH, *a Cl. ob. c. Viol. V. B. Racc. II.*

III. Concerti di C.P.E.BACH, *a Cl. ob. c. Viol. V. B. Racc. III.*

III. Concerti di C.P.E.BACH, *a Cl. ob. c. Viol. V. B. Racc. IV.*

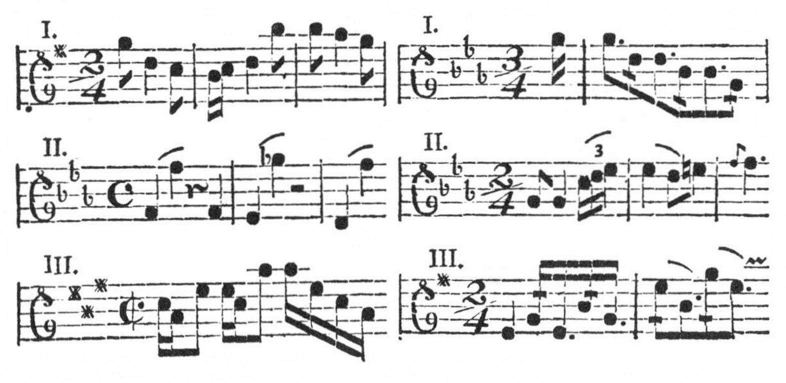

IV. Concerti di George BENDA, *a Cl. obl. c. Viol. V. B.*

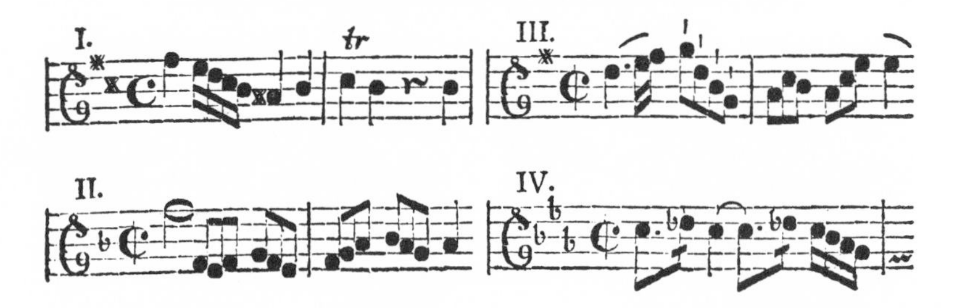

III. Concerti di C.S.BINDER, *a Cl. ob. c. 2 Viol. V. B.*

I. Conc. di BIRCK in Vienna, *a Cl. ob. c. 2 Viol. V. B.*

I. Concerto di J. F. DOLES, *a Cl. ob. c. 2 Viol. V. B.*

III. Concerti di FOERSTER, *a Cl. ob. c. 2 Viol. V. B.*

III. Concerti di C.H.GRAUN, *a Cl. ob. c. 2 Viol. V. B. Racc. I.*

III. Concerti di C.H.GRAUN, *a Cl. ob. c. 2 Viol. V. B. Racc. II.*

III. Concerti di C.H.GRAUN, *a Cl. ob. c. 2 Viol. V. B. Racc. III.*

20 CONCERTI a CEMBALO OBLIGATO.
III. Concerti di C.H.GRAUN, a Cl. ob. c. 2 Viol. V. B. Racc. IV.
II. Concerti di GRUNERT, a Cl. ob. c. 2 Viol. V. B.
II. Concerti di HAYDEN in Vienna, a Cl. ob. c. 2 Viol. V. B.
I. Concerto di HOMILIUS, a Cl. ob. c. 2 Viol. V. B.
I. Concerto di JENICHEN, a Cl. ob. c. 2 Viol. V. B.
I. Conc. di J. F. KIRNBERGER, a Cl. ob. c. 2 Viol. V. B.
I. Concerto di LEFFLOTH, a Cl. ob. c. 2 Viol. V. B.
II. Concerti di MATTHIELLI in Vienna, a Cl. ob. c. 2 Viol. V. B.
II. c. 2 Oboi, 2 Corni, 2 Fl. V. B.
I. Conc. di F.C. MOHRHEIM, a Cl. ob. c. 2 Viol. V. B.
I. Conc. di NICHELMANN, a Cl. ob. c. 2 Viol. V. B.

CONCERTI a CEMBALO OBLIGATO. 21
II. Concerti di Giov. PLATTI, a Cl. ob. c. 2 Viol. V. B.
I. Concerto di Jos. RIEPEL, a Cl. ob. c. Viol. princ. 2 Viol. V. B.
III. Conc. di ROELLIG Jun. in Dresda, a Cl. ob. c. 2 Viol. V. B.
II. Concerti di G. E. ROLLE, a Cl. ob. c. 2 Viol. V. B.
III. Conc. di SCHAFFRATH, a Cl. ob. c. 2 Viol. V. B. Racc. I.
II. Conc. di SCHAFFRATH, a Cl. ob. c. 2 Viol. V. B. Racc. II.
IV. Concerti di Giov. Ad. SCHEIBE, a Cemb. obl.
I. c. 2 Flauti, V. e Basso.
III. c. 2 Fl. e B.
II. c. 2 Viol. V. B.
IV. c. 2 Viol. V. B.

IV. Conc. di G. STEPHANI in Vienna, *a Cl. ob. c. 2 Viol. V. B. Racc. I.*

I. II. *c. 2 Corni.* III. IV.

III. Conc. di G. STEPHANI in Vienna, *a Cl. ob. c. 2 Viol. V. B. Racc. II.*

I. II. III.

I. Conc. di Giov. TISCHER, *a Cl. ob. c. 2 Viol. V. B.*

III. Conc. di C. WAGENSEIL, *a Cl. ob. c. 2 Viol. Violonc. Racc. I.*

I. II. III.

III. Conc. di C. WAGENSEIL, *a Cl. ob. c. 2 Viol. Violonc. Racc. II.*

I. II. III.

III. Conc. di C. WAGENSEIL, *a Cl. ob. c. 2 Viol. Violonc. Racc. III.*

I. II. III.

III. Conc. di C. WAGENSEIL, *a Cl. ob. c. 2 Viol. Violonc. Racc. IV.*

I. II. III.

III. Concerti di WIEDNER, *a Cl. ob. c. 2 Viol. V. B. Racc. I.*

I. II. III.

III. Concerti di WIEDNER, *a Cl. ob. c. 2 Viol. V. B. Racc. II.*

I. *c. 2 Corni.* II. III.

HARPA

SOLI.

I. Sonata di PERENNI, *a Harpa Sola.*

I. Sonata di Georg. Fil. TELEMANN, *a Harpa Sola.*

DUETTI.

II. Duetti di ERNESTI, *a due Harpe.*

TRII.

I. Sonata di CONTIUS, *a Harpa obl. et Violino.*

III. Sonate di HARRER, *a Harpa obl. c. Viol. et Fl.*

I. Sonata di ERNESTI, *a Harpa obl. et Flauto.*

I. Sonata di Ant. MAHAUT, *a Harpa obl. et Viol.*

PARTITE e CONCERTI.

I. Partita di ERNESTI, *a Harpa obl. 2 Viol. e Baſſo.*

III. Partite di ROELLIG, *a Harpa obl. Fl. Viol. Baſſo.*

I. Partita di HARRER, *a Harpa obl. Fl. Chalumeaux, Viol. Baſſo.*

I. Concerto di EYSEL, *a Harpa Concert. e Viola da Gamba.*

Il Fine.

CATALOGO
DE'
QVADRI, PARTITE, DIVERTIMENTI, CASSAT. SCHERZ.
ED
INTRADE
Ô FRANCESE
OUVERTVRES
A
DIVERSI STROMENTI,
CHE
SI TROVANO IN MANOSCRITTO
NELLA OFFICINA MUSICA DI BREITKOPF
IN LIPSIA.

PARTE Vta.
1765.

QUADRI
A
DIVERSI STROMENTI CONCERTANTI.

II. Quadri, del Sigr. G. HARRER, Dirett. della Muſ. in Lipſia.

I. *a Flaut. 2 Viol. e B.* II. *a Carill. 2 Viol. e B.*

I. Quadro del Sigr. HARTWIG, in Zittav.

I. Quadro del Sigr. HENDEL, in Londra.

III. Quadri, del Sigr. J. A. HASSE, Maeſt. di Cap. à Dreſda.

VIII. Quadri, del Sigr. GIVS. HAYDEN, in Vienna.

a 2 Violini, Viol. e B.

VI. Quadri del Sigr. JANITZSCH, in Berolino.

V. Quadri, del Sigr. KRAUSE.

VI. Quadri, del Sigr. REINICKE, Org. in Hamb.

a 2 Violini, Fagotto e B.

II. Quadri, del Sigr. ROSETTI.

I. *a 2 Ob. Viol. picc. B.* II. *a 2 Violin. Flaut. B.*

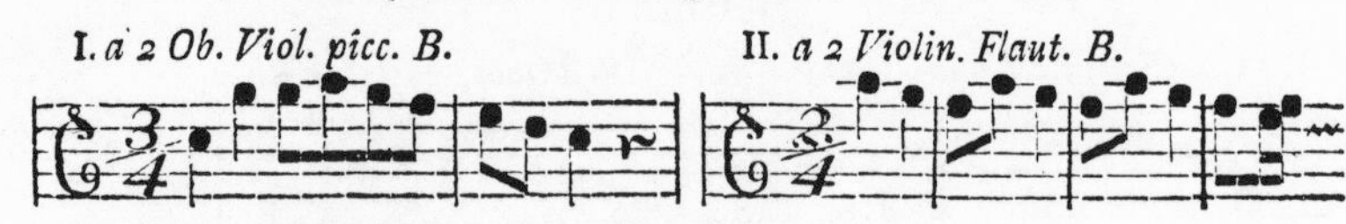

II. Quadri, del Sigr. TELEMANN.

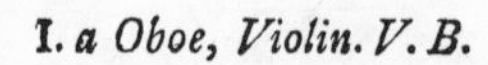

II. *a 2 Viol. V. B.*

VI. Quadri, del Sigr. TOESCHI, *a Flauto trav. Violino, Viola e B.*

II. Quadri da diversi.

I. del Sigr. SCHEIBE, *a Fl. 2 Viol. B.* I. del Sigr. MALZART.

PARTITE *A* DIVERSI STROMENTI.

VI. Partite del Sigr. HARRER, *a 4 e 6 Voci.*

Raccolta I.

I. *a 4 Voci. 2 Viol. Viola, Basso,* IV. *a 6 Voci. 2 Flauti, 2 Viol. V. B.*

II. *a 4 Voci. 2 Viol. V. B.* V. *a 6 Voci. 2 Corni, 2 Viol. V. B.*

III. *a 4 Voci. 2 Viol. V. B.* VI. *a 6 Voci. 2 Corni, 2 Viol. V. B.*

VI. Partite del Sigr. HARRER, *a 6 Voci. 2 Oboi, 2 Violini, Viola, Basso. Racc. II.*

6 PARTITE.
VI. Partite del Sigr. HARRER, a 6 e 8 Voci. Racc. III.
I. 2 Corni, 2 Violini, Viola, Basso.
IV. 2 Oboi, 2 Viol. V. B.
II. 2 Corni, 2 Ob. 2 Viol. V. B.
V. 2 Corni, 2 Viol. V. B.
III. 2 Corni, 2 Ob. 2 Viol. V. B.
VI. 2 Oboi. 2 Viol. V. B.
VI. Partite del Sigr. HARRER, a 4 Voci. 2 Violini, Viola, Basso. Racc. IV.
I.
IV.
II.
V.
III.
VI.

VI. Partite del Sigr. HARRER, a 8 e 10 Voci. Racc. V.
I. a 8 Voci. 2 Corni, 2 Oboi, 2 Viol. Viola, Basso.
IV. a 8 Voci. 2 Corni, 1 Fl. 1 Ob. Viola da Gamba all' Ottav. 2 Viol. c. B.
II. a 8 Voci. 2 Corn. 2 Ob. 2 Viol. V. B.
V. a 10 Voci. 2 Corn. 2 Ob. 1 Fl. tr. 1 Viol. da Gamb. 1 Violonc. oblig. 2 Viol. c. B.
III. a 8 Voci. 2 Corni, 2 Corni Inglesi, 2 Viol. V. B.
VI. a 10 Voci. 2 Corni, 2 Flauti, 2 Oboi, 2 Violini, V. B.

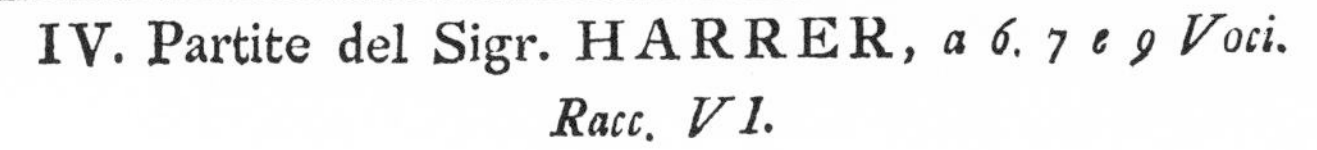
PARTITE. 7
IV. Partite del Sigr. HARRER, a 6. 7 e 9 Voci.

Racc. VI.
I. a 6 Voci. 2 Oboi, 2 Violini, Viola, Basso.
III. 7 Voci. Liuto oblig. 2 Flauti, 2 Viol. V. B.
II. a 6 Voci. 2 Oboi, 2 Violini, Viola, Basso.
IV. a 9 Voci. 2 Corni, 1 Fl. 1 Ob. 1 Viol. di G. 2 Viol. V. B.

VI. Partite del Sigr. HILLER, a 4 Voci. 2 Violini, Viola, Basso. Racc. I.
I.
IV.
II.
V.
III.
VI.

VI. Partite del Sigr. HILLER, a 6 Voci. Racc. II.
I. a 2 Corni, 2 Violini, Viola Basso.
IV. 2 Flauti, 2 Viol. V. B.
II. 2 Corni, 2 Viol. V. B.
V. 2 Fl. 2 Viol. V. B.
III. 2 Oboi, 2 Viol. V. B.
VI. 2 Fl. 2 Viol. V. B.

8 PARTITE.
VI. Partite del Sigr. HORN, a 8 e 6 Voci.
I. 2 Corni, 2 Oboi, 2 Viol. V.B.
IV. 2 Oboi, 2 Viol. V.B.
II. 2 Flauti, 2 Fagotti, 2 Viol. V.B.
V.
III. 2 Flauti.
VI. 2 Oboi, 2 Viol. V.B.
VI. Partite del Sigr. KRAUSE, a 4 e 5 Voci. Racc. I.
I. 2 Viol. V.B.
IV. 2 Viol. V. B.
II. 2 Viol. V. B.
V. 2 Corni, 2 Viol. B.
III. 2 Viol. V.B.
VI. 2 Oboi, 2 Viol. B.
VI. Partite del Sigr. KRAUSE, a 6. 8 e 10 Voci. Racc. II.
I. 2 Oboi, 2 Viol. V.B.
IV. 2 Corni, 2 Flauti, 2 Viol. V.B.
V. 2 Oboi, 2 Fagotti, 2 Viol. V.B.
II. 2 Oboi, 2 Fagotti, 2 Viol. V.B.
III. 2 Corni, 2 Oboi, 2 Viol. V.B.
VI. 2 Corni, 2 Fl. 2 Ob. 2 Viol. V.B.

PARTITE. 9
VI. Partite del Sigr. PFEIFFER, a 4. 5 e 6 Voci.
I. Violino Princip. 2 Viol. V. B.
IV. 2 Viol. V. B.
II. 2 Viol. V. B.
V. 2 Oboi, 2 Viol. V. B.
III. 2 Viol. V. B.
VI. 2 Corn. 1 Ob. d'Amore, 2 Viol. V. B.
VI. Partite del Sigr. ROELLIG, a 4 Voci. Flauto Oblig.
2 Violini, Basso. Racc. I.
I.
IV.
II.
tr
V.
III.
VI.
tr
VI. Partite del Sigr. ROELLIG, a 4 Voci. Racc. II.
I. Flauto, 2 Viol. e B.
IV. 3 Violini, B.
tr
II. 3 Violini, e B.
V. 2 Violini, V. B.
III. 2 Viol. V. B.
VI. 2 Violini, V. B.
tr
tr

VI. Partite del Sigr. ROELLIG, *a 6 Voci, Racc. III.*

I. *2 Corni oblig. 2 Viol. V. B.*

II. *2 Corni obl. 2 Viol. V. B.*

III. *1 Corno, 2 Viol. 1 Fagotto. V. B.*

IV. *2 Flauti, 2 Viol. V. B.*

V. *1 Oboe, 2 Viol. Viola obl. B.*

VI. *1 Flauto, 1 Oboe, 2 Violini, B.*

VI. Partite del Sigr. ROELLIG, *a 6 e 8 Voci. Racc. IV.*

I. *2 Corni, 2 Viol. V. B.*

II. *2 Corni, 2 Viol. V. B.*

III. *2 Corni, 2 Viol. V. B.*

IV. *2 Corni, 2 Oboi, 2 Viol. V. B.*

V. *2 Flauti, 2 Corni, 2 Viol. B.*

VI. *2 Oboi, 2 Viol. V. B.*

VI. Suites del Sigr. ROELLIG, jun. *a 7 Voci. Racc. V.*

I. *2 Clarini, 2 Oboi, 2 Fagotti, B.*

II. *2 Clarini, 2 Oboi, 2 Fagotti, B.*

III. *2 Clarini, 2 Oboi, 2 Fagotti, B.*

IV. *2 Corni, 2 Flauti, 2 Violini, B.*

V. *2 Corni, 2 Oboi, 2 Fagotti, B.*

VI. *2 Corni, 2 Oboi, 2 Fagotti, B.*

III. Partite del Sigr. ROELLIG, *a 6 Voci. Racc. VI.*

I. *2 Oboi, 2 Viol. V. B.*

II. *2 Flauti, 2 Viol. V. B.*

III. *2 Oboi, 2 Viol. V. B.*

II. Partite del Sigr. SIMONETTI, *a 6 Voci. 2 Flauti, 2 Viol. Viola, Basso.*

I.

II.

V. Partite del Sigr. STEINMETZ, *a 6 e 4 Voci.*

I. *2 Oboi, 2 Viol. V. B.*

II. *2 Flauti, 2 Viol. V. B.*

III. *2 Corni, 2 Viol. V. B.*

IV. *2 Corni, 2 Viol. V. B.*

V. *2 Viol. V. B.*

VI. Partite del Sigr. SCHWAEGRICHEN, *a 6 Voci.*

I. *2 Oboi, 2 Viol. V. B.*

II. *2 Corni, 2 Viol. V. B.*

III. *2 Fl. trav. 2 Viol. V. B.*

IV. *2 Fagotti, 2 Viol. V. B.*

V. *1 Corno, 1 Fagott. 2 Viol. V. B.*

VI. *1 Fl. 1 Faggott. 2 Viol. V. B.*

VI. Partite del Sigr. WIEDNER, *a 6 e 4 Voci.*

I. *2 Corni, 2 Viol. V. B.*

II. *2 Corni, 2 Viol. V. B.*

III. *2 Corni, 2 Viol. V. B.*

IV. *2 Corni, 2 Viol. V. B.*

V. *2 Viol. V. B.*

VI. *2 Viol. V. B.*

VI. Partite da diverſi Autori. *Raccolta I.*

I. di Agrelli, *a 6 Voci. 2 Corni, 2 Viol. V. B.*

II. di Brendner, *a 5 V. 1 Viol. d'Amore, 1 Oboe, 1 Corn. 1 Violino, B.*

III. di Brendner, *a 5 V. 1 Liuto, 1 Oboe, 2 Violini, Baſſo.*

IV. di L'Eclair, *a 4 V. 2 Viol. V. B.*

V. di Fœrſter, *a 6 V. 2 Fl. 2 Viol. V. B.*

VI. di Fœrſter, *a 5 V. 2 Fl. 2 Corn. Baſſon.*

VI. Partite da diverſi Autori. *Racc. II.*

I. di Fritſch, *a 6 V. 2 Oboi, 2 Viol. V. B.*

II. di Fritſch, *a 6 V. 2 Corni, 2 Viol. V. B.*

III. di Fritſch, *a 4 V. 2 Viol. V. B.*

IV. di Gebel, *a 4 V. 2 Viol. V. B.*

V. di Gebel, *a 4 V. 2 Viol. V. B.*

VI. di Gebel, *a 4 V. 2 Viol. V. B.*

V. Partite da diverſi Autori. *Racc. III.*

I. di Giraneck, *a 8 Voci. 2 Ob. 2 Faggot. 2 Violini, V. B.*

II. di Giraneck, *a 8 V. 2 Corni, 2 Flauti, 2 Violini, V. B.*

III. di Giraneck, *a 8 V. 2 Flauti, 2 Oboi, 2 Violini, V. B.*

IV. di Gruner, *a 6 V. 2 Corn. 2 Viol. V. B.*

V. di Gruner, *a 6 V. 2 Corn. 2 Viol. V. B.*

VI. Partite da diverſi Autori. *Racc. IV.*

I. di Hoffmann, *a 4 Voci. 2 Viol. V. B.*

Lamento.

II. di Hoffmann, *a 5 V. 2 Ob. d'Amore, 2 Corni, B.*

III. di Kleinknecht, *a 6 V. 2 Corni, 2 Viol. V. B.*

IV. di Kleinkn. *a 6 V. 2 Corn. 2 Viol. V. B.*

V. di Mozart, *a 8 V. 2 Corni, 2 Flauti, 2 Viol. V. B.*

VI. di Mozart, *a 7 V. 2 Corni, 2 Flauti, 2 Violini, B.*

IV. Partite da diverſi Autori. *Racc. V.*

I. di Albinoni, *a 6 V. 2 Violini, 2 Viole, Violonc. e Cembalo.*

II. di Piacentino, *a 4 V. 2 Viol. V. B.*

III. di Wagenſeil, *a 8 V. 2 Corni, 2 Oboi, 2 Viol. V. B.*

IV. di Werner, *a 4 V. 2 Viol. V. e Cemb.*

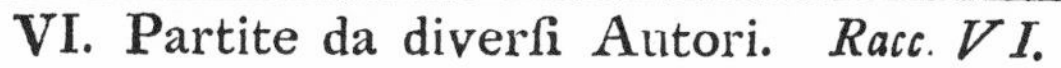

VI. Partite da diversi Autori. *Racc. VI.*

I. di Moecke, *a 5 Voci. 2 Corni, 2 Violini, Basso.*

IV. di Schürer, *a 4 Voci. 2 Violini, Viola, Basso.*

II. di Reichardt, *a 7 Voci. 2 Flauti, 2 Viol. 2 Fagotti, B.*

V. di Trier, *a 6 Voci, 2 Corni, 2 Viol. V. B.*

III. di Scheibe, *a 4 Voci, 1 Flauto obllg. 2 Violini, B.*

VI. di Werner, *a 5 Voci. 2 Corni, 2 Violini, B.*

V. Partite da diversi Anonymi, *a 6 Voci. Racc. VII.*

I. *2 Corni, 2 Violini, Viola, Basso.*

IV. *2 Oboi, 2 Viol. V. B.*

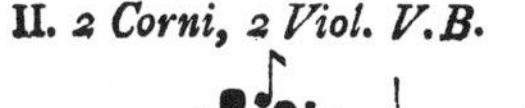

II. *2 Corni, 2 Viol. V. B.*

V. *2 Oboi. 2 Viol. V. B.*

III. *2 Oboi, 2 Viol. V. B.*

DIVERTIMENTI.

VI. Divertimenti del Sigr. Antonio KAMMEL, *a 2 Corni, 2 Violini, 2 Viole e Basso.*

CASSATIONES
Ô NOTTURNI.

VI. Cassationes del Sigr. Gius. HAYDEN.

SCHERZANDI.

VI. Scherzandi del Sigr. Gius. HAYDEN, *a 2 Corni, 2 Oboi, 1 Flauto, 2 Viol. e Basso.*

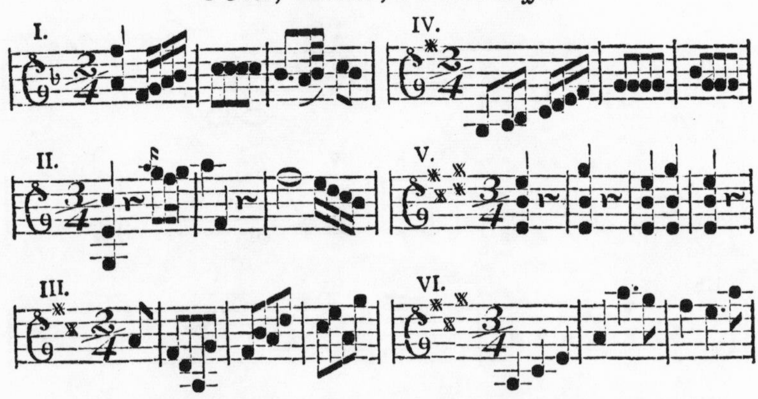

VI. Scherzandi, ô Burlesques, del Anonymo.

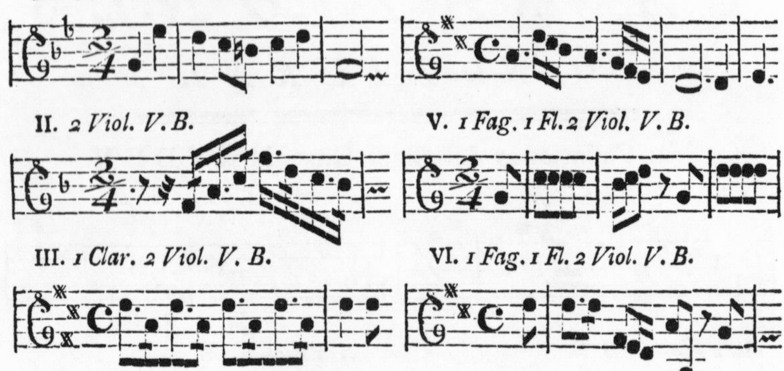

OUVERTURES.

IV. Ouvertures di Anonymo, *a 4. 6 e 7 Voci. Raccolta I.*

I. *3 Clar. Tymp. 2 Oboi, 2 Viol. Conc. 2 Viol. rip. Viola, 2 Fag. e Cemb.*

III. *2 Oboi, Bassono, 2 Violini, Viola, Basso.*

II. *2 Corni, 2 Viol. V. B.* IV. *2 Ob. Bassono, 2 Viol. V. B.*

III. Ouvertures di Anonymo, *a 7 8. 9 Voci. Racc. II.*

I. *2 Oboi, Bassono Oblig. 2 Violini, Viola, Basso.*

III. *2 Corni, 2 Oboi, 2 Viol. Viola, Bassono e Violono.*

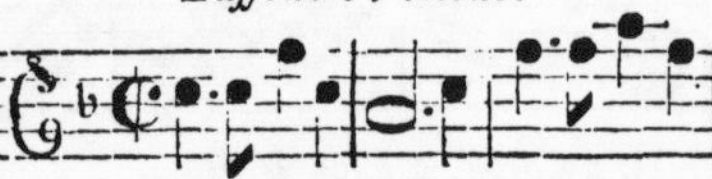

II. *2 Corni, 2 Ob. 2 Viol. V. B.*

VI. Ouvertures del Sigr. FASCH, *a 7 Voci. 2 Oboi, 2 Viol. Viola, Fagotto e Basso. Racc. I.*

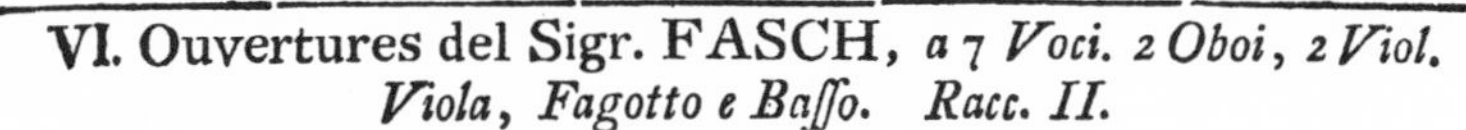

VI. Ouvertures del Sigr. FASCH, *a 7 Voci. 2 Oboi, 2 Viol. Viola, Fagotto e Basso. Racc. II.*

VI. Ouvertures del Sigr. FASCH, *a 7 Voci. 2 Oboi, 2 Viol. Viola, Fagotto e Basso. Racc. III.*

VI. Ouvertures del Sigr. FASCH, *a 7 Voci. 2 Oboi, 2 Viol. Viola, Fagotto e Basso. Racc. IV.*

VI. Ouvertures del Sigr. FASCH, *a 8.9 e 10 Voci. Racc. V.*

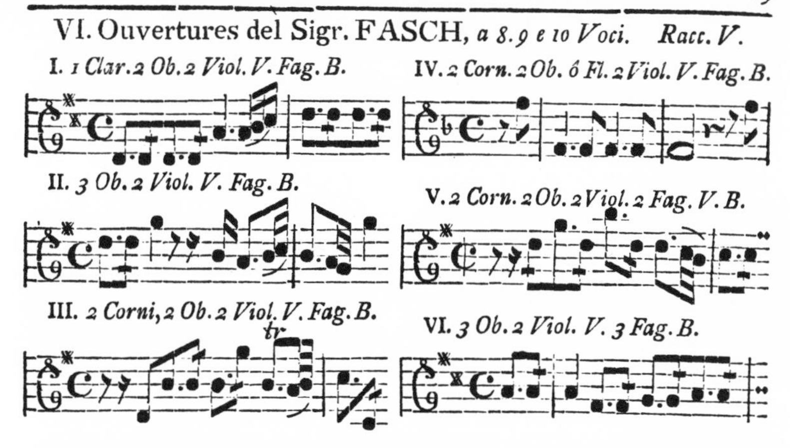

VI. Ouverturds del Sigr. FASCH, *a 11 Voci. Racc. VI.*

VI. Ouvertures del Sigr. FOERSTER, *a 6.7 e 8 Voci. Racc. I.*

VI. Ouvertures del Sigr. GRAUN, a 8 Voci. Racc. I.
I. 2 Cor. 2 Ob. 2 Viol. V. B. Op. Cato.
IV. 2 Viol. V. B. Op. Papirio.
II. 2 Ob. 2 Viol. V. B. Op. Polidor.
V. 2 Corn. 2 Ob. 2 Viol. V. B.
III. 2 Viol. V. B. Op. Pharao.
VI: 2 Violini, V. B.
tr
III. Ouvertures del Sigr. GRAUN, a 4. 6 e 8 Voci. Racc. II.
I. 2 Corni, 2 Viol. V. B.
II. 2 Corni, 2 Ob. 2 Viol. V. B.
III. 2 Viol. V. B.
VI. Ouvertures del Sigr. HARTWIG, a 4 Voci. 2 Violini, Viola, Basso. Racc. I.
I.
IV.
II.
V.
III.
VI.

VI. Ouvertures del Sigr. HARTWIG, a 4. 5 e 8 Voci. Racc. II.
I. 2 Viol. V. B.
IV. Viol. Conc. 2 Viol. V. B.
II. 2 Viol. V. B.
V. 2 Clar. Princ. Tymp. 2 Viol. V. B.
III. Viol. Conc. 2 Viol. V. B.
VI. 2 Corn. 2 Ob. 2 Viol. V. B.
V. Ouvertures del Sigr. HARTWIG, a 6 Voci. Racc. III.
I. 2 Oboi, 2 Viol. V. B.
IV. 2 Corni, 2 Viol. V. B.
II. 2 Corni, 2 Viol. V. B.
V. 2 Oboi, 2 Viol. V. B.
III. 2 Corni, 2 Viol. V. B.
VI. 2 Corn. 2 Violini, V. B.
V. Ouvertures del Sigr. HASSE, a 8. 10 e 13 Voci.
I. 2 Corni, 2 Viol. V. B.
IV. 2 C. 2 O. 2 Fl. 2 V. V. B. Op. Olymp.
II. 2 Oboi, 2 Viol. V. B.
V. 2 Cl. Ty. 2 C. 2 O. 2 Fl. &c. Op. Alcide.
III. 2 C. 2 O. 2 Fl. 2 V. V. B. Op. Irene.
C 3

22 OUVERTURES.
VI. Ouvertures del Sigr. PFEIFFER, a 4 Voci. Racc. I.
I. 2 Violini, Viola, Baſſo.
IV. 2 Viol. V. B.
tr
II. 2 Viol. V. B.
V. 2 Viol. V. B.
III. 2 Viol. V. B.
VI. 1 Viol. Conc. 2 Viol. V. B.
VI. Ouvertures del Sigr. PFEIFFER, a 6 e 9 Voci. Racc. II.
I. 2 Oboi, 2 Viol. V. B.
IV. 2 Oboi, 2 Viol. V. B.
tr
II. 2 Oboi, 2 Viol. V. B.
V. 2 Oboi. 2 Viol. 1 Fag. V. B.
III. 2 Oboi, 2 Viol. V. B.
VI. 3 Oboi, 2 Viol. 2 Fag. V. B.
VI. Ouvertures del Sigr. PFEIFFER, a 6 e 7 Voci, Racc. III.
I. 2 Oboi, 2 Viol. 1 Fag. V. B.
IV. 2 Oboi, 2 Fag, 2 Viol. V. B.
II. 2 Corni, 2 Viol. 1 Fag. V. B.
V. 2 Viol. V. B.
III. 2 Corni, 1 Fag. 2 Viol. V. B.
tr
VI. 2 Ob. 2 Viol. V. B.

OUVERTURES. 23
VI. Ouvertures del Sigr. TELEMANN, a 4 e 5 Voci.
Raccolta I.
I. 2 Violini, Viola, Baſſo.
IV. 1 Viol. Conc. 2 Viol. V. B.
II. 2 Viol. V. B.
V. 2 Viol. V. B.
III. 2 Viol. V. B.
VI. 2 Viol. V. B.
Don Quixotte.
a la Paſtorelle.
VI. Ouvertures del Sigr. TELEMANN, a 6. 7 e 10 Voci.
Raccolta II.
I. 2 Oboi, 2 Viol. V. B.
IV. 2 Oboi, 3 Violini, V. B.
Waßer Ouverture.
II. 2 Corni, 2 Viol. V. B.
V. 3 Tromb. Tymp. Viol. Conc. Fl. Conc. 2 Viol. V. B.
III. 2 Oboi, 2 Viol. V. B.
VI. 2 Ob. 2 Viol. V. B.
IV. Ouvertures del Sigr. TISCHER, a 4 Voci.
2 Violini, Viola, Baſſo.
I.
III.
II.
IV.

VI. Ouvertures da diversi Autori. *Racc. I.*

I. di Fuchs, *a 7 Voci. 2 Ob. 2 Viol. Viola, Bassono, Violono.*

IV. di Hendel, *a 6 Voci. 2 Oboi, 2 Viol. V. B.*

II. di Gebel, *a 7 Voci. Fl. dolce, Fl. trav. Ob. 2 Viol. V. B.*

V. di Hendel, *a 4 Voci. 2 Violini, Viola, Basso.*

III. di Heinsio, *a 4 Voci. 2 Violini, Viola, Basso.*

VI. di Leo, *a 5 Voci. 2 Corni, 2 Violini, Basso.*

VI. Ouvertures da diversi Autori. *Racc. II.*

I. di Schale, *a 4 Voci. 2 Violini, Viola, Basso.*

IV. di Stölzel, *a 4 Voci. 2 Violini. Viola, Basso.*

II. di Stölzel, *a 5 Vobi. Viol. Conc. 2 Viol. V. B.*

V. di Schneider, *a 4 Voci. 2 Viol. Viola, Basso.*

III. di Stölzel, *a 6 Voci. Viol. Conc. 2 Viol. V. Violonc. oblig. e Cemb.*

VI. di Wiedner, *a 4 Voci. 2 Viol. Viola, Basso.*

Il Fine.

CATALOGO
DELLE
ARIE, DUETTI, MADRIGALI
E
CANTATE,
CON
STROMENTI DIVERSI
E CON
CEMBALO SOLO,
CHE
SI TROVANO IN MANOSCRITTO
NELLA OFFICINA MUSICA DI BREITKOPF
IN LIPSIA.

PARTE VIta.

1765.

ARIE, CON STROMENTI.

I. SOPRANO.

CON II. VIOLINI, VIOLA E BASSO.

ANONYMO.
33. Superbo di me stesso di
34. T'aggio vo - lu - to bene
35. Ti sen - to ti sen - to po-
36. Timida no co - si no cosi
37. Tuona adesso il Cielo ira - - to
38. Va trà le selve ir - ca - ne,
39. 1 Tromba. Vi sguardo vi ve - do e
40. Voi ch'al giurai d'un labbro,
ALBUJIO.
1. Op. Artaserse. A. I. Sc. 2. Fra cento affanni e cento, pal-
ARAYA.
1. Povero amante Co - re si
2. 2 Corni. Sappi che in te ri - po - so
BENDA.
1. No non vedre - te mai
BERNASCONI.
1. A - gi - ta - to questo
2. Ah - che s'avesse il seno a
3. Ah - - si resti
4. Ah fre - na - te frenate
BERNASCONI.
5. Arrida il ciel se - reno il
6. Op. Alessandro severo. Ca - ra Madre io vi conosco
7. Op. Ales. sev. Dell' in - fi - do à te
8. Op. Ales. sev. In - fe - li - ce è -
9. Op. Ales. sev. In si tor - bi - do procul
10. Op. Ales. sev. Non dis - pe - ro uon dispero
11. Op. Ales. sev. Parto un' amplesso almeno
12. Op. Ales. sev. Voglio dal tuo do - lo - re
BERNASCONI.
13. Voi non sa - pete quanto
BROSCHI.
1. Che lege spieta - ta che sorte
CALDARA.
1. Op. di Don Chisciote. Che non fece quel cru - dele
CHINZER.
1. Barba - ro tradi - to - re non
CONFORTO.
1. con Recit. Dunque; Ad - di - o;
COSTANZINI.
1. Deh, deh toglie - te agl'occhi
DUNI.
1. Op. Tordinona. Se questo dolce amplesso
2. Op. Tordinona. Se tro - va ri - tegno al

FEO.
1. Op. Ipermestra.
Allorche pugne - rai con
2. Op. Iperm.
Lusinghie - ra la speran-
3. 2 Tromb. 2 Corn. 2 Ob.
Se ai detti tuoi, sospendo
4. Op. Iperm. 2 Ob.
Va più lieto al caro Lido
FINAZZI.
1.
Frà dubbi affetti miei
FIORILLO.
1. 2 Corn.
Da que - sto foglio io
GALUPPI.
1. 2 Corn. 2 Ob.
A - gi - ta ta gelo e tremo
2.
Ca - ra da lu - mi
GALUPPI.
3. 2 Fl.
Lu - ci belle voi - che ar-
4.
Semi vuole oppresso il fato or-
5.
Si si sa ch'un empio
GACOMELLI.
1. Op. Olimpiade.
Non fi - dar - ti del - la
GLUCK.
1.
Care pu - pille pu - pille
2. Op. Issipile.
Im - pal - li - disce in cam - po
3.
Non vi piacque in
HENDEL.
1. con Fag.
Col ardor del tuo bel core
HENDEL.
2. Op. Alcina.
Di cor mio quan - to t'a-
3. Op. Alcina.
Mi lusin - ga il dolce af-
JOMELLI.
1.
A - mor non prometto non
2.
Torna - - te se - - reni be-
KELLERI.
1.
Freddi marmi all' Idol mio
LAMPUGNANI.
1. Op. Olimpiade.
Il do - len - te pastorel - lo
In pen - sar che il fido amico,
2.
Priva del ca - ro be -
3. Op. Olimp.
Su - per - bo di me stesso
LAMPUGNANI.
4. 2 Tromb. 2 Cor. 2 Ob. 4 Viol. 2 V. 2 B.
Troppo fie - ra è la tem-
LATILLA.
1.
Questa è l'ar - te di noi
2. Op. Siroë.
Chi'o mai vi possa lasciar d'a-
3.
Fra mille pensieri, confusa
4. Op. Romolo.
Idol mio nel caso amaro
5.
Jo son qual pas - - saggiero
6.
Non son di quelle, che fan le
7. Op. Romolo.
Scende dal' mon - - - - te

LATILLA.
8. Op. Cameriera.
Son con . fu - fa Pafto-
9.
Svela fe m'ami o ca - ra, il
10. Op. Camer.
Amore è un gran furbetto
11. Op. Siroë.
Ve - de - fte mai ful prato cader
LEO.
1.
A - mor fenza la fpeme tu
2.
I tuoi fdegni e i tuoi la - menti,
3.
Rifponderti vor - rei ma
4.
Vorrei da lac - - -
LOPROSCINO.
1.
Barbaro padre à morte la
2.
Nel penfar, nel pen - far,
3.
Quefto amorofo a - moro - fo
4.
Se mai vo - leffe voleffe
5.
Se intenti fe mi - ri la
6.
Vor - rei nel mio nel
MARCHI.
1.
Non v'è nel mondo duo-
MARTINO.
1.
Torbida not - - te in-

ORLANDINI.
1.
Impallidir ve - drai pria
PAMPANI.
1. Op. Capranica. 1 Tromba folo, 2 Corn. 2 Ob.
Guerriero u - fa - to in Campo
2. 2 Corn. 2 Ob.
Tu vuoi ch'io fen - ta a - more
PARADIE.
1.
Son tanto femplicina fon tanto
PERETZ.
1.
Un raggio di - - fperan-
PALERMITANO.
1.
Qual dolen - te paftorello
PERGOLESI.
1. Op. Tordinona.
Caro fon tua co - fi fon
2.
Co - me na - - - ve,
PERGOLESI.
3.
Grandi è ver fon le tue pene
4.
In braccio à mille furie
5.
In mar turbato e nero
6. Interm. Amor fa l'Uomo cieco.
La Ca - roz - za ci fa rà
7. Op. Merope.
Madre e tu ingiufta
8.
Manca la guida al pie,
9.
Men - tre dormi amor
10.
Mi palpita il co - re, non

PERGOLESI.
11.
Non ha più pace l'amor ge-
12.
O - nell' sen di qual
13.
Perfido ingannatore
14.
Perfido tradi - tore ti
15. Op. Orazio.
Procu-ri la prego la
16.
Quando fremi altie - ra
17. Op. Orazio.
Quanto mai fe-lici
18.
Quel destrier ch'all'Albergo è vi-
PERGOLESI.
19.
Sdegno ingegno affetti
20.
Se cerco, se di-ce, l'amico
21.
Se Ti-ranna se ti-ranna
22.
Se in campo armato vuoi cimen-
23. Op. Orazio.
Sig-nor Lamberto caro caro
24.
Siam navi all'onde algenti lasciate
25. c. Recit. Quanto t'inganni,
Sorge qual lu - ci -
26. La Serva Padrona.
Stizzo-so mio stiz-zoso

PERGOLESI.
27. Op. Tordinona.
Su-per-bo di me stesso
28.
Torbida in volto e nero,
29. Op. Tordin.
Tu di sa-per procu-ra
30.
Vo sol cando un mar crudele
31. Op. Orazio. con Recit.
Nò non vedrai destin tiran-
32.
Vuoi pu - nir l'ingra - to a-
PORPORA.
1. Op. d'Aliberti.
Da te pietade apprende il mio
2. Alle Dame. 1 Sopr. 1 Alto.
Dim-mi, dimmi che m'ami o caro
PORPORA.
3 Op. d'Alib.
Dolce mio ben mia vi - ta
4. Op. d'Alib.
La colomba imprigionata sciolta
5.
Paf-saggier che su la sponda
6. Op. Camilla.
Ramenta - ti chi
7. Op. d'Alib.
Se non dovesse il piè senza
8. Op. d'Alib.
Sia pur cru-dele sia pur in
9. Op. d'Alib.
Spe-ro, spero dal tuo va-
10. Alle Dame.
Torna - te tranquil-le

12 ARIE.
PORPORA.
11. Op. Camilla.
Và per le vene il ſangue
12.
Voi che le mie vi - cende
RUTTINI.
1.
No no non ve-dre-te-
2.
Ve-di quel pianto oh Dio
RINALDO.
1.
Baſta co-ſi t'in-tendo, t'in-
2.
Pallido e meſto in volto di
RISTORI.
1.
La mano di ſa-et-ta
2.
tr
Non ſpinoſo alpeſtre calle,
RISTORI.
3. 2 Fl.
Pe - - - - - no in
4. 2 Fl.
Qual di ſogno ombra leg-
5.
Scherzò, ſcherzò ſcherzò fortuna
6.
Se volgo ta-lo-ra a
7.
So ch'è ſtanco na-vi-
SANTO LAPIS.
1.
Se tutti i ma-li miei
SCALABRINI.
1.
A trionfar mi chiama
SCARLATTI.
1. Op. Iſſipile.
Impallidiſce in cam - po

SOPRANO. 13
SCARLATTI.
1.
Vedrò del tuo ſem-bian-te
SELETTI.
1. Op. Capranica.
Qual torbi - do tor-ren-te
TERRADELLAS.
1.
Al - lor che tu ve-drai
2. Op. L'Aſtarto.
A quell'ingrato core, che
3.
Jo ſon qual Peregri-no, di
UMSTEDT.
1.
Penſa a ſerbami o ca-ra i
VINCI.
1.
Bell'alma vergl'er-ran-ti
2.
Deſtrier che all'armi uſa -
VINCI.
3. Op. Aleſſandro.
Se il Ciel mi divide dal ca-ro
4.
Torto-rella ſe ri - mira
VIVALDI.
1.
Lan-gue. miſe-ro - -
WAGENSEIL.
1.
Quanto fi-do l'a-dorai
ZOPPIS.
1. 2 Corni.
A - gita - to il mio
2.
Dal ſen dal caro ſpoſo
3. Op. Siroë, di Metaſtaſio.
D'og-ni ama-tor la
4. Op. Siroë.
Fra dubbi affet-ti miei

CON II. VIOLINI, VIOLA E BASSO.

LATILLA.
5. Op. Romolo. 2 Tromb. 2 Ob.
Quell' inimico auda - - -
PORPORA.
1. Op. d'Alib. 1 Ob.
Pensa, pensa che sono amante e
6. Op. Romolo. 2 Corn. 2 Ob.
Sde - - - gna chiamato
RISTORI.
1.
Tiran - - - - - - na
LEO.
1.
Mi vuol già mi - sera il
TERADELLAS.
1.
Care pupille ama - te il
2.
Vede che l'onda fre -
VIVALDI.
1.
Non trova mai ripo - so l'a-
LOPROSCINO.
1.
Vorrei del caro bene
2.
Vi - vi dette a giusti

III. TENORE.
CON II. VIOLINI, VIOLA E BASSO.
ANONYMO.
1.
Ah trop - po, piacemi
LATILLA.
1. 2 Corn. 2 Ob.
Se il mio paterno amo - re
BERNASCONI.
1. 4 Corn. 2 Ob.
Odo il suo - no de queruli
2. Op. Orazio.
Ma Canta - ti - na quando è
2. Op. Ales. sev.
Finge il Leon tall' o - ra
PERGOLESI.
1.
Premi o Tiranna altero, tiranna
GALUPPI.
1.
Gelido in ogni ve - na
PORTA.
1.
Fan le colpe una
2.
Veggo le orribili
PORPORA.
1.
A la forra d'un com-
JOMELLI.
1. 2 Corn. 2 Ob.
Super - bo destriero ch'ag-
VIVALDI.
1.
Roma invita ma clemente,

IV. BASSO.

CON II. VIOLINI, VIOLA E BASSO.

ANONYMO.

PERGOLESI.

PFEIFFER.

LATILLA.

D U E T T I.

CON II. VIOLINI, VIOLA E BASSO.

ANONYMO.

LAMPUGNANI.

PERGOLESI.

RINALDO.

TERRADELLAS.

SELLITTI.

T E R C E T T I.

CON II. VIOLINI, VIOLA E BASSO.

LATILLA.

PFEIFFER.

Q V A T E R N O.

CON II. VIOLINI, VIOLA E BASSO.

VINCI.

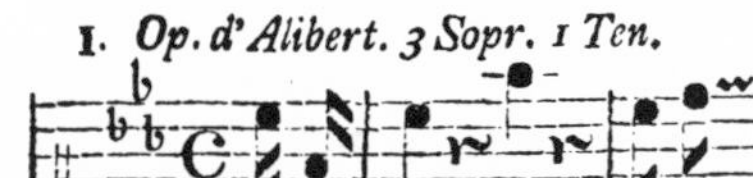

ARIE.

A VOCE CON CEMBALO.

22
ARIE
ORLANDINI.
6.
Ri-cor - - - da - ti-
7.
Perte nel - ca - ro nido
8.
Vesti la gon-na, e'lorin t'in-
9.
Scherza in mar la Na -
10.
Non sempre invendi-ca - ta io
PEREZ.
1. Sopr. solo.
Se mai per-dete l'idol che
PERGOLESI.
1. Sopr. solo.
Contento forse vivere nel
PORPORA.
1. Sopr. solo.
Spera go-der vi-ci-no
PORPORA.
2.
Tù mi dis-prezzi ingrato mà
3.
Non sò se sdegno sia non
4.
Passag-gier che sù la sponda
5.
Vuoi dirmi lo sò lo sò -
6.
Quel vapor che inva-le im.
7.
Voi che le mie vicende
8.
Si pietoso il tuo lu
9.
Il Pastor se torna aprile
CON CEMBALO.
PORPORA.
10.
Vienni vienni che pri
11.
Siete barbare ama - - - te
12.
Vorrei spiegar l'affan-no nas-
13.
Bel pia - cer - sarà d'un
14.
Se intende si poco si poco che hò
15.
Voi non sa - pete quanto gio.
PORPORA.
16. Sop. s.
In braccio à mille furie
17.
Fuggi dà gl'occhi miei
18.
Rondi - nella à cui rapita
SARRO.
1. Sopr. solo.
Sogna co-si la
TERRADELLAS.
1. Sopr. solo.
Per pie - tà bell' i - dol

23

CANTATE
CON
DIVERSI STROMENTI.

ANONYMO.

1. *Sopr. solo, Violino, Viola, Cembalo.*

Porgi ò bella a chi t'adora,

2. *Alto solo, Oboe d'Amore, Cemb.*

Lusinga questo cor -

3. *Alto solo, 2 Viol. Cemb.*

Pa - sto - rel - la, va - ga

4. *Basso solo, 2 Viol. Cemb.*

Pasto - rel - la sola so - la

5. *Sopr. solo, 2 Viol. V. Cemb.*

Vezzo - si Lu - mi a vagheg

BADIA.

1. *Sopr. Cemb. 2 Viol. Viola.*

Festeggian - - - - do

BONONCINI.

1. *Sopr. Cemb. 2 Viol.*

Direi che sei il mio be -

2. *Sopr. Cemb. Viol. Violonç. oblig.*

Sò d'essermi d'Amor, Bel

CONTI.

1. *Sopr. Cemb. Chal. Viol. sord.*

Con più luci di cando - ri

2. *Sopr. Chalmeaux Fl. Viol. sord. Liuti Francesi e Cemb.*

Lontanan - za dell' ama - to

FOERSTER.

1. *Sopr. Basso, 1 Tromb. 2 Viol. 2 Oboi, Viola, Cemb.*

Ini - mi - ca d'amore

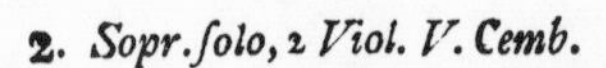

2. *Sopr. solo, 2 Viol. V. Cemb.*

Zef - fi - ret - ti che

FOERSTER.

3. *Recit. Sopr. solo, 2 Viol. V. Basso.*

GRAUN.

3. *Sopr. s. Viol. conc. 2 Viol. V. Cemb. B.*

Clori, sei tutta bella, — Mesto e so - lo - il Russignuo

4. *Sopr. s. 2 Fl. abec, 2 Ob. 2 Viol. V. C.*

4. *Sopr. s. 2 Viol. V. B.*

Vieni ò mor - te a — Qual ti - mor - - - -

GAJARECK.

1. *Sopr. s. 2 Viol. V. Cemb.*

5. *Basso s. 2 Viol. V. Cemb.*

Per - me parlan, quest'a- — Hor che l'Hespera luce tuf-

2. *Recit. Sopr. s. 2 Viol. V. Cemb.*

HARRER.

1. *Sopr. s. 2 Viol. 2 Ob. ad lib. V. B.*

E pur vivo e non spiro? — Doril - la tanti e tan - ti,

3. *Rec. Alto s. 2 Viol. V. Cemb.*

HASSE.

1. *Rec. Sopr. s. Fl. trav. Cemb.*

Lilla mi parto addio — Quel vago seno, ò Fille

4. *Alto solo, 2 Viol. V. Cemb.*

2. *Rec. Sopr. s. 2 Viol. V. Gemb.*

Il piu crudo d'ogni affan- — Tacete pur, ta - cete o

GRAUN.

1. *Basso s. Violino, Viola, Cemb.*

3. *Basso s. 2 Viol. V. Cemb.*

Deh mio bene ancor che — Ti chiedo un guardo

2. *Basso s. 2 Viol. unis. V. Cemb.*

HEINCHEN.

1. *Recit. Sopr. s. Viol. s. Cemb.*

Eh la miei spirti — Nice, se il tuo bel labro,

HEINCHEN.

2. *Rec. Sopr. f. 2 Viol. Cemb.*

3. *Sopr. f. Viol. f. Cemb.*

4. *Sopr. f. 2 Viol. V. Cemb.*

5. *Rec. Alto folo, 2 Viol. V. Cemb.*

6. *Recit. Sopr. f. Viol. Cemb.*

HENDEL.

1. *Sopr. f. 2 Fl. 2 Viol. V. Cemb.*

2. *Sopr. e Baff. 2 Ob. Fag. 2 Viol. V. C.*

3. *Sopr. f. 2 Viol. V. Cemb.*

HENDEL.

4. *Sopr. f. 2 Viol. Cemb.*

5. *Baff. f. 2 Viol. V. Violonc. conc. C.*

6. *Sopr. f. 2 Viol. V. Cemb.*

HOFFMANN.

1. *S. f. 2 V. C.*

KAISER.

1. *Sopr. f. 2 Viol. Cemb.*

2. *Tenore f. 2 Viol. V. Cemb.*

3. *Sopr. f. 2 Viol. Cemb.*

KELLERI.

1. *Sopr. f. 2 Viol. Cemb.*

KOEHLER.

1. *Rec. Sopr. f. Viol. f. Cemb.*

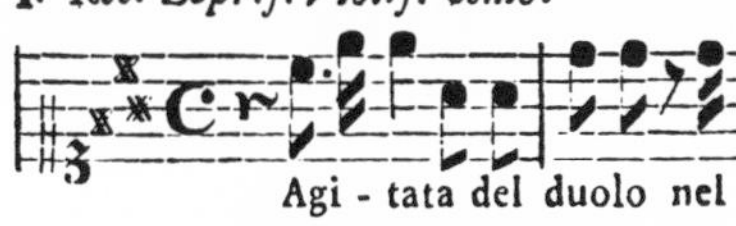

LINICKE.

1. *Sopr. f. 2 Viol. V. Cemb.*

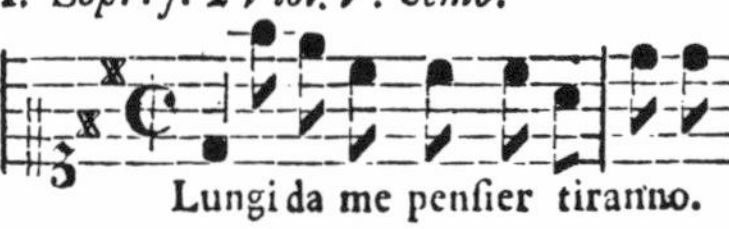

2. *Sopr. folo, Viol. Cemb.*

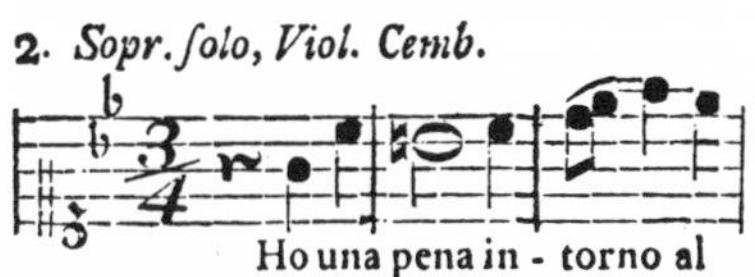

LOTTI.

1. *Sopr. f. 2 Viol. V. Cemb.*

2. *Sopr. f. 2 Viol. V. Cemb.*

PERGOLESI.

1. *S. f. 2 V. V. C.*

PORSILE.

1. *Rec. Sopr. folo, Fl. ô Viol. Cemb.*

SCHEIBE.

1. *Rec. Baffo f. 2 Viol. 2 V. Cemb.*

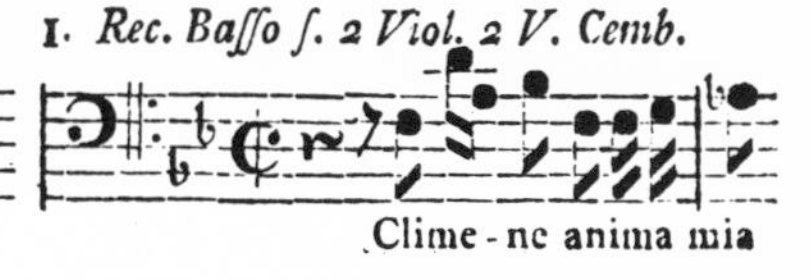

2. *Sopr. Alto, 2 Viol. V. Cemb.*

STOELZEL.

1. *Sopr. f. Viol. V. Cemb.*

2. *Sopr. f. Viol. ô Flauto, V. Cemb.*

TELEMANN.

1. *Sopr. folo. Viol. folo, Cemb.*

VERACINI.

1 *Baffo folo, 3 Viol. Cemb.*

CANTATE
A
VOCE CON CEMBALO.

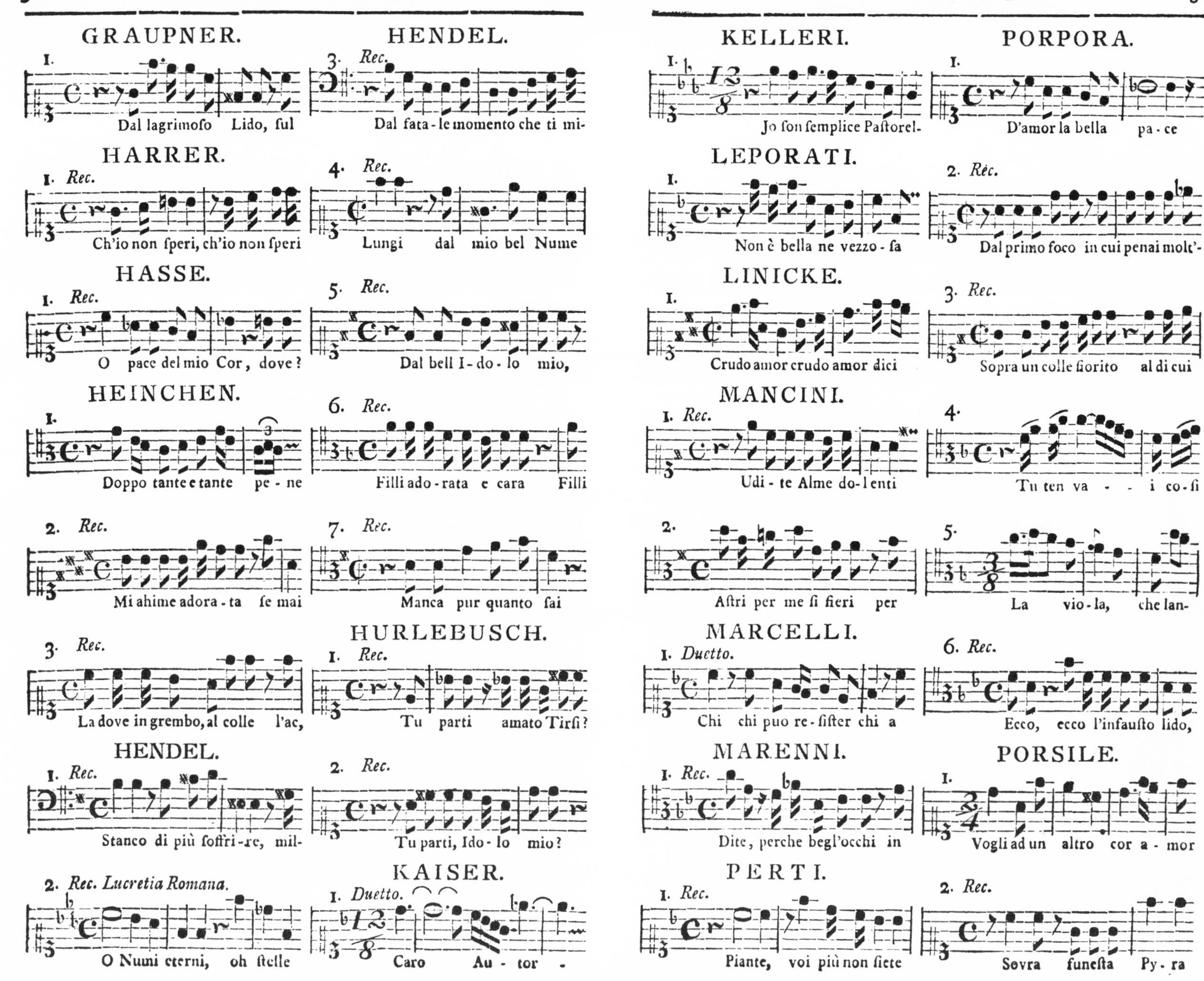
GRAUPNER.
1. Dal lagrimoſo Lido, ſul
HARRER.
1. Rec. Ch'io non ſperi, ch'io non ſperi
HASSE.
1. Rec. O pace del mio Cor, dove?
HEINCHEN.
1. Doppo tante e tante pe - ne
2. Rec. Mi ahime adora - ta ſe mai
3. Rec. La dove in grembo, al colle l'ac,
HENDEL.
1. Rec. Stanco di più ſoffri - re, mil-
2. Rec. Lucretia Romana. O Numi eterni, oh ſtelle
HENDEL.
3. Rec. Dal fata - le momento che ti mi-
4. Rec. Lungi dal mio bel Nume
5. Rec. Dal bell I - do - lo mio,
6. Rec. Filli ado - rata e cara Filli
7. Rec. Manca pur quanto ſai
HURLEBUSCH.
1. Rec. Tu parti amato Tirſi?
2. Rec. Tu parti, Ido - lo mio?
KAISER.
1. Duetto. Caro Au - tor -
KELLERI.
1. Jo ſon ſemplice Paſtorel-
LEPORATI.
1. Non è bella ne vezzo - ſa
LINICKE.
1. Crudo amor crudo amor dici
MANCINI.
1. Rec. Udi - te Alme do - lenti
2. Aſtri per me ſi fieri per
MARCELLI.
1. Duetto. Chi chi puo re - ſiſter chi a
MARENNI.
1. Rec. Dite, perche begl'occhi in
PERTI.
1. Rec. Piante, voi più non ſiete
PORPORA.
1. D'amor la bella pa - ce
2. Rec. Dal primo foco in cui penai molt'-
3. Rec. Sopra un colle fiorito al di cui
4. Tu ten va - - i co - ſi
5. La vio - la, che lan-
6. Rec. Ecco, ecco l'infauſto lido,
PORSILE.
1. Vogli ad un altro cor a - mor
2. Rec. Sovra funeſta Py - ra

32
DUETTI.
PORSILE.
3. Rec.
Ombre amiche ombre care
STOELZEL.
1. Rec.
Deli - ran - - - - - te,
SCARLATTI.
1.
Se Amor con un Contento
ZUCCARI.
1.
Come porrà il mio cor,
DUETTI
A
VOCE CON CEMBALO.
LOTTI.
1. 2 Sopr.
Quella destra si mi
STEFFANI.
4. Sopr. Alto.
M'hai da piange - re m'hai
STEFFANI.
1. Sopr. e Alto.
L'ungi dall' I - dol mio
5. Sopr. Alto.
Rio destin ch'a tutte l'hore
2. Sopr. Alto.
Oc - chi perche piange.
6. Sopr. Alto.
Gia tu par - ti, io che
3. 2 Sopr.
Troppo cru - da è
7. 2 Sopr,
Sal - di mar - mi che copri - te
DUETTI.
33
STEFFANI.
8. Duett. 2 Sopr.
Rauvediti rauve - di - ti
9. Sopr. Alto.
Vorrei dire Vorrei
10. Sopr. Tenore.
Occhi - Belli
11. Sopr. Alto.
Begl'occhl oh Dio, non
12. Alto e Basso.
Ail - - - - re,
13. 2 Soprani.
Pria ch'io faccia altrui pa - lese
14. 2 Soprani.
Quanto care al Cor voi siete
15. 2 Sopr.
Rivel - la - tevi rivel-
STEFFANI.
16. Duett. 2 Soprani.
Sù fie - ri - - - sci
17. Sopr. e Tenore.
E perchè non m'ucci-
18. Sopr. e Tenore.
E co - si mi compati - te
19. Sopr. Basso.
Tengo per in - fal - li - bile
20. 2 Sopr.
Cangia cangia pensier mio
21. 2 Sopr.
Hò scherzato hò scher-
22. Sopr. Tenore.
Ah, che l'ho sempre det - to
23. Sopr. Tenore.
Non venesta - te à ride - re.

STEFFANI.
24. Duett. Alto, Basso.
Sia ma-le-detto Amor
25. Sopr. Basso.
Ge - losia, che vuoi, che vuoi
STEFFANI.
26. Duett. Alto, Tenore.
Mi voglio far in-tende-re
MADRIGALI
A
2. 3. 4 e 5 VOCI CON CEMBALO.
ANONYMO.
L'inganni d'Umanità.
1. Terzetto. Alto, Ten. Bass.
Alla tromba di Marte
2. Duett. Sopr. Alto.
Che vo-lete o cru - de
3. Quartett. Sopr. Alto, Ten. Bass.
Chi vuol a ver feli - ce e
4. Duett. Sopr. Bass.
Dir che gio-vi al mal
ANONYMO.
5. Duett. Sopr. Alto.
La Ca - tena ch'allettan-
6. Duett. Sopr. Alto.
Peggio far non mi può-
7. Duett. Sopr. Basso.
Sol di pian - - - to inondo
8. Duett. 2 Soprani.
Tesoro te-soro di
ANONYMO.
9. Duett. Alto, Ten.
Voi vene penti-rete
10. Duett. 2 Sopr.
Vor-rei sco-prirti
LOTTI.
Incostanza feminile.
1. Duett. Sopr. Basso.
Alcordi Donna aman-te
La querela amorosa.
2. Duett. Sopr. Alto.
Ben dovrei occhi leg-
Lamento di tre Amanti.
3. Terzett. 2 Sopr. Basso.
Ci stringe il co-re a-mor
Al Tabolino.
4. Quintett. 2 Sopr. Alt. Ten. Bass.
Or del ri-gido Ver - no
ROSSI.
1. Duett. 2 Soprani.
Son pur dolci a un cor ch'adora
ROSSI.
2. Duett. Sopr. Basso.
O questo nò. ch'io disperi,
3. Duett. Sopr. Basso.
Pe - - - ne
4. Terzett. Alto, Ten. Bass.
Per bellezza per bellezza
STEFFANI.
1. Duett. Sopr. Alto.
No sò - - chi mi pia-
2. Duett. Sopr. Alto.
Que-sto si lenzio ombroso
TORRI.
1. Duett. Sopr. Alto.
Piag - - - gie
2. Duett. Sopr. Alto.
Lan - gue ge-me

Deutsche scherzhaffte Cantaten.

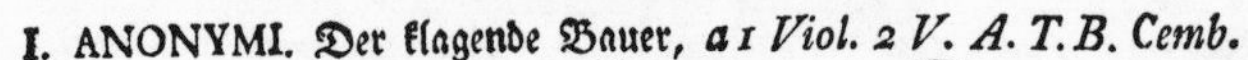

I. ANONYMI. Der klagende Bauer, *a 1 Viol. 2 V. A. T. B. Cemb.*

2. — Der betrogene Geld=Freyer, *a 2 Viol. V. Baß. s. e Fond.*

3. — Die Gevatterinnen, *a 3 Sopr. 1 Baß. con Cemb.*

4. — Der Italiäner, *a 2 Viol. V. Alto solo e Cemb.*

5. — Der weibliche Magister, *a 2 Viol. 1 Baß. solo e Cemb.*

6. — Der verliebte Nachtwächter, *a 2 Viol. V. Baß. solo e Cemb.*

7. — Der junge Soldat, *a 2 Ob. 1 Viol. Baß. solo e Cemb.*

8. — Die Wurmkuchen-Frau, *a Basso e Cemb.*

9. ANONYMI. Der Zahnarzt. *a 2 Viol. V. Basso solo e Cemb.*

10. — Duetto, *Recit.* Der verliebte Zanck, *a Viol. 2 V. e B.*

11. Grauns, Glücksbude des Cupido, *a 2 C. 2 Viol. V. Sopr. e Cemb.*

12. Hassens Filidor, *a 2 Viol. V. Sopr. e Basso.*

13. Herbings, Die Widersprecherinn, *a 2 Viol. V. 2 Fag. Sopr. e B.*

14. Hoffmanns, Dram. Zwischen einem Liebhaber, Jäger und Lauffer. *a Cl. Ob. 2 Viol. 3 Voci. e Basso.*

15. Kuhnaus, Il perfetto Musico. *a 2 Viol. Fag. Tenor. e Basso.*

16. Leleis, Der Jenaische Bursche, *a 2 Viol V. Sopr. Alt. e Baß.*

17. Marpurgs, Die schlauen Mädchen, *a 2 Viol. V. Ten. e Baß.*

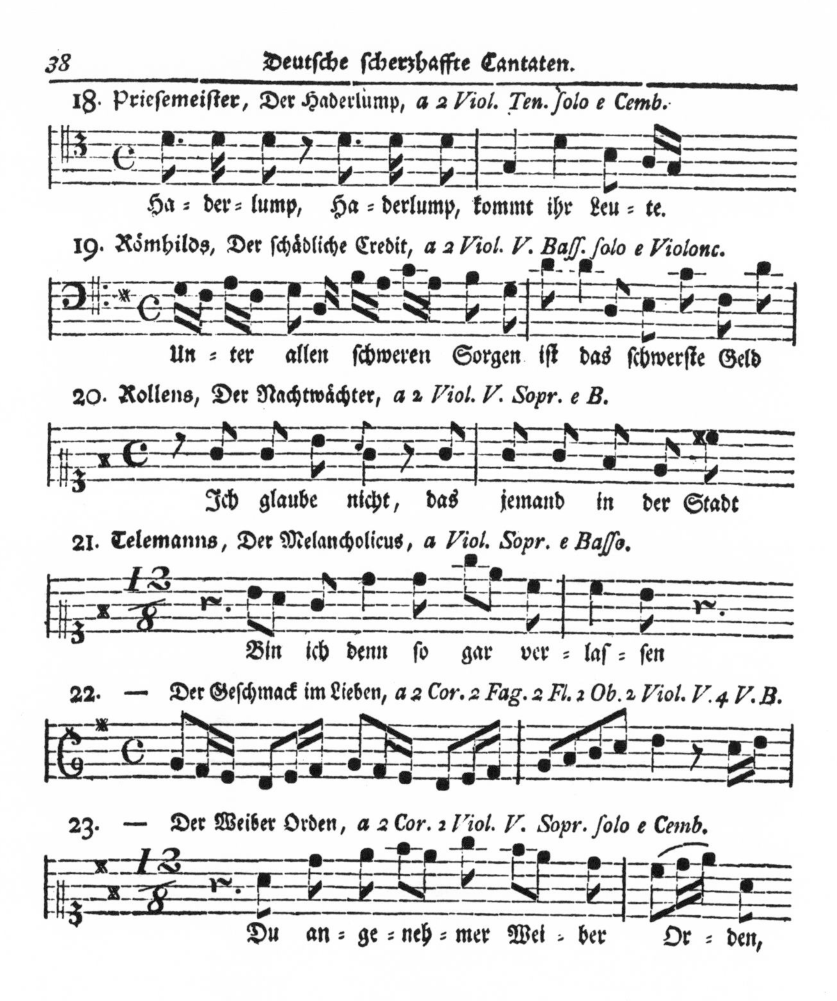

18. Priesemeister, Der Haderlump, *a 2 Viol. Ten. solo e Cemb.*

Ha = der = lump, Ha = derlump, kommt ihr Leu = te.

19. Römhilds, Der schädliche Credit, *a 2 Viol. V. Baß. solo e Violonc.*

Un = ter allen schweren Sorgen ist das schwerste Geld

20. Rollens, Der Nachtwächter, *a 2 Viol. V. Sopr. e B.*

Ich glaube nicht, daß jemand in der Stadt

21. Telemanns, Der Melancholicus, *a Viol. Sopr. e Basso.*

Bin ich denn so gar ver = las = sen

22. — Der Geschmack im Lieben, *a 2 Cor. 2 Fag. 2 Fl. 2 Ob. 2 Viol. V. 4 V. B.*

23. — Der Weiber Orden, *a 2 Cor. 2 Viol. V. Sopr. solo e Cemb.*

Du an = ge = neh = mer Wei = ber Or = den,

Il Fine.

SVPPLEMENTO I.

DEI

CATALOGI

DELLE

SINFONIE, PARTITE, OUVERTURE, SOLI, DUETTI, TRII, QUATTRI

E

CONCERTI

PER IL

VIOLINO, FLAUTO TRAVERSO,

CEMBALO

ED ALTRI STROMENTI.

CHE

SI TROVANO IN MANOSCRITTO

NELLA OFFICINA MUSICA DI BREITKOPF

IN LIPSIA.

1766.

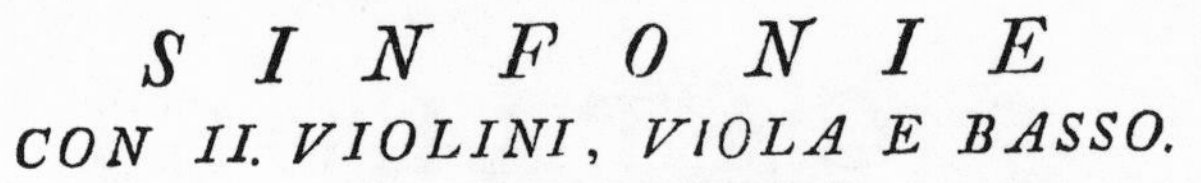
SINFONIE
CON II. VIOLINI, VIOLA E BASSO.

I. Sinf. del Sigr. AGRELL, M. di C. in Nor. a 4 V. Racc. II.
I. Sinfonia del Sigr. ALBINONI, a 6 Voci.
VI. Sinf. del Sigr. ASPELMEYER, a 8 e 9 Voci.
I. a 8 Voci. 2 C. 2 Ob.
IV. a 8 V. 2 C. 2 Ob.
II. a 8 V. 2 C. 2 Ob.
V. a 8 V. 2 C. 2 Ob.
III. a 9 V. 2 C. 2 Ob. 2 V. Violonc. B.
VI. a 8 V. 2 C. 2 Ob.
II. Sinf. del Sigr. C. P. E. BACH, M. di C. in Berol. Racc. II.
I. a 4 Voci.
II. a 4 Voci.
tr
tr
VI. Sinf. del Sigr. J. C. BACH, M. di C. in Londra. a 4. 6 e 8 V.
I. a 8 Voci. 2 C. 2 Ob.
IV.
II.
V.
III. a 8 V. 2 C. 2 Ob.
VI. a 6 Voci. 2 C. oblig.

SINFONIE.
3
I. Sinf. del S. BATONI, a 3 Voci. 2 Viol. Fag.
I. Sinf. del Sigr. BARBA, a 3 Voci.
VI. Sinf. del Sigr. BENDA, M. di C. in Gotha. Racc. II.
I. a 8 Voci. 2 C. 2 Ob.
IV. a 8 V. 2 C. 2 Ob.
II. a 8 V. 2 C. 2 Fl.
V. a 8 V. 2 C. 1 Ob. 1 Fl.
III. a 8 V. 2 C. 1 Ob. 1 Fl.
VI. a 4 Voci.
V. Sinf. del Sigr. BENDA, M. di C. in Gotha. R. III.
I. a 6 V. 2 Fl.
IV. a 6 V. 2 Ob.
II. a 4 Voci.
V. a 8 V. 2 C. 2 Fl.
III. a 4 Voci.
tr
I. Sinf. del S. Fr. BENDA, in Berol. a 4 Voci.
I. Sinf. del S. BEHRWALD, a 4 Voci.
I. Sinf. del S. BERTONI, a 4 V.
I. Sinf. del S. BONNO, a 4 V.

4
SINFONIE.
VI. Sinf. del Sigr. BECK, a 4 Voci.
I.
IV.
II.
V.
III.
VI.
II. Sinf. del Sigr. BESCH.
I. a 8 Voci. 2 C. 2 Ob.
II. a 8 Voci. 2 C. 2 Fl.
II. Sinf. del Sigr. Giov. Franc. BRUSA.
I. a 4 V.
II. a 8 V. 2 C. 2 Ob.
IV. Sinf. del Sigr. CANNABICH.
I. a 8 V. 2 C. 2 Ob.
III. a 8 V. 2 C. 2 Ob.
II. a 8 V. 2 C. 2 Ob.
IV. a 10 V. 2 C. 2 Ob. 2 Fag.
I. Sinf. del Sigr. CALDARA.
a 6 Voci. 2 Cor.
I. Sinf. del Sigr. CONTI. R. II.
a 4 Voci.
SINFONIE.
5
II. Sinf. del Sigr. COCCHI.
I. a 8 Voci. 2 C. 2 Ob.
II. a 9 V. 1 Tromb. 2 C. 2 Ob.
II. Sinf. del Sigr. CROENER.
I. a 7 V. 2 Clar. Tymp.
II. a 6 V. 2 C.
I. Sinf. del Sigr. DELLER.
a 10 V. 2 C. 2 Ob. 2 Fl.
I. Sinf. del Sigr. DUNI.
a 10 V. 2 Tromb. 2 C. 2 Ob.
VI. Sinf. del Sigr. DITTERS.
I. a 9 V. 2 C. 2 Ob. 2 Viole.
IV. a 8 V. 2 C. 2 Ob.
II.
V. a 8 V. 2 C. 2 Ob.
III. a 8 V. 2 C. 2 Ob.
VI. a 8 V. 2 C. 2 Ob.
III. Sinf. del Sigr. DOESKY.
I. a 8 Voci. 2 C. 2 Ob.
II. a 8 V. 2 C. 2 Ob.
III. a 8 V. 2 C. 2 Ob.
I. Sinf. del S. ENTERLEIN.
a 4 Voci.
II. Sinf. di E. T. P. A.
I. a 10 Voci. 2 C. 2 Ob. 2 Fl.
II. a 8 V. 2 C. 2 Ob.

6 SINFONIE.
II. Sinf. del Sigr. FAUNER.
I. a 4 Voci.
II. a 3 Voci.
VI. Sinf. del Sigr. FILTZ, M. di C. in Manheim.
I. a 4 Voci.
IV. a 8 V. 2 C. 2 Fl.
II. a 4 V.
V. a 8 V. 2 C. 2 Ob.
III. a 9 V. 2 Clar. Tymp. 2 Ob.
VI. a 4 V.
VI. Sinf. del Sigr. FILTZ, M. di C. in Manh. Racc. II.
I. a 8 Voci. 2 C. 2 Fl.
IV. a 8 V. 2 C. 2 Fl.
II. a 8 V. 2 C. 2 Fl.
V. a 8 V. 2 C. 2 Ob.
III. a 8 V. 2 C. 2 Fl.
VI. a 4 V.
II. Sinf. del S. FILTZ, M. di C. in Manheim.
I, a 4 V.
II. a 8 V. 2 C. 2 Ob.
II. Sinf. del S. FISCHIETTI.
I. a 8 V. 2 C. 2 Ob.
II. a 8 V. 2 C. 2 Ob.

SINFONIE. 7
II. Sinf. del Sigr. GALLIMBERTI.
I. a 4 Voci.
II. a 6 V. 2 C.
I. Sinf. del S. GAMBARO.
a 4 V.
I. Sinf. del S. GLANTZ.
a 8 V. 2 C. 2 Ob.
I. Sinf. del S. GALUPPI, M. di C. in Venet.
a 8 V. 2 Tromb. 2 Ob.
I. Sinf. del S. GANETTI.
a 8 V. 2 C. 2 Fl.
I. Sinf. del S. GALLINI.
a 6 V. 2 Cor.
I. Sinf. del S. GARZIA.
a 6 V. 2 Cor.
III. Sinf. del S. GASMANN.
I. a 6 Voci.
II. a 10 V. 2 C. 2 Ob. 2 Violonc. obl.
III. a 8 V. 2 C. 2 Ob.
I. Sinf. del S. GEBEL.
a 4 V.
I. Sinf. del S. GERARDO.
a 4 V.
I. Sinf. del S. GERLACH.
a 8 V. 2 Corn. 2 Ob.
II. Sinf. del Sigr. GLUCK.
I. a 8 V. 2 C. 2 Ob.
II. a 6 V. 2 C.

8 SINFONIE.
SINFONIE. 9
VI. Sinf. del Sigr. GRAUN, M. di Conc. in Berol. Racc. VII.
I. a 6 V. 2 C.
IV. a 8 V. 2 C. 2 Fl.
II. a 6 V. 2 Fl.
V. a 11 V. 2 C. 2 Ob. 2 Fl. 1 Fag.
III. a 6 V. 2 C.
VI. a 10 V. 2 C. 2 Ob. 2 Fl.
V. Sinf. del Sigr. GRAUN, M. di Conc. in Berol. Racc. VIII.
I. a 4 V.
IV. a 4 V.
II. a 4 V.
V. a 4 V.
III. a 4 V.
VI. Sinf. del Sigr. HARRER, Dir. dell. Muf. in Lipfia. Raccolta III.
I. a 9 V. 3 C. 2 Ob.
IV. a 9 V. 3 C. 2 Ob.
II. a 11 V. 3 C. 2 Fl. 2 Ob.
V. a 8 V. 2 C. 2 Ob.
III. a 8 V. 2 C. 2 Ob.
VI. a 8 V. 2 C. 2 Fl.
VI. Sinf. del Sigr. HARRER, Dir. dell. Muf. in Lips. R. IV.
I. a 4 Voci.
IV. a 4 V.
II. a 4 V.
V. a 4 V.
III. a 4 V.
VI. a 8 V. 2 Tromb. 2 Ob.
III. Sinf. del Sigr. HARRER, Dir. dell. Muf. in Lips. R. V.
I. a 6 V. 2 Ob.
III. a 4 V.
II. a 4 V.
V. Sinf. del Sigr. HASSE, Pr. M. di Cap. in Dresda.
I. a 10 V. 2 C. 2 Ob. 2 Fl. Clelia.
IV. a 8 V. 2 C. 2 O. Siroë.
II. a 8 V. 2 C. 2 Ob. Zenobia.
V. a 8 V. 2 C. 2 Ob. Egeria.
III. a 8 V. 2 C. 2 Ob. la Nitetti.
II. Sinf. del Sigr. HATTASCH, Muf. di Cam. in Gotha.
I. a 6 V. 2 C.
II. a 6 V. 2 C.

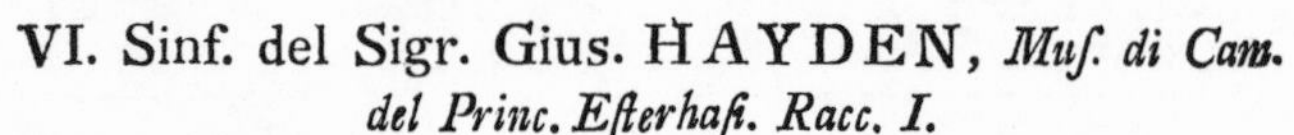

VI. Sinf. dei Sigr. Gius. HAYDEN, *Muf. di Cam. del Princ. Efterhafi. Racc. II.*

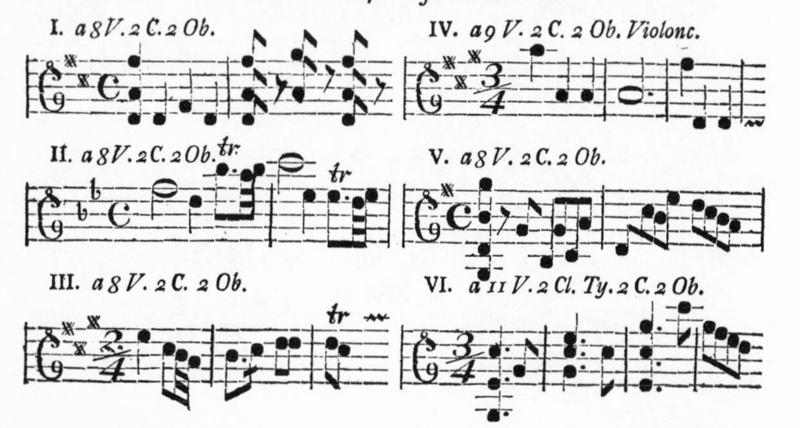

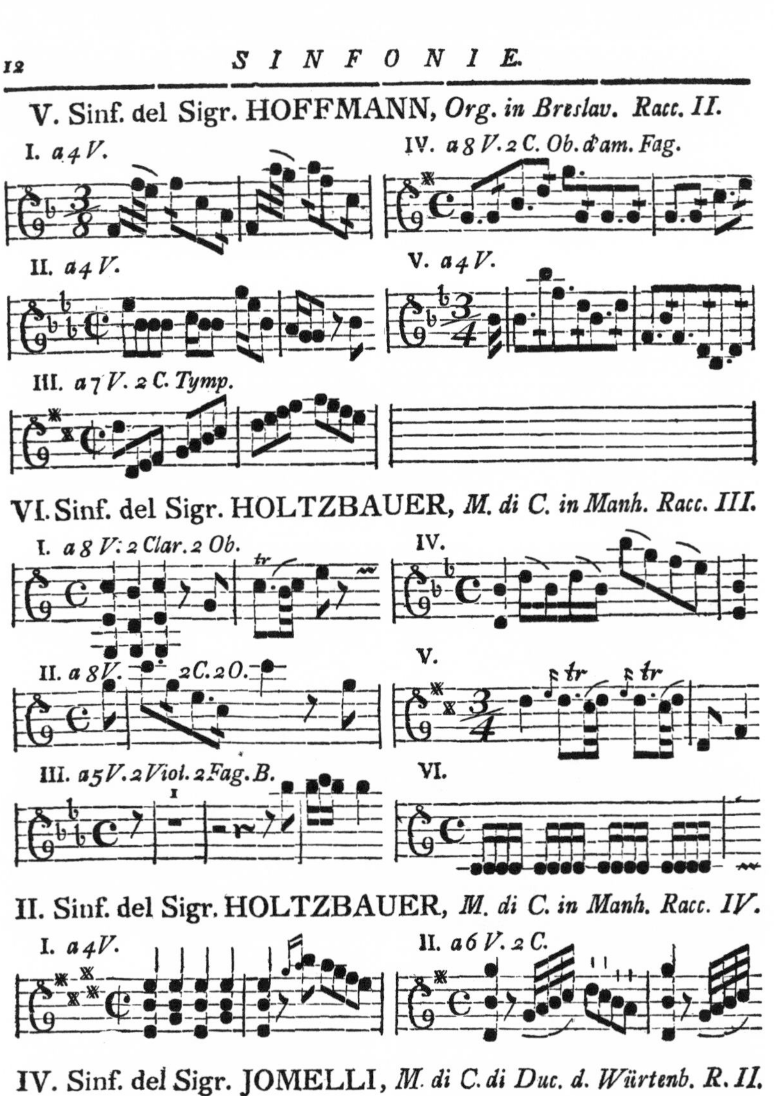

12 SINFONIE.
V. Sinf. del Sigr. HOFFMANN, Org. in Breslav. Racc. II.
I. a 4 V.
IV. a 8 V. 2 C. Ob. d'am. Fag.
II. a 4 V.
V. a 4 V.
III. a 7 V. 2 C. Tymp.
VI. Sinf. del Sigr. HOLTZBAUER, M. di C. in Manh. Racc. III.
I. a 8 V. 2 Clar. 2 Ob.
tr
IV.
II. a 8 V. 2 C. 2 O.
V.
tr
tr
III. a 5 V. 2 Viol. 2 Fag. B.
VI.
II. Sinf. del Sigr. HOLTZBAUER, M. di C. in Manh. Racc. IV.
I. a 4 V.
II. a 6 V. 2 C.

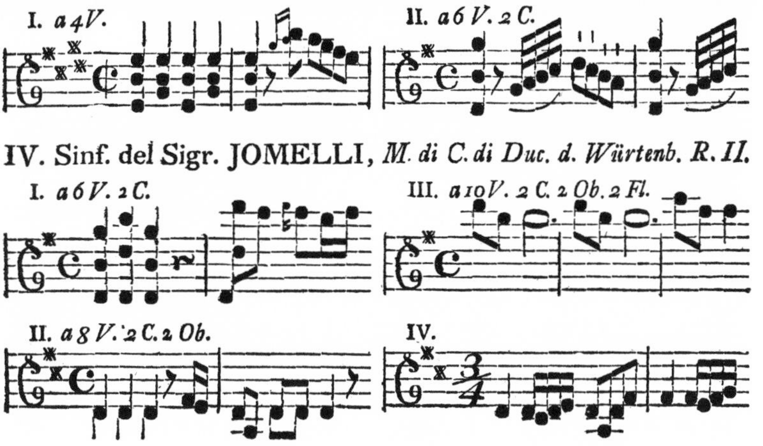

IV. Sinf. del Sigr. JOMELLI, M. di C. di Duc. d. Würtenb. R. II.
I. a 6 V. 2 C.
III. a 10 V. 2 C. 2 Ob. 2 Fl.
II. a 8 V. 2 C. 2 Ob.
IV.

SINFONIE. 13
IV. Sinf. del Sigr. JOMELLI, M. di C. di Duc. d. Würtenb. R. III.
I.
III. a 6 V. 2 C.
fp
II. a 8 V. 2 C. 2 Ob.
IV. a 6 V. 2 C.
I. Sinf. del S. KAISER.
a 6 V. 2 C.
I. Sinf. del S. KELLERI.
a 4 V.
III. Sinf. del Sigr. KIRNBERGER, in Berolino.
I. a 6 V. 2 C.
tr
III. a 4 V.
II. a 4 V.
tr
I. Sinf. del S. KREBS, Org. in Altenb.
a 4 V.
III. Sinf. del Sigr. KUNTZ, Dir. della Mus. in Lubeck.
I. a 9 V. 2 C. 2 Ob. Tymp.
III. a 5 V. Violonc.
tr
II. a 9 V. 3 Clar. Tymp. Violonc.
II. Sinf. del Sigr. LATILLA.
I. a 6 V. 2 C.
II. a 8 V. 2 C. 2 Ob.
I. Sinf. del Sigr. LEO.
I. a 6 V.
I. Sinf. del S. LOCATELLI.
a 4 V.

14
SINFONIE.
I. Sinf. del S. MACCHI.
a 6 Voci. 2 Tromb.
I. Sinf. del S. MARCHI.
a 6 V. 2 Tromb.
II. Sinf. del Sigr. MALZARD.
I. a 6 V. 1 Fl. 1 Viol. 2 C.
II. a 6 V. 1 Fl. 1 Viol. 2 C.
III. Sinf. del Sigr. MARTINO, Racc. IV.
I. a 4 Voci.
III. a 7 V. 2 C. 1 Fl.
II. a 3 V.
I. Sinf. del Sigr. MONN.
a 5 V. 1 Fl.
VI. Sinf. del Sigr. MOZARD, M. di Cam. in Salzb. Racc. II.
I. a 6 V. 2 C.
IV. a 4 V.
II. a 6 V.
V. a 4 V.
III. a 4 V.
VI. a 4 V.
IV. Sinf. del Sigr. MOZARD, M. di Cam. in Salzb. R. III.
I. a 4 V.
III. a 4 V
II. a 6 V. 2 C.
IV. a 4 V.

SINFONIE.
15
II. Sinf. del Sigr. MINGETTI.
I. a 4 Voci.
II. a 4 Voci.
VI. Sinf. del Sigr. NERUDA, M. di Cam. in Dresda. Racc. II.
I. a 6 V. 2 C.
IV. a 6 V. 2 C.
II. a 6 V. 2 Ob.
V. a 6 V. 2 C.
III. a 6 V. 2 C.
VI. a 6 V. 2 C.
IV. Sinf. del Sigr. NERUDA, M. di Cam. in Dresda. R. III.
I. a 4 V.
III. a 6 V. 2 Fl.
II. a 4 V.
IV. a 4 V.
VI. Sinf. del Sigr. NERUDA, M. di Cam. in Dresda. R. IV.
I. a 8 Voci. 2 C. 2 Ob.
IV. a 4 Voci.
II. a 8 V. 2 C. 2 Ob.
V. a 4 Voci.
III. a 8 V. 2 C. 2 Ob.
VI. a 4 Voci.

16 SINFONIE.
IV. Sinf. del Sigr. NAUMANN, Compos. della Corte in Dresda.
I. a 8 V. 2 C. 2 Ob.
III. a 10 V. 2 C. 2 Fl. 2 Ob.
II. a 10 V. 2 C. 2 Fl. 2 Ob.
IV. a 10 V. 2 C. 2 Fl. 2 Ob.
II. Sinf. del Sigr. NICHELMANN, M. di Cam. in Berol.
I. a 4 V.
II. a 4 V.
II. Sinf. del Sigr. ORDONEZ.
I. a 6 V. 2 Ob.
II. a 8 V. 2 C. 2 Ob.
I. Sinf. del S. Dom. d'all OGLIO.
a 4 V.
Sinf. Russa.
I. Sinf. del S. PALADINO.
a 6 V. 2 C.
I. Sf. del S. PALERMITANO.
a 4 V.
I. Sinf. del S. PELLEGRINI.
a 4 V.
IV. Sinf. del Sigr. PUGNANI.
I. a 9 V. 2 C. 2 Ob. 2 V.
III. a 9 V. 2 C. 2 Ob. 2 V.
II. a 9 V. 2 C. 2 Ob. 2 V.
IV. a 9 V. 2 C. 2 Ob. 2 V.
I. Sinf. del S. PERGOLESI.
a 6 V. 2 C.
I. Sinf. del S. PFEIFFER.
a 10 V. 2 Cl. Tymp. 2 Ob. Fag.
SINFONIE. 17
II. Sinf. del Sigr. PERETZ.
I. a 8 V. 2 C. 2 Ob.
II. a 6 V. 2 C.
IV. Sinf. del Sigr. PIRLINGER.
I, a 6 Voci. 2 Ob.
III. a 8 V. 2 C. 2 Ob.
II. a 8 V. 2 C. 2 Ob.
IV. a 9 V. 2 Clar. Tymp. 2 Ob.
f
p
III. Sinf. del Sigr. PORPORA.
I. a 8 Voci. 2 C. 2 Ob.
III. a 4 V.
II. a 4 Voci.
I. Sinf. del S. POLAZZI.
a 4 V.
VII. Sinf. del Sigr. QUERFURTH.
I. a 8 V. 2 C. 2 Ob.
V. a 8 V. 2 Cl. 2 Ob.
II. a 8 V. 2 C. 2 Fl.
IV. a 8 V. 2 C. 2 Ob.
III. a 8 V. 2 C. 2 Ob.
VII. a 8 V. 2 C. 2 Fl.
IV. a 8 V. 2 C. 2 Ob.
I. Sinf. del Sigr. RELUZZI.
a 4 Voci.

18
SINFONIE.
VI. Sinf. del Sigr. Fr. Xav. RICHTER, M. di Cam. in Manheim.
a 6 Voci. 2 Corni. Racc. II.
I.
IV.
II.
V.
III.
tr
VI.
3
V. Sinf. del Sigr. Fr. Xav. RICHTER, M. di Cam. in Manh.
a 4 Voci. Racc. III.
I.
IV.
tr
II.
V.
III.
II. Sinf. del Sigr. RIEPEL, M. di Cam. di Princ. di Turn e Taſſis.
a 6 Voci. 2 Corni.
I.
tr
II.
I. Sinf. del Sigr. ROELLIG,
a 4 V. in Dresda.
I. Sinf. del S. RODEWALD.
a 4 V. in Berol.
tr
tr
I. Sinf. del Sigr. ROMANO.
a 16 V. 2 Tromb. Tymp. 2 C. 2 Fl. 2 Ob.
2 Viol. conc. Violonc. oblig.
I. Sinf. del S. SARTI, M. di Cap.
di Ré di Danem.
a 6 V. 2 C.
SINFONIE.
19
II. Sinf. del Sigr. SCARLATTI,
I. a 3 Voci.
II. a 8 V. 2 C. 2 Ob.
II. Sinf. del Sigr. SCHAFFRATH.
I. a 6 V. 2 C.
II. a 4 V.
VI. Sinf. del Sigr. SCHEIBE, M. di Cap. di Ré di Danem.
a 4 Voci.
all'Paſtorale.
I.
IV.
II.
V.
III.
VI.
VII. Sinf. del Sigr. SCHURER, Comp. di Cort. in Dresd. R. I.
I.
V.
II.
VI. a 6 V. 2 Fl.
III.
VII.
I. Sinf. del Sigr. SCHWA-
NENBERG.
IV.
tr

III. Sinf. del Sigr. SCHLOEGER.

I. a 8 Voci. 2 C. 2 Ob.

III. a 9 V. 2 C. 2 Ob. Viol. conc.

II. a 8 V. 2 C. 2 Ob.

I. Sinf. del Sigr. SCOLARI.

a 6 V. 2 C.

IV. Sinf. del Sigr. SEIFFERT, in Auguſta. a 6 V. 2 Cor. Racc. I.

I.

III.

II.

IV.

VI. Sinf. del Sigr. SEIFFERT, in Auguſta. a 6 V. 2 Cor. R. II.

I.

IV.

II.

V.

tr.

III.

VI.

III. Sinf. del Sigr. STALDERO, a 4 Voci.

I.

III.

II.

I. Sinf. del Sigr. SOLLNITZ.

a 4 Voci.

I. Sinf. del Sigr. STADTLER.

a 4 Voci.

VI. Sinf. del Sigr. STAMITZ, M. di Cam. in Manheim.

I. a 6 V. 2 C.

IV. a 8 V. 2 C. 2 Ob.

II. a 4 V.

V. a 4 V.

III. a 4 V.

VI. a 11 V. 2 Cl. Tymp. 2 C. 2 Ob.

II. Sinf. del Sigr. SUHLE. a 6 Voci. 2 Oboi.

I.

II.

VI. Sinf. del Sigr. Giuſep. STEFFANI. in Vienna.

I. a 8 Voci. 2 Cl. 2 C.

IV. a 6 V. 2 Cl. Tymp.

II. a 7 V. 2 Cl. Tymp.

V. a 4 V.

III. a 6 V. 2 Cl.

VI. a 4 V.

22

SINFONIE.
I. Sinf. del Sigr. TORTI.
a 4 V.
I. Sinf. del Sigr. VINCI.
a 6 V. 2 C.
VI. Sinf. del Sigr. WAGENSEIL, M. di Cap. in Vienna.
Raccolta IV.
I. a 6 V. 2 C.
IV. a 6 V. 2 Ob.
I. a 6 V. 2 C.
V. a 8 V. 2 C. 2 Ob.
III. a 8 V. 2 C. 2 Ob.
VI. a 6 V. 2 Ob.
VI. Sinf. del Sigr. WAGENSEIL, M. di Cap. in Vienna.
Raccolta V.
I. a 8 V. 2 C. 2 Ob.
IV. a 6 V. 2 C.
II. a 8 V. 2 C. 2 Ob.
V. a 6 V. 2 Ob.
III. a 6 V. 2 Ob.
VI. a 6 V. 2 Ob.
II. Sinf. del Sigr. WAGENSEIL, M. di Cap. in Vienna.
Raccolta VI.
I. a 9 V. 2 Tr. Ty. 2 Ob.
II. a 8 V. 2 C. 2 Ob.

SINFONIE. 23
IV. Sinf. del Sigr. VAN-MALTRE, a 4 Voci.
I.
IV.
II.
V.
III.
VI.
I. Sinf. del Sigr. WIRBACH.
a 4 Voci.
I. Sinf. del Sigr. ZANI.
a 4 Voci.
I. Sinf. del Sigr. ZARTH,
in Berolino.
a 4 Voci.
I. Sinf. del Sigr. ZOPPIS.
a 9 Voci. 2 Tromb. 2 Ob. Fag.
III. Sinf. del Sigr. ZACH,
in Mogonza.
III. Sinf. del S. ZIEGLER, in
Vienna. a 8 Voci, 2 C. 2 Ob.
I. a 4 Voci.
I.
II. a 8 V. 2 C. 2 Ob.
II.
III. a 4 Voci.
III.

VIOLINO.

SOLI COL BASSO.

I. Solo del Sigr. AGRELL.

VI. Soli del Sigr. BENDA, *Racc. IX.*

VI. Soli del Sigr. BENDA, *Racc. X.*

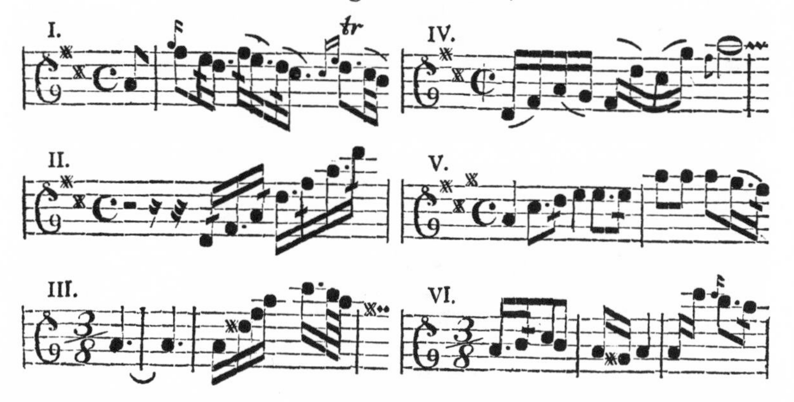

V. Soli del Sigr. BENDA, *Racc. XI.*

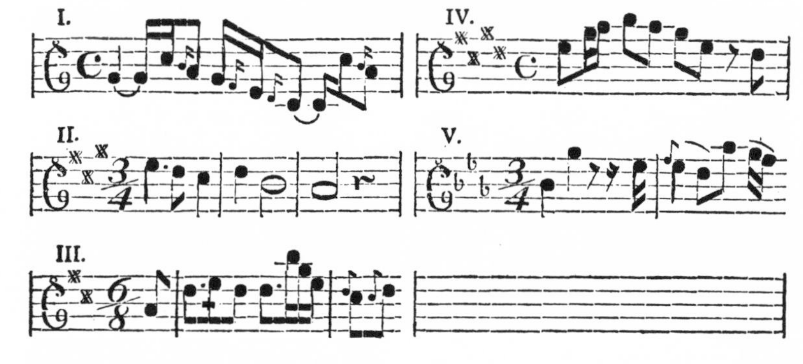

XVII. Capricio, *a Viol. solo senza Basso.*

II. Soli del Sigr. DEGIARDINO.

VII. Soli del Sigr. ENDERLE.

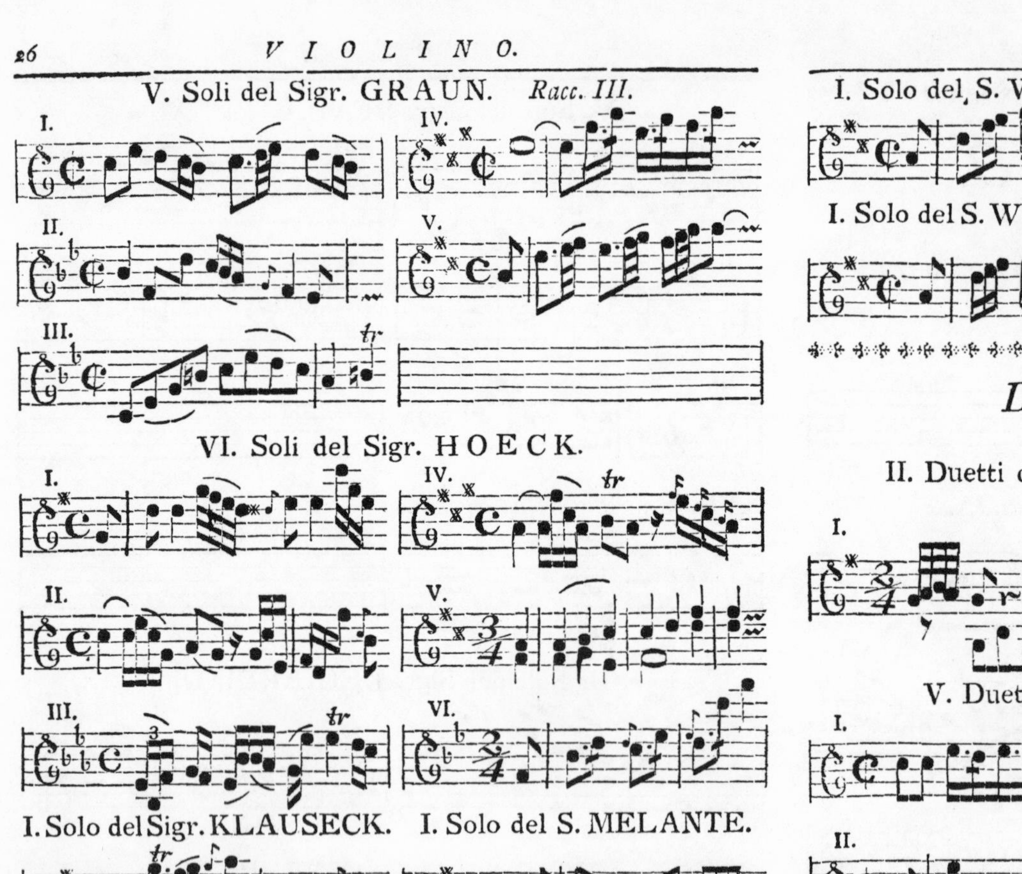
V. Soli del Sigr. GRAUN. Racc. III.
I.
IV.
II.
V.
III.
tr
VI. Soli del Sigr. HOECK.
I.
IV.
tr
II.
V.
III.
tr
VI.
I. Solo del Sigr. KLAUSECK.
tr
I. Solo del S. MELANTE.

VI. Soli del Sigr. STAMITZ.
I.
IV.
II.
V.
III.
VI.

I. Solo del S. VIVALDI.
I. Solo del Sigr. VOGLER.
I. Solo del S. WODIZKA.
DUETTI.
II. Duetti del Sigr. STAMITZ, a Violino solo.
I.
II.
V. Duetti del Sigr. BENDA, a 2 Violini.
I.
IV.
II.
V.
III.
III. Duetti del Sigr. KUNTZ, a 2 Violini.
I.
III.
II.

TRII.

II. Trii del Sigr. APPELMEYER, *a 2 Violini e Basso.*

VI. Trii del Sigr. BACH, *a 2 Viol. e Basso. Racc. I.*

VI. Trii del Sigr. BACH, *a 2 Viol. e Basso. Racc. II.*

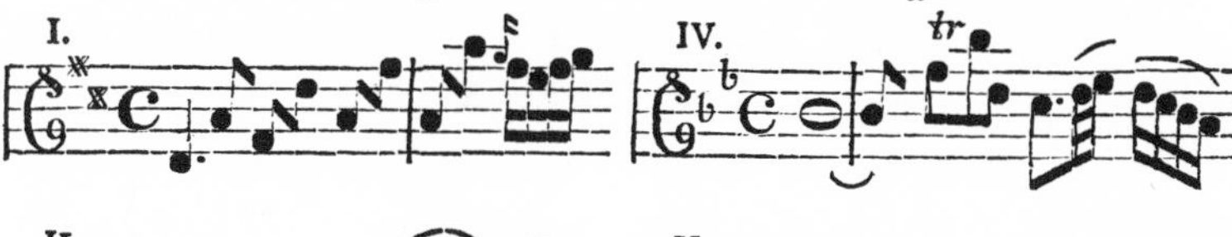

I. Trio del Sigr. BENDA.

I. Trio del Sigr. FASCH.

III. Trii del Sigr. GASMANN, *a 2 Violini e Basso.*

VI. Trii del Sigr. GASPARINI, *a 2 Viol. e Basso. Raccolta I.*

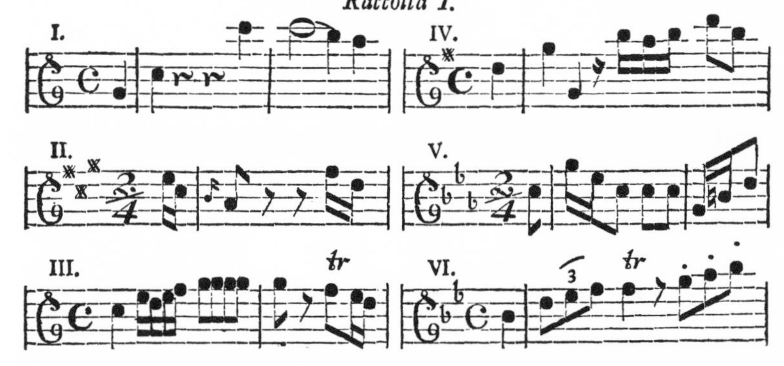

V. Trii del Sigr. GASPARINI, *a 2 Viol. e Basso. Raccolta II.*

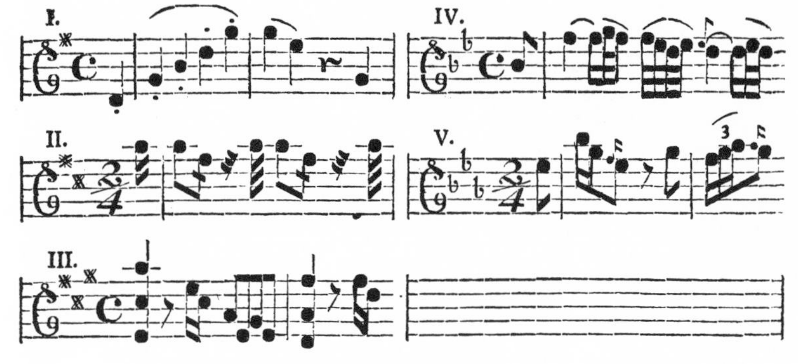

II. Trii del Sigr. GEBEL, *a 2 Viol. e Basso.*

30 VIOLINO.
II. Trii del Sigr. GRAUN, a 2 Viol, e Baſſo. Racc. V.
VI. Trii del Sigr. HEYDEN, a 2 Viol. e Baſſo.
VI. Trii del Sigr. HOFFMANN, a 2 Viol. e Baſſo. Racc. I.
VI. Trii del Sigr. HOFFMANN, a 2 Viol. e Baſſo. Racc. II.

VIOLINO. 31
V. Trii del Sigr. HOECK, a 2 Violini e Baſſo.
I. Trio del Sigr. KOHAUT.
I. Trio del Sigr. KRIEGER.
VI. Trii del Sigr. MARTINI, a 2 Viol. e Baſſo. Racc. VI.
I. Trio del Sigr. ORSLER.
I. Trio del Sigr. PERGOLESI.
I. Trio del Sigr. POSTEL.

VI. Trii del Sigr. SEIFFERT, *a 2 Viol. e Basso.*

IV. Trii del Sigr. WAGENSEIL, *a 2 Viol. e Basso.*

CONCERTI

A VIOLINO CONCERTAT. CON II. VIOLINI, VIOLA E BASSO.

I. Conc. del Sigr. ANTINONI.
a Viol. pr. 2 Viol. conc. B.

III. Conc. del Sigr. Fr. BENDA, *a Viol. conc. 2 Viol. Viola, Basso. Racc. V.*

I. Conc. del S. BIANCOLINI. I. Conc. del S. BISHENDEL.

I. Conc. del S. BOSHOFF. I. Conc. del Sigr. CONTI.

I. Conc. del Sigr. DIO.

VI. Conc. del Sigr. DITTERS.

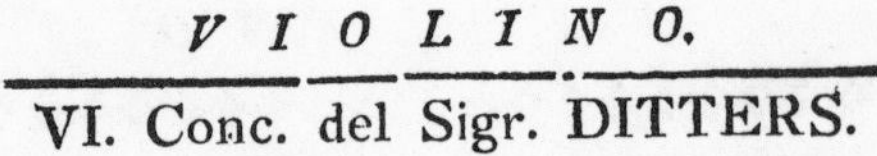

I. *Viol. pr. 2 Viol. obl. 2 Viol. rip. 2 C. V. B. obl. B. rip.*

IV. *2 Viol. princ. 2 Viol. rip. 2 Ob. 2 Corn. V. B.*

II. *Viol. conc. 2 C. 2 Ob. 2 Viol. V. B.*

V. *Viol. conc. 2 Viol. V. B.*

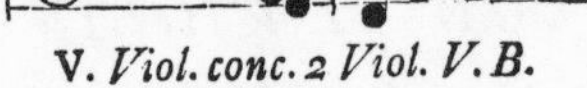

III. *Viol. conc. 2 Viol. V. B.*

VI. *Viol. pr. 2 C. 2 Ob. 2 Viol. V. B.*

I. Conc. del Sigr. DOARI.

I. Conc. del Sigr. ENDERLE.

I. Conc. del S. FERRONATI.

Viol. pr. Viol. 2 do conc. 2 Viol. rip. Viola, Basso.

I. Conc. del Sigr. FIORILLO.

Viol. conc. 2 Viol. V. B.

II. Conc. del Sigr. FOERSTER, *a Viol. princ. 2 Viol. V. B.*

I. II.

I. Conc. del S. GRAUN.

Viol. princ. 2 Viol. V. B.

I. Conc. del Sigr. GRAVINA.

Viol. princ Viol. conc. 2 do. Viol. 3 to. B.

II. Conc. del Sigr. GIRANECK. *a Viol. conc. 2 Viol. V. B.*

I. II.

I. Conc. del Sigr. HARTWIG.

I. Conc. del Sigr. HASSE.

II. Conc. del Sigr. HARRER.

I. *a Viol. conc. 2 Viol. rip. 2 Viole, 2 Violonc. Cemb.*

II. *a Viol. pr. 2 C. 2 Ob. 2 Fag. 2 Viol. V. 2 Violonc. Cemb.*

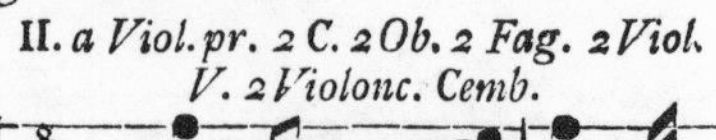

I. Conc. del Sigr. HEIL.

Viol. pr. 2 Viol. conc. 2 V. rip 2 C. V. B.

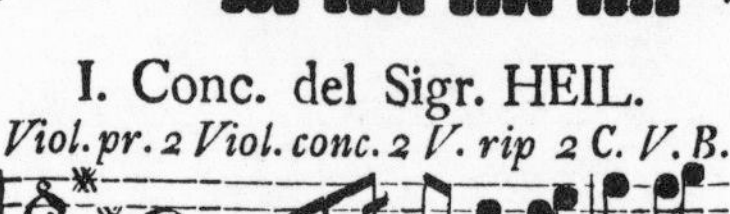

I. Conc. del Sigr. HERING.

Viol. conc. 2 Viol. V. B.

I. Conc. del Sigr. HORN.

I. Conc. del Sigr. HOFFMANN.

I. Conc. del Sigr. KREBS.

I. Conc. del S. KRUMLOWSKY.

I. Conc. del Sigr. MAHAUT.

I. Conc. del Sigr. NARDINI.

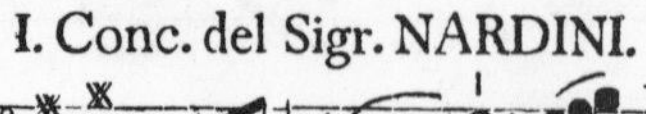

IV. Conc. del Sigr. NERUDA, *a Viol. conc. 2 Viol. V. B. Racc. II.*

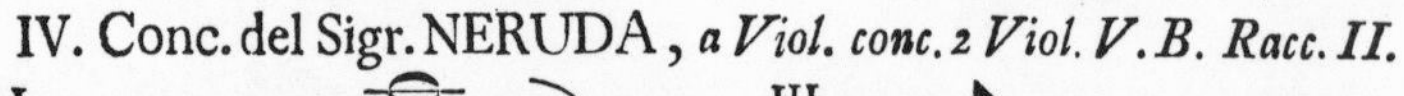

I. III. II. IV.

I. Conc. del Sigr. PERETZ.

a Viol. conc. 3 Viol. Viol. obl. 2 C. B.

VI. Conc. del Sigr. PFEIFFER, *a Viol. conc. 2 Viol. V. B.*
Raccolta V.

I. Conc. del Sigr. PUGNANI.
a Viol. princ. 2 Viol. V. B.

I. Conc. del Sigr. RIEPEL.
a Viol. conc. 2 Ob. 2 Viol. V. B.

I. Conc. del Sigr. RUSSO.
a Viol. conc. 3 Viol. B.

I. Conc. del S. SCHAFFRATH.
a Viol. conc. 2 Viol. V. B.

I. Conc. del Sigr. SCHEIBE.

I. Conc. del Sigr. SEYFFERT.

V. Conc. del Sigr. STAMITZ, *a Viol. conc. 2 Viol. V. B.*

I. Conc. del Sigr. TISCHER.

I. Conc. del Sigr. TZARTH.

I. Concerto del Sigr. ZELLER.

VIOLINO PICCOLO.

CONCERTI.

III. Conc. del Sigr. PFEIFFER, *a Viol. picc. 2 Viol. Vola, Basso.*

VIOLA.

I. Trio, del Sigr. FERRANDINI, *a Viola oblig. Violino, Basso*

VIOLONCELLO.

SOLI.

II. Soli del Sigr. GRETSCH, *a Violoncello, Basso.*

I. Solo del Sigr. VIVALDI.

VIOLA da GAMBA.

QUATTRO.

I. del Sigr. PEPUSCH, *a V. da G. 2 Violini con Cembalo.*

IV. Partite del Sigr. HARRER.

I. *a 10. V. 2 C. 2 Ob. Ingl. V. de Gamb. Liuto. 2 Viol. V. c. B.*

III. *a 8 V. 2 C. 2 Fl. 1 Ob. 1 Viol. d. G. all' Ottav. 2 V. c. B.*

II. *a 10 V. 2 C. 2 Ob. 2 Fl. 1 V. da Gb. 1 Violonc. obl. 2 Viol. c. B.*

IV. *a 9 V. 2 C. 1 Fl. 1 Ob. 1 V. d. Gamb. 2 Viol. V. B.*

FLAUTO TRAVERSO.

SOLI.

III. Soli, del Sigr. BLOCHWITZ.

VI. Soli, del Sigr. WENDLING.

D U E T T I

A II. FLAUTI.

VI. Duetti del Sigr. SIMONETTI. *Raccolta I.*

VI. Duetti del Sigr. SIMONETTI. *Raccolta II.*

TRII

A II. FLAUTI E BASSO.

I. Trio del Sigr. ABEL. *Raccolta II.*

III. Trii del Sigr. KLEINKNECHT, *a 2 Flauti e Basso.*

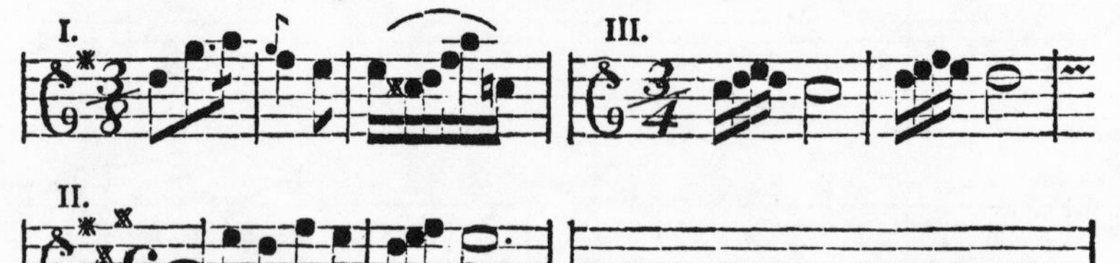

I. Trio del Sigr. LOCATELLI. I. Trio del Sigr. QUANTZ.

TRII

A FLAUTO, VIOLINO E BASSO.

44
FLAUTO TRAVERSO.
CONCERTI
A FLAUTO TRAVERSO.
III. Conc. del ANONYMO.
I. 2 Fl. conc. 2 Viol. B.
III. 1 Fl. conc. 2 Viol. B.
II. 1 Fl. conc. 2 Viol. V. B.
I. Conc. del Sigr. ADAM.
1 Fl. conc. 2 Viol. V. B.
I. Conc. del Sigr. CAPUTTI.
1 Fl. conc. 2 Corn. 2 Viol. B.
I. Conc. del Sigr. DROBISCH.
1 Fl. conc. 2 Viol. V. B.
I. Conc. del Sigr. FOERSTER.
1 Fl. conc. 2 Viol. B.
I. Conc. del Sigr. FASCH.
1 Fl. conc. 2 Viol. V. B.
I. Conc. del Sigr. GRAUN. R. III
1 Fl. conc. 2 Viol. B.
III. Conc. del Sigr. HASSE. Racc. IV.
I. 1 Fl. conc. 2 Viol. V. B.
III. 1 Fl. conc. 2 Viol. B.
II. 1 Fl. conc. 2 Viol. B.
I. Conc. del Sigr. HOFFMANN.
2 Fl. conc. 2 Corn. 4 Viol. V. B.
I. Conc. del Sigr. MALTZARD.

FLAUTO TRAVERSO.
45
III. Conc. del Sigr. QUANTZ,
a Fl. conc. 2 Viol. V. B. Racc. II.
III. Conc. del Sigr. QUANTZ,
a Fl. conc. 2 Viol. V. B. Racc. III.
IV. Conc. del Sigr. QUANTZ, a Fl. conc. 2 Viol. V. B. R. IV.
QUATTRI
A FLAUTO, VIOLINO, VIOLA E BASSO.
VI. Quattri del Sigr. TOESCHI.

SINFON. CASSAT. &c.

A FLAUTO TRAVERSO.

II. Sinf. del Sigr. MALZARD, *a 2 Corn. Fl. Viol. V. B.*

I. Sinfonie del Sigr. MONN, *Flaut. 2 Viol. V. B.*

I. Caſſatio, del Sigr. GEWEY, *2 Corn. 2 Fl. 2 Viol. V. B.*

II. Dell' Academia, del Sigr. MARTINO, *a 2 Corn. 2 Flaut. 2 Viol. B.*

FLAUTO PICCOLO.

V. Trii del ANONYMO, *a 2 Flauti e Baſſo*

OBOE.

SOLI.

I. Solo del Sigr. FOERSTER. *a Oboe, Cembalo.*

I. Solo del Sigr. HEINCHEN. *a Oboe ſolo, Baſſono.*

I. Solo del Sigr. HENDEL. *a Oboe ſolo, Cemb.*

III. Soli del Sigr. QUANTZ, *a Oboe ſolo, Baſſono.*

I. Solo del Sigr. LOCATELLI. *a Oboe ſolo, Baſſo.*

I. Solo del Sigr. STUTICK. *a Oboe ſolo, Baſſo.*

I. Solo del Sigr. STRICKER. *a Oboe ſolo, Baſſo.*

TRII.

I. Trio del Sigr. FASCH.
a 2 Oboi e Bassono.

I. Trio del Sigr. HENDEL.
a 2 Oboi e Basso.

I. Trio del Sigr. LINICKE.
Oboe, Violino, Basso.

I. Trio del Sigr. PEPUSCH.
Oboe, Flauto, Basso.

QUATTRO.

I. Quadro del Sigr. FASCH, *a 2 Oboi, 2 Bassoni.*

CONCERTI.

I. Conc. del Sigr. BACH, *Oboe conc. Viol. princ. 2 Viol. Viola, Basso.*

II. Conc. del Sigr. FOERSTER.

I. *Ob. conc. 2 Viol. V. B.*

II. *Ob. conc. 2 Viol. V. B.*

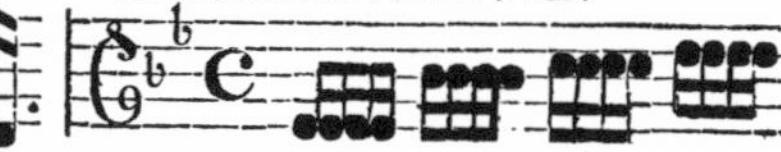

I. Conc. del Sigr. TELEMANN, *Ob. conc. 1 Viol. conc. 2 Viol. V. B.*

OBOE d'AMORE.

I. Trio del Sigr. LOTTI.
a Ob. d'am. Flute trav. e Basso.

I. Conc. del Sigr. FASCH.
a Ob. d'amore, 2 Ob. e Basso.

I. Conc. del Sigr. ULICH, *a Grand Oboe, 2 Violini, Viola, Basso.*

FAGOTTO.

SOLI.

IV. Soli del ANONYMO, *a Fagotto solo con Cembalo.*

TRII.

I. Trio del Sigr. BENDA, *Fagotto oblig. Violino e Cemb.*

II. Trii del Sigr. HASSE, *a Fag. obl. Viol. o Oboe con Basso.*

II. Trii del Sigr. KRAUSE.

CONCERTI.

I. Conc. del ANONYMO, *a Fagott. conc. 2 Viol. Viola, Basso.*

I. Conc. del Sigr. LAUBE. *Fag. conc. 2 Viol. V. B.*

I. Conc. del Sigr. SUHL. *Fag. conc. 2 Viol. V. B.*

CORNO.

I. Conc. del Sigr. TISCHER, *a 2 Corni, 2 Violini, Violone.*

CEMBALO.

SOLI.

I. Solo del Sigr. AGREL.

I. Solo del Sigr. BERLIN.

II. Soli del Sigr. GALUPPI.

I. Concerto del Sigr. HARRER, *a Cemb. solo.*

V. Soli del Sigr. HAYDEN, *a Cemb. solo.*

II. Soli del Sigr. KEUNER, *a Cemb. solo.*

I. Solo del Sigr. PLATTI. I. Solo del Sigr. PAMPANI.

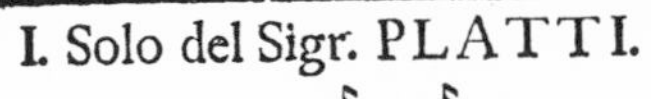

I. Solo del Sigr. PERTI. I. Solo del Sigr. SAXER.

I. Solo del Sigr. SCARLATTI.

TRII

A CEMBALO OBLIGATO CON VIOLINO.

I. Trio del Sigr. BACH. I. Trio del Sigr. BINDER.

I. Trio del Sigr. FRITSCH. I. Trio del Sigr. NERUDA.

VI. Soli del Sigr. WAGENSEIL, *con accomp. Violino.*

TERZETTI

A CEMBALO OBLIGATO.

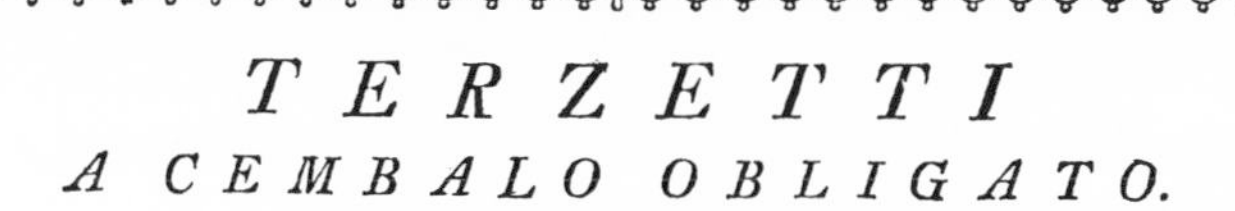

IV. Terzetti del Sigr. HAYDEN, *Cemb. obl. con Violini e Basso.*

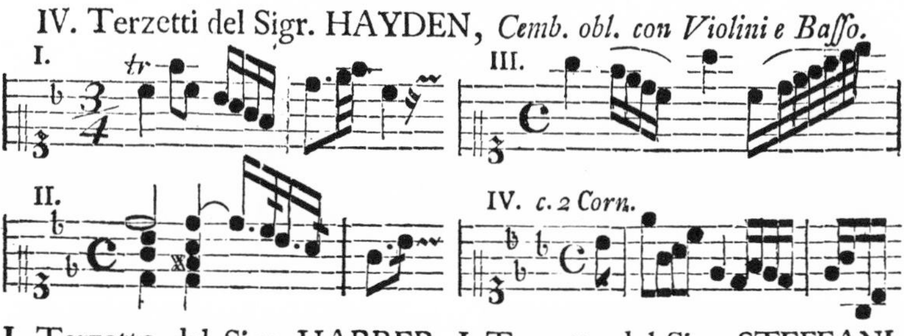

I. Terzetto del Sigr. HARRER. I. Terzetto del Sigr. STEFFANI.

I. Terz. del Sigr. WAGENSEIL.

CONCERTI

A CEMBALO CONCERTAT. II. VIOL. VIOLA, BASSO.

I. Conc. del Sigr. ADAM, *a due Cembali obligati.*

II. Conc. della Sigra. AGNESI. *con 2 Viol. B.* I. Conc. del Sigr. AGRELL. *con 2 Viol. B.*

I. Conc. del Sigr. BINDER. *con 2 Fl.*

54
CEMBALO.
I. Conc. del Sigr. HARRER, con 2 Viol. Viola, Baſſo.
III. Conc. del Sigr. HAYDEN.
I. c. 2 Viol. V. B.
III. c. 2 Corn. 2 Viol. B.
I. Conc. del Sigr. KEHL.
II. c. Viol. princ. 2 Viol. V. B.
c. 2 Viol. V. B.
tr
I. Conc. del Sigr. LELEIN.
c. 2 Viol. V. B.
I. Conc. del Sigr. LANG.
c. 2 Viol. V. B.
tr
I. Conc. del Sigr. SCHOBERT.
c. 2 Viol. V. B.
I. Conc. del Sigr. SENFFT.
c. 2 Viole, B.
III. Conc. del Sigr. STEFFANI. Racc. III.
I. c. Viol. princ. 2 Viol. B.
III. c. 2 Viol. V. B.
tr
II. c. 2 Corn. 2 Viol. V. B.
I. Conc. del Sigr. STAMITZ.
c. 2 Corn. 2 Fl. 2 Viol. V. B.
III. Conc. del Sigr. WAGENSEIL, con 2 Viol. e Baſſo. Racc. V.
I.
III.
II.

CEMBALO.
55
III. Conc. del Sigr. WAGENSEIL, con 2 Viol. V. B. Racc. VI.
I.
tr
III.
II.
III. Conc. del Sigr. WAGENSEIL, con 2 Viol. Baſſo. Racc. VII.
I.
III.
I. Conc. del Sigr. WIEDNER.
II.
HARPA.
I. Trio del Sigr. KIRCHHOF, a Harpa oblig. con Flaut. o Violino.
PARTITE.
III. Partite del Sigr. FUSS, a Harpa oblig. con più Stromenti.
I. c. Fl. Viol. B.
III. c. 2 Viol. B.
II. c. Fl. Viol. B.

IV. Partite del Sigr. GRENTZ, *a Harpa oblig. con più Strome*

ARIA, a Harpa oblig. con 2 Violini e Basso.

Il Fine.

SVPPLEMENTO II.

DEI

CATALOGI

DELLE

SINFONIE, PARTITE, OVERTURE, SOLI, DUETTI, TRII, QUATTRI

E

CONCERTI

PER IL

VIOLINO, FLAUTO TRAVERSO, CEMBALO

ED ALTRI STROMENTI.

CHE

SI TROVANO IN MANOSCRITTO
NELLA OFFICINA MUSICA DI BREITKOPF
IN LIPSIA.

1767.

I. SINFONIE.

VI. Sinfonie di BACH, in Londra. *Raccolta II.*

a 2 Violini, Viola, Basso, Corni, Ob. Fl.

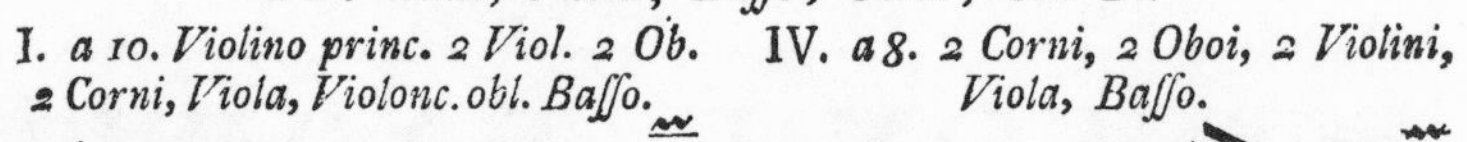

I. *a 10. Violino princ. 2 Viol. 2 Ob. 2 Corni, Viola, Violonc. obl. Basso.*

IV. *a 8. 2 Corni, 2 Oboi, 2 Violini, Viola, Basso.*

II. *a 8. 2 Corn. 2 Ob. 2 Viol. V. B.*

V. *a 8. 2 Corn. 2 Ob. 2 Viol. V. B.*

III. *a 9. 2 Corni, 2 Ob. 2 Violini, 2 Violette, e Basso.*

VI. *a 4. 2 Violini, V. B.*

I. Sinf. di BENDA.

a 2 Corn. 2 Flauti, 2 Viol. V. B.

I. Sinf. di BERWALD.

a 3 Clar. Tymp. 2 Viol. V. B.

I. Sinf. di CHIESA.

a 2 Corni, 2 Violini e Basso.

I. Sinf. di CIAMPI.

a 2 Corn. 2 Ob. 2 Viol. V. B.

VI. Sinf. di DITTERS, *a 2 Corn. 2 Ob. 2 Viol. V. B.*

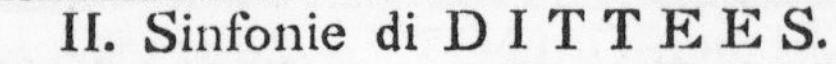

II. Sinfonie di DITTEES.

I. *a 2 Corn. 2 Ob. 2 Viol. V. B.*

II. *a 2 Violini, V. B.*

I. Sinf. di CROIX.

a Violino conc. 2 Viol. V. B.

I. Sinf. di FERANDINI.

a 2 Tromb. 2 Corn. 2 Viol. Viola obl. B.

VI. Sinf. di FILTZ. *Racc. IV.*

I. *a 2 Clar. Tymp. 2 Corni, 2 Oboi, 2 Viol. V. B.*

IV. *a 2 Corn. 2 Fl. 2 Viol. V. B.*

II. *a 2 Corn. 2 Flaut. 2 Viol. V. B.*

V. *a 2 Corn. 2 Ob. 2 Viol. V. B.*

III. *a 2 Corn. 2 Ob. 2 Viol. V. B.*

VI. *a 2 Corn. 2 Ob. 2 Viol. V. B.*

IV. Sinf. di FILTZ. *Racc. V.*

I. *a 2 Corn. 2 Flaut. 2 Viol. V. B.*

III. *a 2 Corn. 2 Ob. 2 Viol. V. B.*

II. *a 2 Corn. 2 Ob. 2 Viol. V. B.*

IV. *a 2 Corn. 2 Ob. 2 Viol. V. B.*

II. Sinf. di FIORILLO.

I. *a 2 Violin. V. B.*

II. Sinf. di GALUPPI.

I. *a 2 Corn. 2 Ob. 2 Fl. 2 Viol. V. B.*

II. *a 2 Viol. V. B.*

II. *a 2 Corn. 2 Ob. 2 Viol. V. B.*

SINFONIE.
III. Sinfonie di GALLO.
I. a 2 Corn. 2 Ob. 2 Viol. V. B.
III. a 2 Viol. V. B.
II. a 2 Viol. V. B.
I. Sinf. di GASMANN.
a 2 Corn. 2 Ob. 2 Viol. V. B.
I. Sinf. di GLANZ.
a 2 Corn. 2 Viol. V. B.
I. Sinf. di GRETSCH.
a 2 Clar. Tymp. 2 Corn. 2 Viol. V. B.
I. Sinf. di GRUNER.
a 2 Viol. V. B.
I. Sinf. di HASSE,
nell' Opera Romolo.
a 2 Tromb. 2 Ob. 2 Corn. 2 Viol. V. B.
VI. Sinf. di HAYDEN. Racc. III.
I. a 2 Corn. 2 Ob. 2 Viol. V. B.
IV. a 2 Corn. 2 Ob. 2 Viol. V. B.
II. a 2 Corn. 2 Flauti, 2 Viol. V. B.
V. a 2 Corn. 2 Ob. 2 Viol. V. B.
III. a 2 Corn. 2 Ob. 2 Viol. V. B.
VI. a 4 Corn. 2 Ob. 2 Viol. Fl. conc.
Violonc. conc. V. B.
IV. Sinf. di HAYDEN. Raccolta IV.
I. a 2 Corn. 2 Ob. 2 Fl. 2 Viol. V. B.
III. a 2 Clar. Tymp. 2 Corn. 2 Ob.
2 Viol. V. B.
II. a 2 Corn. 2 Ob. 2 Viol. V. B.
IV. a 2 Ob. 2 Viol. V. Violonc. obl. B.
Violino 2.
SINFONIE.
5
IV. Sinfonie di HAYDEN. Raccolta V.
I. 2 Corni. 2 Fl. 2 Viol. V. et B.
III. 2 Corni. 2 Viol. V. e B.
IV. 2 Violin. V. et B.
II. 2 Corni. 2 Ob. 2 Violin. V. e B.
VI. Sinfonie di HERFFERT. a 2 Corni. 2 Ob. 2 Violini. Viol. e B.
Raccolta I.
I.
IV.
V.
II.
III.
VI.
tr
I. Sinfonie di HILLER.
I. Sinfonie di HOLZBAUER.
a 2 Corni. 2 Ob. 2 Fl. 2 Viol. V. B.
a 2 Corni. 2 Violin. V. B.
VI. Sinf. di Leopold HOFMANN. 2 Corni. 2 Ob. 2 Viol. V. e B.
Raccolta IV.
I.
IV.
II.
V.
III.
VI. 2 Ob. 2 Viol. V. et B.

I. Sinfonie di KEHL.
a 2 Corn. 2 Fl. 2 Viol. V. e B.
I. Sinfonie di KUNTZ.
a 2 Clarini. 2 Viol. V. e B.
VI. Sinfonie di LANG. Raccolta I.
I. 2 Corn. 2 Ob. 2 Viol. V. e B.
IV. 2 Corni. 2 Fl. 2 Viol. V. e B.
II. 2 Corn. 2 Ob. 2 Violin. V. e B.
V. 2 Corn. 2 Fl. 2 Viol. V. e B.
III. 2 Corn. 2 Ob. 2 Viol. V. e B.
VI. 2 Corn. 2 Ob. 2 Violin. V. e B.
I. Sinf. di MAZZONE.
a 2 Corn. 2 Ob. 2 Viol. V. e B.
tr
I. Sinf. di MALZART.
a 2 Corn. 2 Viol. 2 Ob. V. e B.
I. Sinfonie di NOEL.
a 2 Corn. 2 Ob. 2 Fl. 2 Viol. Fag. V. B.
tr
I. Sinf. dall'OGLIO.
a 2 Clar. Tymp. 2 Violin. B.
I. Sinf. di ORDONEZ.
a 2 Corn. 2 Ob. 2 Viol. V. B.
I. Sinf. di PEREZ.
a 2 Tromb. 2 Corn. 2 Fl. 2 Viol. V. B.
I. Sinf. di PESCH.
a 2 Corn. 2 Fl. 2 Viol. V. B.
I. Sinf. di PFEIFFER.
a 2 Corn. 2 Ob. 2 Fl. 2 Fag. V. B.
I. Sinf. di PICCINI.
a 2 Trombe. 2 Ob. 2 Viol. V. B.
III. Sinfonie di Fr. Xav. RICHTER. 2 Corn. 2 Viol. V. e B.
I.
III.
II.
I. Sinf. di PIRLINGER.
VII. Sinfonie di RIEGEL.
I. 2 Corni. 2 Fl. 2 Violini. V. e Basso.
V. 2 Corn. 2 Fl. 2 Viol. V. e B.
II. 2 Corn. 2 Fl. 2 Viol. V. e B.
VI. 2 Corn. 2 Fl. 2 Viol. V. e B.
III. 2 Corn. 2 Fl. 2 Viol. V. e B.
tr
VII. 2 Corn. 2 Viol. V. e B.
IV. 2 Corn. 2 Fl. 2 Viol. V. e B.
I. Sinf. di RONDINELLO.
a 2 Volin. V. e Basso.
I. Sinf. di ROSENKRANTZ.
a 2 Viol. Viol. Basso.
I. Sinf. di ROY.
a 2 Corn. 2 Ob. 2 Vol. V. e B.
IV. Sinf. di SCHUBERTH.
I. a 2 Corn. 2 Viol. V. e B.
III. a 2 Corni. 2 Fl. 2 Viol. V. e B.
II. a 2 Corn. 2 Viol. V. e B.
IV. a 2 Viol. V. e B.

8
SINFONIE.
I. Sinfonie di RUTINI.
a 2 Corni. 2 Fl. 2 Viol. V. e B.
II. a 2 Corn. 2 Ob. 1 Viol. V. e B.
III. Sinf. di SCHWANENB.
I. 2 Corni. 2 Ob. 2 Viol. V. e B.
III. 2 Corn. 2 Ob. 2 Viol. V. e B.
II. Sinf. di SCHWINDEL.
I. 2 Corn. 2 Ob. 2 Viol. V. e B.
II. 2 Corni. 2 Ob. 2 Viol. V. e B.
VI. Sinfonie di SEIFFERT. Racc. III.
I. 2 Corn. 2 Fl. 2 Violin. Viol. oblig. B.
IV. 2 Corn. 2 Fl. 2 Viol. V. e B.
II. 2 Corn. 2 Fl. 2 Violin. V. e B.
V. 2 Corn. 2 Fl. 2 Viol. V. e B.
III. 2 Corn. 2 Ob. 2 Viol. V. e B.
VI. 2 Corn. 2 Viol. 2 Viol. e B.
VI. Sinfonie di SEIFFERT. Racc. IV.
I. 2 Corn. 2 Viol. V. e B.
IV. 2 Corn. 2 Viol. V. e B.
II. 2 Corn. 2 Viol. V. e B.
V. 2 Corn. 2 Viol. V. e B.
III. 2 Corn. 2 Viol. V. e B.
VI. 2 Corn. 2 Viol. V. e B.
SINFONIE.
9
III. Sinfonie di STAMITZ.
I. a 2 Corn. 2 Ob. 2 Viol. V. B.
III. a 2 Viol. V. B.
II. a 2 Corn. 2 Viol. V. B.
I. Sinf. di SEIFFERTH.
a 2 Viol. V. B.
V. Sinf. di TOESCHI.
I. a 2 Corn. 2 Flauti, 2 Viol. V. B.
IV. a 2 Corn. 2 Ob. 2 Viol. V. B.
II. a 2 Corn. 2 Ob. 2 Fag. 2 Viol. V. B.
V. a 2 Corn. 2 Viol. V. B.
III. a 2 Corn. 2 Ob. 2 Viol. V. B.
I. Sinf. di WAGENSEIL.
a 2 Corn. 2 Ob. 2 Viol. V. B.
Sinfonie intagliate in Parigi.
VI. Sinf. di TOESCHI.
I. a 2 Corn. 2 Ob. 2 Viol. V. B.
IV. a 2 Corn. 2 Flaut. 2 Viol. V. B.
II. a 2 Corn. 2 Ob. 2 Viol. V. B.
V. a 2 Corn. 2 Ob. 2 Viol. V. B.
III. a 2 Corn. 2 Ob. 2 Viol. V. B.
VI. a 2 Corn. 2 Flaut. 2 Clar. Tymp. 2 Viol. V. B.

VI. Sinfonie di van MALDERE, *a 2 Corni, 2 Oboi, 2 Violini, Viola, Basso.*

I. II. III. IV. V. VI.

II. PARTITE, DIVERTIMENTI, CASSATIONES, CONCERTINI.

I. Partita di FILTZ. *a 2 Corn. 2 Ob. 2 Viol. V. B.*

VI. Divertimenti di HAYDEN. *Racc. I.*

I. *a 2 Corn. 2 Ob. 2 Viol. 2 Viole, B.*

IV. *a 2 Corn. 2 Flaut. 2 Violini, B.*

II. *a 2 Corn. 2 Flaut. 2 Viol. 2 Fagot.*

V. *a 2 Viol. 1 Trav. 1 Ob. Violonc. B.*

III. *2 Corn. 2 Corn. Ingl. 2 Viol. V. B.*

VI. *a 2 Viol. 1 Flaut. 2 Viole, B.*

I. Div. di HAYDEN, a Echo. *a 4 Violini, 2 Baffi.*

I. Divert. di Leop. HAYDEN. *a 2 Corn. 2 Flaut. 2 Viol. B.*

I. Concertino di HAYDEN. *a 2 Corn. 2 Ob. 1 Flaut. 4 Viol. Viola, Violonc. Fag. Violono.*

VI. Conc. di Leop. HOFFMANN. *Racc. I.*

I. *a 2 Viol. conc. 1 Viola conc. Violonc. conc. 2 Viol. 2 Ob. 2 Corn. B.*

IV. *1 Viol. conc. Viola conc. Violonc. conc. 2 Viol. V. B.*

II. *2 Viol. conc. 1 Viola conc Violonc. conc. 2 Viol. 2 Ob. 2 Corn. B.*

V. *1 Viol. conc. Violonc. conc. 2 Viol. 2 Ob. 2 Corn. B.*

III. *1 Viol. conc. Viola conc. Violonc. conc. 2 Viol. 2 Ob. 2 Corn. B.*

VI. *1 Viol. conc. Viola conc. Violonc. conc. 2 Violini, B.*

III. Partite di HILLER. *Racc. III.*

I. *a 2 Corn. 2 Ob. 2 Viol. V. B.*

III. *a 2 Corn. 2 Ob. 2 Fl. 2 Viol. V. B.*

II *a 2 Ob. 2 Flaut. 2 Viol. V. B.*

I. Divert. di HILLER. *a 2 Corn. 2 Ob. 2 Fl. 2 Viol. Fag. V. B.*

I. Divert. di KAMMEL. *a 2 Corn. Viol. princip. 2 Viol. 2 Viole, B.*

I. Serenate di KIRMAIR. *a 2 Flaut. 2 Corn. 2 Viol. V. B.*

I. Partita di LELEI. *a 2 Corn. 2 Ob. 2 Flaut. 2 Viol. V. B.*

I. Divert. di MOZART, a Quattro Instrum. Conc. *a Viol. Violonc. 2 Corn. B.*

II. Partite di ROSENCRANTZ, *a 2 Flaut. 2 Viol. V. B.*

I. II.

VIOLINO.

SOLI con BASSO.

II. Soli di BENDA.

I. II.

III. Soli di ENDERLE.

I. *tr* III. *tr*

II.

I. Solo di ERNST.

III. Soli di GRAUN.

I. *tr* III.

II.

I. Solo di HORN.

VI. Soli di HOECKH.

I. IV.

II. V.

III. VI.

DUETTI.

A DUE VIOLINI

TRII.

A DUE VIOLINI CON BASSO.

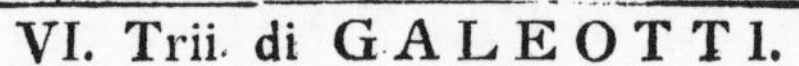

VI. Trii di GALEOTTI.

VI. Trii di HAYDEN.

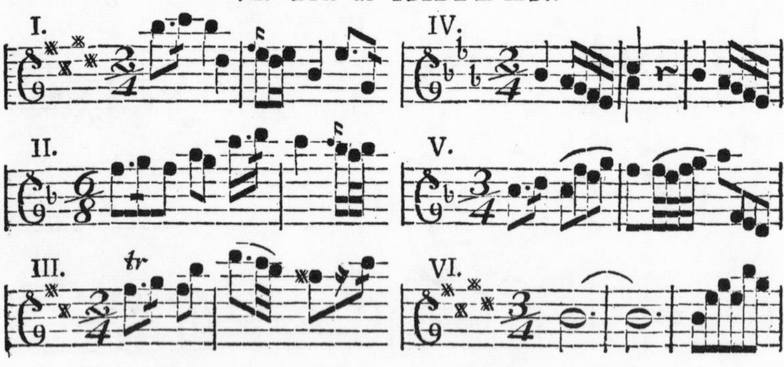

II. Trii con Variazioni di HAYDEN.

II. Trii di MARTINO.

II. Trii di PESCH.

VI. Trii di LIDARTI.

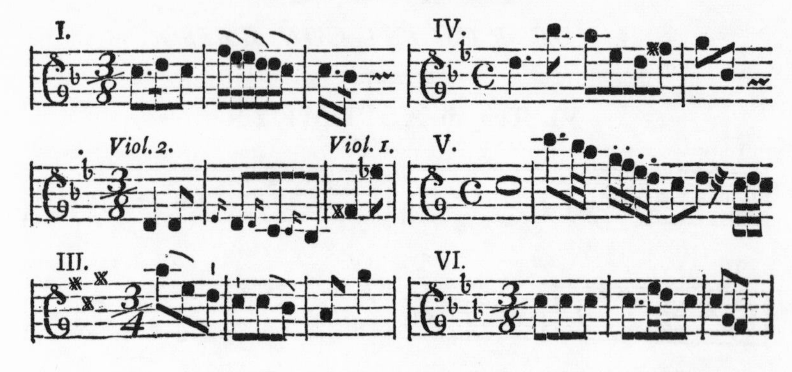

VI. Trii di MISLEWECEK.

VI. Trii di WENTO.

IV. Trii di ZANETTI.

I. Trio di ZAPPA.

Q U A T T R I.

I. Quattro di BARETTI.

V. a 2 Viol. Viola e Basso.

I. Quattro di HAYDEN.

a 2 Violin. Viol. e Basso.

II. Quattri di HOFFSTETER.

VI. Divertimenti di Leop. HOFMANN. *Raccolta I.*
a Flaut. Violino, Viola e Basso.

VI. Divertimenti di Leop. HOFMANN, *a 2 Viol. V. B.*

I. Quattro di KIRMAYR. *a 2 Viol. V. e B.*

I. Quattro di KRAUSE. *a 2 Ob. Violin. Fag. oblig. e Violonc.*

VI. Partite di PESCH, *a Fl. Viol. V. B.*

Q U I N T E T T I.

II. Quintetti di ZANETTI. *a 3 Violini oblig. 2 Violonc.*

I. Quintetto di NERUDA.
a 2 Violini. Viola. Violoncello oblig. e Basso.

CONCERTI.

PER IL VIOLINO CONCERTATO.

III. Conc. di CANNABICH. III. Concerti di DITTERS.

I. *a Viol. Conc. 2 Corn. 2 Viol. V. e B.* I. *a Viol. Conc. 2 Viol. V. e B.*

II. *a Viol. Conc. 2 Viol. V. e B.* II. *a Viol. Conc. 2 Viol. V. e B.*

III. *a Viol. Conc. 2 Viol. V. e B.* III. *a Viol. Conc. 2 Viol. e Baſſo.*

I. Concerto di HASSE. *a Viol. Conc. 2 Viol. rip. V. e B.*

I. Concerto di KREBISCH. *a Violin. Conc. 2 Violin. V. e B.*

I. Concerto di NERUDA. *a Viol. Conc. 2 Viol. V. e B.*

I. Concerto di RIEGEL. *a Viol. Conc. 2 Corn. 2 Fl. 2 Vl. V. e B.*

I. Concerto di RONDINELLI. *a Viol. Conc. 2 Viol. V. e B.*

I. Concerto di PESCH. *a Viol. conc. 2 Cor. 2 Viol. V. e B.*

II. Concerti di STAMITZ.

I. *a Viol. Conc. 2 Viol. V. e B.*

II. *a Viol. Conc. 2 Viol. V. e B.*

VIOLINO discordato. VIOLA e VIOLONCELLO.

FLAUTO TRAV.

TRII.

VI. Trii, di FILTZ. *a Flauto Violino e Violoncello.*

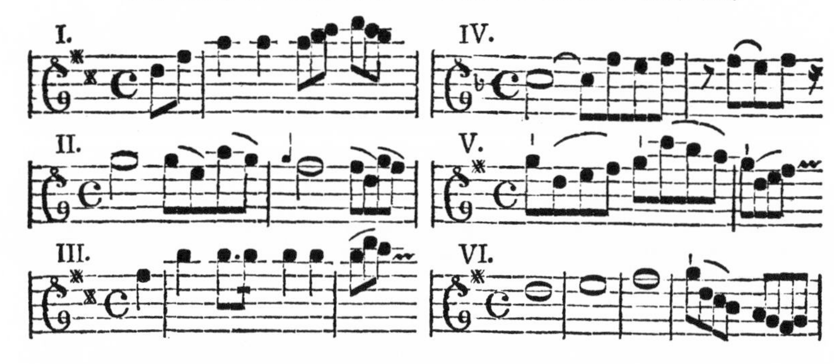

III. Trii di Leop. HOFMANN. *a 2 Flauti col Basso.*

II. Trii di RIEDEL, *a Flauto, Violino e Basso.*

II. Trii di SCHWARTZ.

CONCERTI. à FLAUTO CONCERTATO.

I. Concerto di CONCINNIANO.

a Flauto Conc. 2 Violini e Basso.

III. Concerti di FILS, *a Fl. 2 Viol. V. e B.*

VI. Concerti di GRAF, *a Flaut. Trav. 2 Violin. V. e B.*

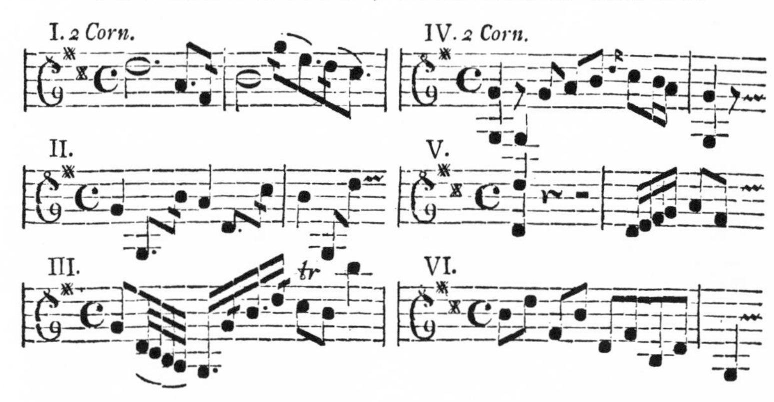

I. Concerto di HOFMANN.

a Flaut. Conc. 2 Viol. V. e B.

I. Concerto di RIEDEL.

a Flaut. Conc. 2 Viol. V. e B.

CEMBALO.

SOLI.

II. Sonate per il Cembalo Solo di AGNESI.

I. Sonata per il Cembalo Solo di ALBERTI.

VI. Divertimenti per il Cembalo Solo di C. S. BINDER.

VI. Sonate per il Cemb. Solo di GALUPPI. *Racc. I.*

VI. Sonate per il Cemb. Solo di GALUPPI. *Racc. II.*

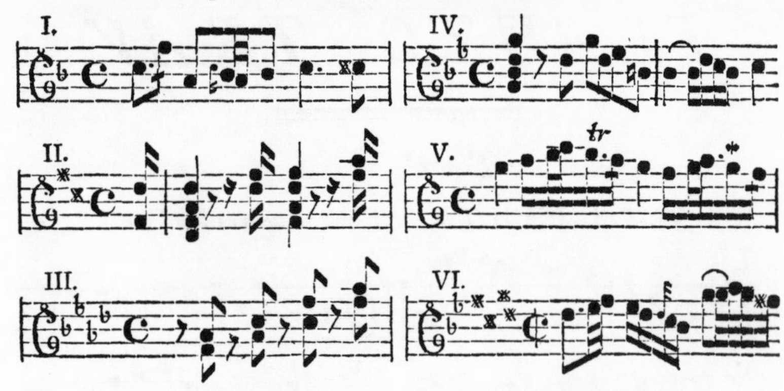

V. Sonate per il Cemb. Solo di HAYDEN.

VI. Divertimenti per il Cemb. Solo di HUNGER.

PARTITE ACCOMODATE al CEMBALO SOLO.

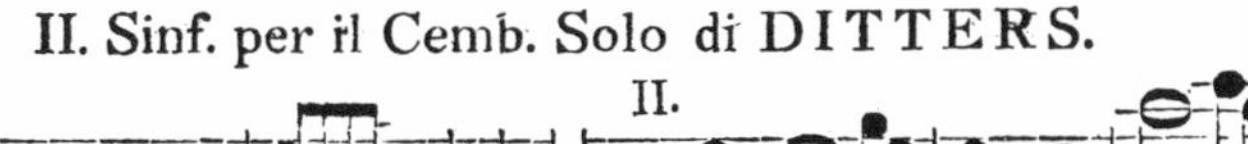

II. Sinf. per il Cemb. Solo di DITTERS.

VI. Scherzandi accomodati per il Cemb. Solo di HAYDEN.

I. Fantasia per il Cemb. nello Circolo degli XXIV modi musici di GRAUN.

Specimen Contrapuncti duplicis in Octava di HARRER.

I. Sonata per il Cemb. Solo di KLEINKNECHT.

Pieces de Clavecin seul par SILBERMANN.

II. Sonate per il Cemb. Solo di WAGENSEIL.

Arietta con XI. Variazioni di ANONYMO.

XII. Sinf. di GRAUN, accomodate per il Cemb. Solo.

VI. Sinf. di HASSE, accomodate per il Cemb. Solo.

VI. Sinfonie accommodate per il Cembalo Solo.

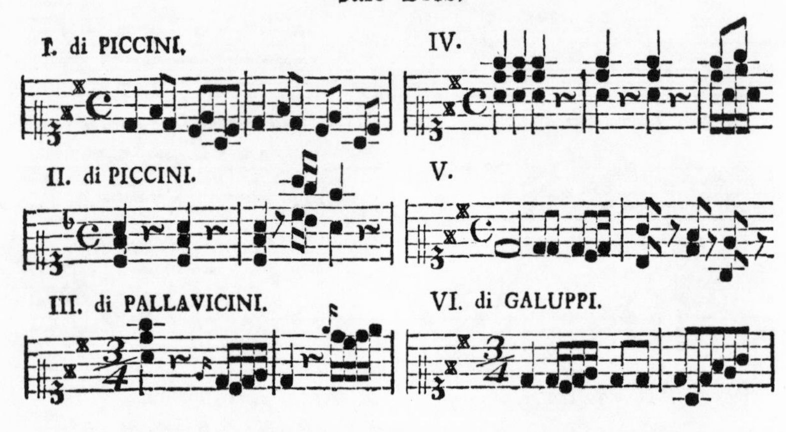

II. Sinfonie di E. T. P. A. accomodate per il Cembalo Solo.

I. Partita accomod. per il Cemb. di WIEDNER.

SONATE a CEMBALO SOLO, intagliate in Parigi.

VI. Sonates par Mr. ECCARD.

VI. Sonates par Mr. HONAÜER.

IV. Sonates pour le Clavecin avec l'Accompagnement de Violon par Mr. MOZARD.

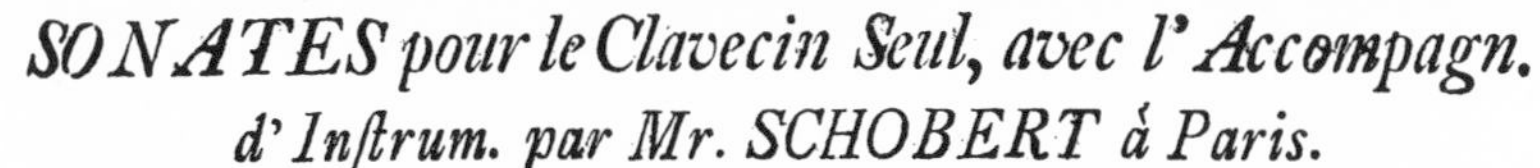
SONATES pour le Clavecin Seul, avec l'Accompagn. d'Instrum. par Mr. SCHOBERT á Paris.

TRII a CEMBALO OBLIGATO con VIOLINO ô TRAVERSO.

I. Trio di BENDA, *a Cembalo oblig. con Violino.*

I. Trio di KLEINKNECHT, *a Cemb. oblig. con Flauto.*

III. Trii di FALKENHAGEN, *a Cembalo oblig. con Liuto oblig.*

I. Trio di KUFFNER, *a Cemb. obligato con Viol.*

II. Trii, di SEIFFERTH, *a Cembalo oblig. con Violino.*

I. Trio di SCHAFFRATH, *a Cemb. oblig. con Flauto.*

I. Trio di SCHWANENBERG *a Cemb. oblig. con Violino.*

VI. Trii di ZACH, *a Cembalo obligato con Violino.*

VI. *con Violino, et Viola.*

TERZETTI a CEMBALO OBLIGATO con VIOLINO ô FLAUTO e BASSO.

I. Terzetto di BENDA. *a Cemb. oblig. con Violino e Basso.*

I. Terzetto di HAYDEN. *a Cemb. oblig. con Violino e Basso.*

III. Terzetti di HOFMANN. *a Cemb. oblig. con Viol. o Trav. e Basso.*

III. Terzetti di KIRSTEN. *a Cemb. oblig. Viol. o Trav. e Basso.*

VI. Terzetti di SEIFFERT, *a Cembalo oblig. con Viol. e Basso.*

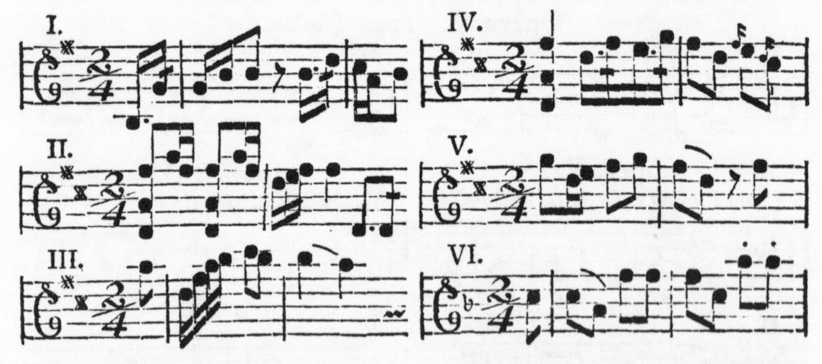

I. Terzetto di STEFFANI. *a Cemb. oblig. con Viol. e Basso.*

I. Terzetto di WAGENSEIL. *a Cemb. oblig. con Viol. e Basso.*

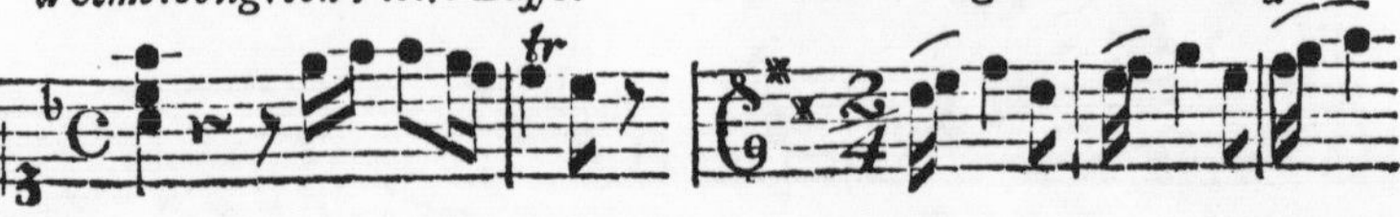

CONCERTI a CEMBALO CONCERTATO,
A DUE VIOLINI, VIOLA e BASSO.

HARPA.

II. Concerti di GRENTZ, *a Harpa concertat. Flauto, Violino Violoncello.*

I. Concerto di CONTE, *a Harpa concert. Flauto Violino e B.*

ARIE e CANZONI.

I. Aria di Giov. BACH, nell' Opera Orione, *a Canto 2 Flauti. 2 Violini Viola e B.*

I. Aria di COCCHI, nell'Opera Semiramide, *a Canto 2 Violini Viola e Basso.*

II. Arie di CONCILIANI, *a Canto 2 Violini Viola e Basso.*

ARIE NELL' OPERE di HASSE.

OPERA IL TRIONFO di CLELIA.

15. 1 Fl. 1 Ob. 2 Viol. Viol. Canto e B.
Tan-to espoſta alle ſven-
18 2 Corn. 2 Ob. 2 Viol. Viol. Canto e B.
In que-ſta ſel-va oſcu-
16. 2 Corn. 2 Fl. 2 Ob. 2 Viol. Viol. Can. e B.
Ah ri - torna età dell'o-
19. 2 Trm. Tymp. 2 C. 2 O. 2 Viol. V. Alt. B.
De' fol-gori di giove
17. 2 Corni 2 Ob. 2 Viol. Viol. Ten. e B.
Speſſo, ſe ben l'affret - ta
20. 2 Tromb. Tymp. 2 C. 2 O. 2 V. V. 4 Voci fondam.
Oggi a te gran Re toſca-
OPERA EGERIA.
1. 2 Corn. 2 Ob. 2 Violin. V. 4 Voci e B.
Da pla-cidi ri-
6. 2 C. 2 Ob. 2 Viol. V. Soprano e B.
Ah ri - - torni al
2. 2 C. 2 Ob. 2 Viol. Viola Alto e B.
Tu gl'oſti-na - - ti
7. 2 C. 2 Ob. 2 Violin. V. Ten. Baſſo e Fag
Ah di pa - be nel pigro
3. 2 Ob. Fag. 2 Violin. Viol. Soprano e B.
E fol - le quel nocchiero
8. 2 C. 2 Fl. 2 Fag. 2 Viol. Viol. Sopr. e B.
Se l'ardor ſolo, o il gie - lo
4. 2 Viol. 2 Ob. Viola Soprano e Baſſo.
Sa - rò qual bra-ma-te ai
9. 2 Tromp. Timp. 2 Ob. 2 Cor. 2 Violin. Viol. 2 S. A. T. e B. Fondam. Fag.
Co-ſi bagna-to di bei
5. 2 Corn. 2 Ob. 2 V V. 3 Sopr. 2 Alt. 2 Ten. 1 Baſſo. Fondam. e Fag.
Sag-gia De - a ta - ce-

OPERA ROMOLO ed ERSILIA.
1. 2 Tromp. 2 Ob. 2 Viol. 4 V. V. B.
Sul tar-pe-o propi - zie
8. 2 Corn. 2 Ob. 2 Viol. V. Ten. B.
Nell penſar che Padre io
2. 2 Ob. 2 Corn. 2 Viol. Viola, Alt. B.
Queſta è la bella
9. 2 Ob. 2 Viol. V. Sopr. B.
Con le ſtelle in van s'a-
3. 2 Ob. 2 Viol. V. Sopr. B.
Sor-prendermi vor - re - -
10. 2 Ob. 2 Viol. V. Sopr. B.
Ah perche quando ap - preſi
4. 2 Ob. 2 Viol. V. Sopr. B.
Si m'inganni e
11. 2 Ob. 2 Viol. V. Sopr. B.
Se tal un non ſà -
5. 2 Ob. 2 Corn. 2 Viol. V. Ten. B.
Molli af - fet - ti dall' alma
12. 2 Corn. 2 Ob. 2 Viol. V. Sopr. B.
Sprezzami pur per ora O-
6. 2 Ob. 2 Viol. V. Sopr. B.
Con vanto men-zo-gnero.
13. 2 Ob. 2 Viol. V. Sopr. B.
Baſtà co-ſi vin - ce - ſti
7. 2 Corn. 2 Ob. 2 Viol. V. Sopr. Alt. B.
Ah che vuol dir quel pianto
14. 2 Tromb. Tymp 2 Corn. 2 Ob. 2 Viol. Viola, Alto, Baſſo.
Con gli amoroſi mirti fra

42 ARIE e CANZONI.

15. 2 Corn. 2 Ob. 2 Viol. V. Ten. B.

Re-ſpi-ra al ſolo a-ſpetto

19. 2 Tromb. Tymp. 2 Corn. 2 Ob. 2 Viol. Viola, Sopr. Alt. Ten. Baſſ. Baſſ.

Serbate o Numi l'Eroe-che

16. 2 Ob. 2 Viol. V. Sopr. B.

Perdo-no al pri-mo ecceſſo.

20. 2 Tromb. Tymp. 2 Corn. 2 Ob. 2 Viol. Viola, Alt. B.

Il te-nor de fati in-

17. 2 Corn. 2 Ob. 2 Viol. V. Sopr. B.

Frà quelle te-ne-re do-

21. 2 Tromb. Tymp. 2 Corn. 2 Ob. 2 Viol. Viola, Sopr. Alt. Ten. Baſſ. Cemb.

Numi che intenti ſiete le ſorti

18. 2 Ob. 2 Viol. V. Sopr. B.

Un'i-ſtan-te al Cor tal-

ARIE NELL'ORATORIO, di Nic. IOMELLI.

LA PASSIONE DI GESU CRISTO.

1. 2 Corn. 2 Ob. 2 Viol. V. Ten. B.

Giac-che mi tre-mi mi

3. 2 Viol. Viola, Sopr. Violonc.

Vorrei dirti il mio do-

2. 2 Viol. Viola, Sopr. Alt. Ten. Baſſo, Violonc.

Quan-to co-ſta il tuo de-

4. 2 Corn. 2 Ob. 2 Viol. Viola, Baſſo, Violonc.

Tor-bi-do mar, che

ARIE e CANZONI. 43

5. 2 Viol. Viola, Alt. Violonc.

Come a vi-ſta di pene

11. 2 Corn. 2 Ob. 2 Viol. V. Baſſ. Violonc.

All' i-dea de tuoi

6. 2 Corni, 2 Ob. 2 Viol. Viola. Sopr. Violonc.

Po-tea quel pian-to

12. 2 Viol. Viola, Ten. Violonc.

Se la pu-pilla in-

7. 2 Viol. Viola, Ten. Violonc.

Tu nel duol nel duol fè-

13. 2 Viol. Viola, Alt. Violonc.

Do-vun-que il guardo il

8. 2 Viol. Viola, Sopr. Ten. Violonc.

Vi ſen-to oh Dio vi

14. 2 Viol. Viola, Sopr. Violonc.

Ai paſ-ſi er-ran-ti

9. 2 Corn. 2 Ob. 2 Viol. Viola, Sopr. Alt. Ten. Baſſ. Violonc.

Di qual ſangue o mortale

15. 2 Corn. 2 Ob. 2 Viol. V. Ten. Violonc.

Se a li-brar - - - - -

10. 2 Viol. Viola, Alt. Violonc.

Ri-tor-ne-rà fra voi

16. 2 Corn. 2 Viol. Viola, Sopr. Alt. Ten. Baſſ. Violonc.

Santa ſpeme, tu ſei

XIV. Arie di SCHWANENBERG.

1. *a Canto. 2 Viol. V. B.*

2. *a Cant. 2 Corn. 2 Viol. V. B.*

3 *a Cant. 2 Corn. 2 Ob. 2 Viol. V. B.*

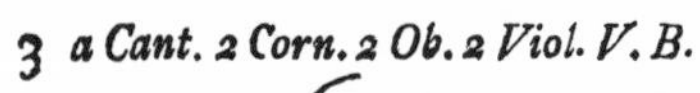

4. *a Cant. 2 Corn. 2 Ob. 2 Viol. V. B.*

5. *a Cant. 2 Corn. 2 Ob. 2 Viol. V. B.*

6. *a Cant. 2 Corn. 2 Ob. 2 V. B.*

Nell' Op. Solimann.
7. *a Sopr. 2 Viol. V. B.*

Nell' Op. Solimann.
8. *a Sopr. 2 Viol. V. B.*

Nell' Op. Zenobia.
9. *a Canto, 2 Viol. V. B.*

Nell' Op. Zenobia.
10. *a Canto, 2 Viol. V. B.*

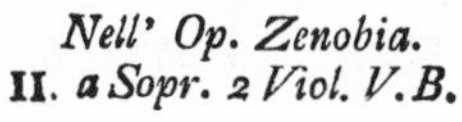

Nell' Op. Zenobia.
11. *a Sopr. 2 Viol. V. B.*

Nell' Op. Zenobia.
12. *a Sopr. 2 Viol. V. B.*

Nell' Op. Didone.
13. *a Sopr. 2 Corn. 2 Ob. 2 Viol. V. B.*

Nell' Op. Didone.
14. *a Sopr. 2 Corn. 2 O. V. B.*

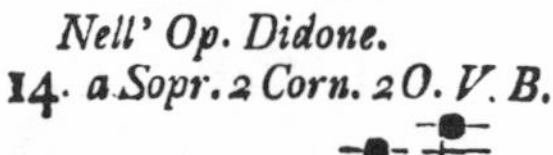

Il Fine.

SUPPLEMENTO III.

DEI

CATALOGI

DELLE

SINFONIE, PARTITE, OVERTURE, SOLI, DUETTI, TRII, QUATTRI E CONCERTI

PER IL

VIOLINO, FLAUTO TRAVERSO, CEMBALO

ED ALTRI STROMENTI.

CHE

SI TROVANO IN MANOSCRITTO
NELLA OFFICINA MUSICA DI BREITKOPF
IN LIPSIA.

1768.

SINFONIE.

V. Sinfonie di Carlo DITTERS.

a 2 Corn. 2 Ob. 2 Violini, Viola e Basso.

I. *Nazionale, a 2 Cor. 2 Ob. 2 Viol. V. e B.* IV. *a Viol. Principale, 2 C. 2 Ob. 1 V. V. e B.*

II. *a 2 Cor. 2 Ob. 2 Viol. V. e B.* V. *a 2 Ob. 2 Viol. V. e B.*

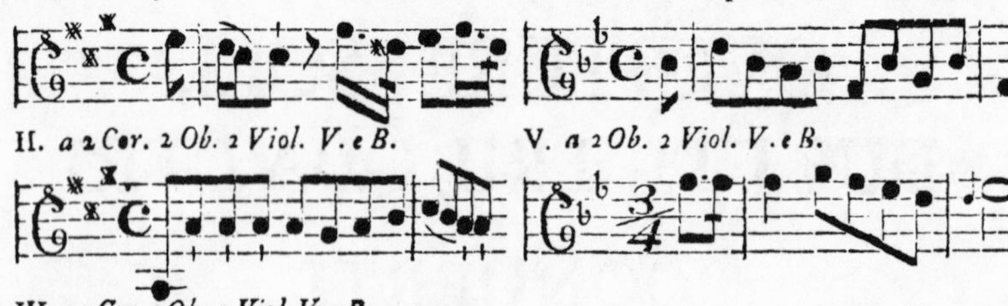

III. *a 2 Cor. 2 Ob. 2 Viol. V. e B.*

II. Sinfonie di Anton. DUNI.

I. *a 2 Corn. 2 Ob. 2 Viol. V. e B.* II. *a 2 Corn. 2 Ob. 2 Viol. 2 Viole e B.*

I. Sinf. di GASMANN. I. Sinf. di Giov. Adolf. HASSE.

a 2 Tromb. Tymp. 2 Cor. 2 Ob. 2 Fl. 2 Viol. Viola 1 Fag. e B.

dell' Opera Partenope. a 2 Tromb. Tymp. 2 Cor. 2 Viol. Viol. e B.

II. Sinfonie di Giuf. HAYDEN.

I. *a 2 Cor. 2 Ob. 2 Viol. V. e B.* II. *a 2 Cor. 2 Ob. 2 Viol. V. e B.*

II. Sinf. di Leop. HOFMANN.

I. *a 2 Cor. 2 Ob. 2 Viol. V. e B.* II. *a 2 Cor. 2 Ob. 2 Viol. V. e B.*

II. Sinfonie di Jean Gab. MEDER.

I. *a 2 Cor. 2 Ob. 2 Viol. V. e B.* II. *a 2 Cor. 2 Ob. 2 Viol. V. e B.*

I. Sinf. di Nicolo PICCINI. I. Sinf. di PIRLINGER.

a 2 Tromb. 2 Ob. 2 Viol. V. e B.

II. Sinf. di SCHMIDTBAUER.

I. *a 2 Cor. 2 Ob. 2 Fl. 2 Fag. 2 Viol. V. e B.* II. *a 2 Cor. 2 Ob. 2 Fl. 2 Fag. 2 Viol. V. e B.*

II. Sinf. di TOESCHI.

I. *a 2 Cor. 2 Fl. 2 Viol. V. e B.* II. *a 2 Cor. 2 Ob. 2 Viol. V. e B.*

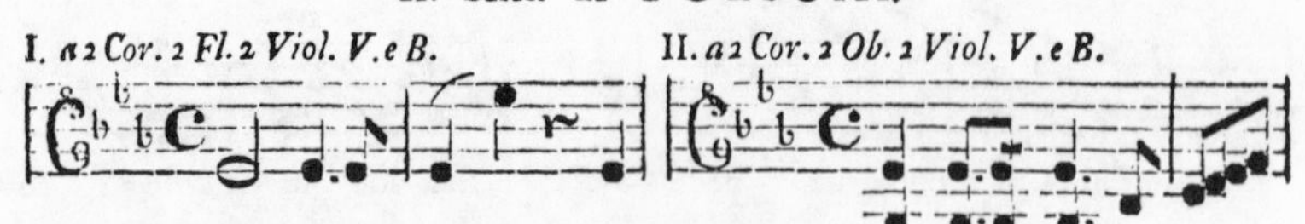

I. Sinf. di TRAJETTA.

a 2 Cor. 2 Viol. V. e B.

II. Sinf. di Giov. VANHALL.

I. *a 2 Cor. Tymb. 2 Clar. 2 Ob. 2 Viol. V. e B.* II. *a 2 Cor. 2 Ob. oblig. 2 Viol. V. e B.*

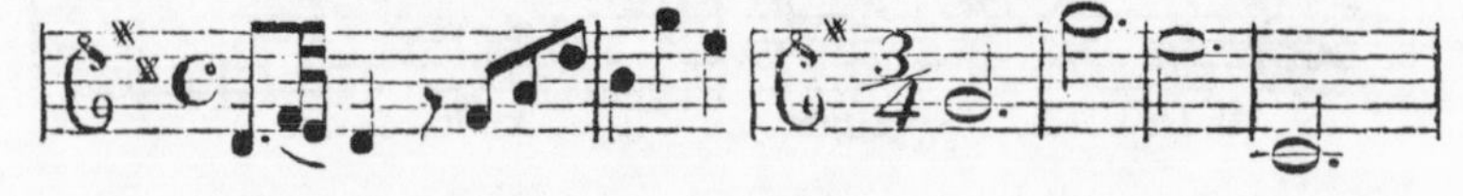

SINFONIE INTAGLIATE IN PARIGI, &c.

VI. Sinf. di Gaudenz. COMI, *a 2 Cor. 2 Ob. 2 V. V. e B.*

VI. Sinfonie di E. F. DELANGE, *a 2 Cor. 2 Viol. V. e B.*

VI. Sinfonie di Giuf. LIDARTI, *a 2 Viol. V. e Basso.*

VI. Sinf. di F. X. RAMBACH, *a 2 Cor. 2 Ob. 2. Viol. V. e B.*

II. Sinfonie di SCHMIDT, *a 2 Corn. 2 Ob. 2 Viol. V. e B.*

III. Sinf. di Carlo STAMITZ, *a 2 Corn. 2 Ob. 2 Viol. V. e B.*

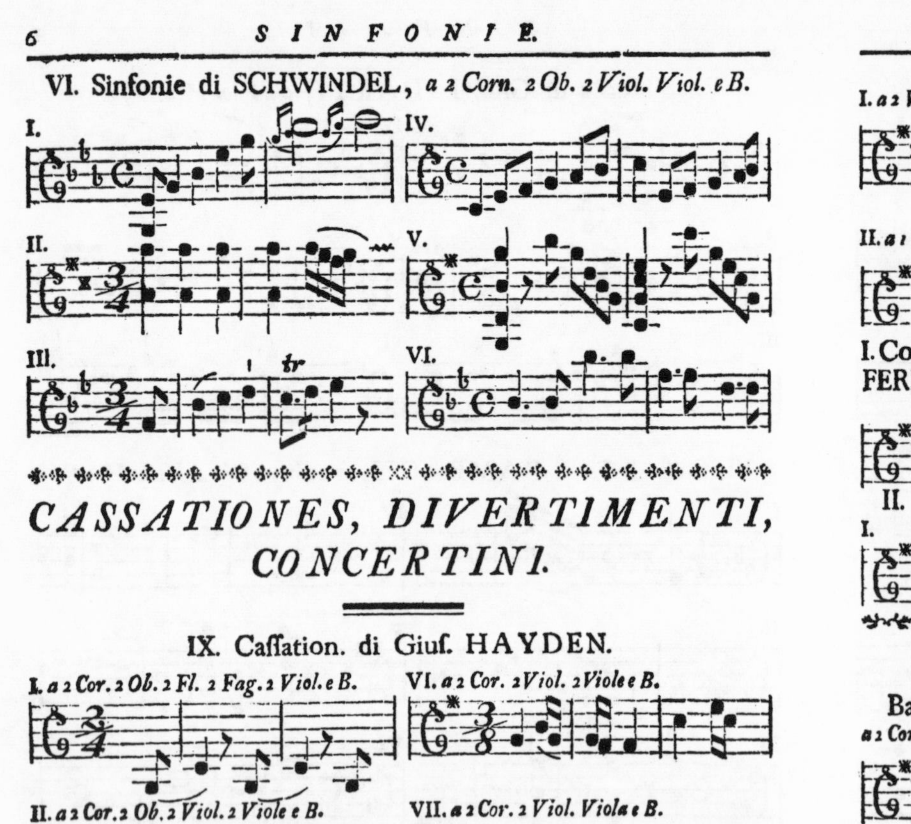

VI. Sinfonie di SCHWINDEL, *a 2 Corn. 2 Ob. 2 Viol. Viol. e B.*

I. IV. II. V. III. VI.

CASSATIONES, DIVERTIMENTI, CONCERTINI.

IX. Caſſation. di Giuſ. HAYDEN.

I. *a 2 Cor. 2 Ob. 2 Fl. 2 Fag. 2 Viol. e B.*

VI. *a 2 Cor. 2 Viol. 2 Viole e B.*

II. *a 2 Cor. 2 Ob. 2 Viol. 2 Viole e B.*

VII. *a 2 Cor. 2 Viol. Viola e B.*

III. *a 2 Cor. 2 Ob. 2 Viol. 2 Viole e B.*

VIII. *a 2 Corn. 1 Viol. Viola e B.*

IV. *a 2 Corn. 2 Viol. 2 Viole e B.*

IX. *a 2 Cor. 1 Viol. V. e B.*

V. *a 1 Flaut. 1 Ob. 2 Viol. Violonc. Violono.*

III. Divertimenti di Giuſ. HAYDEN.

I. *a 2 Viol. 2 Viole e B.*

III. *a 1 Fl. 2 Cor. 2 Viol. Viol. e B.*

I. Concertino di HAYDEN, *a 2 Cor. 2 Viol. V. e B.*

II. *a 1 Fl. 2 Cor. 2 Viol. 2 Viole e B.*

I. Concertino notturno di Carlo FERRARI, *a 2 Cor. 2 Fl. 2 Viol. e B.*

I. Serenada di HAYDEN, *a 2 Corn. 2 Fl, 2 Viol. V. e B.*

II. Caſſation di Anton. ROSETTI, *a 2 Corn. 1 Fl. 2 Viol. e B.*

I. II.

MINUETTI, BALLI, &c.

Ballo, Il Filoſofo amoroſo. *a 2 Corn. 2 Ob. 2 Fl. 2 Viol. V. e B.*

Ballo, la Circe ed Ulyſſe. *a 2 Corn. 2 Ob. 2 Fl. 2 Viol. Viol. e B.*

Ballo Pigmalion. *a 2 Cor. 2 Ob. 2 Fl. 2 Viol. V. e B.*

XXIV. Polonoiſe di FISCHER. *a 2 Cor. 2 Ob. 2 Fl. piccoli 2 Fag. 2 Viol. e B.*

XXIV. G. A. ADAM Dresdn. Redouten, Menuetten Ao. 1769.

XXIV. Dresdner Redouten Menuetten, XXIV. Polonoiſen, Steyeriſch, Maſur. von SIMONETTI Ao. 1768.

XXVI. Dresdner Redouten Menuetten VI. Polonoiſen, Steyeriſch, Maſur. von SIMONETTI, A. 1769. *a 2 Cor. 2 Ob. 2 Fl. 2 V. e B.*

VIOLINO.
SOLI con BASSO.
I. Solo di Georg. BENDA.
I. Solo di Giuf. HAYDEN,
ariofo con variaz.
III. Soli di MANFREDINI.
I.
III.
II.
I. Solo di TZARTH.
Soli intagliati in Parigi &c.
VI. Soli di AVOLIO.
I.
IV.
II.
V
III.
VI.
VI. Soli di Anton. GRONEMANN.
I.
IV.
II.
V.
III.
VI.
tr

VIOLINO.
9
VI. Soli di LOLLI.
I.
IV.
II.
V.
III.
VI.
III. Soli di Francefco LAMOTTA.
I.
III.
II.
tr
VI. Soli di Guilielmo NAVOIGILLE.
I.
IV.
II.
V.
III.
VI.

III. Soli di SPADINA.

DUETTI.

a duoi VIOLINI.

IV. Duetti di MOSELLE.

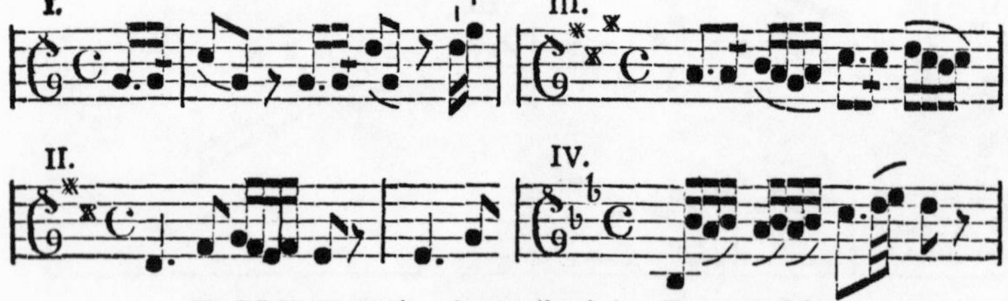

DUETTI, intagliati in Parigi &c.

VI. Duetti di G. KENNIS.

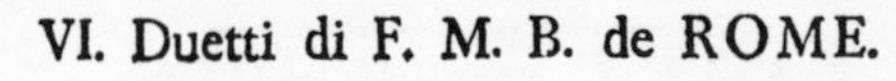

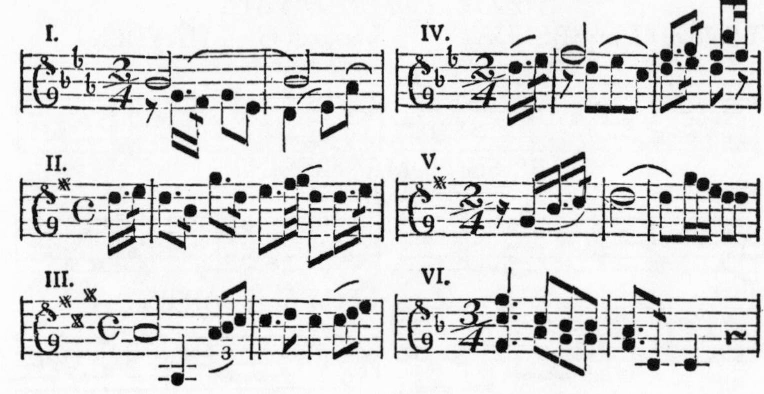

VI. Duets de differents AUTEURS.

TRII.

A DUE VIOLINI CON BASSO.

III. Trii di Leop. HOFFMANN.

V. Trii di ROESER.

Trii intagliati in Parigi etc.

VI. Trii di BERTRAND.

VI. Trii di Luigi BOCCHERINI.

a 2 Viol. e Basso obligato.

VI. Trii di Luigi BOCCHERINI.

VI. Sinfonie à Tre, di Luigi BOCCHERINI.

VI. Sinfonie a Tre, di Gaudenz. COMI.

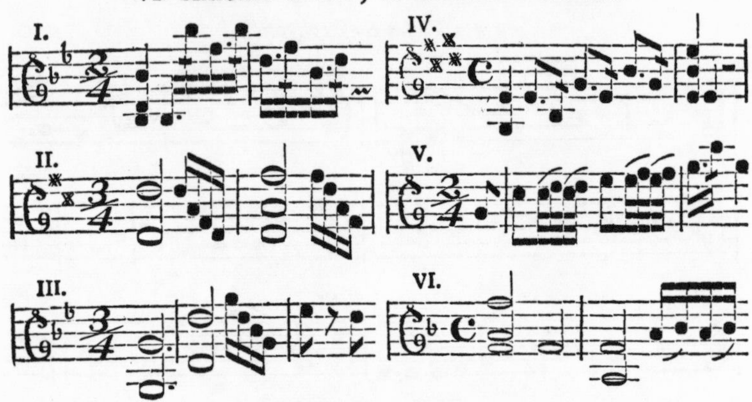

VI. Trii par le DUC l'ainé.

VI. Trii del Conte Giuſ. d'URSENBECK et MASSINI.

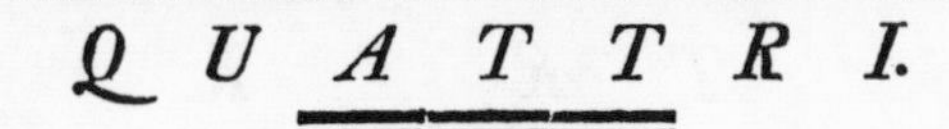

VI. Quattri di ASPELMEURE. *a 2 Viol. Viol. e Baſſo.*

I. Quattro di BISCHOFF. *a 2. Viol. Viol. e Baſſo.*

I. Quattro di HAYDEN. *a 2. Viol. Viol. e Baſſo.*

I. Quattro di KIRMAYER. *a 2 Violin. Viol. e Baſſo.*

Quattri intagliati in Parigi etc.

VI. Quattri di Luigi BOCCHERINI *a 2 Viol. Viol. obl. e Violonc. obl.*

II. Quattri di SCHMIDT *a 2 Violin. Viol. e Baſſo.*

QUINTETTI.

I. Quintetti di KIRMAYER. *a 2 Violin. Viola e Basso.*

II. Quintetti di ZANETTI. *a 3 Viol. 2 Violoncelli.*

Quintetti intagliati in Parigi.

VI. Quintetti di Giuſ. MISLEWECEK. *a 2 Violini 2 Viole e Basso.*

II. Quintetti di SCHMIDT. *a 2 Cor. 2 Viol. 2 Viol. e Basso.*

CONCERTI.

PER IL VIOLINO CONCERTATO.

I. Conc. di CROENER. *a Viol. conc. 2 Viol. V. e B.*

I. Conc. di Carlo DITTERS. *a Viol. conc. 2 Cor. 2 Viol. V. e B.*

I. Conc. di Leop. HOFFMANN. *a Viol. conc. 2. Viol. V. e B.*

II. Conc. di Giov. Batt. NERUDA. *a Viol. conc. 2 Viol. V. e B.*

I. Conc. di RIEPEL.

V. Conc. di Giuſ. TOESCHI.

II. Conc. di FRAENZEL. *Intagliati in Parigi.*

VIOLA d' AMORE.

IX. Duetti del Sign. KRUMLOFFSKY *a 2 Viole d' Amore.*

TRII.

I. Trio di KRUMLOFFSKY. *a Viola d' Amore, Violino e Basso.*

I. Trio di ZACH. *a Viola d' Amore, Viol. e Basso.*

I. Trio di SIMONETTI. *a Viola d' Amore e Cembalo.*

VIOLONCELLO.

Intagliati in Parigi.

VI. Soli di CANAVAS. *a Violoncello e Basso.*

Intagliati in Lüttich.

VI. Soli di MASSART.

DUETTI.

II. Duetti di Leop. HOFFMANN. *a Violonc. e Violino.*

TRII.

I. Trio di L. HOFFMANN. *a Violonc. Violino e Basso.*

I. Trio di KIRSTEN. *a Viola, Violonc. e Violono.*

CONCERTI.

I. Conc. di HOFFMANN. *a Violonc. conc. 2 Viol. e Basso.*

FLAUTO TRAVERSO.

VI. Soli di Messiandro BESOZZI.

DUETTI.

I. Duetto di BERTONI, *a 2 Flauti.*

IV. Duetti di Leop. HOFFMANN.

I. Duetto di MANCINELLI.

TRII.

a Flauto, Violino e Basso.

I. Trio di BERINGER.

VI. Trii di BUTINI.

22 FLAUTO TRAVERSO.
VI. Trii di Anton. FILS.
I.
IV.
II.
V.
III.
VI.
III. Trii di Leop. HOFFMANN.
I. a 2 Flauti e Baſſo.
III. a Flauto, Viol. e Baſſo.
tr
II. a 2 Flauti e Baſſo.
I. Trio di Giuſ. HAYDEN.
a Flauto, Viol. e Baſſo.
VI. Trii di WENDLING, a Fl. Viol. e B.
I.
IV.
II.
V.
III.
VI.

FLAUTO TRAVERSO. 23
QUATTRI.
II. Quattri di Giuſ. TOESCHI.
I. a Flauto Viol. V. e B.
II. a Flauto Viol. V. e B.
CONCERTI
à
FLAUTO CONCERTATO.
III. Concerti di FILS.
I. a Flauto conc. 2 Viol. Viol. e Baſſo.
III. a Flauto conc. 2 Corn. 2 Viol. Viol. e B.
tr
II. a Fl. conc. 2 Cor. 2 Viol. V. e B.
V. Concerti di GRAF. a Fl. conc. 2 Viol. Viol. e B.
I.
IV.
II.
V.
III. 2 Corni.
I. Concerti di KLEINKNECHT.
a Fl. conc. 2 Viol. V. e B.
I. Conc. di RICHTER.
tr

CEMBALO.

SOLI.

VI. Soli di J. C. BACH Milanese.

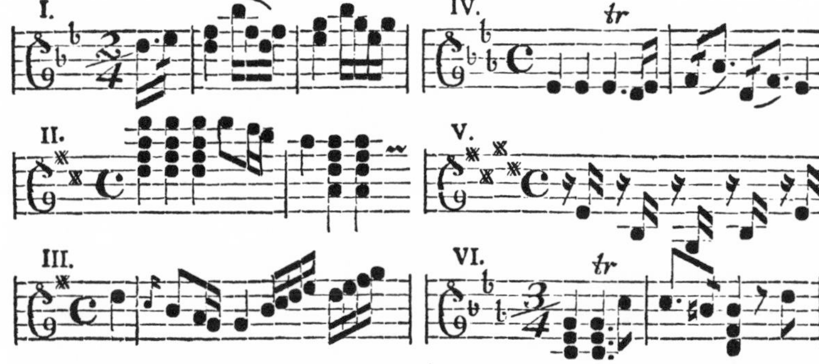

II. Soli di BINDER.

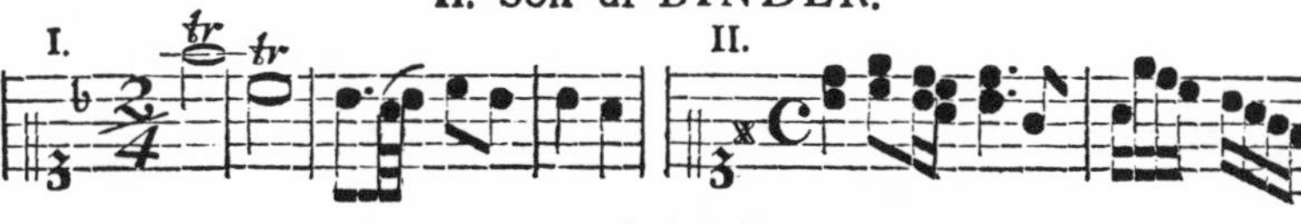

II. Soli di CORNELIUS.

VI. Soli di Giov. SCHWANBERG jun.

VI. Soli di Giov. SCHWANBERG. jun.

VI. Soli di STEFFANI.

Soli intagliati in Parigi.

VI. Soli di Don Idelfonso de ROSSI.

VIII. Soli di Domenico ALBERTI.

XXIV. Poloneſi di GOLDBERG.

Sonata per dui in uno Clavicembalo.

TRII a Cembalo obligato.

CON VIOLINO O TRAVERSO.

I. Trio di GRAF. *a Cemb. e Viol.* I. Trio di SCHWINDEL. *a C. e Fl.*

Intagliati in Amſterdam.

VI. Trii di Wolffgang. MOZARD. *a Cemb. e Violino.*

TERZETTI a Cembalo obligato.

CON VIOLINO O FLAUTO E BASSO.

I. Terzetto di BODE. *a Cemb. Viol. e Baſſo.*

I. Terzetto di GRAUN. *a Cemb. Viol. e Baſſo.*

III. Terzetti di KREISIG. *a Cemb. Violino e Baſſo.*

Intagliati in Parigi etc.

IV. Terzetti di SCHOBERT. *a Cemb. Viol. e Basso.*

I. III.

II. IV.

CONCERTI a Cembalo concertato.

CON PIU STROMENTI.

IV. Conc. di BINDER.

I. *a Cemb. conc. 2 Ob. obl. 2 Viol. V. e B.* III. *a Cemb. conc. 2 Cor. 2 Ob. 1 Fl. 2 V. V. B.*

II. *a Cemb. conc. 2 Ob. 2 Viol. V. e B.* IV. *a Cemb. conc. 2 Viol. Viol. e Basso.*

I. Conc. di DURANT. *a Cemb. conc. Liuto obl. Violonc. obl. 2 V. B.*

I. Conc. di FILS. *a Cemb. conc. 2 Viol. e Basso.*

I. Conc. di FORSTMEYER. *a Cemb. conc. 2 Cor. 2 Viol. e Basso.*

III. Conc. di Leop. HOFFMANN.

I. *a Cemb. conc. 2 Viol. Viol. e Basso.* III. *a Cemb. conc. 2 Viol. Viol. e Basso.*

II. *a Cemb. conc. Flaut. conc. 2 Viol. B.*

II. Conc. di JOMELLI.

I. *a Cemb. conc. 2 Cor. Tymp. 2 Ob. 2 Flaut. 2 Viol. Viola e Basso.* II. *a Cemb. conc. 2 Cor. 2 Flaut. 2 Violin. Viola, Violonc. e Basso.*

II. Conc. di MICHAELIS. *a Cemb. conc. 2 Viol. Viola e Basso.*

I. II.

II. Conc. di POCORNI.

I. *a Cemb. conc. 2 Cor. 2 Fl. 2 Viol. V. B.* II. *a Cemb. conc. 2 Fl. 2 Viol. e B.*

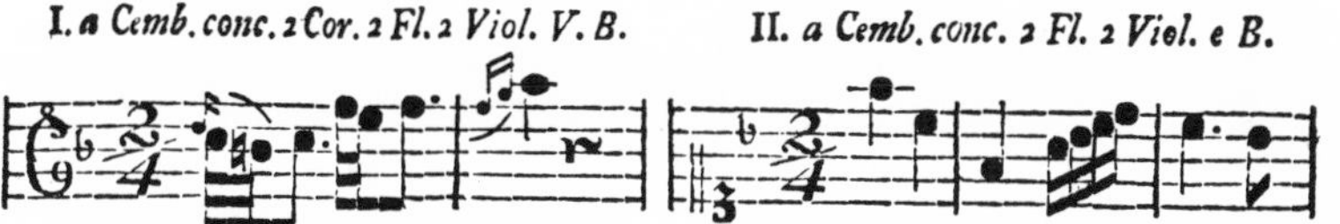

I. Conc. di RICHTER. *a Cemb. conc. 2 Viol. V. e B.*

I. Conc. di SEIFERT. *a Cemb. conc. Fl. conc. 2 Cor. 2 Viol. V. e B.*

I. Conc. di STAMITZ. *a Cemb. conc. 2 Viol. V. e B.*

I. Conc. di SCHOBERT, *a Cemb. conc. 2 Cor. 2 Fl. 2 Viol. V. e B.*

I. Conc. di WAGENSEIL. *a Cemb. conc. 2 Cor. 2 Ob. 2 Fl. 2 V. 2 V. e B.*

I. Conc. di WOLF. *a Cemb. conc. 2 Viol. Viola e Basso.*

I. Partita di SIMONETTI.

a Cemb. oblig. Viola oblig. Violonc. oblig. 2 Flaut. e Violono.

ARIE E CANTATE.

CON PIU STROMENTI.

I. Cantata di CONTI. *a Sopr. 2 Violin. Viol. e Basso.*

II. Cantate di FOERSTER. *a Sopr. 2 Viol. V. e Basso.*

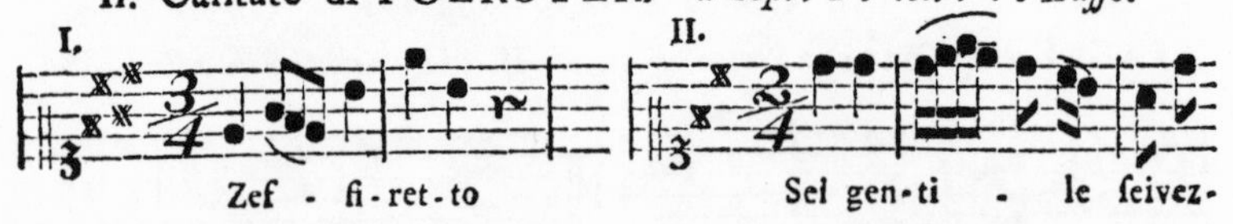

I. Cantata di GAJARECK. *a Sopr. 2 Viol. unis. V. e B.*

V. Cantate di GRAUN. *a Sopr. 2 Viol. Viol. e Basso.*

V. Cantate di HASSE.

I. *a Alto solo e Flaut. Trav.* IV. *a Sopr. 2 Viol. unis. e Basso.*

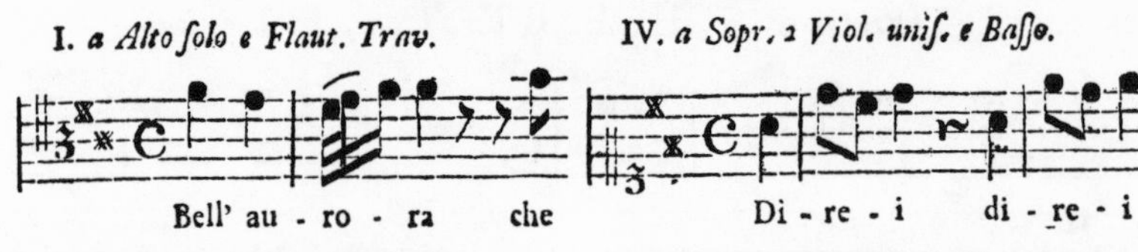

II. *a Sopr. 2 Viol. Viol. e Basso.*

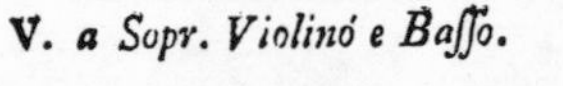

III. *a Sopr. 2 Viol. Viol. e Basso.*

III. Arie di HENDEL.

I. *a Sopr. 2 Viol. Viol. e Basso.* III. *a Sopr. 2 Viol. unis. e Basso.*

II. *a Sopr. 2 Viol. e Basso.*

III. Cantate di HENDEL.

I. *a Sopr. 2 Viol. e Basso.* III. *a Sopr. 2 Viol. Viol. e Basso.*

I. Cant. di HURLEBUSCH. *a Sopr. 2. Viol. Viol. e Basso.*

I. Cantata di LOTTI. *a Sopr. Oboe obl. 2 Viol. V. e B.*

II. Arie di RISTORI.

I. *a Sopr. 2 Viol. unis. Viol. e Basso.*

II. *a Sopr. 2 Viol. Viol. e Basso.*

Der Schulmeister in der Singschule del Sign. FEHRE.
a Basso voce, 2 Viol. Viola e Basso.

Die zwey Wächter. di Sign. HERBING.
a Soprano, 2 Viol. Viola e Basso.

ARIE NELL' OPERA PARTHENOPE del Sgr. HASSE.

ARIE NELL' OPERA AMORE e PSICHE del Sgr. Flor. GASMANN, in Vienna.

36 ARIE e CANZONI.

ARIE, NELL' OPERA, IL BARONE DI TORRE FORTE, del Sgr. NIC. PICCINI.

Terzetto.

1 2 Cor. 2 Viol. Viola, 3 Voci e Basso.

Una po-ve-ra don-

2 2 Cor. 2 Ob. 2 Viol. Viol. e B.

Quell' occhio vez-zoso, quel

3. 2 Viol. Viola e Basso.

Chi dice ad un aman-te

Quartetto.

4. 2 Cor. 2 Ob. 2 Viol. Viola, 4 Voci e B.

Salta il core e salto

5. 2 Viol. Viola e Basso.

Son le donne Pa-dron mio

6. 2 Cor. 2 Ob. 2 Violin. Viola e B.

Si: lo giuro, oh ninfa bella

7. 2 Cor. 2 Viol. 2 Viol. e B.

Suentu-ra-ta, poue-

Quartetto.

8. 2 Cor. 2 Ob. 2 Viol. Viola 4 Voci e B.

Attenti Pa-droni, la pri-

9. 2 Corn. 4 Viol. Viola e B.

Via zit-to, compren-do,

Duetto.

10. 2 Cor. 2 Ob. 2 Viol. Viola e Basso.

Queste a-ma-bi-li fio-ret-

11. 2 Cor. 2 Ob. 2 Viol. Viola e B.

Sta nel vol-to un

12. 2 Viol. Viola e Basso.

A-mato mio be-ne

13. 2 Cor. 2 Ob. 2 Violini, Viola e B.

Vedete che ri-di-co-

14. 2 Corn. 2 Ob. 2 Violini, Viola e B.

Mesta e fle-bi-le mi dice

15. 2 Corn. 2 Violin. Viola e B.

Oh che not-te

Duetto.

16. 2 Corn 2 Ob. 2 Violini, Viola e B.

Se la vaga Lodo-letta

Quartetto.

17. 2 Tromb. 2 Ob. 2 Violini, Viola e B.

Oh ve-de-te che sog-

SVPPLEMENTO IV.

DEI

CATALOGI

DELLE

SINFONIE, PARTITE, OVERTURE, SOLI, DUETTI, TRII, QUATTRI

E

CONCERTI

PER IL

VIOLINO, FLAUTO TRAVERSO,

CEMBALO

ED ALTRI STROMENTI.

CHE

SI TROVANO IN MANOSCRITTO NELLA OFFICINA MUSICA DI BREITKOPF IN LIPSIA.

1769.

SINFONIE.

I. Sinf. di ASPLMAYR, *a 2 Clar. Tymp. 2 Cor. 2 Ob. 2 Viol. V. e B.*

II. Sinfonie di Carlo DITTERS.

I. *a 2 Cor. 2 Ob. 2 Viol. V. e B.* II. *a 2 Cor. 2 Ob. 2 Viol. V. e B.*

I. Sinf. di Giov. Adolf HASSE, *dell' Opera Piramo e Tisbe.*

a 2 Cor. 2 Ob. 2 Flaut. Trav. 2 Viol. V. e B.

IV. Sinfonie di Giuſ. HAYDEN.

I. *a 2 Cor. 2 Ob. Fl. Trav. 2 Viol. V. e B.* III. *a 2 Cor. 2 Ob. Violino e Violonc. obl. 2 Viol. V. e B.*

II. *2 Clar. Tymp. 2 Cor. 2 Ob. 2 V. e B.* IV. *a 2 Cor. 2 Ob. 2 Viol. V. e B.*

VI. Sinfonie di Frederico HENNIG.

I. *a 2 Cor. 2 Ob. 2 Viol. V. e B.* IV. *a 2 Cor. 2 Fl. Trav. 2 Viol. V. e B.*

II. *a 2 Cor. 2 Ob. 2 Viol. V. e B.* V. *a 2 Cor. 2 Ob. 2 Viol. V. e B.*

III. *a 2 Cor. 2 Ob. 2 Fag. 2 Viol. V. e B.* VI. *a 2 Clar. T. 2 Cor. 2 Ob. 2 Viol. V. e B.*

SINFONIE. 3

II. Sinfonie di G. A. HILLER.

I. *a 2 Cor. 2 Ob. 2 Viol. V. e B.* II. *a 2 Cor. 2 Ob. 2 Fl. Trav. 2 Viol. V. e B.*

I. Sinfonie di KOZELUCH. *a 2 Clar. 2 Ob. 2 Flaut. 2 Fag. 2 Viol. V. e B.*

III. Sinfonie di Giuſ. MISLEWECEK, *a 2 Cor. 2 Ob. 2 Viol. V. e B.*

I. III.

II.

I. Sinf. di Gio. Amad. NAUMANN.

a 2 Cor. 2 Ob. 2 Viol. V. e B.

I. Sinf. di Carlo d'ORDONEZ.

a 2 Cor. 2 Ob. 2 Viol. V. e B.

III. Sinfonie di Wenzeslao PICHEL.

I. Terpſiche, *a 2 Cor. 2 Flauti & 2 Fagotti oblig. 2 Viol. V. e B.* III. Urania, *a 2 Cor. 2 Ob. 2 Viol. Viola e Baſſo.*

II. Euterpe, *a 2 C. 2 Ob. obl. 2 Viol. V. e B.*

V. Sinfonie di Giuſ. TOESCHI.

I. *a 2 Cor. 2 Flaut. Trav. 2 Viol. V. e B.* IV. *a 2 Cor. 2 Ob. 2 Viol. V. e B.*

II. *a 2 Cor. 2 Ob. 2 Viol. V. e B.* V. *a 2 Cor. 2 Ob. 2 Viol. V. e B.*

III. *a 2 Cor. 2 Ob. 2 Viol. V. e B.*

SINFONIE intagliate in Parigi, &c.

VI. Sinfonie di Giov. BACH, *a 2 Cor. 2 Ob. 2 Viol. V. e B.*
Opera VI.

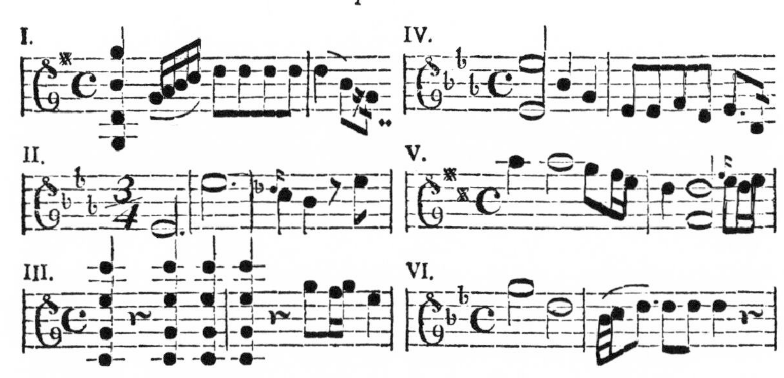

VI. Sinf. di Carolo DITTERS, *a 2 Cor. 2 Ob. 2 Viol. V. e B. Opera IV.*

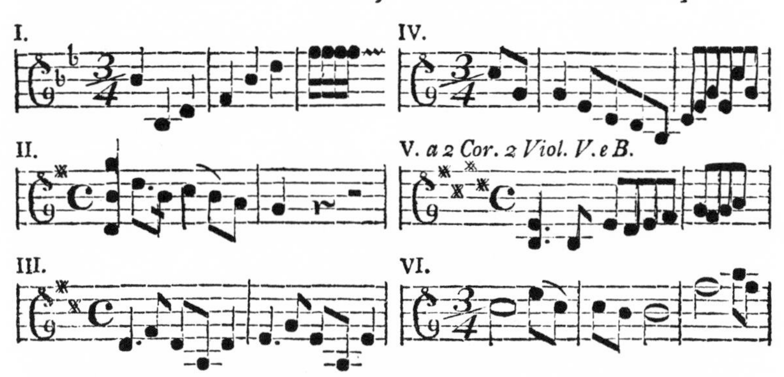

III. Sinf. di Carlo DITTERS, *a 2 Cor. 2 Ob. 2 Viol. V. e B.*
Opera V.

VI. Sinf. di GOSSEK, *a 2 Cor. 2 Ob. 2 Viol. V. e B.*
Opera XII.

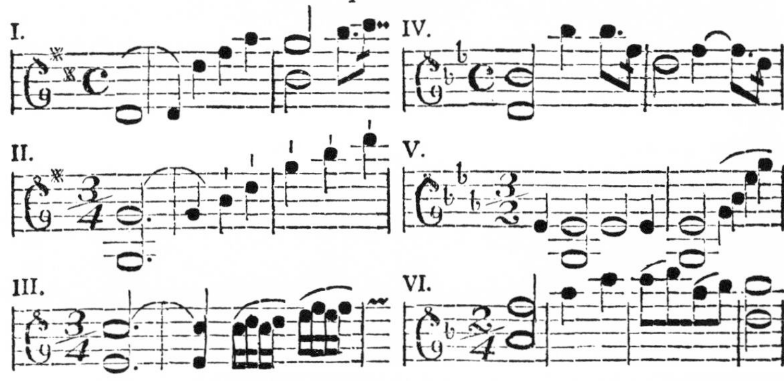

VI. Sinf. di Giuf. HAYDEN, *a 2 Cor. 2 Ob. 2 Viol. V. e B.*
Oper. VII.

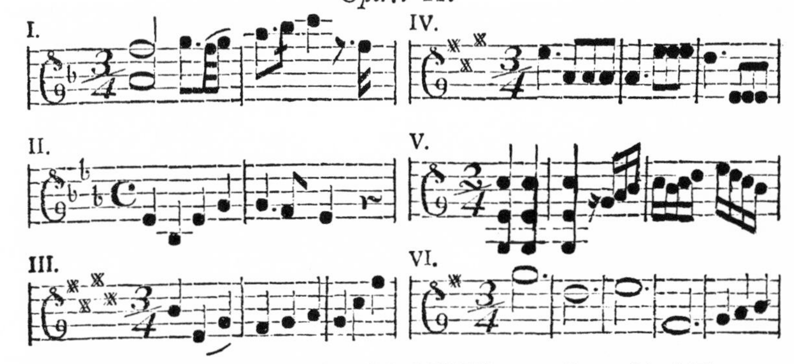

VI. Sinf. di Ignatio HOLZBAUER, *a 2 Cor. 2 Ob. ô Flauti, 2 Viol. V. e B. Opera III.*

6 SINFONIE.
III. Sinfonie di Ignatio HOLZBAUER. Opera IV.
I. a 2 Cor. 2 Ob. 2 Viol. V. e B.
III. a 2 Cor. 2 Fag. 2 Ob. 2 Viol. V. e B.
II. a 2 Cor. 2 Flaut. Trav. 2 Viol. V. e B.
VI. Sinf. di MARTINI, il Tedesco a 2 Viol. V. e B. Opera V.
I.
IV.
II.
V.
III.
VI.
VI. Sinf. di Xavieri RICHTER, a 2 Cor. 2 Ob. 2 Viol. V. e B.
Opera VII.
I.
IV.
II.
V.
III.
VI.

SINFONIE. 7
II. Sinfonie di Giuſ. TOESCHI.
I. a 2 Cor. 2 Ob. 2 Viol. V. e B.
II. a 2 Cor. 2 Flaut. Trav. 2 Viol. V. e B.
VI. Sinf. di VANMALDERE, a 2 Cor. 2 Ob. 2 Viol. V. e B.
Opera V.
I.
IV.
II.
V. a 2 Viol. V. e B.
III.
VI.
I. Sinf. di VANNAL, a 2 Viol. V. e B.
PARTITE, DIVERTIMENTI,
CASSATIONES &c.
I. Partita di B. T. BREITKOPF, a 2 Cor. 2 Flauti, 2 Viol. V. e B.
I. Divertimento di Carlo
DITTERS.
a 2 Cor. Violino Solo, Oboe Solo, 2 Viole,
e Baſſo.
I. Caſſatio di Carlo DITTERS.
a 2 Corni, Violino, Viola e Baſſo.

VIOLINO.

SOLI con BASSO.

VIII. Soli di Carolo DITTERS.

SOLI, intagliati in Parigi &c.

VI. Soli di BERTHEAUME.

VI. Soli di Conrad BREUNIG. *Opera II.*

VI. Soli di CAPRON. *Opera I.*

VI. Soli di DEMACHI. *Opera I.*

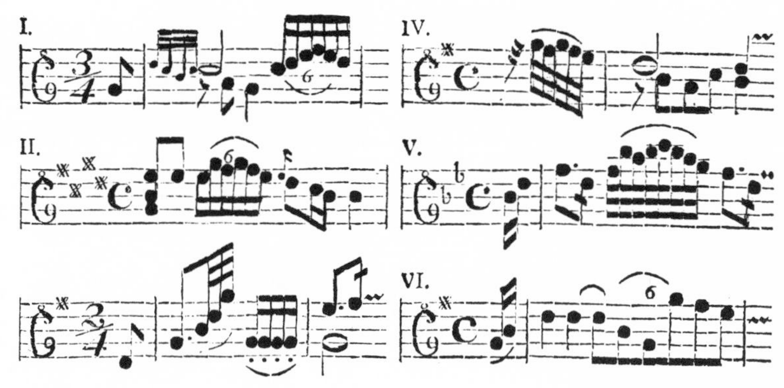

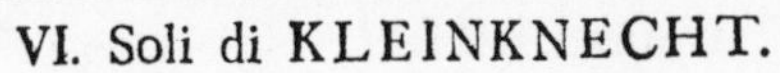

VI. Soli di KLEINKNECHT.

VI. Soli di Filippo MANFREDI. *Opera I.*

VI. Soli dell'Abbate Alexandro ROBINEAU.

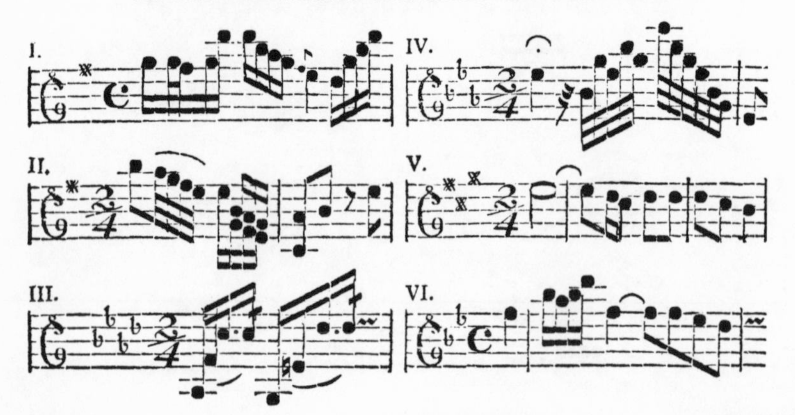

VI. Soli di VACHON. *Opera III.*

DUETTI.

A DUOI VIOLINI.

VI. Duetti di EISELT.

DUETTI, intagliati in Parigi.

VI. Duetti di Conrad BREUNIG. *Opera I.*

VI. Duetti di Felice DEGIARDINO. *Opera X.*

VI. Duetti di REY, *a Violino I & II. ó Violoncello.*

TRII.

A DUE VIOLINI CON BASSO.

VI. Trii di Carolo DITTERS.

VI. Trii di Giuf. MISLEWECEK.

TRII, intagliati in Parigi, &c.

VI. Trii di Guillelme CRAMER. *Opera I.*

VI. Trii di Bartolomeo MENESINI, *London.*

VI. Sinfonie a trè di Andrea OCH. *Opera I.*

VI. Trii di Giov. Andrea SABATINI, *London.*
Opera I.

VI. Trii di SCHLEGER. *Opera I.*

VI. Trii di Gregorio SCIROLI. *Opera I.*

VI. Trii di Ludovico SIRMEN. *Opera I.*

VI. Trii di Francesco UTTINI, *Opera I. London.*

QUATTRI, intagliati in Parigi &c.

VI. QUATTRI di ASPELMAYR, *a 2 Viol. V. e B. Opera II.*

VI. Quattri di BARBICI, *a 2 Viol. V. e B. Opera I.*

VI. Quattri di Giov. FRANCISCONI, *a 2 Viol. V. e B. Opera II.*

VI. Quattri di GEBART, *a 2 Viol. V. e B. Opera I.*

CONCERTI, per il Violino concertato.

VIOLA d'AMORE.

I. Trio di NOVY.
a Viola d'Amore, Flauto Trav. e B.

I. Concerto di KRUMLOFFSKY.
a Viola d'Amore conc. 2 Viol. V. e B.

VIOLONCELLO.

SOLI, intagliati in Parigi, &c.

VI. Soli di PIN, *a Violoncello e Basso.*

DUETTI.

VI. Duetti di NEYDING, *a due Violoncelli.*

VI. Duetti di NEYDING, *a Flaut. Trav. e Violoncello.*

II. Duetti di NEYDING, *a Violoncello e Violino.*

I. Trio di Leop. HOFFMANN, *a Violoncello, Violino e Basso.*

FLAUTO TRAVERSO.

VI. Soli di Filippo PROVER, *intagliati in Parigi. Opera I.*

DUETTI.

III. Duetti di Leop. HOFFMANN. *a due Flauti.*

VI. Duetti di KLEINKNECHT, *a 2 Flauti Traversi.*

TRII.

A DUE FLAUTI e BASSO.

VI. Trii di KLEINKNECHT, *a 2 Flauti e Basso.*

intagliati in Parigi. Opera III.

A FLAUTO, VIOLINO e BASSO.

V. Trii di Leop. GASMANN, *a Flauto, Violino e Basso.*

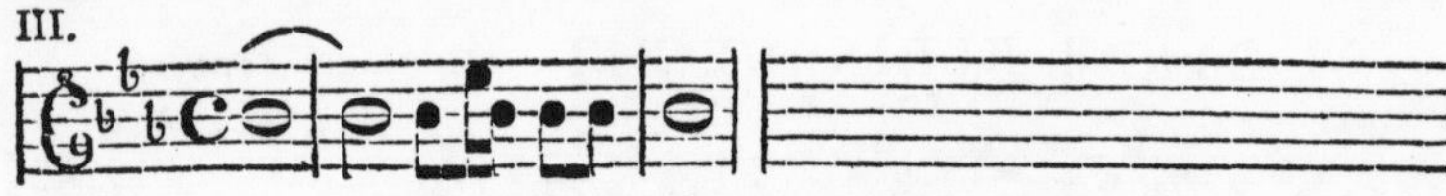

II. Trii di Giuſ. HAYDEN.

I. *a Flauto, Violino e Baſſo.* **II. *a Flauto, Viola e Baſſo.***

I. Trio di Leop. HOFFMANN, *a Flauto Violino e Baſſo.*

III. Trii di STALDER, *a Flauto, Violino e Baſſo.*

QUATTRI, *intagliati in Parigi &c.*

VI. Quattri di Leop. GASMANN. *Opera I.*

QUINTETTI, *intagliati in Parigi &c.*

VI. Quintetti di Chriſtiano CANNABICH, *a 2 Flauti, Violino, Viola & Violoncello obligato. Opera VII.*

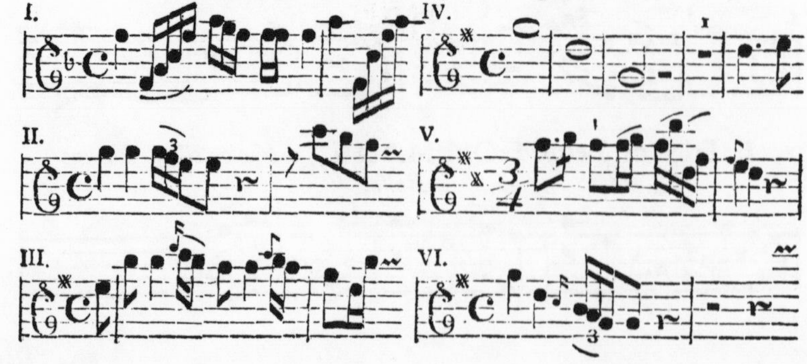

CONCERTI.

A FLAUTO TRAVERSO CONCERTATO.

I. Concerto di CANNABICH, *a Flauto conc. 2 Viol. V. e B.*

II. Concerti di Anton. FILS, *a Fl. conc. 2 Cor. 2 Viol. V. e B.*

I. II.

V. Concerti di Leop. HOFFMANN.

I. *a Fl. conc. 2 V. Viola oblig. e Basso.* IV. *a Fl. conc. 2 Cor. 2 Viol. V. e B.*

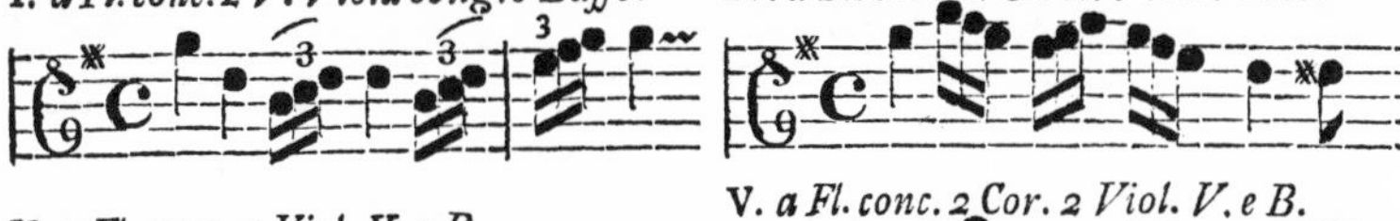

II. *a Fl. conc. 2 Viol. V. e B.*

V. *a Fl. conc. 2 Cor. 2 Viol. V. e B.*

III. *a Fl. conc. 2 Viol. V. e B.*

II. Concerti di HOLZBOGEN.

I. *a Fl. conc. 2 Cor. 2 Viol. V. e B.* II. *a Fl. conc. 2 Viol. V. e B.*

I. Conc. di Giuſ. TOESCHI.

II. Concerti di WENDLING.

I. *a Flaut. conc. 2 Clar. Tymp. 2 Cor. 2 Ob. 2 Viol. V. e B.*

II. *a Flaut. conc. 2 Viol. V. e B.*

II. Conc. di WENDLING, *a Flaut. conc. 2 Cor. 2 Viol. V. e B. intagliati in Parigi. Opera IV.*

I. II.

OBOE.

VI. Sonate a Oboe ſolo di PROVER, *vid. Flaut. Trav. p. 21.*

II. Conc. di FISCHER, *a Oboe conc. 2 Violini, Viola e B.*

I. II.

I. Conc. di ROELLIG, *a Oboe conc. 2 Viol. V. e Baſſo.*

CORNO.

II. Concerti di HAMPEL, *a 2 Corn. concert. 2 Viol. V. e B.*

I. II.

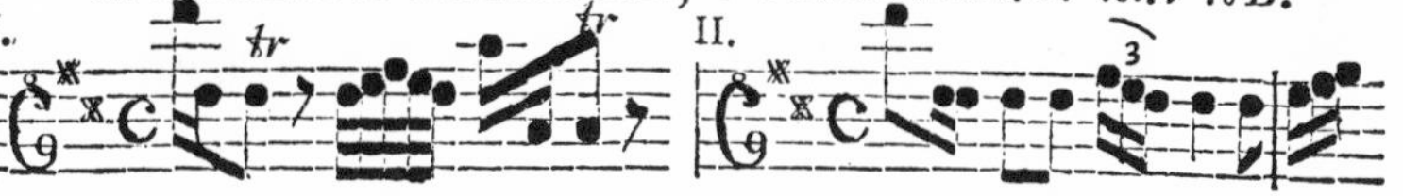

II. Concerti di LAU, *a Corno conc. 2 Viol. Viola e B.*

I. II.

FAGOTTO.

I. Concerto di ZIMMERMANN, *a Fagotto conc. 2 Viol. V. e B.*

CEMBALO.

SOLI.

VI. Divertimenti di Leop. HOFFMANN, *a Clavicembalo solo.*

I. Fantasia di STEFFANI *a Cembalo solo.*

Sonate, a Cembalo Solo, intagliate in Parigi &c.

VI. Sonate di BAMBINI, *a Cembalo Solo.*

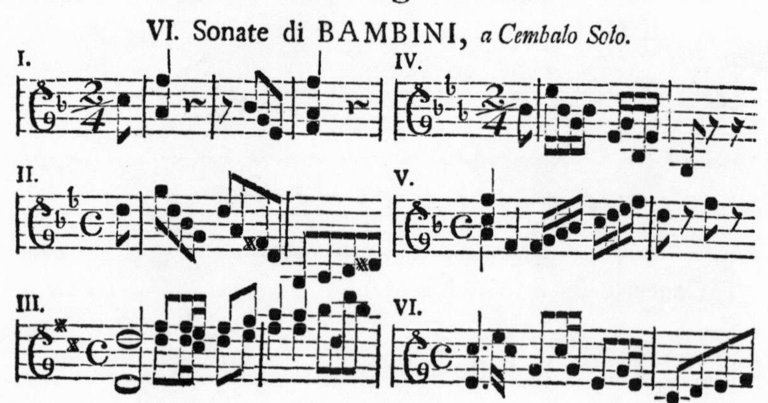

III. Sonate della Sigra. BAYON. *a Cembalo Solo, intagliate in Parigi. Opera I.*

VI. Sonate di BEECKE, *a Cembalo Solo. Opera V.*

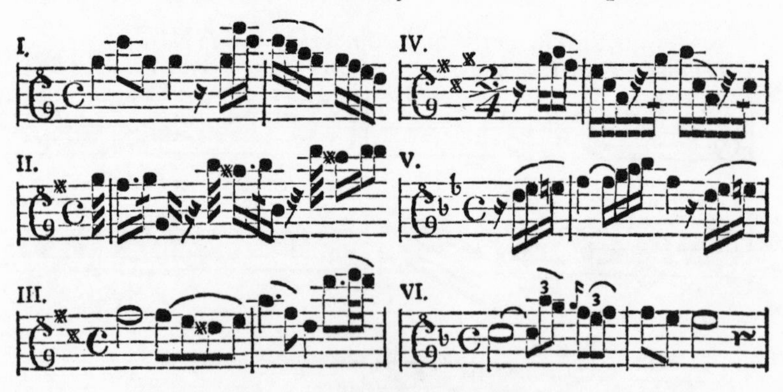

VI. Sonate di Giac. CROCE, *a Cembalo Solo. Stampate in Londra.*

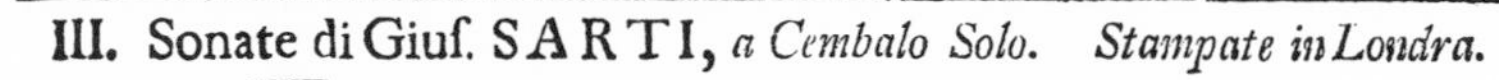

III. Sonate di Giuſ. SARTI, *a Cembalo Solo.* *Stampate in Londra.*

TRII.

A CEMBALO OBLIGATO CON VIOLINO.

I. Trio di BINDER, *a Cembalo e Violino.*

I. Terzetto di HAYDEN, *a Cembalo, Violino e Baſſo.*

III. Trii della Sigra. BAYON, *a Cembalo e Violino, intagliati in Parigi. Opera I.*

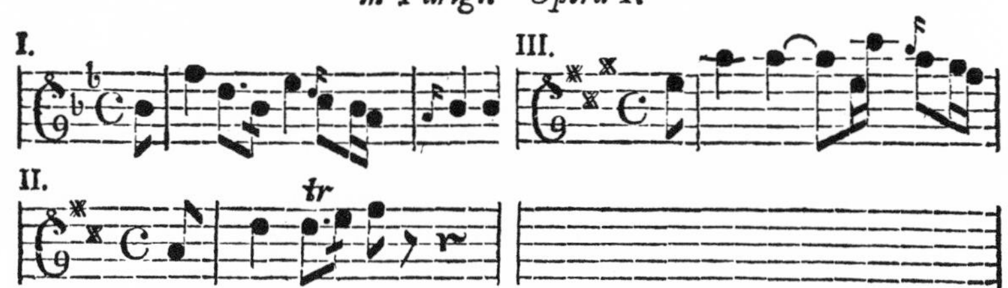

VI. Trii di Luigi BOCHERINI, *a Cembalo e Violino. intagliati in Parigi.*

CONCERTI e CONCERTINI a Cembalo concertato con più Stromenti.

VI. Concerti di Chriſtiano BACH, *a Cemb. conc. 2 Cor. 2 V. V. e B.*

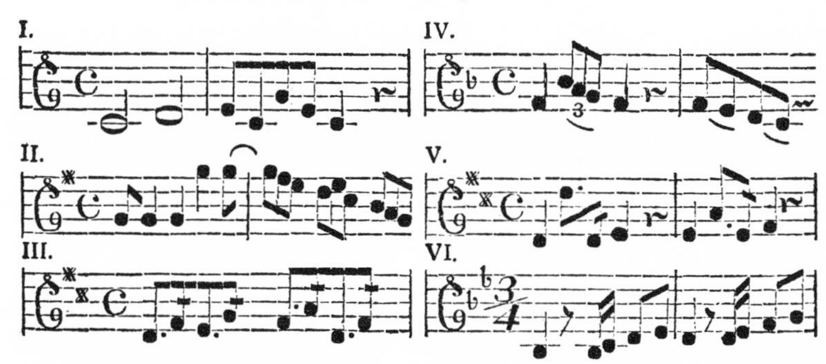

I. Conc. di BINDER. *a Cemb. conc. 2 V. V. e B.*

I. Conc. di CHARPENTIER. *a Cemb. conc. 2. V. e B.*

III. Concerti di Leop. HOFFMANN.

I. *a Cemb. conc. Oboe conc. 2 V. V. e B.*

III. *a Cemb. conc. 2 Cor. 2 V. V. e B.*

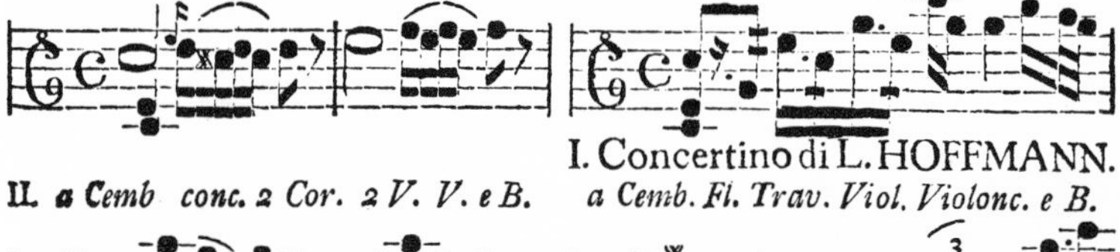

II. *a Cemb conc. 2 Cor. 2 V. V. e B.*

I. Concertino di L. HOFFMANN. *a Cemb. Fl. Trav. Viol. Violonc. e B.*

II. Concerti di ROLLE, *a Cemb. conc. 2 V. V. e B.*

I. Concerto di SCHALE.

II. Concertini di Giuſ. STEFFANI.

I. *a Cemb. conc. 2 Cor. Flauto Trav. Violino e Baſſo.* II. *a Cemb. conc. Flauto Trav. Violino e Violoncello.*

II. Concerti di WOLF.

I. *a Cemb. conc. 2 V. V. e B.* II. *a Cemb. conc. 2 Flaut. 2 V. V. e B.*

VI. Notturni di MARTINI, *a Cembalo oblig. o Harpa, 2 Viol. e Baſſo. intagliati in Parigi. Opera IV.*

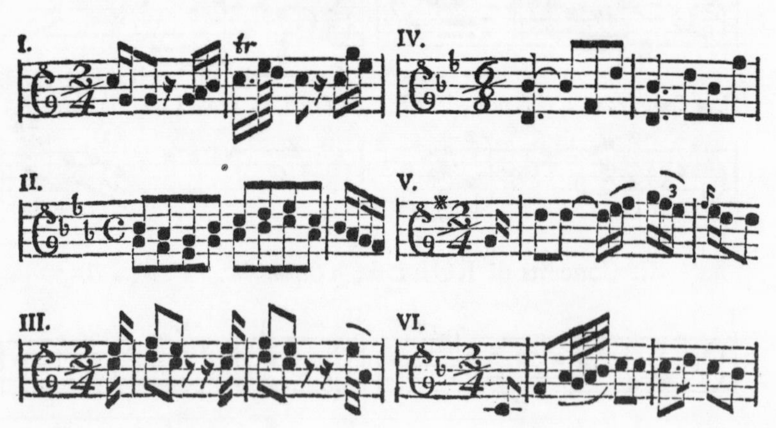

HARPA.

MOREAU *airs choiſis pour la Harpe, intagliate in Parigi.*

VI. Sonate per l' Harpa e Violino di Franceſco PETRINI, *intagliate in Parigi. Opera I.*

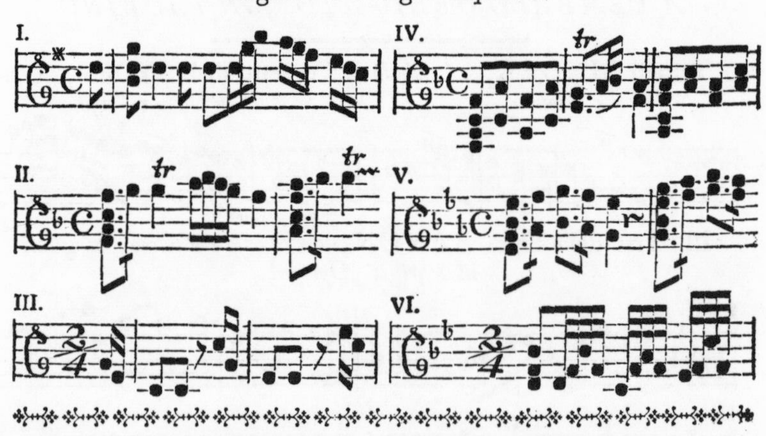

ARIE DELL' INTERMEZZO PIRAMO e TISBE del Sgr. HASSE.

PARTITE PER IL LIUTO SOLO.

LXVI. Partite del Sgr. S. L. WEISS.

VI. Partite grandi.

PARTITE PER IL LIUTO SOLO.

B dur.

C dur.

C moll.

D dur.

23. Allemande.
27. Prelude.
24. Prelude.
28. Fantasia con Fuga.
25. Allemande.
29. Fuga seul.
26. Prelude.

D moll.

30. Allemande.
32. Fantasie.
31. Prelude.
33. Allemande.

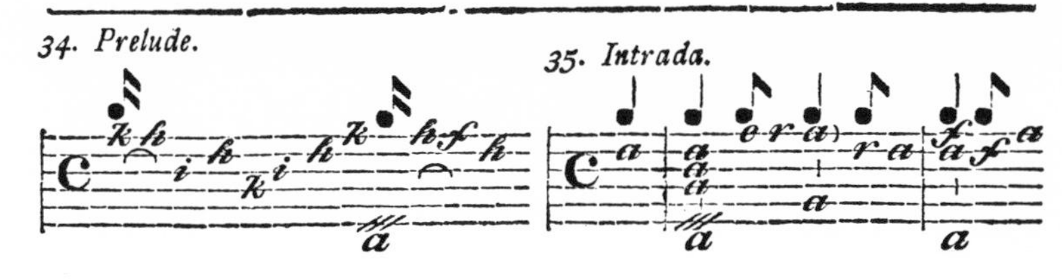
34. Prelude.
35. Intrada.

Dis dur.
36. Allemande.

F dur.
37. Fantasie.
41. Prelude.
38. Prelude.
42. Largo.

39. Allemande.

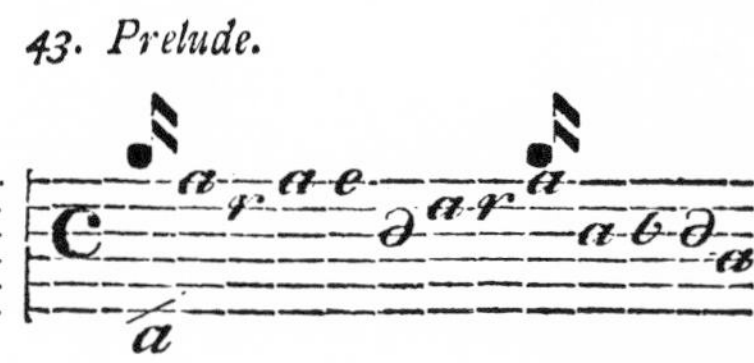
43. Prelude.

40. Allemande.

44. Entrée.

45. Vivace.
46. Moderato.
F moll.
47. Allemande.
48. Allemande.
Fis moll.
49. Allemande.
G dur.
50. Prelude.
51. Fantasie.
52. Allemande.
53. Adagio.
54. Allemande.
55. Largo.
56. Allemande.
G moll.
57. Allemande.
58. Lentement.
59. Fantasie.
60. Prelude.
VI. Soli di DURANT.
1. Cantabile. A dur.
2. Prelude. A moll.
3. Adagio. H moll.
4. Siciliana. Dis dur.
5. Saturnina. F dur.
6. Fantasie. A moll.

IX. Solos del Sgr. I. B. v. HAGEN.

SVPPLEMENTO V.

DEI

CATALOGI

DELLE

SINFONIE, PARTITE, OVERTURE, SOLI, DUETTI, TRII, QUATTRI E CONCERTI

PER IL

VIOLINO, FLAUTO TRAVERSO,

CEMBALO

ED ALTRI STROMENTI.

CHE

SI TROVANO IN MANOSCRITTO
NELLA OFFICINA MUSICA DI BREITKOPF
IN LIPSIA.

1770.

SINFONIE.

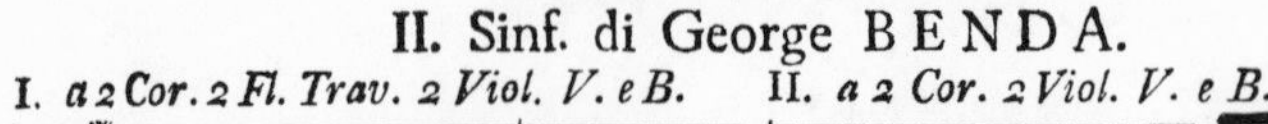

II. Sinf. di George BENDA.

I. a 2 Cor. 2 Fl. Trav. 2 Viol. V. e B. II. a 2 Cor. 2 Viol. V. e B.

II. Sinf. di Christiano CANNABICH.

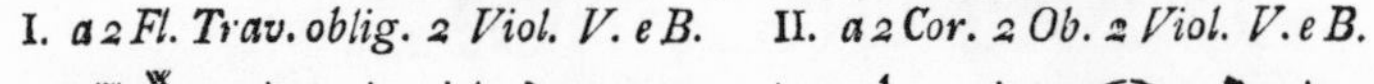

I. a 2 Fl. Trav. oblig. 2 Viol. V. e B. II. a 2 Cor. 2 Ob. 2 Viol. V. e B.

I. Sinf. di Carlo DITTTRS, *a 2 Cor. 2 Ob. 2 Viol. e B.*

I. Sinf. di Flor. GASMANN, *a 2 Cor. 2 Fl. Trav. 2 Viol. V. e B.*

VI. Sinfonie di Frederico HENNIG.

I. a 2 Ob. 2 Viol. V. e B. IV. a 2 Cor. 2 Ob. 2 Flaut. 2 Viol. V. e B.

II. a 2 Cor. 2 Ob. 2 Viol. V. e B. V. a 2 Cor. 2 Ob. 2 Fagott. 2 Viol. V. e B.

III. a 2 Clar. Tymp. 2 Ob. 2 Viol. V. e B. VI. a 2 Cor. 2 Ob. 2 Viol. V. e B.

II. Sinf. di G. A. HILLER.

I. a 2 Cor. 2 Ob. 2 Viol. V. e B. II. a 2 Cor. 2 Ob. 2 Fl. Tr. 2 Viol. V. e B.

I. Sinf. di PESCH.

a 2 Cor. 2 Ob. 2 Viol. V. e B.

I. Sinf. di Gio. Amad. NAUMANN, *nell' Opera il Villano geloso.*

a 2 Cor. 2 Ob. 2 Flauti, 2 Viol. V. e B.

I. Sinf. di Nicolo PICCINI, *nel opera la Pescatrice.*

a 2 Tromb. 2 Cor. 2 Ob. 2 Viol. V. e B.

II. Sinf. di ROESER.

I. a 2 Clar. 2 Cor. 2 Viol. V. e B. II. a 2 Clar. 2 Cor. 2 Viol. V. e B.

VI. Sinf. di VANHALL, *a 2 Cor. 2 Ob. 2 Viol. V. e B.*

I. IV. II. V. III. VI.

I. Sinf. di WESTENHOLTZ.

a 2 Clar. Tymp. 2 Cor. 2 Fag. 2 V. V. e B.

I. Sinf. di WOLF.

a 2 Cor. 2 Ob. 2 Viol. V. e B.

MINUETTI.

XXIV Dresdn. Redout. Men. &c. di SIMONETTI, ao. 1771.

XII. Dresdn. Redout. Men. &c. del Sign. HENNIG, ao. 1771.

XII Polonoisen del Sign. ENGEL, *in Varsovia*, ao. 1771.

SINFONIE intagliate in Parigi, &c.

VI. Sinfonie di I. C. BACH, *a 2 Cor. 2 Ob. 2 Viol. V. e B. Opera VI. Amſterd.*

VI. Sinf. di Franceſco BECK, *a 2 Cor. 2 Ob. 2 Viol. V. e B. Opera IV. Parigi.*

VI. Sinf. di Gaſparo FRITZ, *a 2 Cor. 2 Flaut. Trav. 2 Viol. V. e B. Opera VI. Parigi.*

VI. Sinf. di C. F. GRAAF, *a 2 Cor. 2 Flaut. 2 Viol. V e. B. Opera IX. Amſterd.*

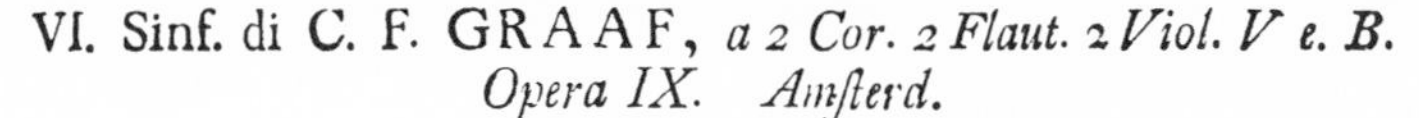

I. Sinf. di GREINER. *Amſterd. a 2 Flaut. 2 Viol. 2 Viole e B.*

I. Sinf. di Giuſ. TOESCHI. *Pari. a 2 Cor. 2 Ob. 2 Viol. V. e B.*

Sinfon. Periodique, *intagliati in Amſterdam.*

I. di TOESCHI, *a 2 Cor. 2 Ob. 2 Viol. V. e B.*

V. di KREUSER, *a 2 Cor. 2 Flaut. 2 Viol. V. e B.*

II. di SCHWINDEL, *a 2 Cor. 2 Ob. 2 Viol. V. e B.*

VI. di SCHWEITZER, *a 2 Cor. 2 Ob. 2 Viol. V. e B.*

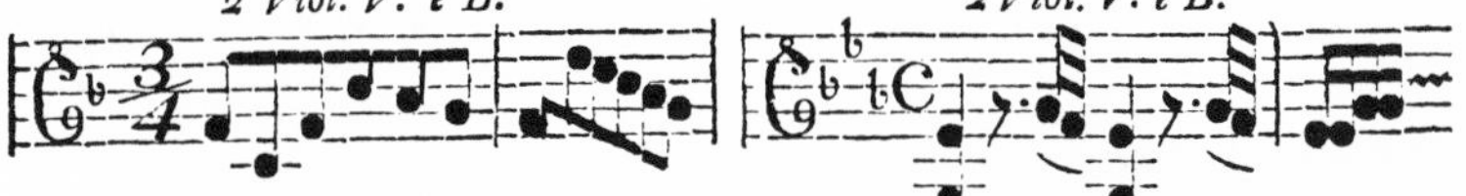

III. di KLOEFFLER. *a 2 Cor. 2 Flaut. 2 Viol. V. e B.*

VII. di HARTMANN, *a 2 Cor. 2 Ob. 2 Viol. V. e B.*

IV. di DITTERS, *a 2 Cor. 2 Ob. 2 Viol. 2 Viole e B.*

VIII. di DITTERS, *a 2 Cor. 2 Ob. 2 Viol. V. e B.*

IX. di TOESCHI, *a 2 Cor. 2 Flaut. 2 Viol. V. e B.* XI. di SCHMIDT, *a 2 Cor. 2 Ob. 2 Viol. V. e B.*

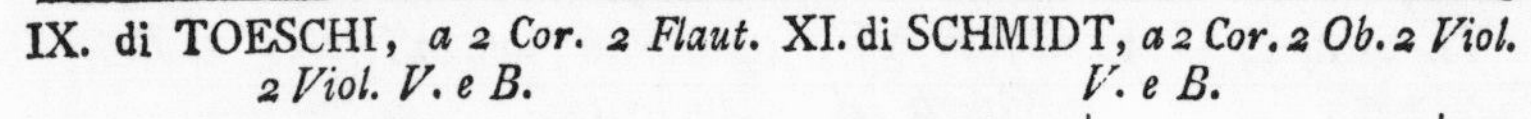

X. di DITTERS, *a 2 Cor. 2 Ob. 2 Viol. V. e B.* XII. di DITTERS, *a 2 Cor. 2 Ob. 2 Viol. V. e B.*

VIOLINO.

SOLI con BASSO.

VI. Soli di ANNONVILLE.

VI. Soli di Pietro NARDINI, *intagliati in Londra. Opera V.*

DUETTI.

A DUE VIOLINI.

VI. Duetti di GAVIGNE'.

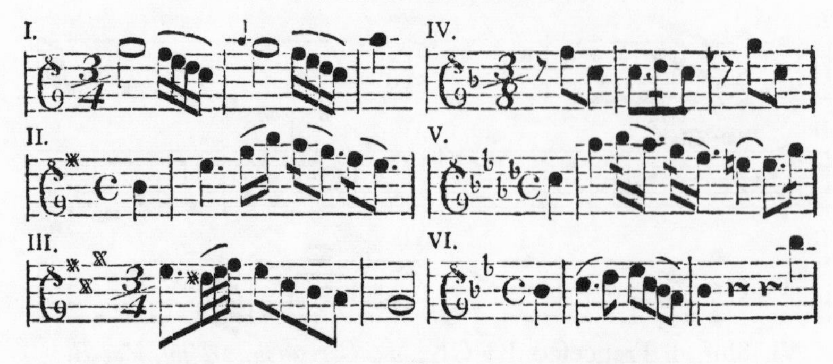

VI. Duetti di Francesco LAMOTTA.

VI. Duetti di SIMON. *Racc. I.*

8
VIOLINO.
VI. Duetti di SIMON. Racc. II.
VI. Duetti di SIMON. Racc. III.
DUETTI intagliati in Parigi &c.
VI. Duetti di AVOLIO. Opera II. Parigi.
VIOLINO.
9
VI. Duetti di AVOLIO. Opera III. Parigi.
VI. Duetti di FAUTINI. Opera I. Parigi.
(laufen im Mspt. unter den Namen PESCH.)
VI. Duetti di Giuſ. HAYDEN. Opera VI. Amſterd.
(laufen im Mspt. unter den Namen KAMMEL.)

VI. Duetti di Antonio KAMMEL. *Opera II. Amſterd.*

VI. Duetti di LALOYAU. *Opera I. Parigi.*

TRII.

A DUE VIOLINI CON BASO intagliati in Parigi &c.

VI. Converſazioni *a 2 Violini e Baſſo*, di L. BOCHERINI. *Opera VII. Parigi.*

VI. Trii di B. HUPFELD. *Opera II. Amſterd.*

VI. Trii di Giov. MARTINI, *il Tedeſco. Opera VI. Parigi.*

VI. Trii di Madame Lombardini SIRMEN. *Op. I. Amſterd.*
con Violoncello obligato.

VI. Trii di Carlo STAMITZ. *Opera II. Parigi.*

QUATTRI.

VI. Quattri di HENNIG, *a 2 Viol. Viola e Baſſo.*

QUATTRI, *intagliati in Parigi &c.*

VI. Quattri di L. BOCHERINI, *a 2 Viol. V. e Vilc. obl. Op. VI. Par.*

VI. Quattri di Carlo STAMITZ, *a 2 Viol. V. e B. Opera I. Parigi.*

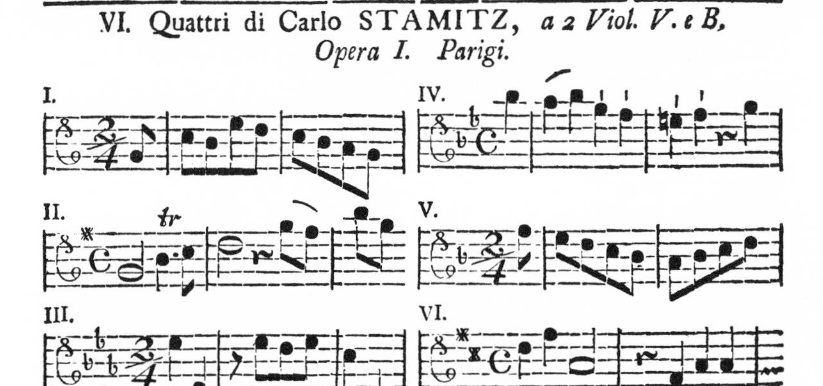

VI. Sonate da VELLA, *Malteſe, a 3 Violini e Baſſo. Opera I. Parigi.*

QUINTETTI.

I. Quintetto di HENNIG, *a 2 Viol. 2 Viole e Baſſo.*

I. Quintetto di Giov. Chr. BACH, *a 2 Viol. ó Oboi, Viola, Violoncello ó Fagotto, e Baſſo. Parigi.*

CONCERTI, *per il Violino concertato.*

I. Conc. di FESTONI, *a 2 C. 2 Ob. oblig. 2 Viol. e Violonc. concertati, 2 Viol. V. e B.*

I. Conc. di Leop. HOFFMANN. *a Viol. conc. 2 Viol. V. e B.*

I. Conc. di Giuſ. MISLEWECEK. *a 2 Cor. 2 Ob. Viol. conc. 2 Viol. V. e B.*

I. Conc. di PUGNANI. *a Viol. conc. 2 Viol. V. e B.*

I. Conc. di SCOLARI. *a Viol. conc. 2 Viol. V. e B.*

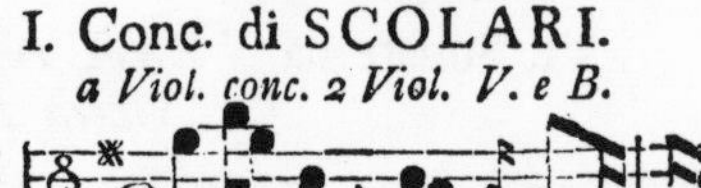

I. Conc. di Giuſ. TOESCHI. *a 2 Cor. Viol. conc. 2 Viol. V. e B.*

I. Conc. di VANHALL. *a Viol. conc. 2 Viol. V. e B.*

I. Concerto di d'AVAUX, *a Viol. conc. 2 Viol. V. e B. intagl. in Parigi.*

VIOLONCELLO.

VI. Soli di GRETSCH, *a Violoncello e Baſſo.*

II. Soli di FILS, *a Violoncello e Baſſo.*

I. Solo di HIMMELPAUR. *a Violoncello e Baſſo.*

I. Solo di MISLEWEZEK. *a Violoncello e Baſſo.*

I. Solo di PREYSING, *a Violoncello e Baſſo.*

II. Soli di WERNER, *a Violoncello e Baſſo.*

IV. Sonate di AVONDANO, *a Violoncello ſolo e Baſſo,* e II. Duetti *per due Violoncelli, intagliati in Parigi.*

DUETTI.

I. Duetto di SCHINDLER, *a due Violoncelli.* I. Duetto di Giuſ. TOESCHI, *a due Violoncelli.*

VI. Duetti di SCHWINDEL, *a Violoncello e Violino, intagl. in Amſterdam. Op. VI.*

TRII.

V. Trii di Leop. HOFFMANN, *a Violoncello, Viol. e B.*

CONCERTI, *per il Violoncello concertato.*

II. Concerti di FILTZ.

I. *a Violonc. conc. 2 Viol. V. e B.* II. *a Violonc. conc. 2 C. 2 Ob. 2 Viol. V. e B.*

I. Conc. di GRETSCH. *a Violonc. conc. 2 C. 2 Clar. 2 V. V. e B.* I. Conc. di KLEINKNECHT. *a Violonc. conc. 2 Viol. V. e B.*

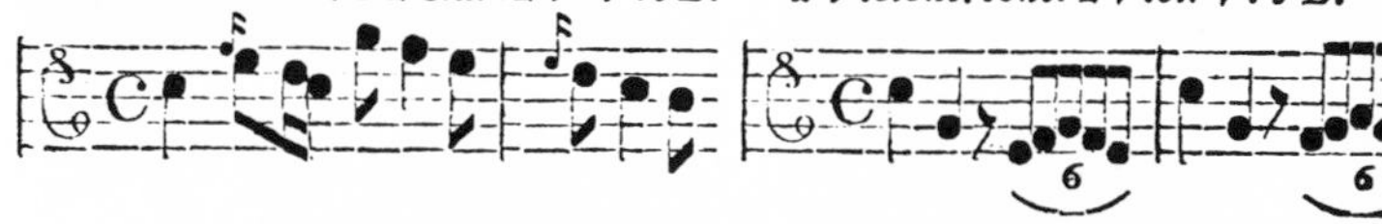

II. Concerti di Leop. HOFFMANN.

I. *a Violonc. conc. 2 Viol. V. e B.* II. *a Violonc. conc. 2 Viol. V. e B.*

I. Conc. di MEGOLI. *a Violonc. conc. 2 Cor. 2 Ob. 2 Viol. V. e B.* I. Conc. di SCHINDLER. *a Violonc. conc. 2 Cor. 2 Viol. V. e B.*

I. Concerto di TZSCHETKY, *a Violonc. conc. 2 Viol. V. e Baſſo.*

I. Concerto di L. BOCHERINI, *a Violonc. conc. 2 Viol. V. e B. intagliati in Parigi.*

FLAUTO TRAVERSO.

I. Solo di GRAFF, *con* XVIII. Variazioni.

VI. Duetti di T. GREINER, *a due Flauti. Op. 1. Amſterd.*

T R I I.

A DUE FLAUTI E BASSO.

I. Trio di Giac. Feder. KLEINKNECHT, *a 2 Flauti e Baſſo.*

VI. Trii di SCHWINDEL, *a 2 Flauti e Baſſo.*

TRII A FLAUTO, VIOLINO E BASSO.

IV. Trii di VANHALL, *a Flauto, Viol. e Baſſo.*

VI. Trii, III. *a Flauto, Violino e Baſſo*, e III. *a due Flauti e Baſſo*, di I. C. MULLER. *Op. I. Amſterdam.*

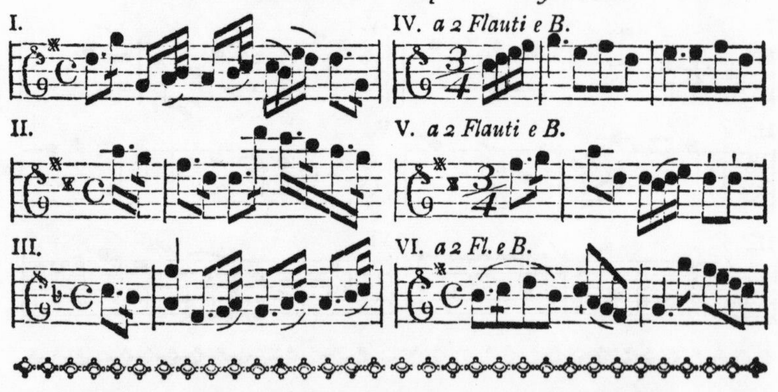

QUATTRI, intagliati in Parigi &c.

VI. Quattri di GOSSEC, *a Flauto ò Violino, Violino, Viola, e Baſſo. Op. XIV. Parigi.*

V. Quattri di Giuſ. HAYDEN, *a Flauto, Violino, Viola e Baſſo. Opera V. Amſterdam.*

VI. Quattri di Giov. MARTINI, *Tedeſco, a Fl. Viol. Viola e Baſſo. Opera I. Parigi.*

VI. Quattri di Giuſ. SCHMIDT, *a Flauto, Violino, Viola e Baſſo. Opera III. Amſterd.*

QUINTETTI.

VI. Quint. di C.E. GRAAF, *a Fl. Viol. V. Violonc. e B. Op. VIII. Amſt.*

CONCERTI.

A FLAUTO TRAVERSO CONCERTATO.

I. Conc. di CANNABICH. *a Fl. conc. 2 Viol. V. e B.* I. Conc. di FILTZ. *a Fl. conc. 2 Cor. 2 Viol. V. e B.*

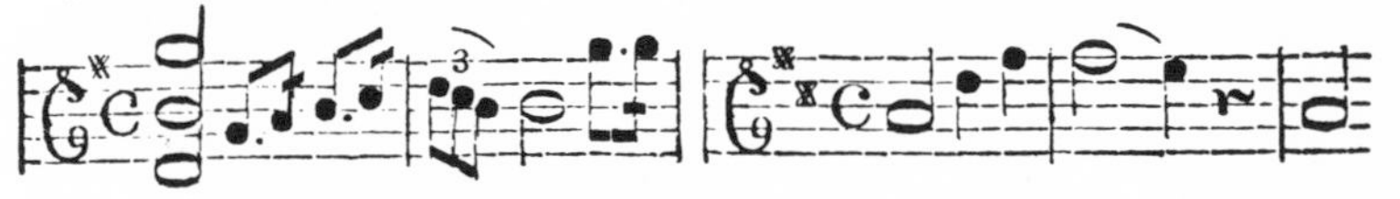

I. Conc. di GLOESCH, *a Fl. conc. 2 Viol. V. e B.*

II. Concerti di STAMITZ, *a Fl. conc. 2 Viol. V. e B.*

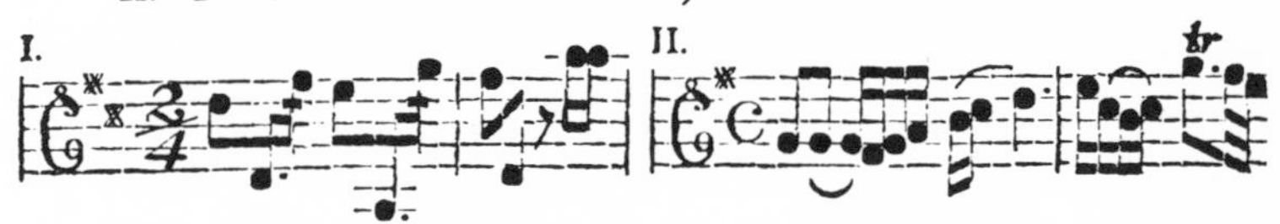

CONCERTI, intagliati in Amſterdam.

I. Conc. di B. HUPFELD, *a Fl. conc. 2 Cor. 2 Viol. V. e B.*

III. Conc. di KLOEFFLER, *a Fl. conc. 2 Cor. 2 Viol. V. e B. Op. II.*

I. Conc. di I. W. LEEDER.
a Fl. conc. 2 Cor. 2 Viol. V. e B.

OBOE.

VI. Sonate di Alessandro BESOZZI, *a 2 Oboi e Basso.*

VI. Trii di BLAS, *a 2 Oboi e Basso.*

II. Partite di SIMON, *a Oboe oblig. Fag. oblig. 2 Viol. e Basso.*

CONCERTI.

I. Conc. di Leop. HOFFMANN.
a Oboe conc. 2 Viol. V. e B.

I. Conc. di FILS.
a Oboe conc. 2 Cor. obl. 2 Viol. V. e B.

CEMBALO.

SOLI.

Sonate, a Cembalo Solo, intagliate in Amst. &c.

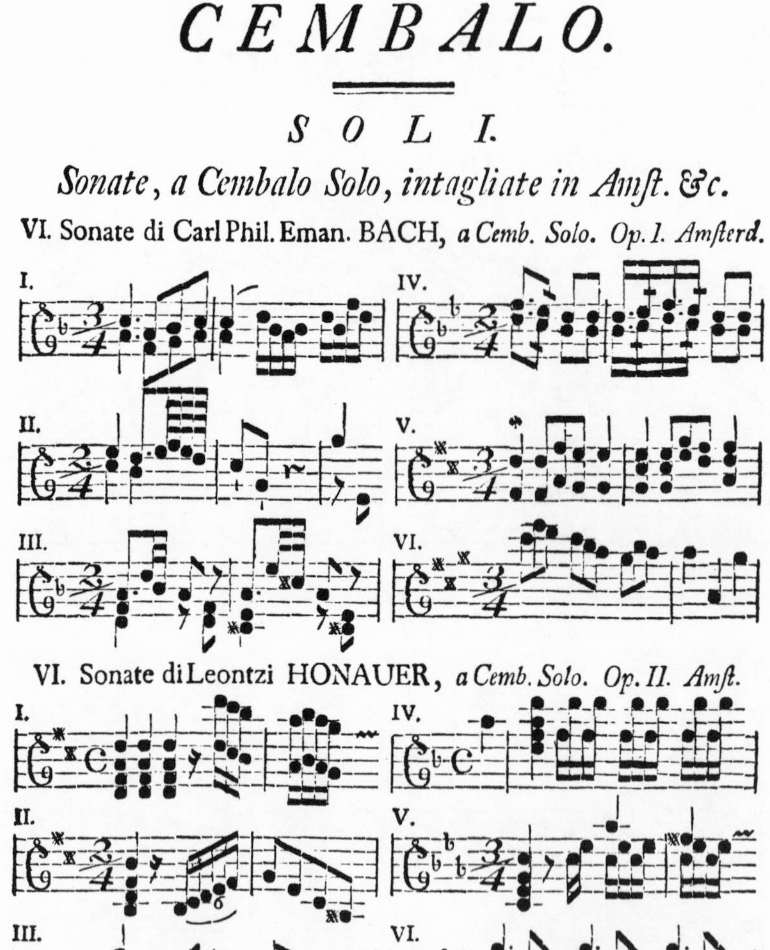

VI. Sonate di Carl Phil. Eman. BACH, *a Cemb. Solo. Op. I. Amsterd.*

VI. Sonate di Leontzi HONAUER, *a Cemb. Solo. Op. II. Amst.*

VI. Sonate di Ferdin. HORN, *a Cemb. Solo. Op. I. Londra.*

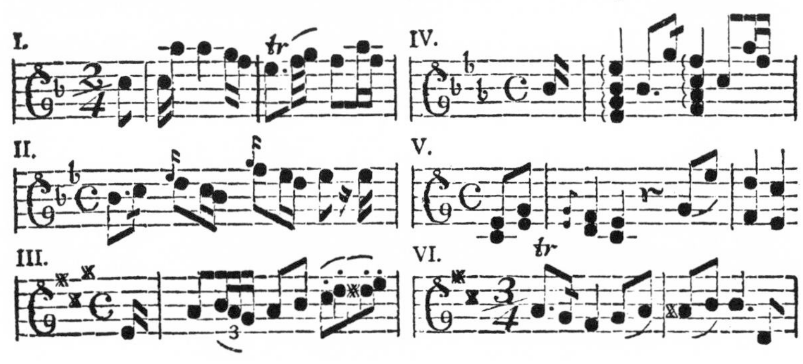

VI. Sonatines, *pour le Clavecin a l'usage des Commencans, par* I. A. IUST, *Amsterd.*

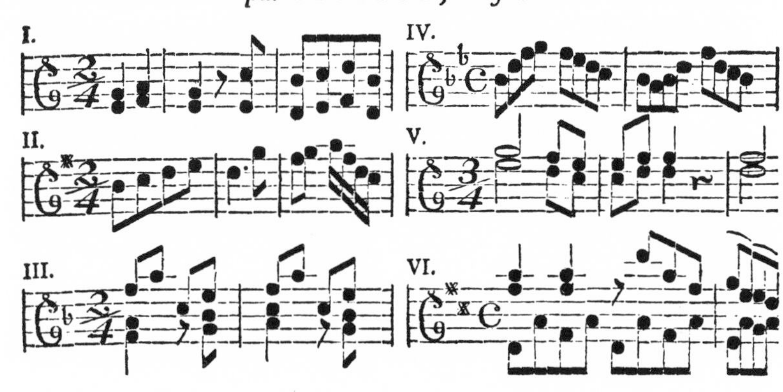

VI. Fuges par H. P. JOHNSEN, *pour les Orgues ou le Clavecin. Amsterd.*

VI. Partite di Giorg. Simon. LELEI, *per il Cembalo Solo, intagl. in Lipsia. Opera I.*

VI. Sonate di G. S. LELEI, *per il Cembalo. Op. II.*

VI. Partite di G. S. LELEI, *Opera III.*

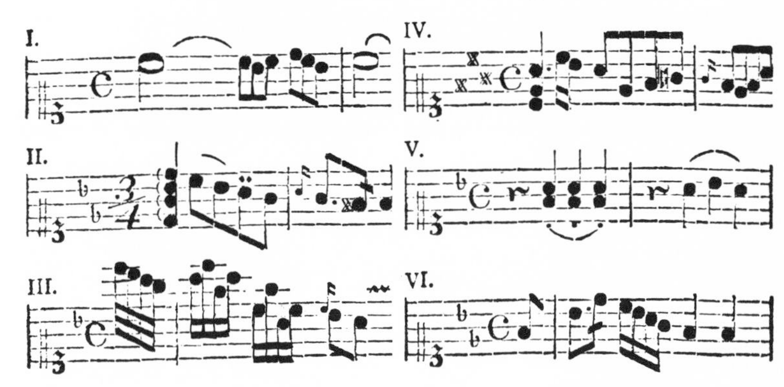

VI. Sonate di Bened. LEONI, *a Cembalo Solo. Londra.*

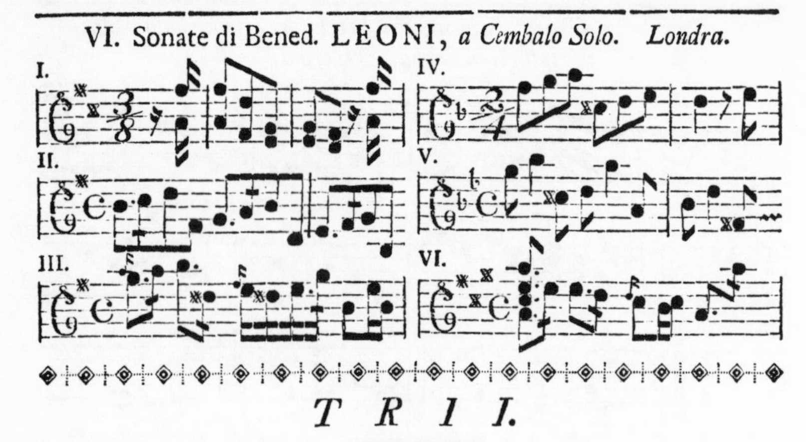

T R I I.

A CEMBALO OBLIGATO, CON VIOLINO O TRAVERSO.

I. Trio di BENDA, *a Cembalo e Flauto.*

TRII, intagliati in Amſterdam.

VI. Trii di I. W. LEEDER, *a Cemb. e Viol. oblig. Amſterd.*

VI. Trii di SCHOBERT, *a Cemb. e Viol. Op. IV. Amſterd.*

TERZETTI, a Cembalo obligato.

CON VIOLINO ó FLAUTO e BASSO, intagliati in Parigi &c.

III. Sonate di Ern. EICHNER, *a Cemb. Violino e Violonc. Opera II. Parigi.*

III. Sonate di W. N. HAUEISEN, *a Cembalo, Violino, e Violoncello. Op. I. Amſterd.*

VI. Terzetti, di Giov. MARTINI, *Tedesco. a Cembalo, Violino e Violoncello. Op. II. Parigi.*

VI. Sonate di Gaetano PUGNANI, *a Cemb. Viol. o Fl. Trav. e Violoncello. Op. VI. Amsterd.*

QUATTRI E DIVERTIMENTI.

I. Divertim. di G. BENDA, *a Cemb. 2 Viol. V. e Basso.*

II. Divertim. di Leop. HOFFMANN.

I. *à Cemb. 2 Violini e Basso.* II. *a Cemb. 2 Flaut. Trav. e Basso.*

III. Quartetti di Gius. BAUR, *a Cembalo ò Harpa, Fl. Trav. Violino e Basso. Op. II. Parigi.*

VI. Quattri di Pietro GUGLIELMI, *a Cemb. 2 Viol. e Basso, intagliati in Londra.*

IV. Divertim. di Giov. MARTINI, *Tedesco, a Cembalo, 2 Violini e Basso. Op. III. Parigi.*

CONCERTI, *a Cembalo concertato, con più Stromenti.*

I. Conc. di BAUER. *a Cemb. conc. 2 Cor. 2 Fl. 2 Viol. V. e B.*

I. Conc. di Georg. BENDA. *a Cemb. conc. 2 Viol. V. e B.*

I. Conc. di BINDER.
a Cemb. conc. 2 Ob. 2 Viol. V. e B.
I. Conc. di CHARPENTIER.
a Cemb. conc. 2 Viol. e Basso.
V. Concerti di Leop. HOFFMANN.
I. a Cemb. conc. 2 Viol. e B.
IV. a Cemb. conc. 2 Viol. V. e B.
II. a Cemb. conc. 2 Cor. 2 Viol. V. e B.
V. a Cemb. conc. 2 Cor. 2 Viol. e B.
I. Conc. di HOLTZBAUER.
a Cemb. conc. 2 Viol. V. e B.
III. a Cemb. conc. 2 Viol. V. e B.
I. Conc. di KUFFNER.
a Cemb. conc. 2 Viol. V. e B.
I. Conc. di POCORNI.
a Cemb. conc. 2 Cor. 2 Ob. 2 Viol. V. e B.
VI. Concerti di I. C. BACH, a Cemb. conc. 2 Viol. e Violonc.
Op. VII. intagliati in Amsterd.
I.
IV.
II.
V.
III.
VI.
I. Conc. di Ern. EICHNER, a Cemb. ô Harp. 2 C. 2 Fl. 2 Viol. V. e B. Par.

ARIE DELL' OPERA il VILANO GELOSO,
del Sign. G. A. NAUMANN, Dresd. 1770.
Atto primo.
I. Terzetto. a 2 Cor. 2 Fl. 2 Ob. 2 Viol. V. 2 Sop. B. Fond.
La cam-pa-gna co-sì
2. Aria. a 2 C. 2 Ob. 2 Fl. 2 Vi. V. Fag. e B.
Sono qual To-ro indormito.
3. Aria. a 2 C. 2 Fl. 2 Ob. 2 Vi. V. Fag. e B.
Se tu vedesti il co-re
4. Aria. a 2 Fl. 2 Ob. 2 Vi. V. Fag. e B.
Semplicina, modestina, senza
5. Aria. a 2 Ob. 2 Vi. Viola, Fag. e B.
Donne ca-re, io non vi
6. Fin. a 3 Sop. Ten. Bss. 2 Cor. 2 Ob. 2 Vi. Viola, Fag. e B.
Se Giannina affè mi vuole,
Atto secondo.
7. Aria. a 2 C. 2 Fl. 2 Ob. 2 Vi. V. Fag. e B.
Per pietà bell' I-dol-mi-o
8. Aria. 2 Cor. 2 Ob. 2 Viol. V. Fag. e B.
Quan-to mai fe-li-
9. Aria. a 2 Fl. 2 Ob. 2 Viol. V. Fag. e B.
Se cre-dessi di vo-la-re
10. Aria. a 2 C. 2 O. 2 Vi. V. 1 Fag. obl. e B.
La not-te oh Di-o non
11. Aria. a 2 Fl. 2 Ob. 2 Vi. V. Fag. e B.
Jo fò quel che costumano
12. Aria. a 2 Ob. 2 Violini, V. Fag. e B.
Gianni-na lo spera
13. Aria. a 2 C. 2 Ob. 2 Fl. 2 Vi. V. Fag. e B.
Ado-ra-te mie capan-ne
14. Finale, a 2 Sop. 2 Ten. Bass. 2 Cor 2 Ob. 2 Violini, Viola, Fag. e Basso.
Il caso si fa brutto, e
Atto terzo.
15. Aria. 2 C. 2 Ob. 2 Vi. V. Fag. e B.
Ah che pur troppo e vero
16. Aria. 2 Fl. 2 Ob. 2 C. 2 Viol. V. Fag. e B.
Fra can-ti, suo-ni, e giubili
17. Finale, a 2. Sop. 2 Ten. B. 2 C. 2 Fl. 2 Vi. V. Fag. e B.
Vanne pur vanne pur lascia d'a-

ARIE DELL' OPERA LA PESCATRICE.
del Sigr. PICCINI.

IL LIUTO.

Von Herrn Hillers Operetten sind auf die Laute aptirt zu haben:

XIX. Arien von der Opera: Lottchen am Hofe.
XVI. — — — — Die Liebe auf dem Lande.
IX. — — — — Die Jagd.

SVPPLEMENTO VI.

DEI

CATALOGI

DELLE

SINFONIE, PARTITE, OVERTURE, SOLI, DUETTI, TRII, QUATTRI

E

CONCERTI

PER IL

VIOLINO, FLAUTO TRAVERSO,

CEMBALO

ED ALTRI STROMENTI,

CHE

SI TROVANO IN MANOSCRITTO
NELLA OFFICINA MUSICA DI BREITKOPF
IN LIPSIA.

1771.

SINFONIE.

II. Sinfonie di Carlo DITTERS, *a 2 Cor. 2 Ob. 2 Viol. V. e B.*

I. II.

I. Sinf. di GRENTZER, *a 2 Cor. 2 Ob. 2 Viol. V. e B.*

II. Sinf. di B. HUPFELD.

I. *a 2 C. 2 Ob. 6 Fl. 2 Fag. 2 Viol. V. e B.* II. *a 2 Cor. 2 Flaut. 2 Fag. 2 Viol. V. e B.*

III. Sinf. di Giov. Batt. NERUDA.

I. *a 2 Ob. oblig. 2 Viol. 2 Viole e B.* III. *a 2 Cor. 2 Ob. 2 Flaut. 2 Viol. V. e B.*

II. *a 2 Cor. 2 Ob. 2 Viol. V. e B.*

VI. Sinf. di Carlo STEGMANN. *Racc. I.*

I. *a 2 C. Tymb. 2 Tr. 2 Ob. 2 Viol. V. e B.* IV. *a 2 Cor. 2 Ob. 2 Viol. V. e B.*

II. *a 2 Fl. oblig. 2 Viol. V. e B.* V. *a 2 Cor. 2 Ob. 2 Viol. V. e B.*

III. *a 2 Cor. 2 Ob. 2 Viol. V. e B.* VI. *a 2 C. Tymp. 2 Tr. 2 Ob. 2 Viol. V. e B.*

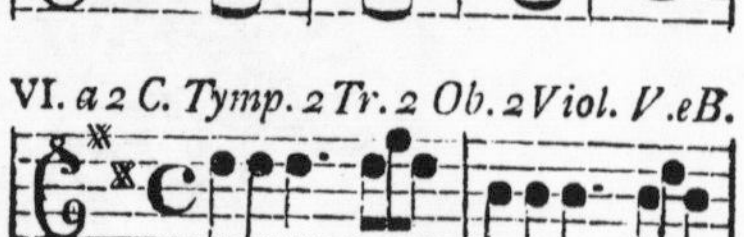

III. Sinf. di Carlo STEGMANN. *Racc. II.*

I. *a 2 Cor. 2 Ob. 2 Viol. V. e B.* III. *a 2 Viol. V. e B.*

II. *a 2 Cor. 2 Ob. 2 Viol. V. e B.*

I. Sinf. di TUERCKE, *a 2 Cor. 2 Ob. 2 Viol. V. e B.*

VIII. Sinf. di Giov. VANHALL.

I. *a 2 Cor. 2 Ob. 2 Viol. V. e B.* V. *a 4 C. 2 O. Vilcl. e Viola obl. 2 Vi. V. e B.*

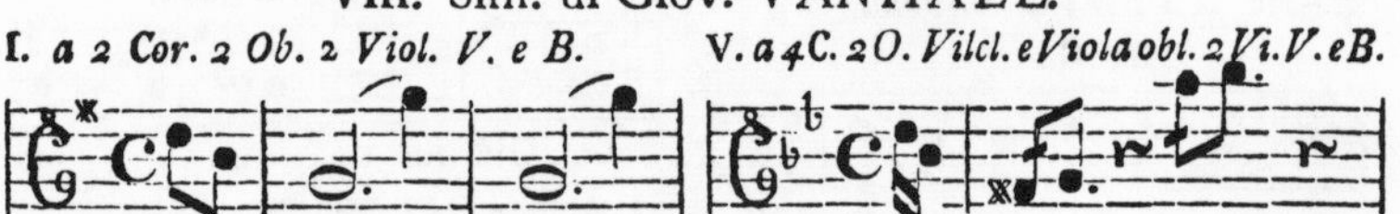

II. *a 2 C. Tymp. 2 Cl. 2 Ob. 2 Viol. V. e B.* VI. *a 2 C. 2 O. Violonc. e Fl. obl. 2 Vi. V. e B.*

III. *a 2 Cor. 2 Ob. Violonc. 2 Viol. V. e B.* VII. *a 2 Cor. 2 Ob. 2 Viol. V. e B.*

IV. *a 4 Cor. 2 Ob. 2 Viol. V. e B.* VIII. *a 2 Viol. V. e Basso.*

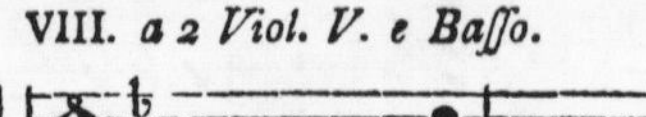

MINUETTI.

XXIV. Dresdn. Redout. Men. etc. di SIMONETTI, ao. 1772.

VI. Polonoisen di SIMONETTI, ao. 1772.

SINFONIE intagliate in Amsterdam.

VI. Sinfonie di C. Fr. ABEL, *a 2 Cor. 2 Ob. 2 Viol. V. e B. Op. VII. Amsterd.*

VI. Sinf. di KREUSSER, *a 2 Cor. 2 Ob. 2 Viol. V. e B. Op. II. Amst.*

SINFONIES PERIODIQUES, intagl. in Lond.

I. d'ARNE, *a 2 Cor. 2 Ob. 2 Fag. 2 Viol. V. e B.* I. di HERSCHEL, *a 2 Cor. 2 Ob. 2 Viol. V. e B.*

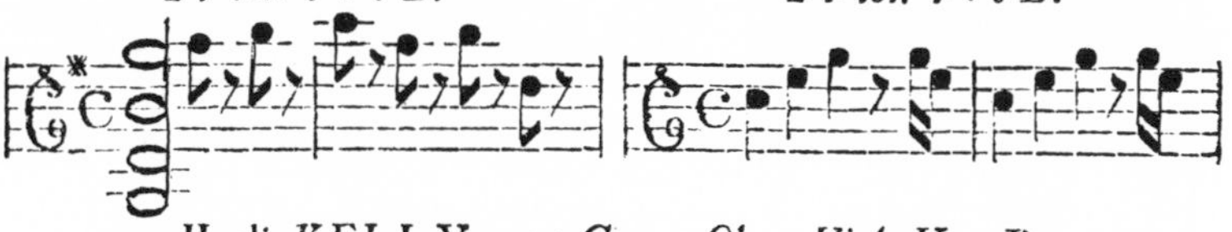

II. di KELLY, *a 2 Cor. 2 Ob. 2 Viol. V. e B.*

CONCERTINI e DIVERTIMENTI.

VI. Concertini di Leop. HOFFMANN.

I. *a Violino conc. Violonc. conc. Viola conc. 2 Viol. 2 Cor. 2 Ob. e B.* IV. *a Violino conc. Violoncello conc. Viola conc. 2 Violini e B.*

II. *a Violino conc. Violonc. conc. 2 Viol. 2 Cor. 2 Ob. Viola e B.* V. *a Violonc. conc. Viola conc. 2 Viol. 2 Cor. 2 Ob. Tymp. e B.*

III. *a Viola prima conc. Viola sec. conc. Violonc. conc. 2 Viol. 2 C. 2 Ob. e B.* VI. *a Violonc. conc. Viola conc. 2 Viol. e Basso.*

I. Concertino di Giuf. TOESCHI, *a Fl. Viol. Viola, Violonc. obl. e B.*

I. Divertim. di Giov. VANHALL. I. Divert. di DUSCHECK, *a 2 Cor. oblig. 2 Viol. V. e B.*

VIOLINO.

SOLI con BASSO.

VI. Soli di Carlo DITTERS.

I. Solo di Antonio KAMMEL.
II. Soli di Francefco LAMOTTA.
VI. Soli di VACHON, intagliati in Londra.
DUETTI.
A DUE VIOLINI.
VI. Duetti di PESCH.
II. Duetti di SCHIATTI.

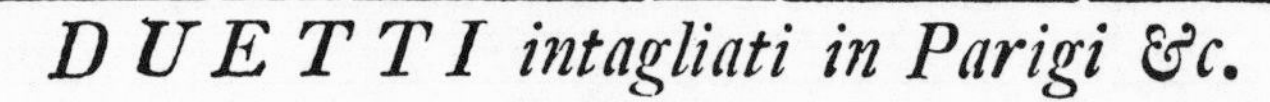
DUETTI intagliati in Parigi &c.

VI. Duetti del Conte BENEVENTO. Londra.

VI. Duetti di Luigi BOCHERINI. Opera V. Parigi.

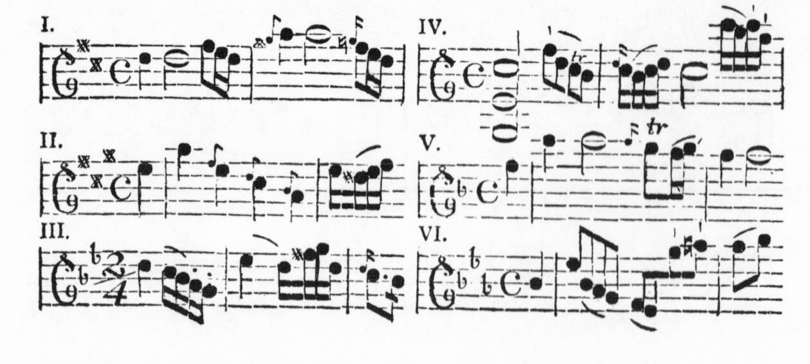
VI. Duetti di I. G. BUERCKHOEFFER, il Tedefco. Op. III. Parigi.

VI. Duetti di Francesco GOSSEC. *Op. VII. Parigi.*

I. IV. II. V. III. VI.

TRII.

A DUE VIOLINI CON BASSO.

VI. Trii di Carlo DITTERS.

I. IV. II. V. III. VI.

II. Trii di LAUBE.

I. II.

VI. Trii di PESCH.

I. IV. II. V. III. VI.

VI. Trii di Giov. VANHALL.

I. IV. II. V. III. VI.

VI. Trii di F. ZANNETTI, *intagliati in Londra. Op. IV.*

I. IV. II. V. III. VI.

QUATTRI.

II. Quattri di DUSCHEK, *a 2 Viol. Viola e Basso.*

VI. Quattri di Giuſ. HAYDEN, *a 2 Viol. Viola e Basso.*

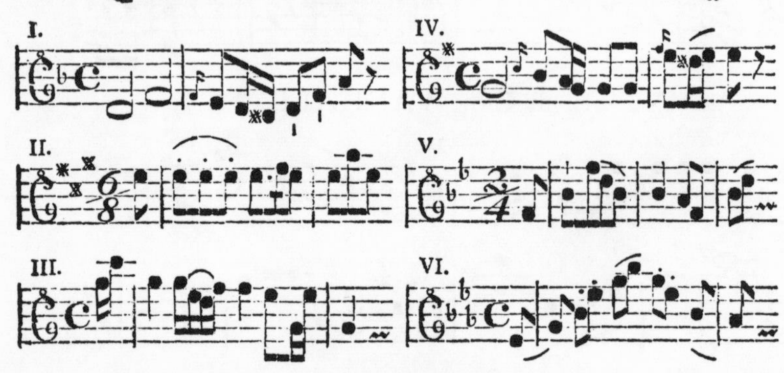

V. Quattri del Sigr. de KOSPOTH, *a 2 Viol. Viola e Basso.*

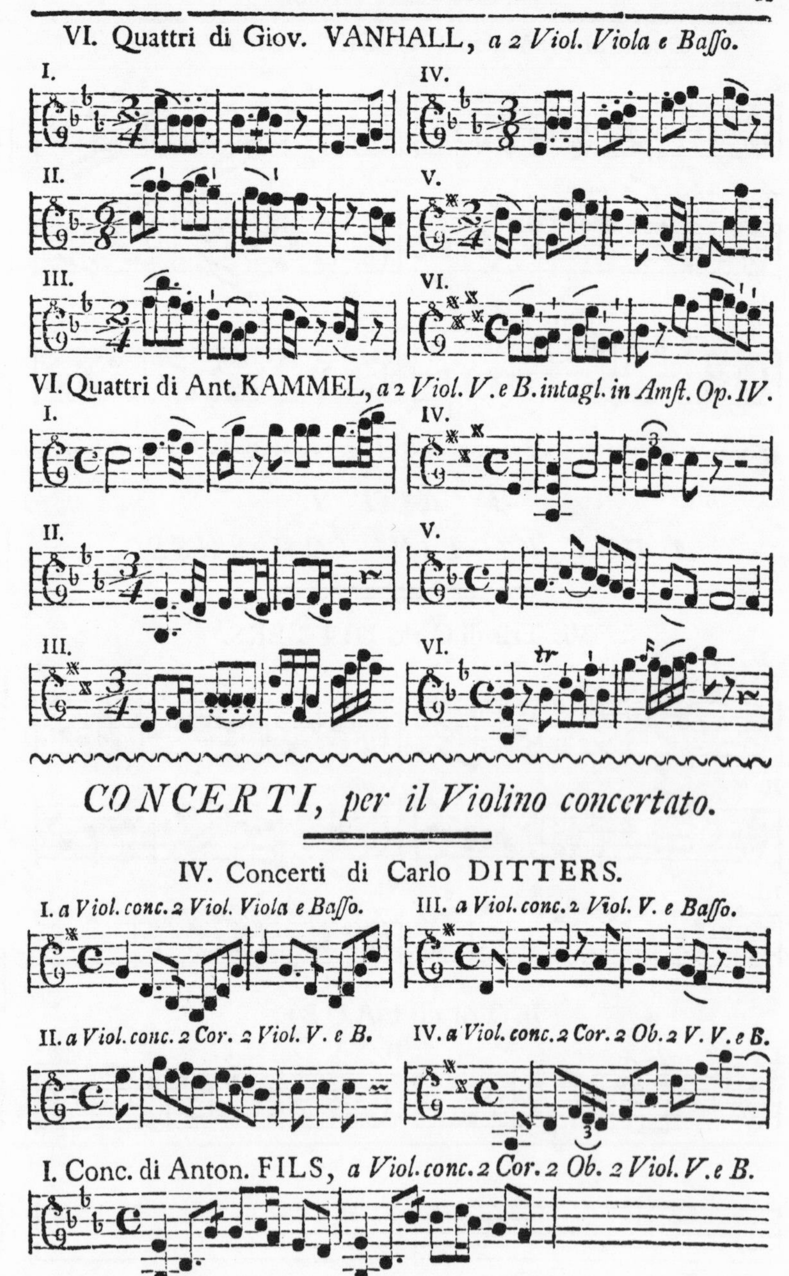

VI. Quattri di Giov. VANHALL, *a 2 Viol. Viola e Basso.*

VI. Quattri di Ant. KAMMEL, *a 2 Viol. V. e B. intagl. in Amst. Op. IV.*

CONCERTI, *per il Violino concertato.*

IV. Concerti di Carlo DITTERS.

I. Conc. di Anton. FILS, *a Viol. conc. 2 Cor. 2 Ob. 2 Viol. V. e B.*

12 VIOLA.
II. Conc. di Mich. HAYDEN, a Viol. conc. 2 Viol. V. e B.
I.
II.
II. Conc. di Leop. HOFFMANN, a Viol. conc. 2 Viol. V. e B.
I.
II.
I. Conc. di Wentzel HOFFMANN, a Viol. conc. 2 Viol. V. e B.
I. Conc. di Giov. Fred. REICHARDT, a Viol. conc. 2 Viol. V. e B.
II. Conc. di Giuf. TOESCHI.
I. a Viol. conc. 2 Cor. 2 Flaut. 2 V. V. e B.
II. a Viol. conc. 2 Viol. V. e B.
I. Conc. di Giuf. VANHALL, a Viol. conc. 2 Viol. V. e B.
VIOLA.
III. Trii di Leop. HOFFMANN, a Viola, Flauto Trav. e B.
I.
III.
II.
I. Trio di SIMON.
a Viola, Violino e Basso.

VIOLONCELLO. 13
VIOLONCELLO.
I. Solo di Anton. FILS, a Violoncello e Basso.
II. Soli di GRETSCH, a Violoncello e Basso.
I.
II.
V. Soli di Leop. HOFFMANN, a Violoncello e Basso.
I.
IV.
II.
V.
III.
II. Soli di SCHETTKY, a Violoncello e Basso.
I.
II.
I. Solo di VODISCA, a Violoncello e Basso.
I. Solo di WENZEL, a Violoncello e Basso.

DUETTI.

VI. Duetti di CAMPIONI, *a Violino e Violoncello.*

I. Duetto di Ant. FILS, *a Viol. e Vioncello.*

I. Duetto di KLEINKNECHT, *a 2 Violoncelli.*

TRII.

II. Trii di ANONYMO.

I. *a Violoncello, Viola e Basso.* II. *a Violoncello, Violino e Basso.*

I. Trio di Leop. HOFFMANN, *a 2 Violoncelli e Basso.*

II. Trii di SCHETTKY, *a Violoncello, Violino e Basso.*

II. Trii di SIPRATINI, *a 2 Violoncelli e Basso.*

CONCERTI, *per il Violoncello concertato.*

I. Conc. di GRAF, *a Violoncello conc. 2 Viol. Viola e Basso.*

I. Conc. di Giuſ. HAYDEN, *a Violonc. conc. 2 Corni, 2 V. V. e B.*

III. Conc. di Leop. HOFFMANN, *a Violonc. conc. 2 Viol. V. e B.*

II. *2 Corni.*

I. Conc. di Ign. HOLTZBAUER, *a Violonc. conc. 2 Viol. V. e B.*

I. Conc. di MEGOLI, *a Violonc. conc. 2 Cor. 2 Ob. 2 Viol. V. e B.*

IV. Conc. di SCHETTKY.

I. *a Violonc. conc. 2 Viol. V. e B.* III. *a Violonc. conc. 2 Flaut. 2 V. e B.*

II. *a Violonc. conc. 2 Cor. 2 V. V. e B.* IV. *a Violonc. c. 2 Cor. 2 Ob. 2 V. V. e B.*

II. Conc. di SCHINDLER, *a Violonc. conc. 2 Viol. V. e B.*

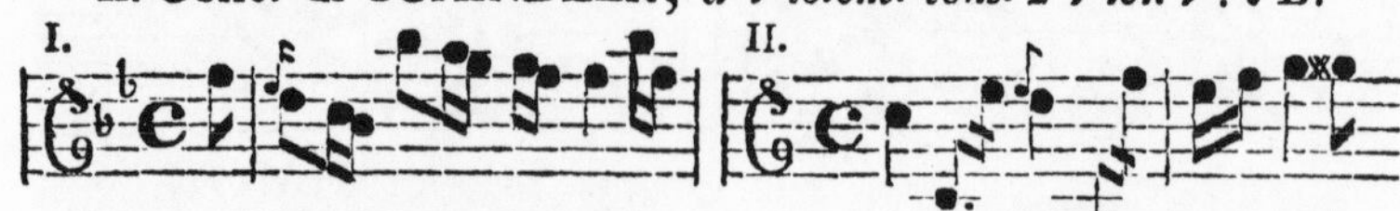

I. Conc. di WENTZEL, *a Violonc. conc. 2 Viol. V. e B.*

FLAUTO TRAVERSO.

IV. Soli di C. F. ABEL.

I. Solo di DOTEL.

III. Soli di Leop. HOFFMANN.

DUETTI.

VI. Duetti a due Flauti di LIBERT.

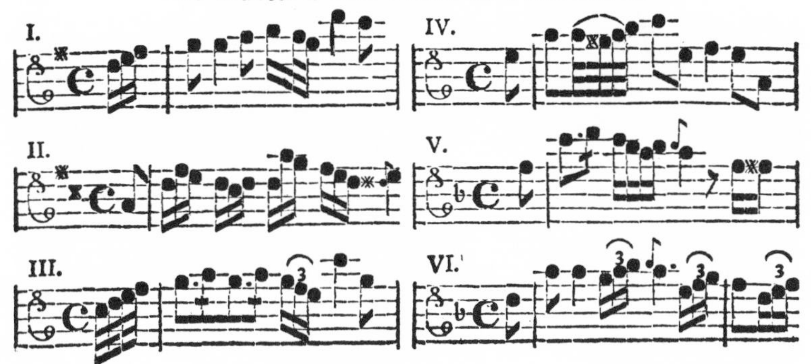

VI. Duetti di WOLF, *a due Flauti.*

TRII.

VI. Trii di Giuſ. TOESCHI, *a 2 Flauti e Baſſo.*

I. Trio di BRAUN, *a Flauto, Violino e B.*

I. Trio di SCHWANENBERG, *a Flauto, Violonc. e Baſſo.*

II. Trii di MARTINI, *a Flaut. Violoncello e Baſſo.*

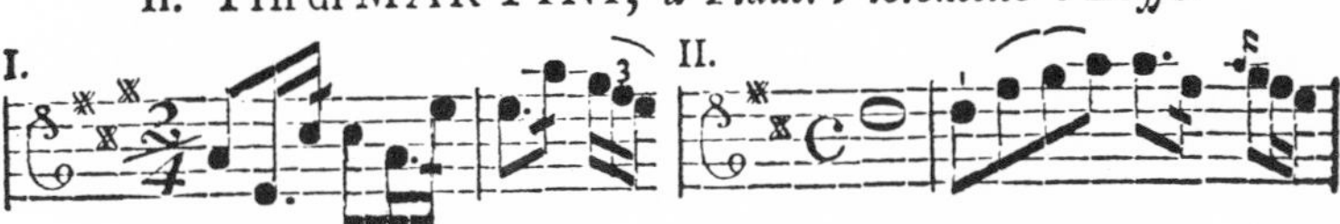

I. Trio di WOLF, *a Flauto, Violino e Baſſo.*

VI. Trii di I. B. WENDLING, *a Flauto, Viol. e B. Op. 11. Amst.*

QUATTRI.

III. Quattri di KELLNER.

I. *a Flauto, Violino Viola e Basso.* III. *a Flauto o Oboe, 2 Viol. e Basso.*

II. *a Flauto, Oboe, Violino e Basso.*

II. Quattri di WOLF, *a Flauto, Oboe, Fag. e Violoncello.*

VI. Quattri di Fred. SCHWINDEL, *a Flauto ô Viol. primo, Viol. second. Viola e B. intagl. in Amsterd. Op. VII.*

QUINTETTI.

VI. Quint. del Sig. de KOSBOTH, *a Fl. Viol. Viola, Violonc. e B.*

III. Quintetti di KELLNER.

I. *a Fl. Ob. Viol. Violoncello e Basso.* III. *a Flauto, Oboe, Viol. Viola e Basso.*

II. *a Flauto ô Oboe, 2 Viol. Viola e B.*

CONCERTI.

A FLAUTO TRAVERSO CONCERTATO.

I. Conc. di CANNABICH. *a Fl. conc. 2 Cor. 2 Viol. V. e B.*

I. Conc. di Carlo DITTERS. *a Fl. conc. 2 Cor. 2 Viol. V. e B.*

I. Conc. di Ant. FILS. *a Fl. conc. 2 Cor. 2 Viol. V. e B.*

I. Conc. di FISCHER. *a Fl. conc. 2 Cor. 2 Viol. V. e B.*

I. Conc. di GEHRA. *a Fl. conc. 2 Viol. V. e B.*

I. Conc. di HAYDEN. *a Fl. conc. 2 Viol. V. e B.*

I. Conc. di Wenzesl. HOFFMANN, *a 2 Flaut. conc. 2 Viol. V. e B.*

II. Concerti di HUPFELD, *a Flaut. conc. 2 Viol. V. e B.*

I. II.

II. Concerto di LANGE.

I. *a Flaut. conc. 2 Cor. 2 Ob. 2 Viol. V. e B.* II. *a Fl. conc. 2 Cor. 2 Viol. V. e B.*

I. Concerti di Giuſ. TOESCHI, *a Fl. conc. 2 Cor. 2 Viol. V. e B.*

II. Concerti di WENDLING, *a Fl. conc. 2 Viol. V. e B.*

I. III.

III. Concerti di I. F. KLÖFFLER, *a 2 Fl. conc. 2 Cor. 2 Viol. V. e B.*
intagliati in Amſterdam. Opera. III.

I. II. II.

OBOE.

VI. Quintetti di Giov. VANHALL, *a 2 Ob. 2 Cor. e Fagotto.*

I. IV. II. V. III. VI.

CONCERTI.

I. Concerto di FISCHER. *a Oboe conc. 2 Viol. V. e B.*

I. Concerto di Giov. Batt. BLAS. *a Oboe conc. 2 Viol. V. e B.*

IV. Concerti Militari da diverſi Maeſtri, *intagl. in Londra.*
a 2 Oboi o Flauti, 2 Corni, 2 Clarini & 2 Fagotti.

I. III. II. IV.

CEMBALO.

SOLI.

Petites Pieces pour le Clavecin, de Mr. George BENDA, à Gotha.

I. Allegro. II. Minuetto con Variazioni.

I. HAYDEN *Minuetto con 20. Variaz. a Cembalo Solo.*

I. Leop. HOFFMANN *Min. e Trio a Cemb. Solo con 3 Variaz.*

II. Leop. HOFFMANN Soli.

I. II.

VI. Sonate di Giov. VANHALL, *a Cembalo Solo.*

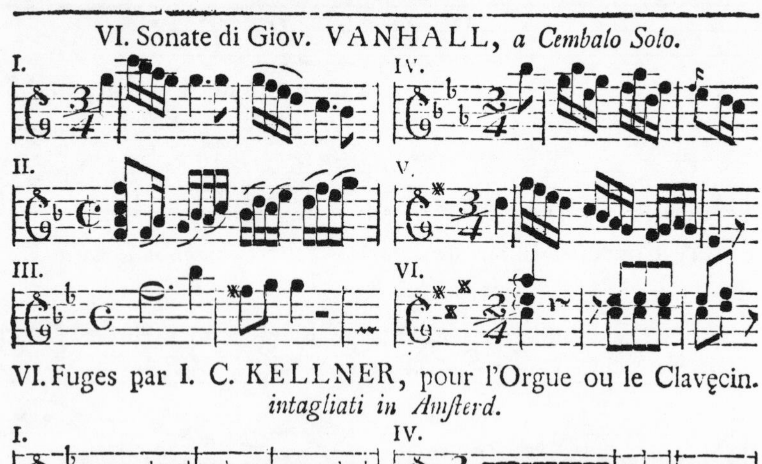

VI. Fuges par I. C. KELLNER, pour l'Orgue ou le Claveçin. *intagliati in Amsterd.*

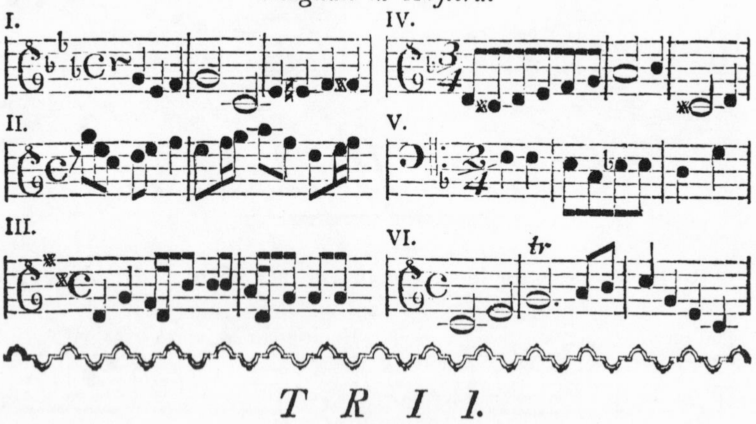

TRII.

VI. Trii di Pietro GUGLIELMI, *a Cembalo e Violino, intagl. in Londra.*

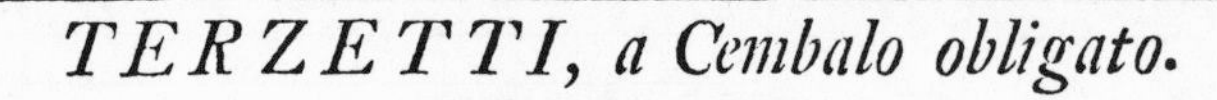

TERZETTI, *a Cembalo obligato.*

IV. Divert. di Giuſ. HAYDEN, *a Cemb. Violino e Baſſo.*

II. Terz. di Carlo BURNEY, *a Cemb. Viol. e B. intagl. in Londra.*

QUATTRI et DIVERTIMENTI.

I. Divertim. di G. BENDA, *a Cemb. 2 Viol. Viola e Baſſo.*

II. Divert. di Leop. HOFFMANN, *a Cemb. 2 Viol. e Baſſo.*

II. Quattri di LANGE, *a Cemb. Flauto, Violino e Violonc. conc.*

CONCERTI, *a Cemb. conc. con piu Stromenti.*

I. Conc. di G. BENDA. *a Cemb. conc. 2 Viol. V. e B.*

II. *a Cemb. 2 Viol. e B.*

III. Conc. di Giuſ. HAYDEN. I. *a Cemb. conc. 2 Viol. e Baſſo.*

III. *a Cemb. conc. 2 Viol. V. e B.*

VI. Conc. di Leop. HOFFMANN.

I. *a Cemb. conc. 2 Viol. V. e B.*

IV. *a Cemb. ed Oboe conc. 2 V. V. e B.*

II. *a Cemb. conc. 2 Viol. e B.*

V. *a Cemb. conc. 2 Cor. 2 Viol. e B.*

III. *a Cemb. conc. 2 Cor. 2 Viol. e B.*

VI. *a Cemb. conc. 2 Cor. 2 Viol. e B.*

I. Conc. di KIRNBERGER, *a Cemb. conc. 2 Viol. V. e Basso.*

III. Conc. di LANGE.

I. *a Cemb. conc. 2 Viol. V. e B.*

III. *a Cemb. conc. 2 Cor. 2 Viol. V. e B.*

II. *a Cemb. conc. 2 Cor. 2 Flaut. 2 V. V. e B.*

I. Conc. di Pompeo SALES. *a Cemb. conc. 2 Cor. 2 Viol. V. e B.*

I. Conc. di TOUCHEMOLIN. *a Cemb. conc. 2 Flaut. 2 Viol. V. e B.*

I. Conc. di WILLFURT. *a Cemb. conc. 2 Cor. 2 Flaut. 2 V. V. B.*

I. Conc. di WSCHETYNSKI. *a Cemb. conc. 2 Cor. 2 V. V. e B.*

II. Conc. di WOLF, *a Cemb. conc. 2 Viol. V. e B.*

I.

II.

ARIE DELL'OPERA: L'ISOLA D'AMORE del Sgr. SACCINI.

Atto primo.

1. Duetto. *2 Corni, 2 Oboi 2 Viol. Viola, Canto, Tenore e Fond.*

Bravi, bravi, bel pen-fiero

2. Cavatina. *2 Viol. Canto, Tenore e Basso.*

Mi fò rof-fa, mi vergogno.

3. Aria. *2 Cor. 2 Ob. 2 Viol. V. Ten. e Basso.*

Nel partir, carina mia, ftrano.

4. Aria. *2 C. 2 Ob. 2 Viol. V. Canto e Basso.*

Lo fa il Ciel s'io diceva di - no

5. Aria. *2 Cor. 2 Ob. 2 V. V. Basso e Fondam.*

Ma che fo? non e paz-zi-a

6. Cavatina. *2 Cor. 2 Ob. 2 Viol. V. Canto e Basso.*

Dove fon? dove fon chi mi configlia

7. Aria. *2 Cor. 2 Ob. 2 Viol. V. Canto e Basso.*

Si piangendo io par-ti-ro.

8. Quartetto. *2 Cor. 2 Ob. 2 Viol. V. 2 Canti, Tenore, Basso, e Fondam.*

Non vorre-i nell mio contento.

Atto Secondo.

9. Aria. *2 Ob. 2 Viol. V. Canto e Basso.*

Pove-ri affet-ti, povera

10. Aria. *2 Cor. 2 Ob. 2 V. V. Tenore e Basso.*

Quefto acciaro, e quefto argento

11. Aria. *2 Viol. V. Canto e Basso.*

Re - fta pur con chi ti piace

12. Aria. *2 Cor. 2 Viol. V. Canto e Basso.*

Se pie-ta de in Ciel non

13. Aria. *2 Cor. 2 Ob. 2 Viol. Va. Tenore, e Basso.*

Con la ge-li-da Sal ma

14. Duetto. *2 Cor. 2 Ob. 2 Viol. V. Canto, e Basso, e Fond.*

Non fon poi co - fi tiranna

15. Duetto. *2 Viol. Canto, Tenor. e Fond.*

Se mi rendi il

16. Quartetto. *2 Cor. 2 Ob. 2 V. V. 2 Canti, Tenore, Basso, e Fondam.*

Spe - ranze lu-fing hiere

II. Arie di Antonio DUNI.

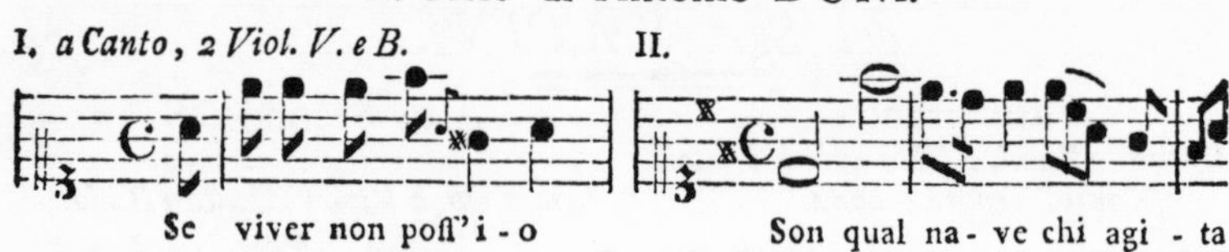

VI. Motetti di Ant. DUNI, *a Canto solo, 2 Viol. V. e B.*

GUITARRE.

XII. Chansons françois, tirés de differentes Opera comiques.

Die Laute.

Arien aus Herrn Hillers Operetten in die Laute übersetzt.

Aus der Jagd.

28
Aus der Liebe auf dem Lande.
Ach! meines Mägdchens Lämmchen ist.
Es ist ein schlanker Bauerjunge.
Wie wird mir bange.
Es trug einst Gretchen.
Was sich neckt, das liebet sich.
Ich suche, such auch du.
Nur für mein Mägdchen allein.
Man sperre mich mit Lieschen ein.
Ein Mägdchen das auf Ehre hielt.
Sehn sie meinen Thränen fließen.
Hab ich einmal ihn zum Mann.
Das kleine Lieschen sticht dem Schösser.

29
Die Liebe, die dieß Paar entzündet,
Der Strauß, den ich hier binde.
Nur in süßer Einsamkeit.
Ein alter Dieb hat unser Lamm.
Aus Lottchen am Hofe.
Lustig zur Arbeit ihr Schwestern.
Ach! Lotte geht davon.
Bald pflück ich mir Rosen zu Kränzen.
Nicht Schätze reizen mich.
Ich muß darüber lachen.
Stille, Gürgel, schäme dich.

30
Es ist die Mode so.
Wie artig ist er nicht.
Auf unsrer Bluhmenreichen Flur.
Schelm beßre dich.
So wie die Glock im Dorfe schlägt.
Lebe wohl mit aller deiner Pracht.
Ein blendend Weiß mit sanftem roth.
O macht mir doch von ewger Treu.
Schon beym frühen Morgenroth.
Wie schön, wen Rang und Hoheit schmückt.
Das ist schön, ey das muß ich doch.
Rauschend geht er auf und zu.

31
Aus dem Aerndtekranze.
Vom Puder glänzt sein lockigt Haar.
Meine Tochter, traue nicht.
Das beste Guth im Dorf ist sein.
Wie schnell entfloh die schöne Zeit.
Seht den jungen Zephyr streichen.
Ich war ein Junge, kaum so groß.
Ein junges Bauermägdchen kam oft.
Ich bin ein kleiner Naseweiß.
Ich hab ein viel zu gutes Herz.
Hier seh ich, mir zu Füßen, Vergiß mein
Ich bin noch allzusehr ein Kind.
Ein Edelmann, sehr wohl gebaut.

SVPPLEMENTO VII.

DEI

CATALOGI

DELLE

SINFONIE, PARTITE, OVERTURE, SOLI, DUETTI, TRII, QUATTRI E CONCERTI

PER IL

VIOLINO, FLAUTO TRAVERSO,

CEMBALO

ED ALTRI STROMENTI,

CHE

SI TROVANO IN MANOSCRITTO
NELLA OFFICINA MUSICA DI BREITKOPF
IN LIPSIA.

1772.

SINFONIE.

III. Sinf. di Carlo DITTERS.

I. *a 2 Cor. 2 Ob. Fiauto, 2 Viol. V. e B.* III. *a 2 Cor. 2 Ob. 2 Viol. V. e B.*

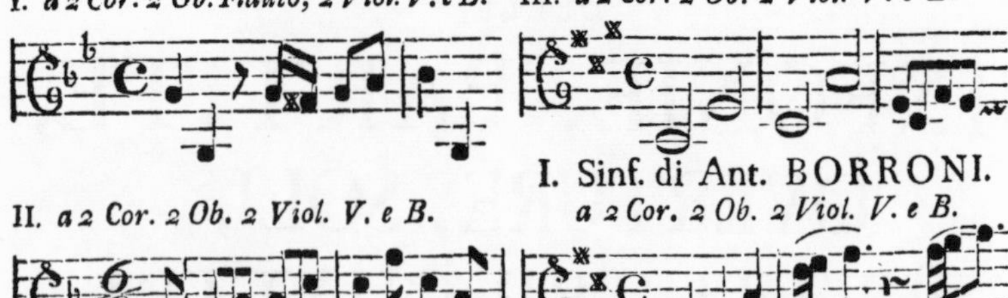

II. Sinf. di Bald. GALUPPI.

I. *a 2 Cor. 2 Ob. 2 Viol. V. e B.* II. *a 2 Cor. 2 Ob. 2 Viol. V. e B.*

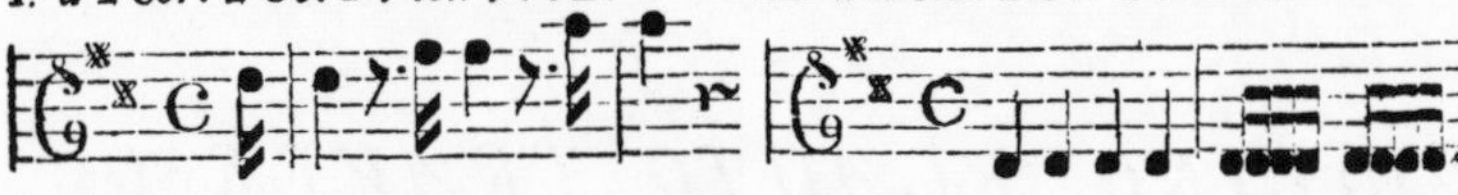

III. Sinf. di Flor. GASMANN.

I. *a 2 Cor. 2 Ob. 2 Viol. V. e B.* III. *a 2 Cor. 2 Ob. Fag. obl. 2 Viol. V. e B.*

I. Sinf. di Pietro GUGLIELMI.

II. *a 2 Cor. 2 Ob. 2 Viol. V. e B.* *a 2 Cor. 2 Ob. 2 Viol. V. e B.*

III. Sinf. di Giuſ. HAYDEN.

I. *a 2 Cor. 2 Ob. 2 Viol. V. e B.* III. *a 2 Cor. 2 Ob. 2 Viol. V. e B.*

II. *a 2 Cor. 2 Ob. 2 Viol. V. e B.*

I. Sinf. di HEMBEL, *a 2 Cor. 2 Ob. 2 Viol. V. e B.*

VII. Sinf. di Giov. VANHALL.

I. *a 2 C. 2 Ob. 2 Cl. Tymp. 2 Viol. V. e B.* V. *a 4 Cor. 2 O. 2 Viol. V. e B.*

II. *a 2 C. 2 Ob. 2 Cl. Tymp. 2 Viol. V. e B.* VI. *a 2 Cor. 2 Ob. 2 Viol. V. e B.*

III. *a 2 Cor. 2 Ob. 2 Viol. V. e B.* VII. *a 2 C. 2 O. 2 Cl. Tymp. 2 Viol. V. e B.*

IV. *a 2 Cor. 2 Ob. 2 Viol. V. e B.*

III. Sinf. di WOLF.

I. *a 2 Cor. 2 Ob. 2 Viol. V. e B.* III. *a 2 Cor. 2 Ob. 2 Fl. 2 Viol. V. e B.*

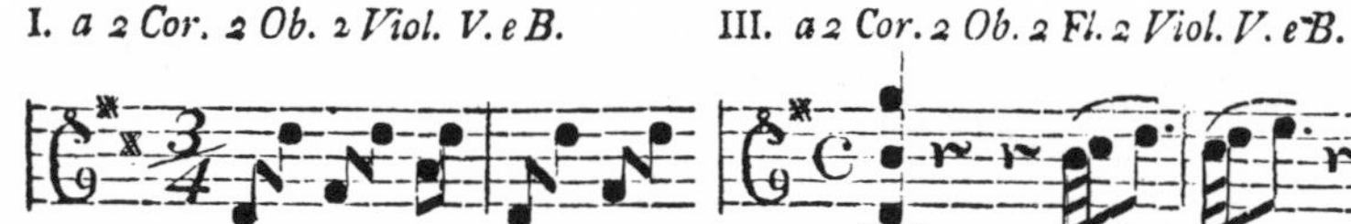

II. *a 2 Cor. 2 Ob. 2 Fl. 2 Viol. V. e B.*

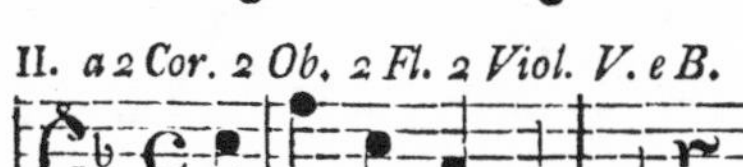

III. Sinf. di ZIMMERMANN.

I. *a 2 Cor. 2 Ob. 2 Viol. V. e B.* III. *a 2 Cor. 2 Ob. 2 Viol. 2 Viole obl. e B.*

II. *a 2 Cor. 2 Fl. 2 Viol. V. e B.*

SINFONIE intagliate e ſtampate.

VI. Sinf. di C. F. ABEL, *a 2 Cor. 2 Ob. 2 Viol. V. e B.*

Opera X. London.

VI. Sinf. di ENGEL, *a 2 Cor. 2 Ob. 2 Viol. V. e B. Varſavia.*

VI. Sinf. di C. E. GRAAF, *a 2 Cor. 2 Fl. 2 Viol. V. e B.*

Opera XI. Amſterd.

VI. Sinf. di Gio. Th. GREINER, *a 2 Cor. 2 Ob. 2 Fl. 2 Viol. V. e B. Opera II. Amsterd.*

III. Sinf. di Giuf. HAYDEN, *a 2 Cor. 2 Fl. o Ob. 2 Viol. V. e B. Opera X. Amsterd.*

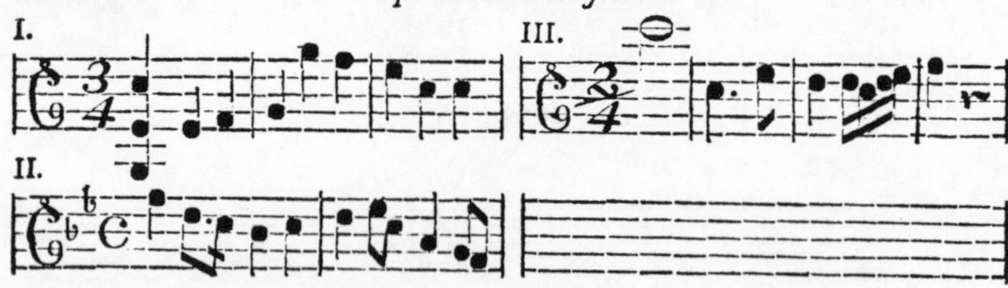

VI. Sinf. di Urban HOFFSTETTER, *a 2 Cor. 2 Ob. 2 Fl. 2 Cl. 2 Viol. V. e B. Opera I. Norimberga.*

VI. Sinf. di B. HOUPFELD, *a 2 Cor. 2 Ob. 2 Viol. V. e B. Amsterd.*

VI. Sinf. di G. A. KREUSSER, *a 2 Cor. 2 Ob. o Fl. 2 Viol. V. e B. Opera V. Amsterd.*

III. Sinf. di H. LEEHMANS, *a 2 Cor. 2 Ob. 2 Fag. 2 Viol. V. e B. Opera IV. Parigi.*

VI. Sinf. di Ant. LORENZITI, a 2 Viol. V. e B.
Opera II. Parigi.
I.
IV.
II.
V.
III.
VI.
I. Sinf. di VEICHTNER, a 2 Cor. 2 Fl. 2 Viol. V. e B.
IV. Sinf. di VEICHTNER, a 2 Cor. 2 Ob. 2 Fl. 2 Viol. V. e B.
I.
III.
II.
IV.
SINFONIES PERIODIQUES. Amst.
I. di DITTERS, a 2 Cor. 2 Fl. 2 Viol. V. e B.
II. di KLOEFFLER, a 2 Cor. 2 Fl. o Ob. 2 Viol. V. e B.
I.
I. di HAYDEN, a 2 Cor. 2 Ob. o Fl. 2 Viol. V. e B.
II.
I. di MILANDRE, a 2 Ob. Fag. 2 Viol. V. e B.
I. di SCHMITT, a 2 Cor. 2 Fl. o Ob. 2 Viol. V. e B.
I. di Iof. SCHMITT, a 2 Cor. 2 Fl. 2 Viol. V. e B.
I. di TOESCHI, a 2 Cor. 2 Fl. 2 Viol. V. e B.
PARTITE, OVERT. DIVERTIMENTI.
I. Partita di REICHARDT, a 2 Cor. 2 Fl. 2 Viol. V. e B.
I. Overtura di MARTINI Tedefco, a 2 Cor. 2 Ob. 2 Viol. V. e B.
I. Divert. di MARTINI Ted. a 2 Cor. 2 Ob. 2 Viol. V. e B.
I. Partita di NEEFE, a 2 C. 2 Ob. 2 Fl. 2 Fag. 2 Viol. V. e B.
I. Partita di ROLLE, a 2 Ob. 2 Fag. 2 Viol. V. e B.
I. Partita di WEINLICH, a 2 Cor. 2 Ob. 2 Fl. 2 Viol. V. e B.

VIOLINO.

SOLI con BASSO.

XII. Soli di HEMBEL.

SOLI, *intagliati*.

I. FISCHER, Rondeau varié, pour le Violon.

Amsterd.

VI. Soli di F. MÜLLER, *Parigi*.

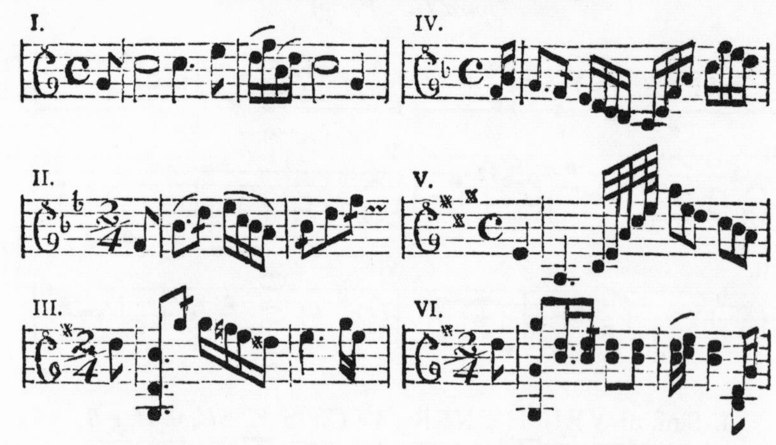

XII. Soli di Giuſ. TARTINI. *Opera II. Roma.*

DUETTI, *intagliati.*

VI. Duetti di Franc. GUERINI. *Opera V.* *Amſterd.*

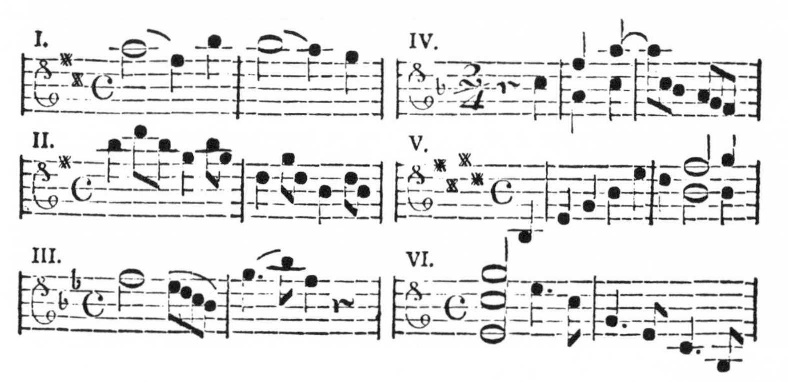

VI. Duetti di Franc. GUERINI. *Opera X.* *Amſterd.*

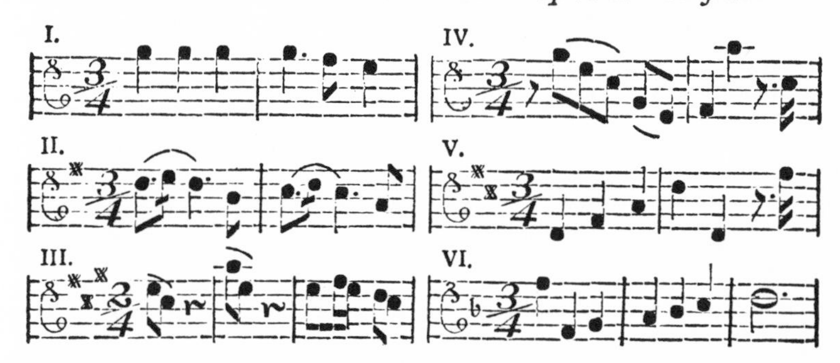

VI. Duetti di C. F. KERNTL. *Opera I.* *Amſterd.*

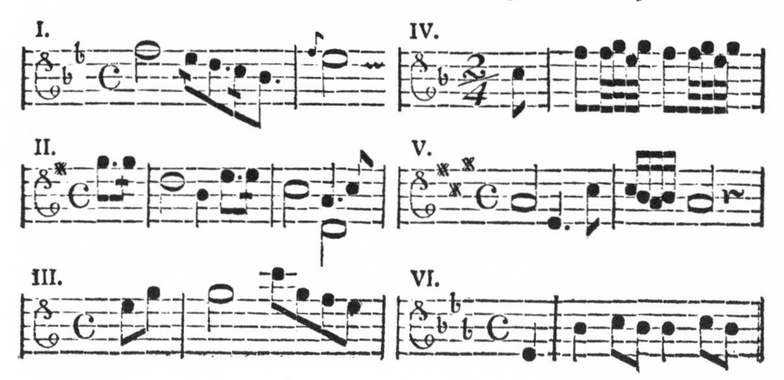

VI. Duetti di G. A. KREUSSER. *Opera III. Amſterd.*

VI. Duetti di G. A. KREUSSER. *Opera IV. Amſterd.*

VI. Duetti di Henrico SCHROETER. *Amſterd.*

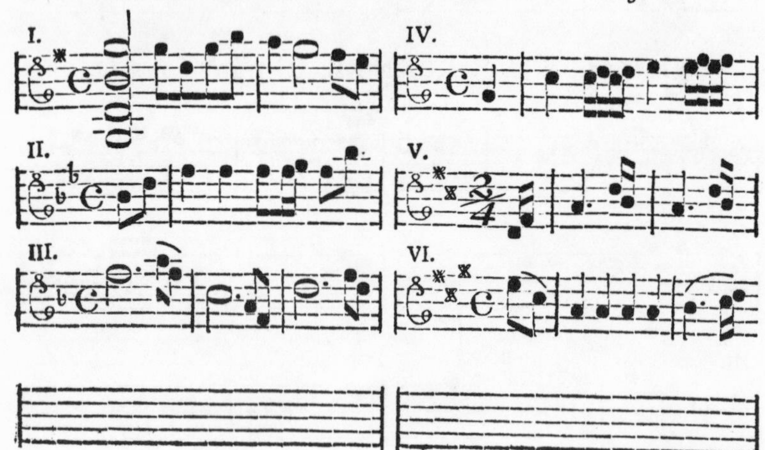

VI. Duetti di Gio. Batiſta NOFERI. *Amſterd.*

XII. Divertiſſements di F. SCHWINDL. *Op. IV. Amſt.*

16 VIOLINO.
VI. Duetti di Steffano N. detto SPADINA. Opera VI. Amſterd.
I.
IV.
II.
V.
III.
VI.
TRII.
A DUE VIOLINI CON BASSO.
VI. Trii di L. BOCHERINI. Opera IX. London.
I.
IV.
II.
V.
III.
tr
VI.
VI. Trii di C. E. GRAAF. Opera X. a la Haye.
I.
IV.
II.
V.
III.
VI.
VIOLINO. 17
VI. Trii di Antonio KAMMEL. Opera VII. a la Haye.
I.
IV.
II.
V.
III.
VI.
VI. Trii di M. le MARCHAND. Parigi.
I.
IV.
II.
V.
III.
3
3
VI.
VI. Trii di Ioſeph SCHMITT. Opera IV. Amſterd.
I.
IV.
II.
V.
III.
VI.

QUATTRI.

II. Quattri di SCHMIDT. *a 2. Viol. V. e B.*

QUATTRI, intagliati.

VI. Quattri di I. C. BACH. *a 2. Viol. V. e B. Parigi.*

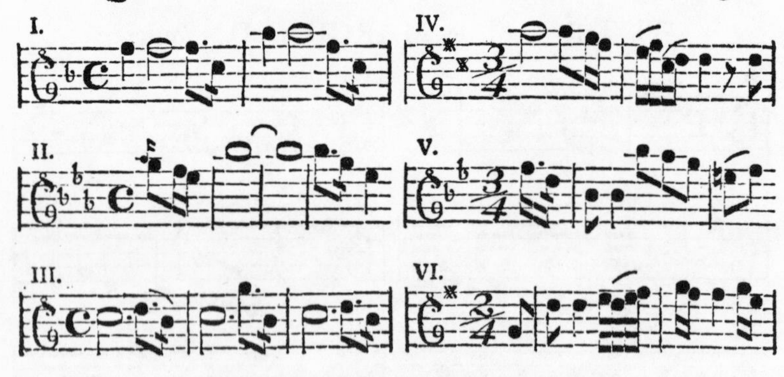

VI. Quattri notturni di Ignazio FRAENZL.

a 2. Viol. V. e B. Opera III. Parigi.

VI. Quattri di F. I. GOSSEC. *a 2. Viol. V. e B. Opera I.*

VI. Quattri di Giuſ. HAYDEN. *a 2. Viol. V. e Baſſo.*

Opera IX. Amſterdam.

VI. Quatri di Rom. HOFFSTETTER. *a 2. Viol. V. e B.*

Amſterdam.

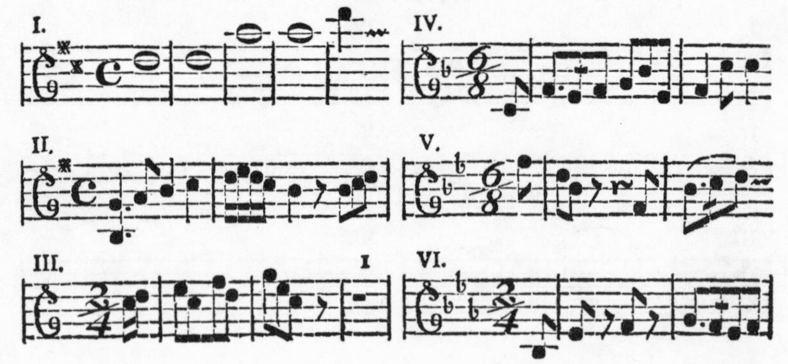

VI. Quattri di Giov. VANHALL. *a 2 Viol. V. e B. Opera IX. Parigi.*

I. II. III. IV. V. VI.

CONCERTI, per il Violino concertato.

I. Conc. di BISCHOFF. *a Viol. conc. 2 O. 2. Cl. T. 2 V. V. e B.*

I. Conc. di CANNABICH. *a Viol. conc. 2 Viol. V. e Basso.*

I. Conc. di HEMBEL. *a Viol. conc. 2 Viol. V. e Basso.*

I. Conc. di Leop. HOFFMANN. *a Viol. conc. 2 Cor. 2. Ob. 2 Viol. V. e B.*

I. Conc. di VANHALL. *a Viol. conc. 2 Cor. 2 Viol. V. e B.*

I. Conc. di Adam VEICHTNER. *a Viol. conc. 2 Cor. 2 Viol. V. e B.*

CONCERTI intagliati e stampati.

I. Conc. di REICHARDT. *a Viol. conc. 2. Viol. V. e B. a Riga.*

I. Conc. di Ign. RAIMONDI. *a plusieurs Instrum. Op. II. Amst.*

I. Conc. di Alex. ROBINEAU. *a Viol. conc. 2 Cor. 2 Ob. 2 V. e B. Parigi.*

III. Conc. di M. L. SYRMEN. *a Viol. conc. 2 Cor. 2 Ob. 2. Viol. V. e B. Op. II. Amsterd.*

I. II. III.

III. Conc. di M. L. SYRMEN. *a Viol. conc. 2 Cor. 2 Ob. 2 Viol. V. e B. Op. III. Amsterd.*

I. II. III.

VIOLA.

VI. Duetti di Pancrazio HUBER. *a Violino e Viola. Op. I. Amst.*

I. II. III. IV. V. VI.

VI. Trii di Gius. HAYDEN. *a Viol. Viola e Basso.*

I. II. III. IV. V. VI.

VIOLONCELLO.

I. Solo di PREYSING. *a Violoncello e Baſſo.*

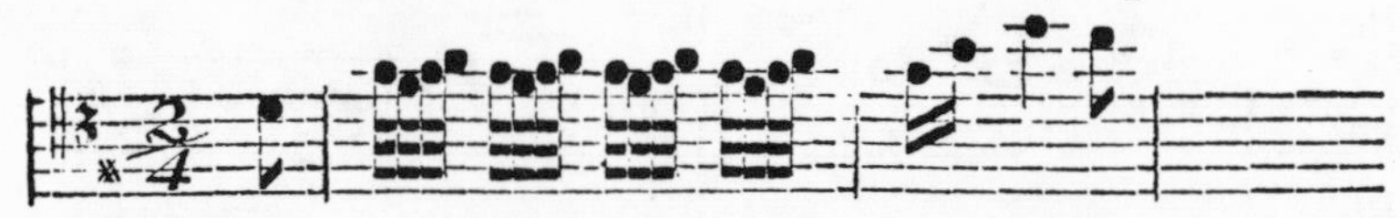

VI. Soli di L. BOCCHERINI. *a Violonc. e Baſſo. London.*

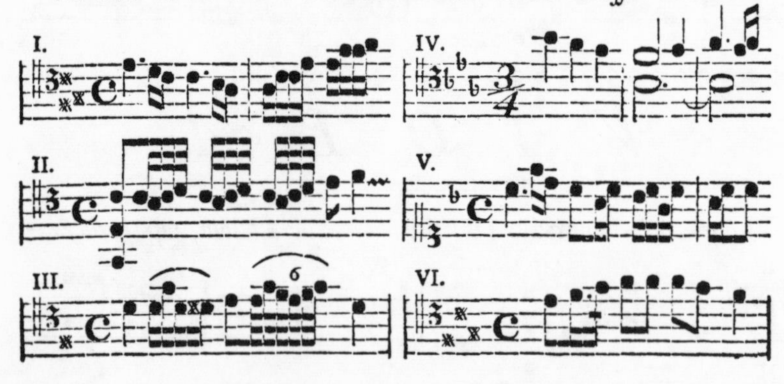

D U E T T I.

VI. Divertiſſements *a deux Baſſe (à l'uſage des Commençans)* par Mr. BARETTE. *Oeuv. I. Amſterd.*

VI. Duetti di Fred. SCHROETER. *a Viol. e Violoncello. Amſterd.*

V. Trii di Giuſ. HAYDEN. *a Violonc. Viola e Baſſo.*

CONCERTI, *per il Violoncello concertato.*

I. Con. di Giuſ. HAYDEN. *a Violonc. conc. 2 Viol. V. e B.*

II. Concerti di ZYCKA. *a Violonc. conc. 2 Viol. V. e B.*

II. Concerti di L. BOCHERINI. *a Violonc. conc. 2 Viol. V. e B. intagliati in Parigi.*

FLAUTO TRAVERSO.

D U E T T I.

VI. Duetti di DOTHEL. *a 2 Flauti Traversi.*

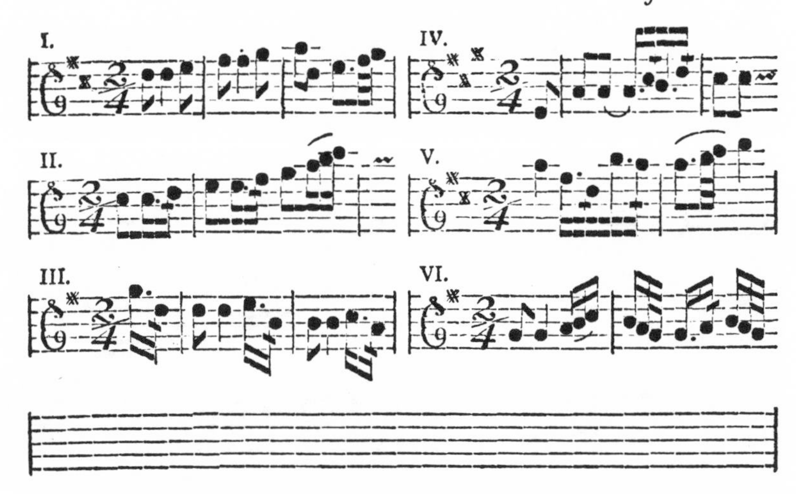

VI. Duetti di KLOEFFLER. *a 2 Flauti Traversi.*

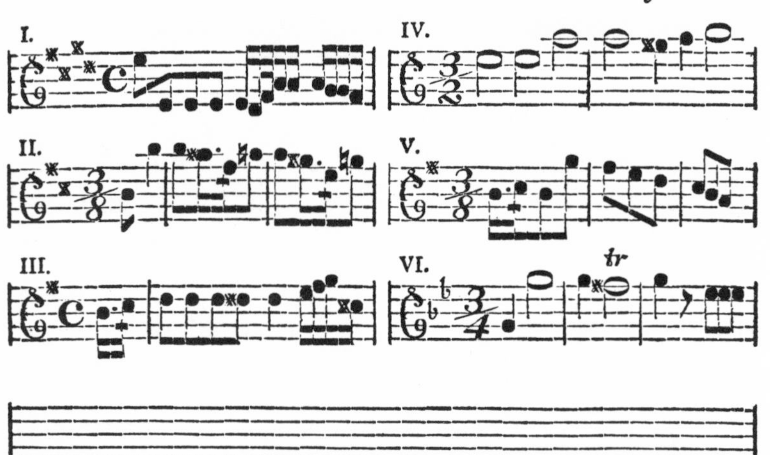

D U E T T I, *intagliati.*

VI. Duetti di T. GREINER. *a 2 Flauti. Opera I. Amsterd.*

VI. Divertiss. di C. F. KERNTL. *a 2 Flauti. Opera II. Amsterd.*

VI. Duetti di PLA. *a 2 Flauti. Opera I. Amsterd.*

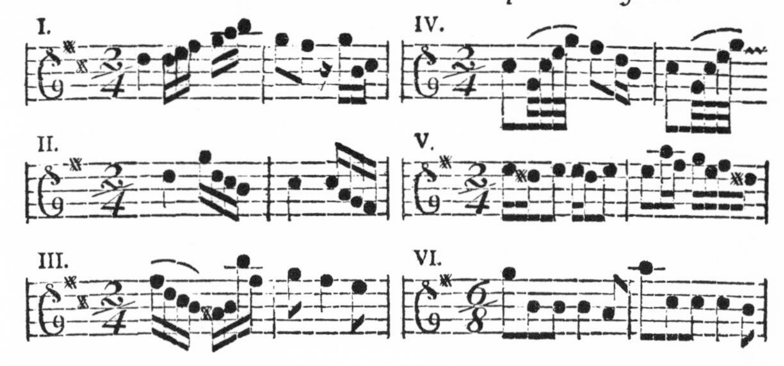

VI. Duetti di Mattia STABINGHER. *a 2 Flauti. Op. I. Parigi.*

VI. Duetti di I. B. WENDLING. *a 2 Flauti. Op. IV. Amſterd.*

T R I I.

VI. Trii di C. WEISS. *a Flauto, Viol. e Baſſo. London.*

VI. Trii di Giuſ. HAYDEN. *a 2 Flauti, e Baſſo. Op. XI. Amſt.*

VI. Trii di I. B. WENDLING. *a Flauto, Viol. e B. Op. III.*

Q U A T T R I,

A FLAUTO, VIOLINO, VIOLA E BASSO.

I. Quattro di NEYDING.

III. Quattri di PANNENBERG.

QUATTRI, *intagliati.*

VI. Quattri di C. E. GRAAF. *a Flauto, Violino, Viola e Basso. Opera XII. Amsterdam.*

VI. Quattri di Giuſ. TOESCHI. *a Flauto, Violino, Viol. e Basso. Opera V. Amsterdam.*

VI. Quattri di VANHALL. *a Flauto, Viol. V. e B. Op. VII. Parigi.*

CONCERTI

A FLAUTO TRAVERSO CONCERTATO.

VI. Con. di GOEZEL. *a Flauto conc. 2 Viol. Viola e B.*

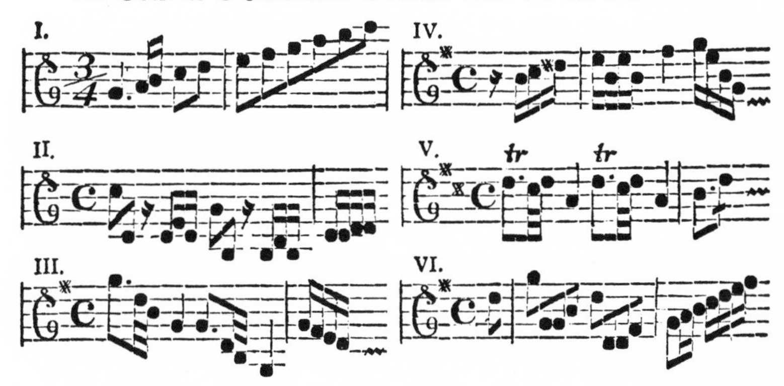

II. Concerti di Leop. HOFFMANN. *a Flauto conc. 2 Cor. 2 Viol. Viola e Basso.*

II. Concerti di Giac. Feder. KLEINKNECHT. *a Flauto conc. 2 Cor. 2 Viol. Viola e Basso.*

I. Concerto di SCHWINDEL. *a Flauto concertato, 2 Cor. 2 Viol. Viola e Basso.*

O B O E.

I. Conc. di HEMBEL. *a Oboe conc. 2 Viol. Viola e B.*

I. Conc. di FISCHER. *a Oboe conc. 2 Cor. 2 Viol. V. e B. London.*

CLARINETTO.

I. Conc. di STARCK. *a Clarinetto conc. 2. Viol. Viola e B.*

F A G O T T O.

II. Concerti di WEINLICH. *a Fagotto concertato, 2 Cor. 2 Ob. 2 Violini, Viola e Baſſo.*

I.

II.

H A R P A.

II. Divertimenti di GERA.

I. *a Harpa conc. Flauto, 2 Viol. e B.* II. *a Harpa conc. Flauto, Viol. e B.*

C E M B A L O.

S O L I.

I. di BENDA. I. di SCHWANENBERG.

I. Sinfonia Pantomima di Giov. VANHALL.

S O N A T E, *intagliate e ſtampate.*

VI. Sonate di C. F. ABEL. *Amſterdam.*

I. IV.

II. V.

III. VI.

VI. Sonate di Giov. Feder. DOLES. *a Cembalo Solo.*
Riga.

XII. Sonate di Chr. G. NEEFE. *a Cembalo Solo.*
Leipzig.

TRII, *intagliati.*

VI. Sonate di I. B. BAMBINI, *a Cemb. e Viol. Op. IV. Parigi.*

VI. Sonate di A. E. FORSTMEYER, *a Cembalo e Viol. Op. I. Francfort sur le Main.*

VI. Sonate di Andrea LUCHESI, *a Cemb. e Violino, in Bonn.*

VI. Sonate di Franc. ZAPPA, *a Cemb. e Viol. Op. VI. Parigi.*

TERZETTI, *a Cembalo obligato,*

CON VIOLINO O FLAUTO E BASSO.

I. Sonata di GERBER, *a Cemb. Fl. o Viol. e Violonc.*

VI. Sonate di H. RIGEL, *a Cemb. Viol. e Violonc.*

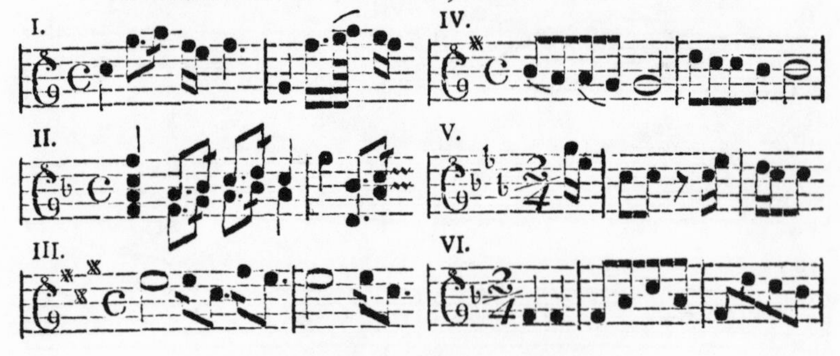

TERZETTI, *intagliati.*

II. Sonate di BURNEY, *a Cemb. Viol. e Basso. London.*

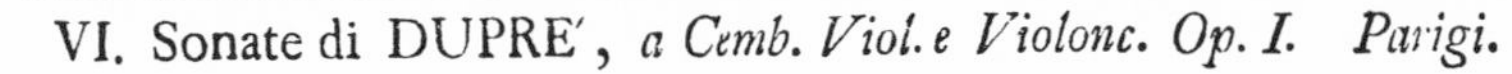
VI. Sonate di DUPRE', *a Cemb. Viol. e Violonc. Op. I. Parigi.*

VI. Sonate di I. S. SCHRÖTER, *a Cemb. Viol. e Violonc. Op. II. Amſterd.*

VI. Sonate di G. S. LOEHLEIN, *a Cemb. Viol. o Fl. e Violonc. Coll. I. et II. Leipſic.*

QUATTRI e DIVERTIMENTI.

I. Divertim. di Giuſ. HAYDEN, *a Cemb. 2 Viol. e B.*

VI. Quattri di G. HERSCHEL, *a Cemb. 2 Viol. e B. Op. I. Amſterd.*

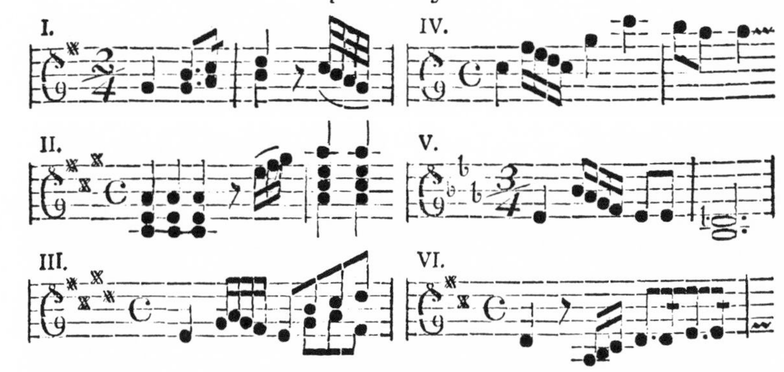

I. Quintetto di C. B. UBER, *a Cemb. 2 Cor. V. e B. Breslau.*

CONCERTI, a Cemb. conc. con più Stromenti.

IV. Conc. di DEGEN, *a Cemb. conc. 2 Viol. V. e B.*

I. Conc. di Carlo DITTERS, *a Cemb. conc. 2 Viol. e Baſſo.*

38 CEMBALO.
II. Concerti di FRECH, a Cemb. conc. 2 Viol. V. e B.
I.
II.
I. Conc. di HAUSCHILD.
a Cemb. conc. 2 Viol. V. e B.
I. Conc. di Giuſ. HAYDEN.
a Cemb. conc. 2 Viol. e Baſſo.
II. Concerti di Leop. HOFFMANN, a Cemb. conc. 2 Viol. V. e B.
I.
II.
I. Conc. di KELLNER.
a Cemb. conc. 2 Cor. 2 Viol. V. e B.
I. Conc. di KÜFFNER.
a Cemb. conc. 2 Fl. 2 Viol. V. e B.
III. Concerti di LANGE.
I. a Cemb. conc. 2 Fl. 2 Viol. V. e B.
III. a Cemb. conc. 2 C. 2 Fl. 2 Vi. V. e B.
I. Conc. di LIPPE.
a Cemb. conc. 2 Viol. V. e B.
II. a Cemb. conc. 2 C. 2 Ob. 2 Vi. V. e B.
VI. Concerti di G. F. MEISSLER, Org. in Lubbenau.
I. a Cemb. conc. 2 Viol. V. e B.
IV. a Cemb. conc. 2 Ob. 2 Viol. V. e B.
II. a Cemb. conc. 2 C. 2 Viol. V. e B.
V. a Cemb. conc. 2 Fl. 2 Viol. V. e B.
III. a Cemb. conc. 2 C. 2 Viol. V. e B.
VI. a Cemb. conc. 2 Clar. 2 Viol. V. e B.

CEMBALO. 39
I. Conc. di POCORNI, a Cemb. conc. 2 Cor. 2 Ob. 2 Viol. V. e B.
II. Concerti di RIEGEL.
I. a Cemb. conc. 2 C. 2 Ob. 2 Viol. V. e B.
II. a Cemb. conc. 2 Cor. 2 Viol. V. e B.
IV. Concerti di ZEIDLER.
I. a Cemb. conc. 2 Fl. 2 Fag. 2 Vi. V. e B.
III. a Cemb. conc. 2 Fl. 2 Fg. 2 Vi. V. e B.
II. a Cemb. conc. 2 Viol. V. e B.
IV. a Cemb. conc. 2 Viol. V. e B.
VI. Conc. di C. P. E. BACH, a Cemb. conc. 2 Viol. V. e B.
ſtamp. in Hamburgo.
I.
IV.
II.
V.
III.
VI.
I. Conc. di W. N. HAUEISEN.
a Cemb. 2 C. 2 Viol. V. e B. Op. V. Frf.
I. Conc. di G. F. REICHARDT.
a Cemb. conc. 2 Vi. V. e B. ſtamp. in Riga.

SVPPLEMENTO VIII.

DEI

CATALOGI

DELLE

SINFONIE, PARTITE, OVERTURE, SOLI, DUETTI, TRII, QUATTRI E CONCERTI

PER IL

VIOLINO, FLAUTO TRAVERSO,

CEMBALO

ED ALTRI STROMENTI,

CHE

SI TROVANO IN MANOSCRITTO
NELLA OFFICINA MUSICA DI BREITKOPF
IN LIPSIA.

1773.

SINFONIE.
I. Sinf. dal Conte J. di BACHTA.
a 2 Cor. 2 Ob. Fag. 2 Viol. V. e B.
I. Sinf. da BARSIELLO.
a 2 Cor. 2 Ob. 2 Viol. 2 Viole e B.
II. Sinf. da Carlo DITTERS.
I. a 2 Cor. 2 Ob. 2 Viol. V. e B.
II. a 2 Cor. 2 Ob. 2 Viol. V. Fag. e B.
I. Sinf. da Franc. DUSCHEK.
a 2 Cor. 2 Viol. V. e B.
I. Sinf. da GAZANIGA.
a 2 Cor. 2 Ob. 2 Viol. V. e B.
IX. Sinf. da Flor. GASMANN.
I. a 2 Cor. 2 Ob. Fag. 2 Viol. V. e B.
VI. a 2 C. 2 Ob. 2 Cl. 2 Fl. Fag. 2 Vi. V. e B.
II. a 2 Cor. 2 Ob. 2 Viol. V. e B.
VII. a 2 C. 2 Ob. 2 Fl. Fag. 2 Viol. V. e B.
III. a 2 Cor. 2 Ob. 2 Viol. V. e B.
VIII. a 2 Cor. 2 Ob. 2 Fag. 2 Viol. V. e B.
IV. a 2 Cor. 2 Ob. 2 Viol. V. e B.
IX. a 2 C. 2 O. Fg. obl. Vlc. obl. 2 Vi. V. e B.
V. a 2 Cor. 2 Ob. 2 Viol. V. e B.
I. Sinf. da F. I. GOSSEK.
a 2 Cor. 2 Ob. 2 Clar. 2 Trombe. Tymp. 2 Fag. 2 Viol. 2 Viole e B.

SINFONIE. 3
VI. Sinf. da Giuf. HAYDEN.
I. a 2 Cor. 2 Ob. 2 Viol. V. e B.
IV. a 2 Cor. 2 Ob. 2 Viol. V. e B.
II. a 2 C. in G. 2 C. in B. 2 O. 2 Vi. V. e B.
V. a 2 C. 2 O. 2. Trom. Tymp. 2 Vi. V. e B.
III. a 2 Cor. 2 Ob. 2 Viol. V. e B.
VI. a 2 Cor. 2 Ob. 2 Viol. V. e B.
II. Sinf. da Leop. HOFMANN.
I. a 2 Cor. 2 Ob. 2 Viol. V. e B.
II. a 2 C. 2 Ob. 2 Fl. 2 Cl. Tp. 2 Vi. V. e B.
VI. Sinf. da HOLZBOGEN.
I. a 2 Cor. 2 Fl. 2 Viol. V. e B.
IV. a 2 Cor. 2 Ob. 2 Viol. V. e B.
II. a 2 Cor. 2 Fl. 2 Viol. V. e B.
V. a 2 Cor. 2 Viol. V. e B.
III. a 2 Cor. 2 Ob. 2 Viol. V. e B.
VI. a 2 Cor. 2 Viol. V. e B.
I. Sinf. da KOZELUCH, a 2 Cor. 2 Ob. 2 Fl. 2 Fag. 2 Viol. 2 Viole. 2 Tromb. Tymp. e B.
I. Sinf. da MISLEWEZECK.
a 2 Cor. 2 Ob. o Fl. 2 Viol. V. e B.
I. Sinf. da PICHL. al's DITTERS.
a 2 Cor. 2 Ob. 2 Viol. V. e B.

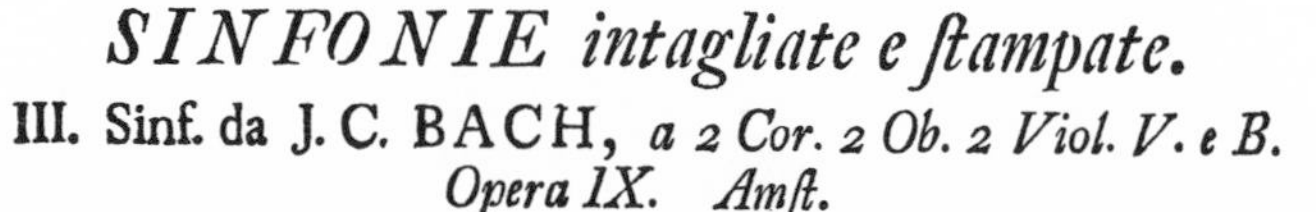

III. Sinf. da Carlo DITTERS, *a 2 Cor. 2 Ob. 2 Viol. V. e B.*
Opera VI. Parigi.

IV. Sinf. da Carlo DITTERS, *a 2 Cor. 2 Ob. 2 Fl. o Clarinetti. 2 Viol. V. e B. Opera VII. Parigi.*

III. Sinf. da Carlo DITTERS, *a 2 Cor. 2 Ob. 2 Viol. V. e B.*
Opera VIII. Parigi.

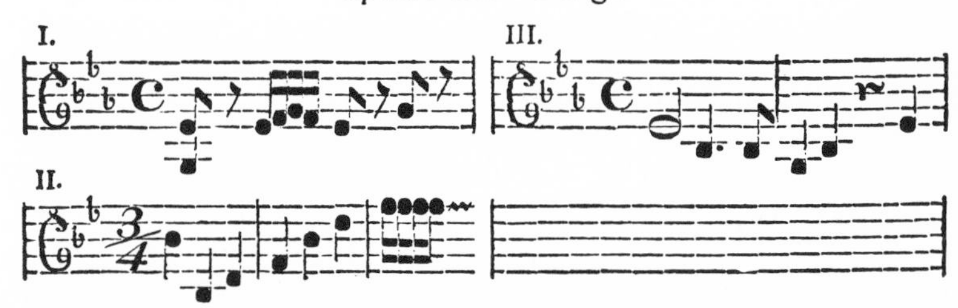

VI. Sinf. da Ern. EICHNER, *a 2 Cor. 2 Ob. o Fl. 2 Viol. V. e B.*
Opera I. Parigi.

VI. Sinf. da Giuſ. HAYDEN, *a 2 Cor. 2 Ob. 2 Viol. V. e B.*
Opera VIII. Parigi.

VI. Sinf. da Giuſ. HAYDEN, *a 2 Cor. 2 Ob. 2 Viol. V. e B.*
Opera IX. Parigi.

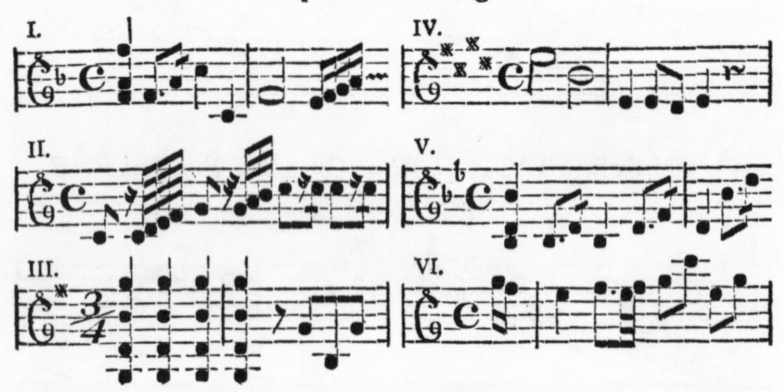

III. Sinf. da LUCHESI, *a 2 Cor. 2 Fl. o Ob. 2 Viol. V. e B.*
Opera II. Bonn.

VI. Sinf. da SCHMITT, *a 2 Cor. 2 Ob. 2 Viol. V. e B.*
Opera VI. Amſt.

VI. Sinf. da C. STAMITZ, *a 2 Cor. 2 Ob. 2 Viol. V. e B.*
Opera VI. Parigi.

II. Sinf. da C. STAMITZ, *Parigi.*
I. *a 2 Cor. 2 Ob. 6 Clarin. 2 Viol. 2 V. e B.* II. *a 2 Cor. 2 Ob. 2 Viol. V. e. B.*

II. Sinf. da GIOV. VANHALL, *a 2 C. 2 Ob. 2 Vi. V. e B. Op. X. Parigi.*

DIVERTIMENTI. CASSATIONES, OVERTURE etc.

I. Divert. da Giuſ. HAYDEN, *a Viol. conc. 2 Cor. 2 Ob. 2 Viol. Viola. Flauto Solo. Violoncl. obl. Fag. obl. Contra Baſſo obl. e B.*

II. Overture dal Barone HENET, *a 2 Viol. V. e B.*

I. Caſſatio da SCHMITT, *a 2 Cor. Fl. Viol. V. e B.*

VI. Divert. di Giov. VANHALL, *a Viol. princ. Viol. 2do. V. e B.*

SOLI con BASSO.

VI. Soli di PUGNANI, *Opera I. Parigi.*

VIOLINO.

VI. Soli da Gioachimo TRAVERSA, *Opera II. Parigi.*

DUETTI, intagliati.

VI. Duetti da Ignazio CELLONIETTI, *Opera I. Parigi.*

VI. Duetti da Giuſ. DEMACHI. *Parigi.*

VI. Duetti da G. FRANCISCONI, *Opera I. Amst.*

VI. Duetti da Gull. Gommar KENNIS, *Opera X. Parigi.*

VI. Duetti da Ignazio RAIMONDI, *Opera IV. Amst.*

TRII.

PER DUE VIOLINI CON BASSO.

IV. Da HOLZBOGEN.

VI. Trii da Anton KAMMEL.

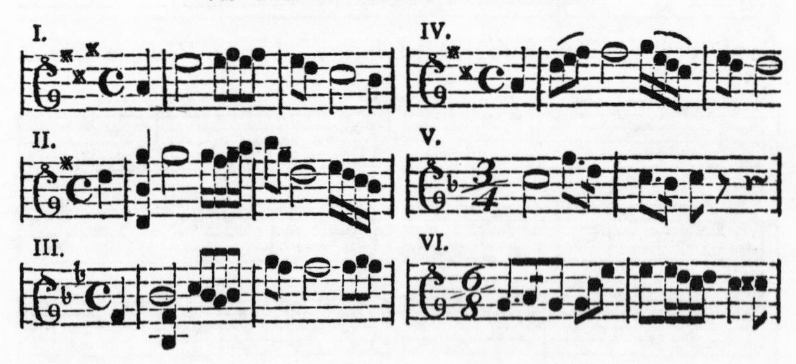

VI. Trii da Anton KOPPAUR.

VIII. Trii da KLEINKNECHT.

VI. Trii da KREUSER.

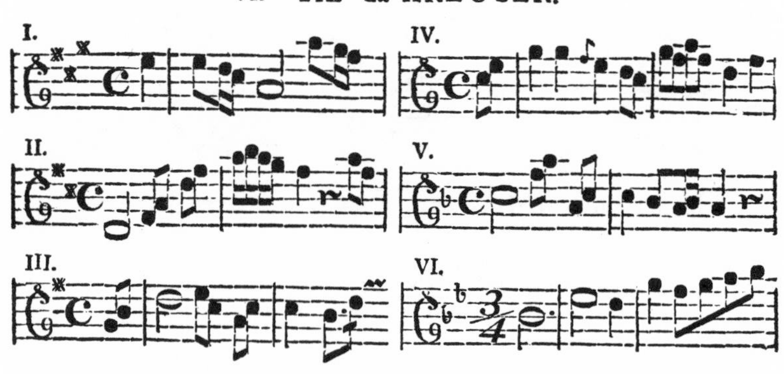

III. Trii da Georgio LANG.

VI. Trii da Giuſ. SCHMIDT.

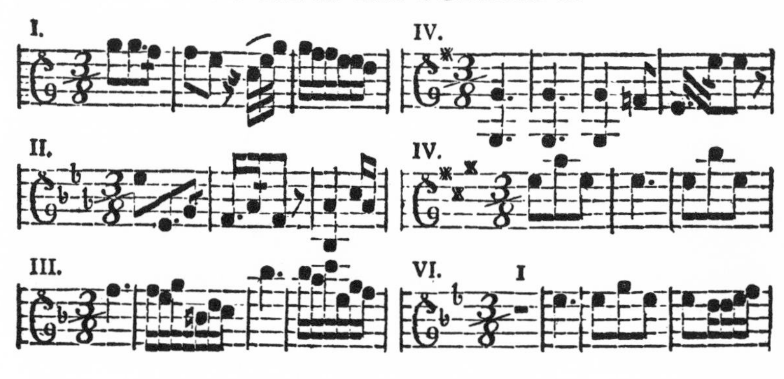

TRII intagliati.

VI. Trii da Carlo DITTERS, *Opera VI. Parigi.*

VI. Trii da Le DUC *l'ainé. Opera V. Parigi.*

VI. Trii da FRAENZEL. *Opera II. Parigi.*

VI. Trii da Gull. NAVOIGILLE. *Opera I. Parigi.*

I. Periodical Trio da PERGOLESI. *London.*

III. Trii da F. T. SCHUMANN. *Opera I. Amst.*

VI. Trii da VANHALL. *Opera IV. Parigi.*

VI. Trii da VANHALL. *Opera XI. Parigi.*

VI. Trii da DEMACHI, *a 3 Violini. Opera V. Geneve.*

QUATTRI.

VI. Quattri da BACHSCHMIDT, *a 2 Viol. V. e B.*

VI. Quattri da Giuf. MICHL, *a 2 Viol. V. e B.*

V. Quattri da Giuf. SCHMITT, *a 2 Viol. V. e B.*

VI. Quattri da Sigism. B. de RUMLINGE, *a Viol. V. e B.*

QUATTRI *intagliati.*

VI. Quattri da d'AVAUX, *a 2 Viol. V. e B. Opera VI. Parigi.*

IV. Quattri da M. BAUERSCHMITT, *a 2 Viol. V. e B. Parigi.*

VI. Quattri da BOCCHERINI, *a 2 Viol. V. e B. Opera X. Parigi.*

VI. Quattri da CAPRON, *a 2 Viol. V. e B. Opera II. Parigi.*

IV. Quattri da COLIZZI, *a 2 Viol. V. e B. Opera II.*

VI. Quattri da J. GIORDANI, *a 2 Viol. V. e B. Opera II. Parigi.*

VI. Quattri da Giuſ. SCHMITT, *a 2 Viol. V. e B. Opera V. Amſterd.*

VI. Quattri da Giuſ. SIGNORETTI, *a 2 Viol. V. e B. Opera XII. Parigi.*

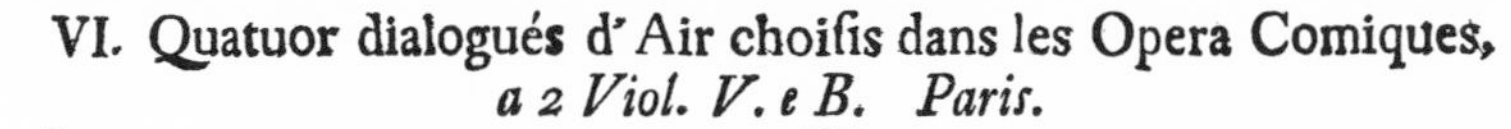

VI. Quatuor dialogués d'Air choisis dans les Opera Comiques, *a 2 Viol. V. e B. Paris.*

VI. Quattri da P. VACHON, *a 2 Viol. V. e B. Opera VII. Parigi.*

QUINTETTI.

II. Quintetti da Giuf. SCHMITT, *a 2 Cor. 2 Viol. 2 Viole e B.*

QUINTETTI, *intagliati.*

VI. Quintetti da L. GASMANN, *a 2 Viol. 2 Viole e B. Opera II. Parigi.*

III. Quintetti da PUGNANI, *a 2 Viol. 2 Ob. ó Fl. e B. 2 Cor. ad lib. Opera VII. Amst.*

CONCERTI, *per il Violino concertato.*

I. Conc. da HOECK, *a Viol. conc. 2 Viol. V. e B.*

II. Conc. da KLEINKNECHT, *a Viol conc. 2 Corn. 2 Fl. 2 Viol. V. e B.*

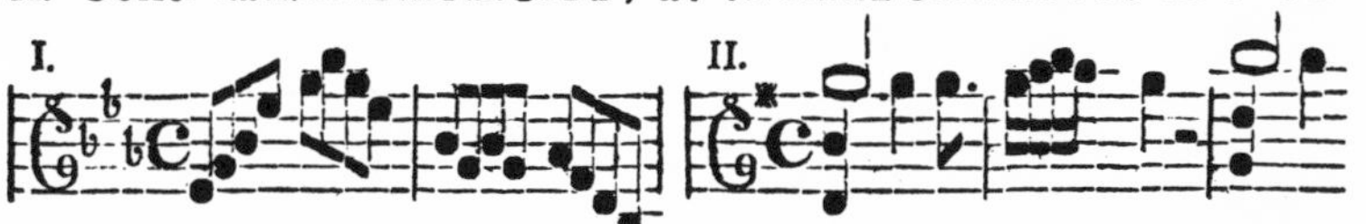

II. Conc. da LOLLI, *a Viol. conc. 2 Cor. 2 Fl 2 Viol. V. e B.*

I. Conc. da PICHL, *a Viol. conc. 2 Cor. 2 Ob. 2 Viol. V. e B.*

II. Conc. da STAMITZ, *a Viol. conc. 2 Viol. V. e B.*

I. Conc. da TARTINI, *a Viol conc. 2 Viol. V. e B.*

II. Serenate da Benj. UBER.

a Viol. princ. 2 C. 2 Fl. 2 Viol. V. e B. *a 2 C. 2 Fl. 2 Fag. 2 Viol. 2 Viole e B.*

VIOLA.

VI. Trii da VANHALL, *a Viol. Viola e B. 2 Cor. ad lib. Op. XII. Pari.*

VIOLONCELLO.

I. Solo da BRODETZ, *a Violonc. e B.* I. Solo da KLOB, *a Violonc. e B.*

II. Soli da THOMAS, *a Violoncello e Basso.*

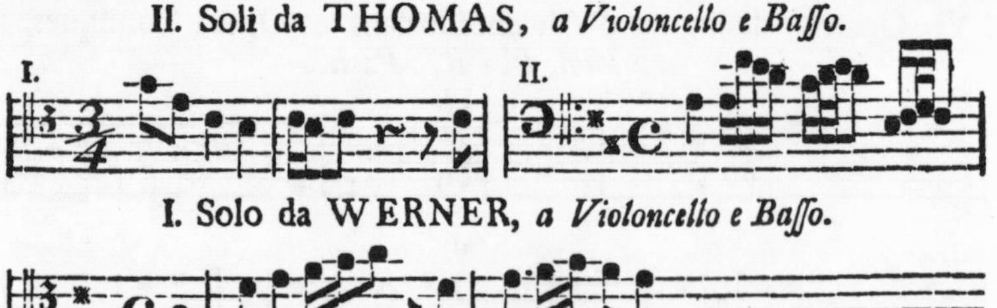

I. Solo da WERNER, *a Violoncello e Basso.*

DUETTI.

II. Duetti da HIMMELBAUER, *a Violino e Violoncello concertanti.*

VI. Duetti da AUBERTI, *à 2 Violoncelli. Opera II. Parigi.*

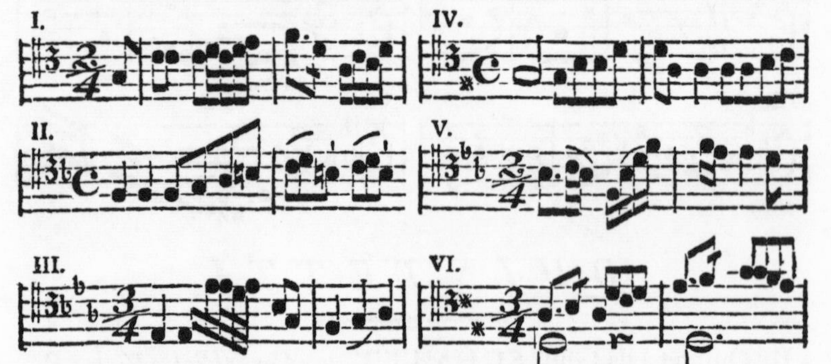

III. Duetti da CUPIS, *a 2 Violoncelli. Opera V. Parigi.*

III. Trii da F. T. SCHUHMANN, *a Violino, Violonc. e B. Op 1. Amst.*

CONCERTI, per il Violoncello concertato.

I. Conc. da ANONYMO. *a Violonc. conc. 2 Viol. V. e B.*

I. Conc. da BAUMGARTEN. *a Violonc. con. 2 Cor. 2 Viol. V. e B.*

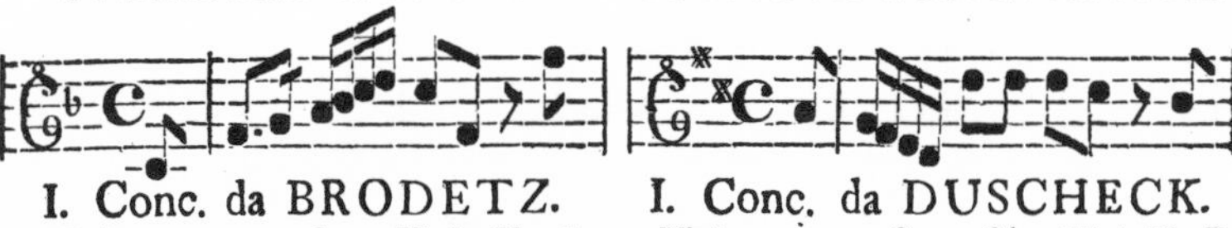

I. Conc. da BRODETZ. *a Violonc. conc. 2 C. 2 Viol. V. e B.*

I. Conc. da DUSCHECK. *a Violonc. conc. 2 Cor. 2 Ob. 2 Viol. V. e B.*

I. Conc. da EITHNER, *a Violonc. conc. 2 Viol. V. e B.*

II. Conc. da FILS.

I. *a Violonc. conc. 2 Clar. Tymp. 2 Vi. V. e B.* II. *a Violonc. conc. 2 Cor. 2 Viol. V. e B.*

II. Concerti da GRETSCH.

I. *a Violonc. conc. 2 Viol. V. e B.* II. *a Violonc. conc. 2 Cor. 2 Viol. V. e B.*

I. Concerto da HAYDEN. *a Violonc. conc. 2 Viol. V. e B.*

I. Concerto da KLOB. *a Violonc. conc. 2 Cor. 2 Viol. V. e B.*

I. Conc. da KÜFFLER. *a Violonc. conc. 2 Viol. V. e B.*

I. Conc. da NEYMANN. *a Violonc. conc. 2 Viol. V. e B.*

I. Conc. da PICHL. *a Violonc. conc. 2 Cor. 2 Viol. V. e B.*

I. Conc. da WERNER. *a Violonc. conc. 2 Viol. V. e Basso.*

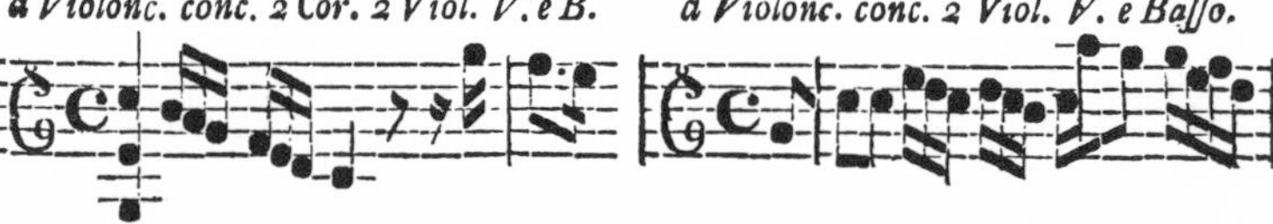

I. Concertino da KLOB, *a Violonc. obl. Viola obl. 2 Cor. 2 Clar. 2 Viol. V. e B.*

I. Divertimento da SÜSSIG, *a Violonc. obl. Flauto. V. e B.*

FLAUTO TRAVERSO.

VI. Soli da WILLHELMY, *a Flauto con Basso.*

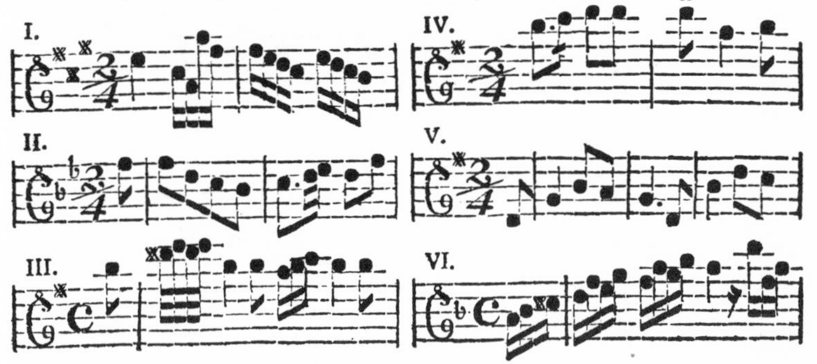

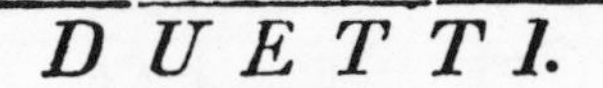

DUETTI.

VI. Duetti da GROS, *a 2 Flauti Traversi.*

VI. Duetti da L. HOFFMANN, *a 2 Flauti Trav.* Parigi.

TRII.

IV. Trii da KLEINKNECHT, *a 2 Flauti e Basso.*

I. Trio da RICHTER, *a 2 Flauti e Basso.*

II. Trii da HOLZBOGEN, *a Flauto, Violino e B.*

VI. Trii da PICHL, *a Flauto, Violino e Basso.*

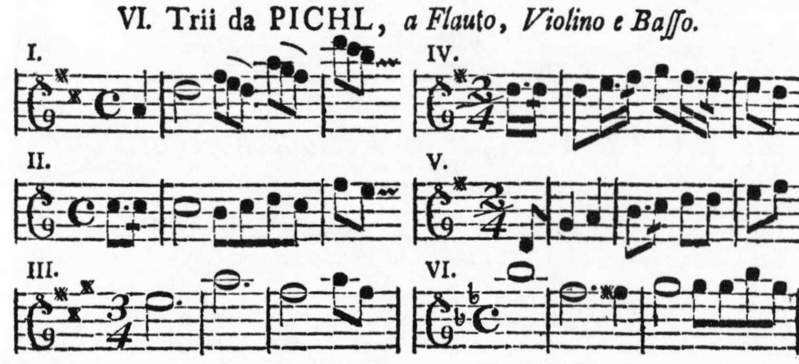

QUATTRI,

A FLAUTO, VIOLINO, VIOLA E BASSO.

VI. Quattri da Antonio RIGEL.

QUATTRI intagliati.

II. Quattri da BAUERSCHMIDT, *a Flauto, Viol. V. e B.* Parigi.

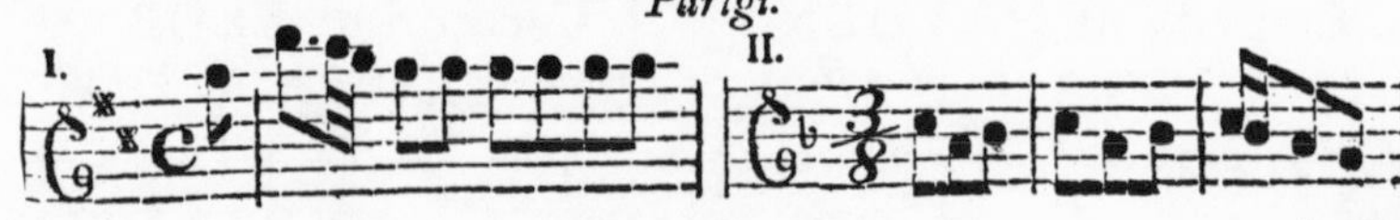

CONCERTI
A FLAUTO TRAVERSO CONCERTATO.

II. Conc. da HUPFELD, *a Flauto conc. 2 Cor. 2 Viol. V. e B.*
I. II.

I. Conc. da RIEGEL, *a Fl. conc. 2 Cor. 2 Ob. 2 Tromb. Tymp. 2 Viol. V. e B.*

I. Conc. da SCHÖPS, *a Flauto conc. 2 Cor. 2 Viol. V. e B.*

CONCERTINI.

II. Concertini da SCHÖPS.
I. *a Flauto conc. Viol. conc. Viola conc. Violonc. conc. 2 Corni obl. e B.*

II. *a Flauto conc. Viol. conc. Viola conc. Violonc. conc. Corno obl. e B.*

OBOE.

I. Conc. da FISCHER, *a Oboe conc. 2 Cor. 2 Viol. V. e B.*

CLARINETTO.

VI. Soli da PROCKSCH. *Opera V. Parigi.*

TRII.

VI. Trii da PROCKSCH, *a Clarinetto, Violino e Basso. Opera IV. Parigi.*

QUATTRI.

VI. Quattri da GASPARD, *a Clarinetto, Viol. V. e B. Parigi.*

VI. Quattri da KICHLER, *a Clarinetto. Viol. V. e B. Opera I. Parigi.*

IV. Quattri da C. STAMITZ, *a Clarinetto. Viol. V. e B. Opera VIII. Parigi.*

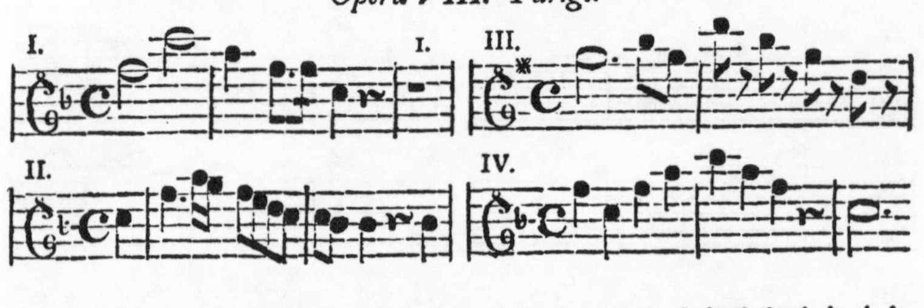

CORNO.

VI. Sonate da COMI, *a Corno e Basso. Parigi.*

CEMBALO.

SOLI.

IX. Sonate da Francesco DUSCHECK.

I. Sonata da Leop. KOZELUCH.

SONATE, intagliate e ſtampate.

I. Sonata da Franc. DUSCHECK. *Praga.*

VI. Sonate da Charles BURNEY. *London.*

VI. Sonate da Peter GUGLIELMI, *Opera III. London.*

VI. Sonate da Gius. HAYDEN. *Vienna.*

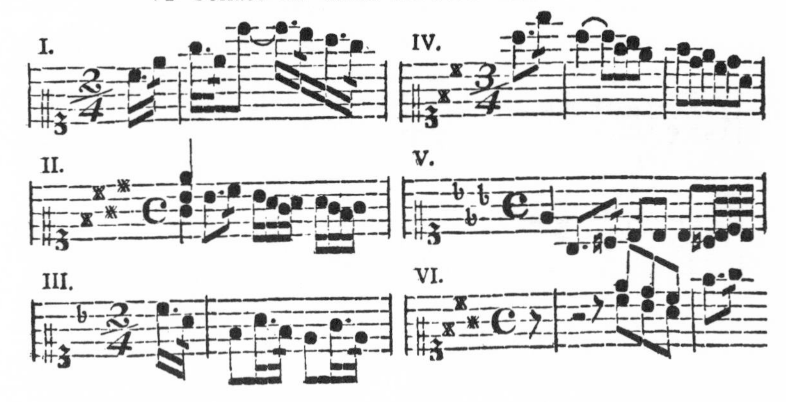

TRII,

A CEMBALO OBLIGATO CON VIOLINO O FLAUTO.

I. Sonata da BECKI, *a Cemb. e Viol.* I. Sonata da LANG, *a Cemb. e Viol.*

II. Sonate da SCHÖPS, *a Cembalo e Violino.*

II. Sonate da Benjam. UBER, *a Cembalo e Violino.*

TRII, *intagliati.*

III. Sonate da M. * * *. *a Cembalo e Violino. Opera I. Parigi.*

VI. Sonate da I. C. BACH, *a Cembalo e Violino. Opera X. Amst.*

III. Sonate da COURSELLO, *a Cembalo e Violino. Opera I. Parigi.*

VI. Sonate da DESPREAUX, *a Cembalo e Violino. Opera I. Parigi.*

IV. Sonate da G. F. RICHTER, *a Cembalo e Violino. Opera I. Amſterd.*

I. Sonata da LUCHESI, *a Cembalo e Violino.*

TERZETTI *intagliati.*

VI. Sonate da Giuſ. DIETZ, *a Cemb. Viol. e B. Opera I. Amſt.*

III. Sonate da Ern. EICHNER, *a Cemb. Viol. e B. London.*

I. Concertino da Fr. DUSCHEK. *a Cemb. obl. Viol. obl. e Baſſo.*

QUATTRI e DIVERTIMENTI.

I. Divertiment. da G. BENDA, *a Cemb. conc. 2 Viol. V e B.*

I. Divertim. da Gius. HAYDEN, *a Cemb. 2 Viol. e Baſſo.*

QUATTRI *intagliati.*

III. Quattri da BAUER, *a Cemb. Flauto, Viol. e B. Opera III. Francf. ſur le Main.*

VI. Quattri da Carlo BONI, *a Harpa o Cembalo, Viol. V. e B. Parigi.*

CONCERTI *a Cemb. con più Stromenti.*

I. Conc. da BECKE, *a Cemb. conc. 2 Cor. 2 Fl. 2 Viol. V. e B.*

IV. Conc. da COLIZZI, *a Cemb. conc. 2 Cor. 2 Viol. V. e B.*

II. Conc. da C. DITTERS, *a Cemb. conc. 2 Cor. 2 Viol. e B.*

I. II.

II. Conc. da Franc. DUSCHEK, *a Cemb. conc. 2 Cor. 2 Viol. V. e B.*

I. II.

I. Conc. da FOERSTER, *a Cemb. conc. 2 Viol. V. e B.*

V. Concerti da KÜFFNER.

I. *a Cemb. conc. 2 Cor. 2 Ob. 2 Viol. e B.* IV. *a Cemb. conc. 2 C. 2 Fl. 2 Vi. V. e B.*

II. *a Cemb. conc. 2 Cor. 2 Fl. 2 Vi. V. e B.* V. *a Cemb. conc. 2 Ob. 2 Viol. e B.*

III. *a Cemb. conc. 2 C. 2 O. 2 Fl. 2 Vi. 2 Fag. e B.*

I. Conc. da LANGE, *a Cemb. conc. 2 Viol. V. e B.*

I. Conc. da POKORNI, *a Cemb. conc. Fl. obl. 2 Cor. 2 Viol. e B.*

II. Concerti da Benjam. UBER.

I. *a Cemb. conc. 2 Fl. 2 Viol. V. e B.* II. *a Cemb. conc. 2 Cor. 2 Viol. V. e B.*

II. Concerti da ZEIDLER.

I. *a Cemb. conc. 2 Fl. 2 Fag. 2 Vi. V. e B.* II. *a Cemb. conc. 2 Viol. V. e B.*

CONCERTI *intagliati.*

I. Conc. da W. N. HAUEISEN, *a Cemb. conc. 2 Cor. 2 Viol. V. e B. Opera VI. Francf. sur le Main.*

I. Conc. da LUCHESI, *a Cemb. conc. 2 Cor. 2 Ob. 2 Viol. V. e B. Bonn.*

VI. Concerti da Ferd. PELLEGRINO, *a Cemb. conc. 2 Viol. V. e B. Parigi.*

SVPPLEMENTO IX.

DEI

CATALOGI

DELLE

SINFONIE, PARTITE, OVERTURE, SOLI, DUETTI, TRII, QUATTRI E CONCERTI

PER IL

VIOLINO, FLAUTO TRAVERSO, CEMBALO

ED ALTRI STROMENTI,

CHE

SI TROVANO IN MANOSCRITTO NELLA OFFICINA MUSICA DI BREITKOPF IN LIPSIA.

1774.

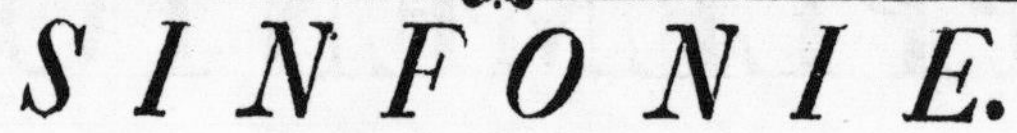
SINFONIE.

II. Sinf. da BARTA.
I. a 2 Cor. 2 Fl. 2 Viol. V. e B.
II. a 2 Cor. 2 Fl. 2 Viol. V. e B.
VI. Sinf. da BRODSKY.
I. a 2 Cor. 2 Fl. 2 Viol. V. e B.
IV. a 2 Cor. 2 Fl. 2 Viol. V. e B.
II. a 2 Cor. 2 Fl. 2 Viol. V. e B.
V. a 2 Cor. 2 Fl. 2 Viol. V. e B.
III. a 2 Cor. 2 Fl. 2 Viol. V. e B.
VI. a 2 Cor. 2 Fl. 2 Viol. V. e B.
II. Sinf. da Carlo DITTERS.
I. a 2 Cor. 2 Ob. 2 Viol. V. e B.
II. a 2 Cor. 2 Ob. 2 Viol. V. e B.
I. Sinf. da Franc. DUSCHEK.
a 2 Cor. 2 Ob. 2 Viol. 2 Viole e B.
I. Sinf. da F. I. GOSSEK.
a 2 Cor. 2 Ob. 2 Fag. 2 Viol. V. e B.
I. Sinf. da GLUCK.
a 2 Cor. 2 Ob. 2 Viol. V. e Baſſo.
I. Sinf. da Giuſ. HAYDEN.
a 2 Cor. 2 Ob. 2 Viol. V. e B.
I. Sinf. da HENNIG.
a 2 Cor. 2 Ob. 2 Viol. V. e Baſſo.
I. Sinf. da KARAUSCHEK.
a 2 Cor. 2 Ob. 2 Viol. V. e B.

III. Sinf da KOZELUCH.
I. a 2 Cor. 2 Fl. 2 Viol. V. e B.
III. a 2 Cor. 2 Ob. 2 Viol. V. e B.
II. a 2 Cor. 2 Ob. 2 Viol. V. e B.
III. Sinf. da W. LEEDER.
I. a 2 Cor. 2 Fl. 2 Viol. V. e B.
III. a 2 Cor. 2 Ob. 2 Viol. V. e B.
II. a 2 Cor. 2 Ob. 2 Viol. V. e B.
II. Sinf. da MISLEWECZECK.
I. a 2 Cor. 2 Ob. 2 Viol. 2 Viole e B.
II. a 2 Cor. 2 Ob. 2 Viol. V. e B.
I. Sinf. da Carlo ORDONEZ.
a 2 Cor. 2 Viol. V. e B.
I. Sinf. da PICHL.
a 2 Cor. 2 Ob. 2 Viol. V. e Baſſo.
I. Sinf. da SCHOEPS.
a 2 Ob. o Fl. 2 C. o Cl. Tymp. 2 Vi. V. e B.
I. Sinf. da Giuſ. SCHMIDT.
a 2 Cor. 2 Ob. 2 Viol. V. e B.
II. Sinf. da SCHMIDTBAUER.
I. a 2 Cor. 2 Ob. 2 Viol. V. e B.
II. a 2 C. 2 Ob. 2 Fl. 2 Fag. 2 Viol. V. e B.
I. Sinf. da SCHWINDEL, a 2 Cor. 2 Fl. 2 Viol. V. e B.

III. Sinf. da Antonio ZIMMERMANN.

SINFONIE intagliate e ſtampate.

IV. Sinf. da Antonio BULANT. *a 2 Cor. 2 Ob. 2 Viol. V. e B.*
Op. V. Parigi.

II. Sinf. da COMY, *a 2 Cor. 2 Fl. 2 Viol. V. e B.*
Op. V. Parigi.

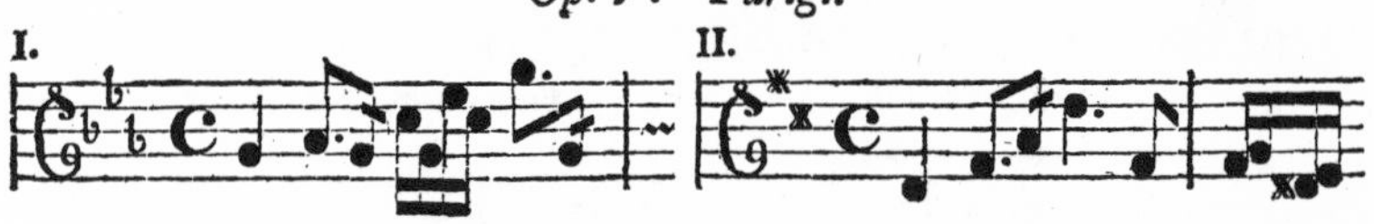

III. Sinf. da HAYDEN, *a 2 Cor. 2 Ob. 2 Viol. V. e B. Parigi.*

6 SINFONIE.

VI. Sinf. da G. A. KREUSSER, *a 2 Cor. 2 Ob. 2 Viol. V. e B. Op. VII. Amsterdam.*

I. II. III. IV. V. VI.

VI. Sinf. da Giuf. MISLEWECZECK, *a 2 Cor. 2 Ob. 2 Viol. V. e B. Op. I. Norimberga.*

I. II. III. IV. V. VI.

IV. Sinf. da Giov. VANHALL. *Op. XVI. Parigi.*

I. *vid. Suppl. VI. No. VI.* III. *vide Suppl. VI. No. II.*

II. IV. *vid. Suppl. VII. No. VI.*

II. Sinf. Periodiques par Jof. SCHMIDT, *a 2 Cor. 2 Ob. o Fl. 2 Viol. V. e B. Amsterdam.*

I. II.

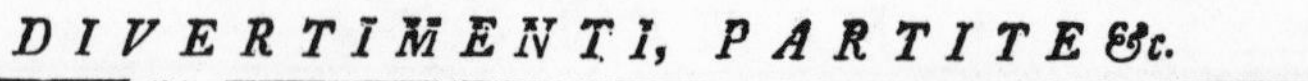

DIVERTIMENTI, CONCERTINI, PARTITE, &c.

I. Divert. da HAYDEN, *a 2 Cor. Flauto, Violino, V. e B.*

II. Partite da NEEFE.

I. *a 2 Cor. 2 Ob. 2 Viol. V. e B.* II. *a 2 Ob. 2 Viol. V. e B.*

Concertino da Giuf. SCHMIDT, *a 2 Cor. 2 Viol. 2 Viole e B. Amst.*

VIOLINO.

SOLI con BASSO.

I. Solo da PICHL.

SOLI intagliati.

VI. Soli da P. GAVINIES. *Op. I. Parigi.*

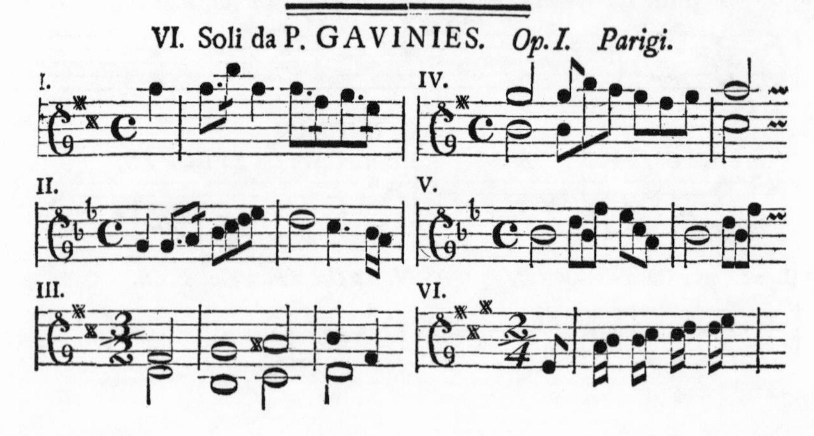
I. II. III. IV. V. VI.

8 VIOLINO.
VI. Soli da HUPFELD. Op. I. Amsterdam.
I.
IV.
II.
V.
III.
VI.
VI. Soli da A. KAMMEL. Op. XIII. Parigi.
I.
IV.
II.
V.
III.
VI.
VI. Soli par MIROGLIO le jeune. Op. I. Paris.
I.
IV.
II.
V.
III.
VI.
VIOLINO. 9
VI. Soli da PUGNANI. Op. VIII. Amsterdam.
I.
IV.
II.
V.
III.
VI.
DUETTI intagliati.
VI. Duetti da Antonio KAMMEL. Op. V. a la Hayè.
I.
IV.
II.
V.
III.
VI.
VI. Duetti da PUGNANI. Op. IV. Amsterdam.
I.
IV.
II.
V.
III.
VI.

VI. Duetti da Giuſ. SCHMITT, *a 2 Violini, o Violino e Violonc.* *Op. VIII. Amſterdam.*

TRII.

A DUE VIOLINI CON BASSO.

VI. Trii da CARDON. *Op. X. Parigi.*

VI. Trii da Giuſ. HAYDEN. *Op. VIII. Amſterdam.*

I. *vid. Suppl. II. No. IV.* IV. *vid. Suppl. I. No. VI.*

II. *vid. Suppl. I. No. I.* V.

III. *vid. Suppl. II. No. III.* VI.

VI. Trii da F. A. HEMBERGER. *Op. I. Parigi.*

12
VIOLINO.
VI. Trii da HELBERT. Op. III. Parigi.
I.
IV.
II.
V.
III.
VI.
VI. Trii da LEBRUN. Op. I. Mannheim.
I.
IV.
II.
V.
III.
VI.
VI. Trii da F. P. RICCI. London.
I.
IV.
II.
V.
III.
VI.

VIOLINO.
13
VI. Trii da Giuſ. SCHMITT. Op. VII. Amſterdam.
I.
IV.
o 2 Flauti.
II.
V.
o 2 Flauti.
III.
VI.
o 2 Flauti.
VI. Trii da Giov. VANHALL. Op. VII. Parigi.
I.
IV.
II.
V.
III.
VI.
QUATTRI intagliati.
VI. Quattri da C. F. ABEL, a 2 Viol. V. e B. Op. XII. London.
I.
IV.
II.
V.
III.
VI.

VI. Quattri da L. BOCCHERINI, *a 2 Viol. V. e B.*
Op. VIII. Amsterdam.

VI. Quattri da Flor. GASMANN, *a 2 Viol. V. e B.*
Op. I. Amsterdam.

VI. Quattri da GRETRY, *a 2 Viol. V. e B. Op. III. Parigi.*

VI. Quattri da Giorgio HAYDEN, *a 2 Viol. V. e B.*
Op. XVIII. Parigi.

VI. Quattri da A. KAMMEL, *a 2 Viol. V. e B. Op. XIV.*
Parigi.

VI. Quattri concert. da KUCHELER, *a 2 Viol. V. e B.*
Op. IV. Parigi.

QUINTETTI intagliati.

VI. Quintetti da ZANNETTI, *a 3 Viol. e 2 Violoncelli. Op. II. London.*

CONCERTI per il Violino concertato.

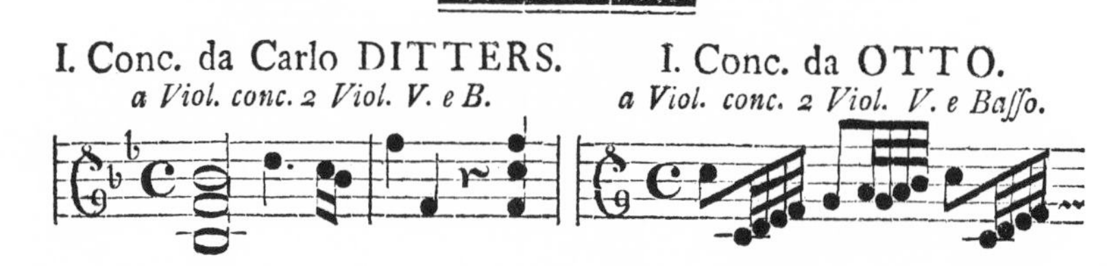

I. Conc. da JARNOVIK, *a Viol. conc. 2 Cor. 2 Ob. 2 Viol. V. e B.* Parigi.

III. Concerti da REIPEL, *a Viol. conc. 2 Viol. V. e B.* Op. I. Parigi.

VIOLA.

VI. Quattri da M. STAMITZ, le Fils, *a Violino, 2 Viole e B.* Parigi.

I. Concerto da PESCH, *a Viola conc. 2 Viol. V. e B.*

II. Concerti da STAMITZ.

I. *a Viola conc. 2 Cor. 2 Clar. 2 Violini, 2 Viole e B.* Parigi. II. *a Viola conc. 2 Cor. 2 Fl. 2 Violini, 2 Viole e B.* Parigi.

VIOLONCELLO.

VI. Soli da MARA, *a Violonc. e B.*

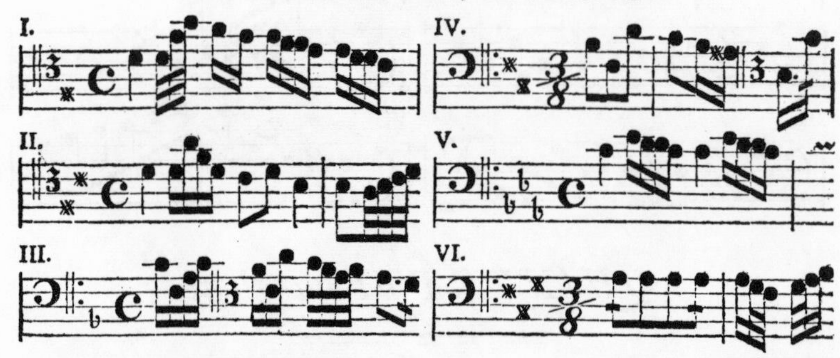

CONCERTI *per il Violoncello concertato.*

II. Concerti da FILS.

I. *a Violonc. conc. 2 Viol. V. e B.* II. *a Violonc. conc. 2 Cor. 2 Viol. V. e B.*

I. Concerto da KLEINKNECHT, *a Violonc. conc. 2 Cor. 2 Fl. 2 Viol. V. e B.*

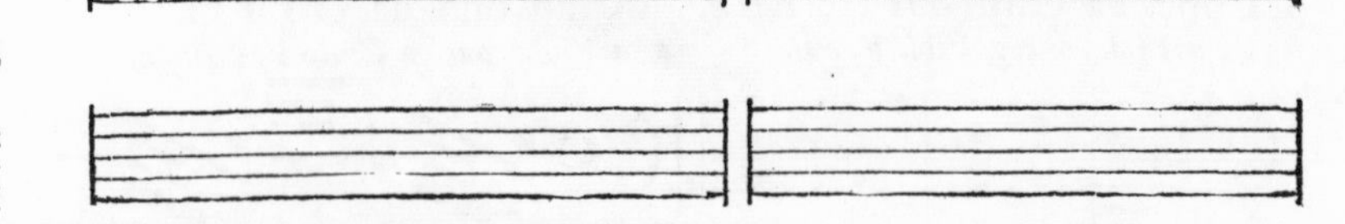

FLAUTO TRAVERSO.

I. Solo da Giov. VANHALL, *a Flauto con Basso.*

VI. Soli da WENDLING, *a Flauto con Basso. Op. IV. Parigi.*

DUETTI *intagliati.*

VI. Duetti da T. GIORDANI, *a 2 Flauti. Op. I. Parigi.*

I. II. III. IV. V. VI.

VI. Duetti da SCHWINDL, *a 2 Flauti. Op. I. Parigi.*

TRII.

I. Trio da FILS, *a Flauto, Violonc. e B.*

TRII *intagliati.*

VI. Trii da Conrad BREUNIG, *a Flauto, Violino e B. Op. IV. Francf. sur le Main.*

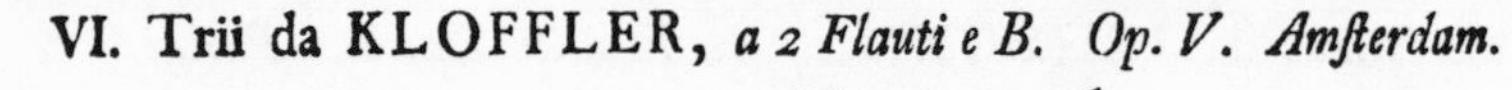

VI. Trii da KLOFFLER, *a 2 Flauti e B. Op. V. Amſterdam.*

VI. Trii da Gio. Batt. WENDLING, *a Flauto, Violino e B. Op. VII. Amſterdam.*

QUATTRI.

A FLAUTO, VIOLINO, VIOLA E BASSO.

I. Quattro da Giov. VAAHALL.

VI. Quattri da SCHMIDT.

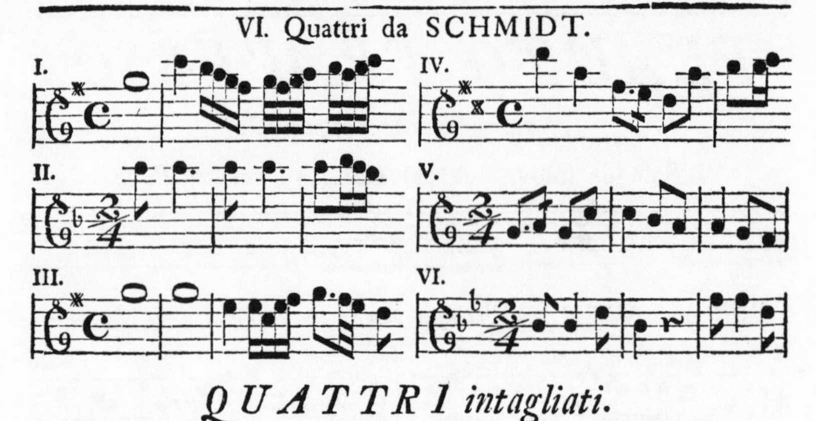

QUATTRI intagliati.

VI. Quattri da CANNABICH, *a Flauto, Viol. V. e B. Op. I. Amſterdam.*

VI. Quattri da J. Aug. Louis FATKEN, *a Flauto, Violino, V. e B. Op. I. Amſterdam.*

VI. Quattri da G. A. KREUSSER, *a Flauto, Viol. V. e B. Op. VIII. Amsterdam.*

VI. Quattri da M. J. SCHMITBAUR, *a Flauto, 2 Viol. e B. Op. I. Mannheim.*

VI. Quattri da Giov. VANHALL, *a Fl. Viol. V. e B. Op. XIV. Parigi.*
vide sopra Quattri da KREUSSER.

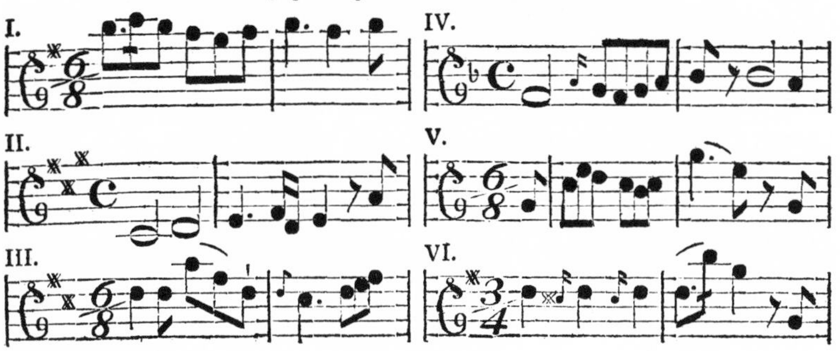

I. Quattro da Giuf. TOESCHI, *a Flauto, Viol. V. e B. Mannheim.*

CONCERTI.

A FLAUTO TRAVERSO CONCERTATO.

I. Concerto da KEHL, *a Flauto conc. 2 Viol. V. e B.*

II. Concerti da Fred. KLEINKNECHT.
I. *a Flauto conc. 2 Viol. V. e B.* II. *a Fl. conc. 2 C. 2 Vi. V. Bassono obl. e B.*

CONCERTI intagliati.

I. Conc. da BESOZZI, *a Flauto conc. 2 Viol. V. e B. Amsterdam.*

II. Concerti da C. STAMITZ, *a Fl. conc. 2 Viol. V. e B. Parigi.*

III. Concerti da TROMLITZ, *a Fl. conc. 2 Viol. V. e B. Op. I. Amsterdam.*

FAGOTTO.

I. Solo da MAERZ, *a Fagotto solo con Basso.*

I. Trio da MAERZ, *a Fagotto, Flauto e B.*

CONCERTI.

II. Concerti da BESOZZI.

I. *a Fag. conc. 2 Viol. V. e B.*

II. *a Fag. conc. 2 Viol. V. e B.*

I. Concerto da GROSS, *a Fag. conc. 2 Viol. V. e B.*

I. Concerto da HENNIG, *a Fag. conc. 2 Cor. 2 Ob. 2 Viol. V. e B.*

I. Concerto da MAERZ, *a Fag. conc. 2 Viol. V. e B.*

CEMBALO.

SOLI.

XIV. Polonoisen da BACH, *in Halla.*

I. Sonata da G. BENDA, *a 2 Cembali.*

VII. Sonate da Francesco DUSCHECK.

Minuetto da Gius. HAYDEN, *con XII Variazioni a Cembalo.*

VI. Sonate da MEISLER.

SONATE intagliate e ſtampate.

VI. Sonatinen, von Chriſt. Gottlieb Ahneſorgen. *Hamburg.*

III. Sonate da J. BACH. *Op. III. Parigi.*

VI. Sonate da J. F. KLÖFFLER. *Op. VI. Amſterdäm.*

VI. Ouverture da C. F. ABEL. *London.*

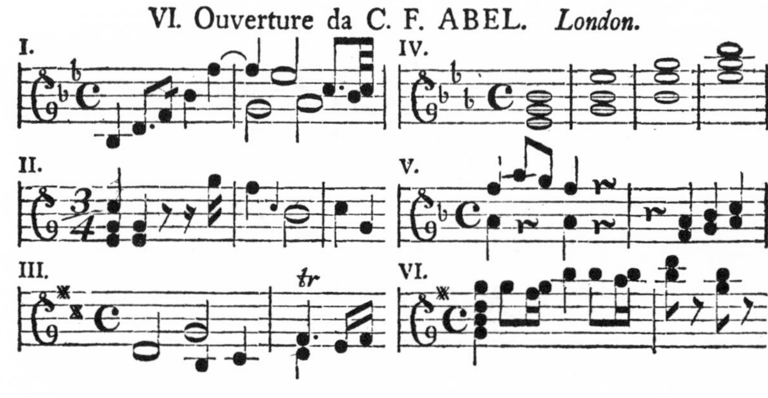

T R I I,

A CEMBALO OBLIGATO CON VIOLINO O FLAUTO.

I. Sonata da DUSCHECK, *a Cembalo e Violino.*

I. Sonata da SCHOBERT, *a Cembalo e Violino.*

TRII intagliati.

III. Sonate da J. BACH, *a Cembalo e Violino. Op. III. Parigi.*

VI. Sonate da P. GUGLIELMI, *a Cembalo e Violino. London.*

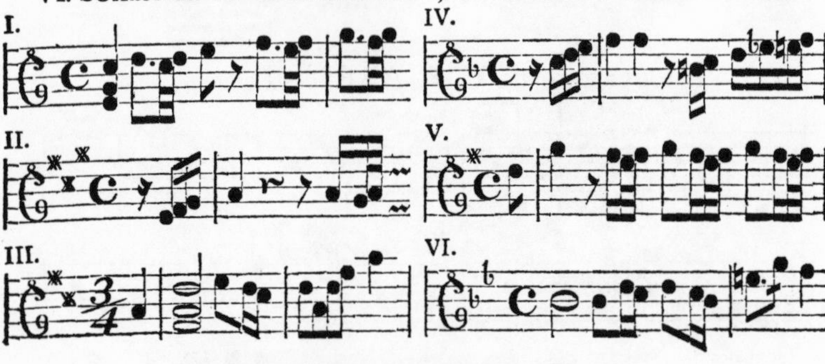

TERZETTI.

II. Sonate da JUST, *a Cembalo, Viol. e B.*

TERZETTI intagliati.

III. Sonate da HAUEISEN, *a Cembalo, Violino e B. Op. III.*
Francf. sur le Main.

III. Sonate da Fred. HELLMUTH, *a Cembalo, Viol. e B.*
Op. I. Offenbach.

VI. Sonate da LIBER, *a Cembalo, Viol. e B. Mannheim.*

III. Sonate da J. F. STERKEL. *a Cembalo, Viol. e B. Op. I. Francf. sur le Main.*

III. Sonate da J. F. STERKEL. *a Cembalo, Viol. e B. Op. II. Francf. sur le Main.*

VI. Sonate da Giov. VANHALL, *a Cemb. Viol. e B.* *Op. I.* *Offenbach.*

DIVERTIMENTI e PARTITE.

I. Concertino da Fr. DUSCHECK, *a Cemb. Flauto, Viol. Violoncello e B.*

I. Divertim. da HAMPEL, *a Cemb. Flauto, 2 Viol. e B.*

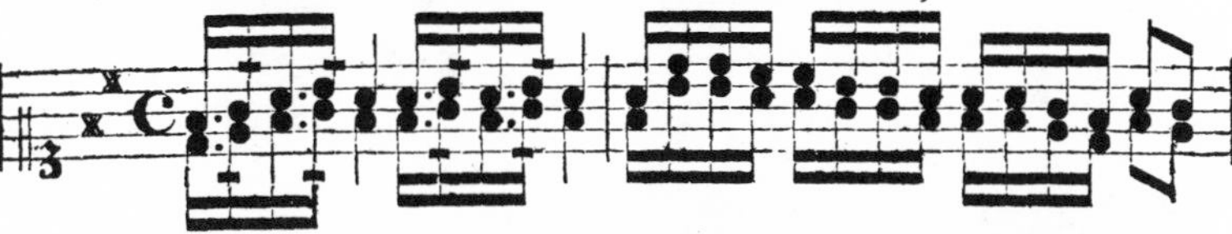

I. Partita da Giuſ. HAYDEN, *a Cemb. Violino ſolo e B.*

I. Partita da Giuſ. HAYDEN, *a Cemb. 2 Viol. e Baſſono.*

I. Sinfonia da KOLB, *a Cemb. Violino, Viola e B.*

QUATTRI intagliati.

II. Quattri da GRETRY, *a Cemb. Flauto, Viol. e B.* *Op. I.* *Offenbach.*

VI. Quattri da L. I. SCHULTZ, *a Cemb. Flauto, Viol. e B.* *Op. I.* *Amſterdam.*

CONCERTI, a Cemb. con più Stromenti.

I. Conc. da Sebaſt. BACH, *a 3 Cemb. 2 Viol. V. e B.*

I. Conc. da Fr. BRIXY, *a Cemb. conc. 2 Cor. 2 Viol. V. e B.*

I. Conc. da Dominco BRIXY, *a Organo ſolo, 2 Clar. 2 Viol. V. e B.*

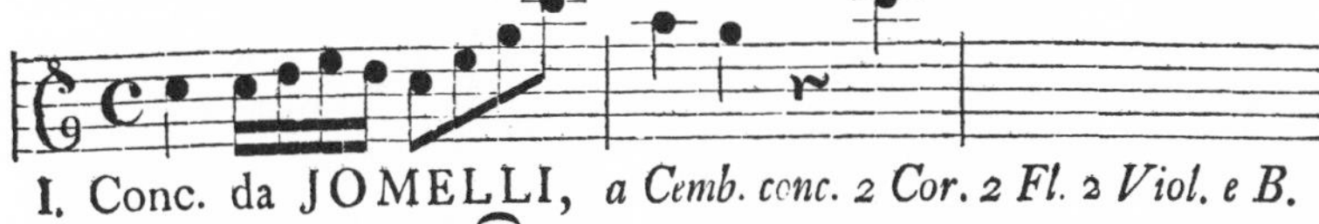

I. Conc. da JOMELLI, *a Cemb. conc. 2 Cor. 2 Fl. 2 Viol. e B.*

I. Conc. da MOELLER, *a Cemb. conc. 2 C. 2 Fl. 2 Viol. V. e B.*

I. Conc. da SCHINDLER, *a Cemb. conc. 2 Cor. 2 Ob. 2 Fl. 2 Fag. 2 Viol. V. e B.*

I. Conc. da SCHOBERT, *a Cemb. conc. 2 Cor. 2 Viol. V. e B.*

I. Conc. da SCHOEPS, *a Cemb. conc. 2 Viol. V. e B.*

I. Conc. da WAGENSEIL, *a Organo, 2 Viol. e B.*

CONCERTI intagliati.

VI. Conc. da C. F. ABEL, *a Cemb. conc. 2 Viol. e B. Op. XI. Londra.*

II. Conc. da EICHNER, *a Cemb. conc. 2 Cor. 2 Fl. 2 Viol. V. e B. Op. V. Amsterdam.*

I. Conc. da G. C. KELLNER, *a Cemb. conc. 2 Cor. 2 Viol. V. e B. Op. III. Francf. sur le Main.*

I. Conc. da KELLNER, *a Cemb. conc. 2 Cor. 2 Viol. V. e B. Amsterdam.*

II. Conc. da Giorgio RUSCH, *a Cemb. conc. 2 Cor. 2 Ob. 2 Viol. e B. a la Haye.*

VI. Conc. da G. S. SCHROETER, *a Cemb. conc. 2 Viol. e B. Op. III. Londra.*

HARPA.

I. Conc. da SCHOEPS, *a Harpa conc. 2 Viol. e B.*

ARIE DELL' OPERA LA CONTESSINA, dal Sign. FLORIANO GASMANN.

Atto primo.

1. Terz. *a 2 C. 2 Ob. 2 Viol. Viola, 2 Ten. Baſſo e Fond.*

2. Terz. *a 2 Ob. 2 Viol. V. Fag, 2 Ten. Baſſo e Fond.*

3. Aria. *a 2 Cor. 2 Ob. 2 Viol. V. Fag. Baſſo e Fond.*

4. Cavatina. *a 2 C. 2 Ob. 2 Viol. V. Fag. Soprano e Fond.*

5. Cavatina. *a 2 Viol. V. Fagotto, Sopr. e Tenore, e Fond.*

6. Aria. *a 2 Cor. 2 Ob. 2 Viol. V. Fagotti. Tenore e Fond.*

7. Aria. *a 2 Cor. 2 Ob. 2 Viol. V. Fagotto, Soprano e Fond.*

8. Aria. *a 2 C. 2 Ob. 2 Viol. V. Fagotti. Tenore e Fond.*

9. Aria. *a 2 Cor. 2 Ob. 2 Viol. 2 Viole, Soprano e Fond.*

10. Aria. *a 2 Cor. 2 Ob. 2 Viol. V. Fag. Soprano e Fond.*

11. Aria. *a 2 C. 2 Ob. 2 Viol. V. Fagotti. Baſſo e Fond.*

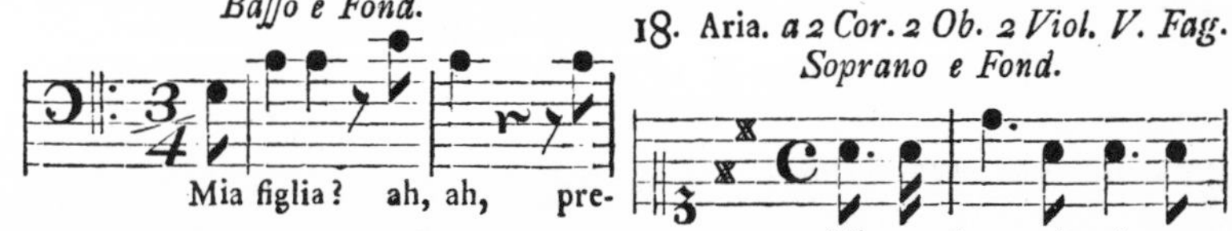

12. Finale. *a 2 C. 2 Ob. 2 Viol. V. Fag. 1 Sopr. 2 Ten. e Baſſo, Violonc. e Fond.*

Atto ſecondo.

13. Terzetto. *a 2 C. 2 Ob. 2 Viol. V. Fag. 3 Tenori e Fond.*

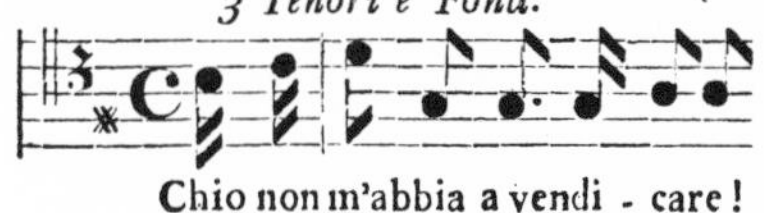

14. Aria. *a 2 C. 2 Ob. 2 Viol. V. Fagotto. Tenore e Fond.*

15. Terzetto. *a 2 Viol. V. 2 Soprani, Baſſo e Fond.*

16. Aria *a 2 C. 2 Ob. 2 Viol. V. Tenore e Fond.*

Per voi ſola, o mio bel

17. Aria. *a 2 Cor. 2 Ob. 2 Viol. 2 Viole, 2 Fagotti, Baſſo e Fond.*

Per e - ſempio, quando

18. Aria. *a 2 Cor. 2 Ob. 2 Viol. V. Fag. Soprano e Fond.*

19. Aria. *a 2 Cor. 2 Ob. 2 Viol. Viola, Soprano e Fond.*

20. Aria. *a 2 Ob. 2 Viol. V. Fagotto, Soprano e Fond.*

N'ho vi - ſte tan - te e

21. Terzetto. *a 2 Cor. 2 Ob. 2 Viol. 2 V. Fagotto, 2 Ten. Baſſo e Fond.*

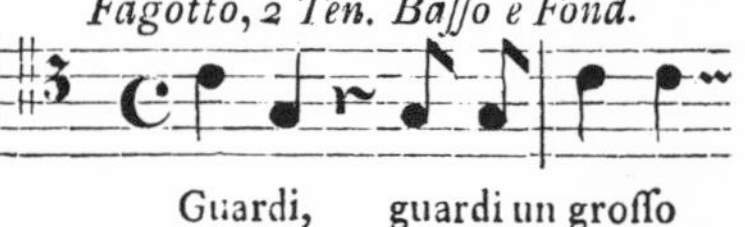

22. Finale. *a 2 C. 2 Ob. 2 Viol. V. Fag. 1 Soprano, 3 Tenori, Baſſo e Fond.*

Folgende Stücke sind in Partitur und in Stimmen zu haben.

Italiänische Opern.

Piccini — la buona figliola.
— — la buona figliola maritata.

Teutsche Opern.

Hillers — Lisuart und Dariolette.
— — Lottchen am Hofe.
— — Liebe auf dem Lande.
— — Jagd.
— — verwandelte Weiber.
— — Dorfbalbier.
— — lustiger Schuster.
— — Aerndtekranz.
— — Krieg.
— — Jubelhochzeit.
Neefens — Apotheke.
— — Amors Guckkasten.
— — Einsprüche.
Schweitzers — Elisium.
— — Alceste.
— — Dorf-Galla.
Stegmanns — Deserteur.
Ubers — Clarisse.
Wolfs — Rosenfest.
— — Dorfdeputirten.
— — treue Köhler.
— — Gärtnermädchen.
— — Abend im Walde.
— — großes Loos.

Italiänische Oratoria.

Fischetti La Morte d'Abele.
Hasse Sant Elena, neue Compos. 1773.

Teutsche Oratoria.

Ein Oratorium von Carl Phil. Em. Bach.
Wolfs leidender Erlöser.

Nach-

Nachricht.

Die Ausgabe dieses IXten Supplements hat sich wider Vermuthen so lange verzögert; man wollte dem Vorwurfe vorbeugen, daß man alte Musicalien unter die neuen mische, oder andere unter unrechten Nahmen bekannt mache, und deswegen desto vorsichtiger dabey verfahren. Dieser Vorwurf ist immer **den geschriebenen Musicalien** gemacht worden; ob aber die Liebhaber sicherer gehen, welche sich deswegen an **gestochene und gedruckte Musicalien** halten, wird die 11. 16. 24. und 35. Seite dieses Supplements entscheiden; denn der Herr Cammerm. Eichner zu Berlin versichert, daß die auf letzterer Seite angezeigten 2 Clavierconcerte nicht von ihm sind. Wir versichern wenigstens das Publicum, das dergleichen Unrichtigkeiten nicht vorsetzlich von uns veranstaltet werden, und wir uns eher Mühe geben, solche zu entdecken, als davon Vortheil zu ziehen.

Leipzig,
den 25. Julii 1775.

B. C. B. u. S.

SUPPLEMENTO X.
DEI
CATALOGI
DELLE
SINFONIE, PARTITE, OVERTURE, SOLI, DUETTI, TRII, QUATTRI E CONCERTI

PER IL
VIOLINO, FLAUTO TRAVERSO,
CEMBALO
ED ALTRI STROMENTI,
CHE
SI TROVANO IN MANOSCRITTO
NELLA OFFICINA MUSICA DI BREITKOPF
IN LIPSIA.

1775.

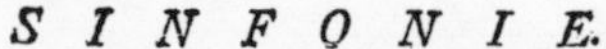
S I N F O N I E.

2
SINFONIE.
I. Sinf. da BOEMO.
a 2 Cor. 2 Ob. 2 Viol. V. e. B.
I. Sinf. da BOLOGNA.
a 2 Cor. 2 Ob. 2 Viol. V. e B.
V. Sinf. da G. D. CRUSE.
I. a 2 Cor. 2 Fl. 2 Viol. V. e B.
IV. a 2 Cor. 2 Ob. 2 Viol. V. e B.
II. a 2 Cor. 2 Ob. 2 Viol. V. e B.
V. a 2 Cor. 2 Ob. 2 Viol. V. e B.
III. 2 Cor. 2 Ob. 2 Viol. V. e. B.
V. Sinf. da Carlo DITTERS.
I. a 2 C. 2 O. 2 Fl. 2 Fag. 2 Viol. V. e B.
IV. a 2 Cor. 2 Ob. 2 Viol. V. e B.
II. a 2 Cor. 2 Ob. 2 Viol. V. e B.
V. a 2 C. 2 Ob. Fl. Fag. 2. Viol. V. e B.
I. Sinf. da FAGHETTI.
III. a 2 Cor. 2 Ob. 2 Viol. V. e B.
a 2 Cor. 2 Ob. 2 Viol. 2 Viole e B.
II. Sinf. da Flor. GASMANN.
I. a 2 Cor. 2 Ob. 2 Fag. 2 Viol. V. e. B.
II. a 2 Cor. 2 Ob. 2 Clar. Tymp. 2 Viol. V. Violoncel. e B.
3
I. Sinf da Gius. HAYDEN. a 2 Cor. 2 Ob. 2 Viol. V. e B.
I. Sinf. da HOLTZBAUER. a 2 Cor. 2 Ob. 2 Viol. V. e B.
III. Sinf. da HUBER.
I. a 2 Cor. 2 Ob. Flauto 2 Viol. V. e B.
III. a 2 C. 2 O. 2 Cl. Tymp. 2 Viol. V. e B.
II. a 2 Cor. 2 Ob. 2 Viol. V. e B.
I. Sinf. da KOZELUCH. a 2 C. 2 Ob. 2 Clar. 2 Fl. 2 Fag. 2 Viol. V. e B.
II. Sinf. da LANGE.
I. a 2 Cor. 2 Ob. 2 Viol. V. e B.
II. a 2 Cor. 2 Fl. 2 Viol. V. e B.
II. Sinf. da Gius. MISLEWECZECK.
I. a 2 Cor. 2 Ob. 2. Viol. V. e B.
II. a 2 Cor. 2 Ob. 2 Viol. V. e B.
II. Sinf. da L. MOZART.
I. a 2 Cor. 2 Ob. 2 Viol. V. e B.
II. a 2 Cor. 2 Ob. 2 Viol. V. e B.
I. Sinf. da Carlo ORDONEZ. a 2 Cor. 2 Ob. 2 Viol. V. e B.

4 SINFONIE.
VII. Sinf. da PICHL.
I. a 2 C. 2 O. 2 Clar. Tymp. 2 Viol. V. e B.
V. a 2 Cor. 2 Ob. 2 Viol. V. e B.
II. a 2 Cor. 2 Ob. 2 Viol. V. e B.
VI. a 2 C. 2 O. 2 Clarinetti 2 Viol. V. e B.
III. 2 C. 2 Ob. Andante Fl. 2 Vi. V. e B.
VII. 2 Cor. 2 Ob. 2 Viol. V. e B.
IV. a 2 Cor. 2 Ob. 2 Viol. V. e B.
X. Sinf. da SCHMIDTBAUER.
I. a 2 C. 2 O. 2 Clar. Tymp. 2 Viol. V. e B.
VI. a 2 Cor. 2 Ob. 2 Fl. 2 Viol. V. e B.
II. a 2 Cor. 2 Ob. 2 Fl. 2 Viol. V. e B.
VII. a 2 Cor. 2 Ob. 2 Fl. 2 Viol. V. e B.
III. a 2 C. 2 O. 2 Fl. 2 Fag. 2 Viol. V. e B.
VIII. a 2 C. 2 O. 2 Fl. Fag. 2 Vi. 2 V. e B.
IV. a 2 Cor. 2 Ob. 2 Fl. 2 Viol. V. e B.
IX. a 2 C. 2 O. 2 Fl. 2 Fag. 2 Viol. V. e B.
V. a 2 C. 2 Ob. 2 Cl. Tymp. 2 Viol. V. e B.
X. a 2 Cor. 2 Ob. 2 Fl. 2 Viol. V. e B.

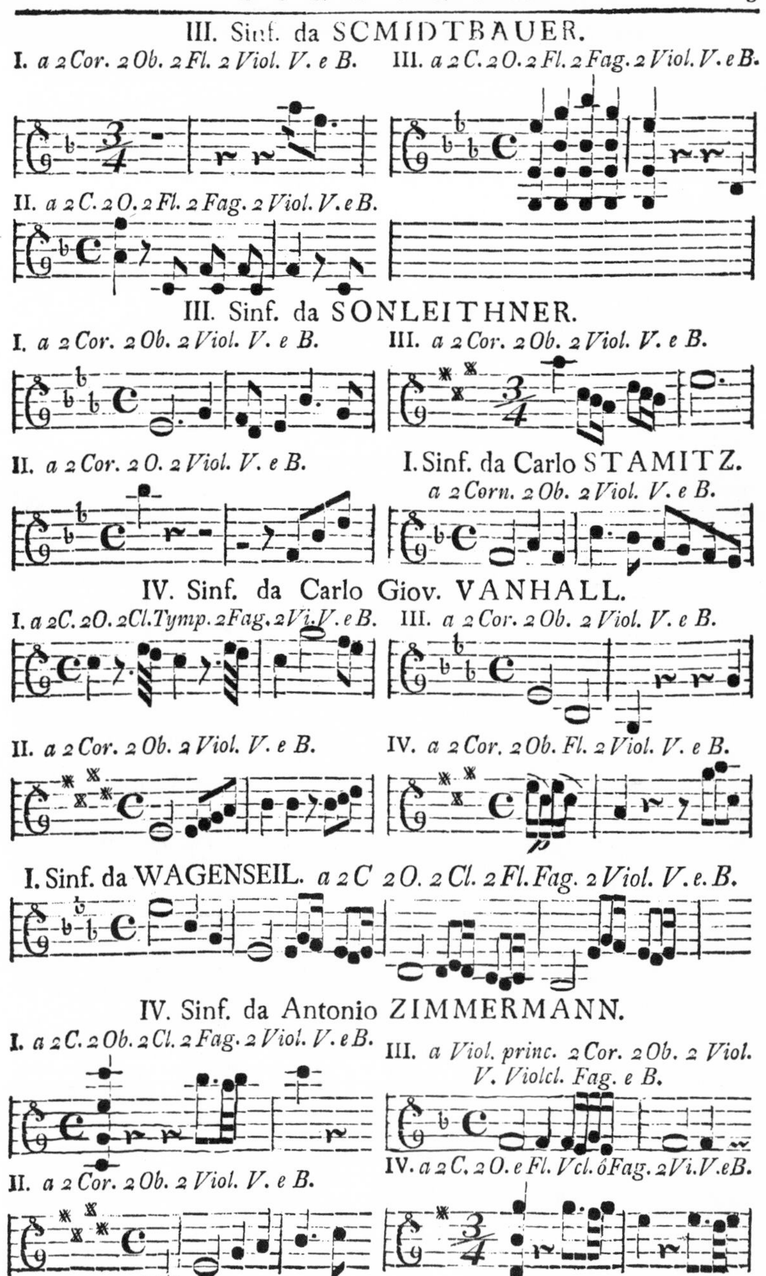
SINFONIE. 5
III. Sinf. da SCMIDTBAUER.
I. a 2 Cor. 2 Ob. 2 Fl. 2 Viol. V. e B.
III. a 2 C. 2 O. 2 Fl. 2 Fag. 2 Viol. V. e B.
II. a 2 C. 2 O. 2 Fl. 2 Fag. 2 Viol. V. e B.
III. Sinf. da SONLEITHNER.
I. a 2 Cor. 2 Ob. 2 Viol. V. e B.
III. a 2 Cor. 2 Ob. 2 Viol. V. e B.
II. a 2 Cor. 2 O. 2 Viol. V. e B.
I. Sinf. da Carlo STAMITZ.
a 2 Corn. 2 Ob. 2 Viol. V. e B.
IV. Sinf. da Carlo Giov. VANHALL.
I. a 2C. 2O. 2Cl. Tymp. 2Fag. 2Vi. V. e B.
III. a 2 Cor. 2 Ob. 2 Viol. V. e B.
II. a 2 Cor. 2 Ob. 2 Viol. V. e B.
IV. a 2 Cor. 2 Ob. Fl. 2 Viol. V. e B.
I. Sinf. da WAGENSEIL. a 2 C 2 O. 2 Cl. 2 Fl. Fag. 2 Viol. V. e. B.
IV. Sinf. da Antonio ZIMMERMANN.
I. a 2 C. 2 Ob. 2 Cl. 2 Fag. 2 Viol. V. e B.
III. a Viol. princ. 2 Cor. 2 Ob. 2 Viol. V. Violcl. Fag. e B.
II. a 2 Cor. 2 Ob. 2 Viol. V. e B.
IV. a 2 C. 2 O. e Fl. Vcl. ô Fag. 2 Vi. V. e B.

SINFONIE intagliate e ftampate.

I. Sinf. da I. C. BACH. à Viol. obl. Violcl obl. 2 C. 2 Ob. 2 Viol. V. e B. N. 1. Offenbach.

VI. Sinf. da Francefco BECK. a 2 Cor. 2 Ob. 2 Viol. V. e B. Op. IV. Parigi.

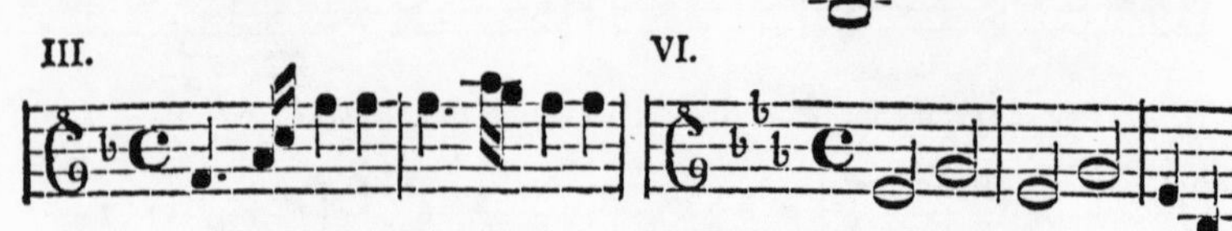

VI. Sinf. da Fr. BECK. a 2 Viol. V. e B. Op. II. Parigi.

I. 2 Corni. IV.

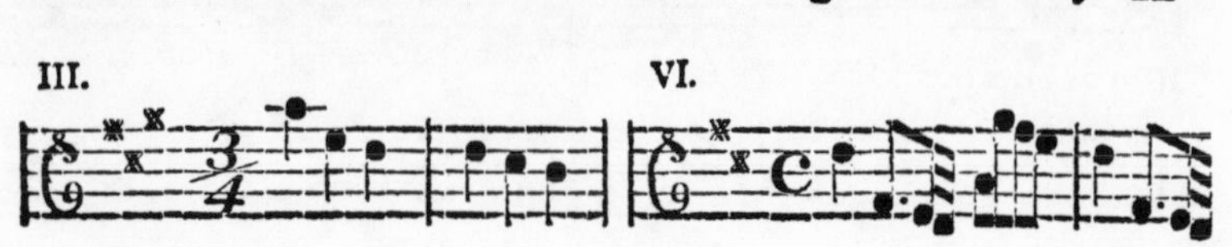

SINFONIES PERIODIQUES.

VI. da C. E. GRAAF. La Haye.

I. a 2 C. 2 Ob. 2 Cl. Tymp. 2 Viol. V. e B. IV. a 2 Cor. 2 Fl. 2 Viol. V. e B.

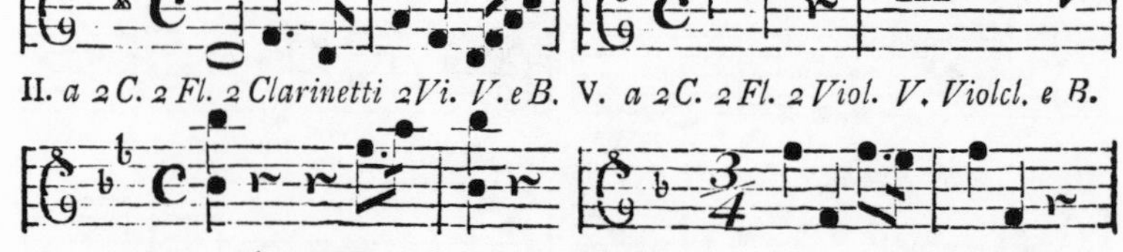

II. a 2 C. 2 Fl. 2 Clarinetti 2 Vi. V. e B. V. a 2 C. 2 Fl. 2 Viol. V. Violcl. e B.

III. a 2 Cor. 2 Ob. 2 Viol. 2 Viole e B. VI. a 2 Cor. 2 Ob. 2 Viol. V. e B.

I. da F. P. RICCI. a 2 Cor. 2 Ob. 2 Viol. Viola obl. e B.

I. Concertino da Barone de SCHACHT. a Corno obl. Clarinetto obl. Fag. obl. 2 Fl. 2 Tallie 2 Viol. V. e B.

VIOLINO.

VI. Solie da I. G. BURCKHOFFER. Opera I. Parigi.

8 VIOLINO.
VI. Soli da Antoine LOLLI. Op. III. Amſterdam.
TRII.
A DUE VIOLINI CON BASSO.
VI. Trii da A. KAMMEL.
TRII intagliati.
VI. Trii da C. A. PESCH. Op. II. London.

VIOLINO. 9
VI. Trii da C. A. PESCH. Op. III. London.
QUATTRI.
III. Quattri da Giuſeppe HAYDEN. a 2 Viol. V. e. B.
VI. Quattri da Leop. HOFFMANN. a 2 Viol. V. e B.

10 VIOLINO.
IX. Quattri da Carlo STAMITZ, a 2 Viol. V. e B.
I.
VI.
II.
VII.
III.
VIII.
IV.
IX.
V.
VI. Quattri da Giov. VANHALL, a 2 Viol. V. e B.
I.
IV.
II.
V.
III.
VI.
VIOLINO. 11
QUATTRI intagliati.
III. Quattri da Gius. HAYDEN. a 2 Viol. V. e B. Op. XVII.
Offenbach.
I.
III.
II.
CONCERTI per il Violino concertato.
II. Concerti da CRAMER.
I. a Viol. conc. 2 Viol. V. e B.
II. a Viol. conc. 2 C. 2 Ob. 2 Viol. V. e B.
II. Concerti da G. D. CRUSE.
I. a Viol. conc. 2 Viol. V. e B.
II. a Viol. conc. 2 C. 2 Ob. 2 Viol. V. e B.
I. Conc. da LEEDER.
a Viol. conc. 2 Cor. 2 Fl. 2 Viol. V. e B.
I. Conc. da PICHL.
a Viol. conc. 2 Viol. V. e B.
III. Concerti da Carlo STAMITZ.
I. a Viol. conc. 2 Viol. V. e B.
III. a Viol. conc. 2 C. 2 Ob. 2 Viol. V. e B.
II. a Viol. conc. 2 Viol. V. e B.

III. Concerti da Giov. VANHALL.

I. *a Viol. conc. 2 C. 2 Ob. 2 Viol. V. e B.* III. *a Viol. conc. 2 Viol. V. e B.*

II. *a Viol. conc. 2 Cor. 2 Viol. V. e B.*

VIOLONCELLO.

I. Solo da VANDINI, *a Violoncello con Basso.*

I. Concerto da Leop. HOFFMANN, *a Violcl. conc. 2 C. 2 Viol. V. e B.*

FLAUTO TRAVERSO.

DUETTI *intagliati.*

VI. Duetti da CANNABICH, *a Flauto con Violino. Op. IV. Mannh.*

I. IV.

II. V.

III. VI.

QUATTRI.

A FLAUTO, VIOLINO VIOLA e BASSO.

V. Quattri da G. D. CRUSE.

I. IV.

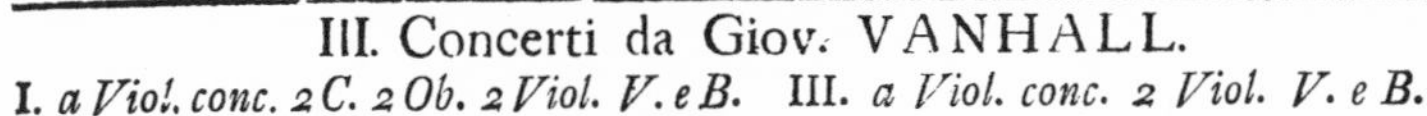

II. V.

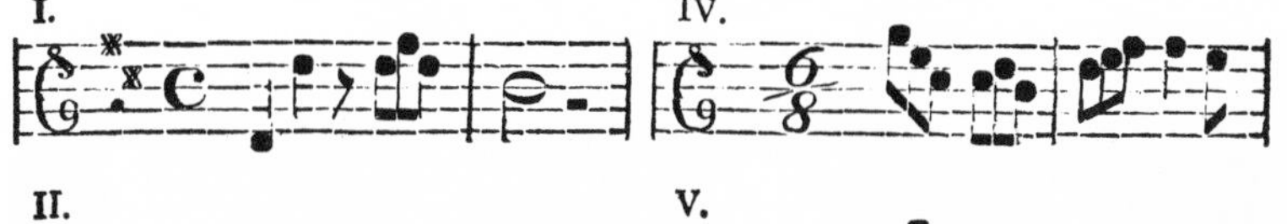

III.

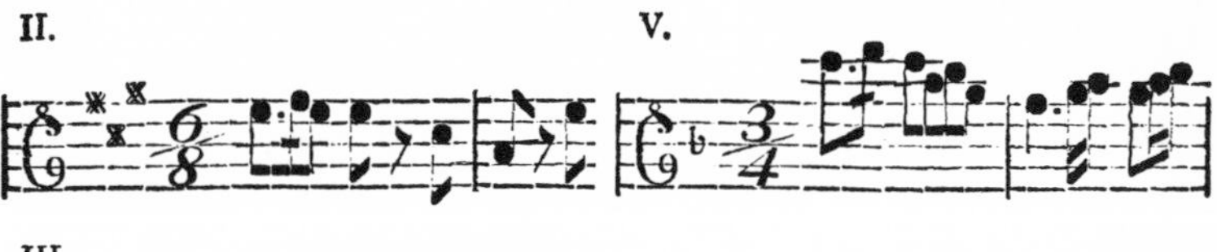

I. Quattro da Ern. Gugl. WOLFF, *a Flauto, Oboe o Viol. Fag. o Violonc. e B. Breslau.*

CONCERTI.

A FLAUTO TRAVERSO CONCERTATO.

VI. Concerti da HUPFELD.

I. *a Fl. conc. 2 Cor. 2 Viol. V. e B.* IV. *a Fl. conc. 2 Cor. 2 Viol. V. e B.*

II. *a Fl. conc. 2 Cor. 2 Viol. V. e B.* V. *a Fl. conc. 2 C. 2 Viol. V. 2 Fag. e B.*

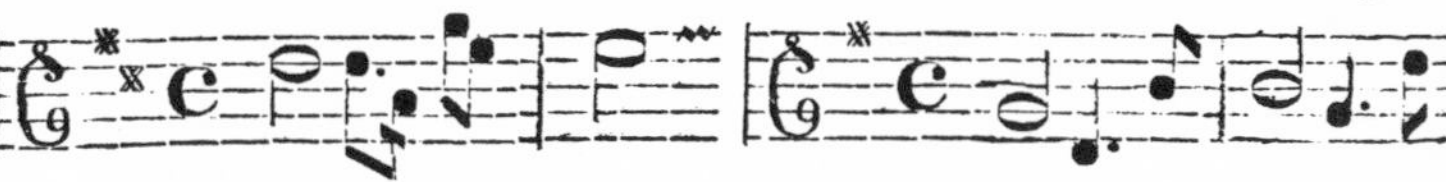

III. *a Fl. conc. 2 Cor. 2 Viol. V. e B.* VI. *a Fl. conc. 2 C. 2 Fl. rhinf. 2 Vi. V. e B.*

IV. Concerti da Giov. VANHALL.

I. *a Fl. conc. 2 Cor. 2 Viol. V. e B.* III.

II. *a Fl. conc. 2 Cor. 2 Viol. V. e B.* IV. *a Fl. conc. 2 Cor. 2 Viol. V. e B.*

O B O E.

CONCERTI *a* OBOE CONCERTATO.

I. Concerto da BESOZZI, *a Ob. conc. 2 Viol. V. e B.*

III. Concerti da Carlo DITTERS.

I. *a Ob. conc. 2 Viol. V. e B.* III. *a Ob. conc. 2 Cor. 2 Viol. V. e B.*

II. *a Ob. conc. 2 Cor. 2 Viol. V. e B.*

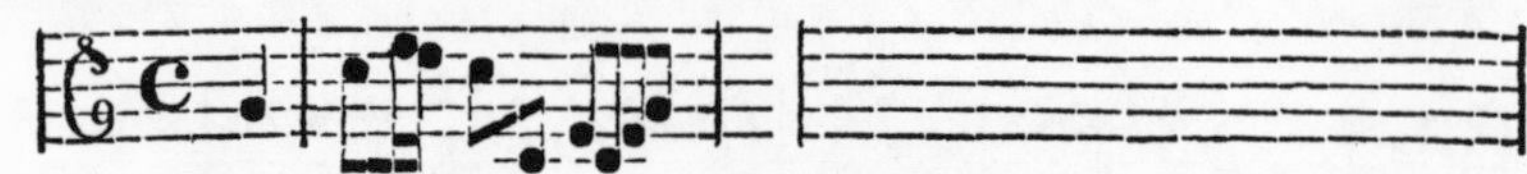

I. Concerto da E. EICHNER, *a Ob. conc. 2 C. 2 Fl. 2 Viol. V. e Basso.*

I. Concerto da KLEINKNECHT, *a Ob. conc. 2 Viol. V. e B.*

XIII. Concerti Militari da diversi Maestri, *intagliati in Londra.* Vid. Suppl. VI. p. 21.

a 2 Oboi o Flauti 2 Corni 2 Clarinetti e Fagotto.

CLARINETTO.

VII. Sonate da A. RATHGEN. *a 2 Clarinetti 2 Corni e Basson* *Op. I. London.*

CEMBALO.

SOLI.

SONATE intagliate e stampate.

VI Clavier - Suiten da Gottlob Willhelm BURMANN. *Berlin und Leipzig.*

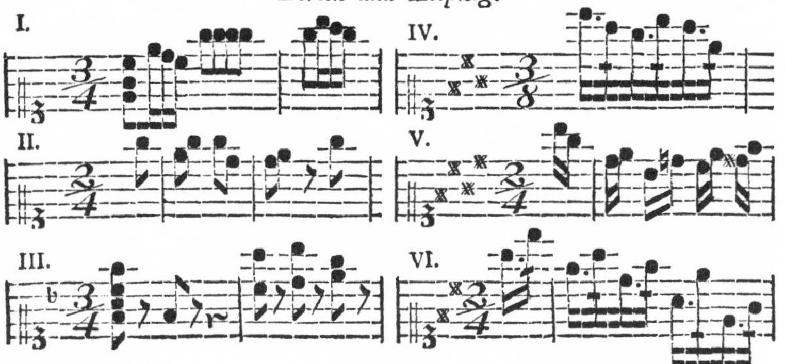

III. Sonate da Leonardo FRISCHMUTH. *Amsterd.*

VI. Sonate da Ioh. Guil. HAESSLER. *Leipzig.*

VI. Sonate da Giov. Federico REICHARDT. *Berlin.*

VI. Sonate da I. F. W. WENKEL. *Hamburg.*

VI. Sonate da E. G. WOLFF.

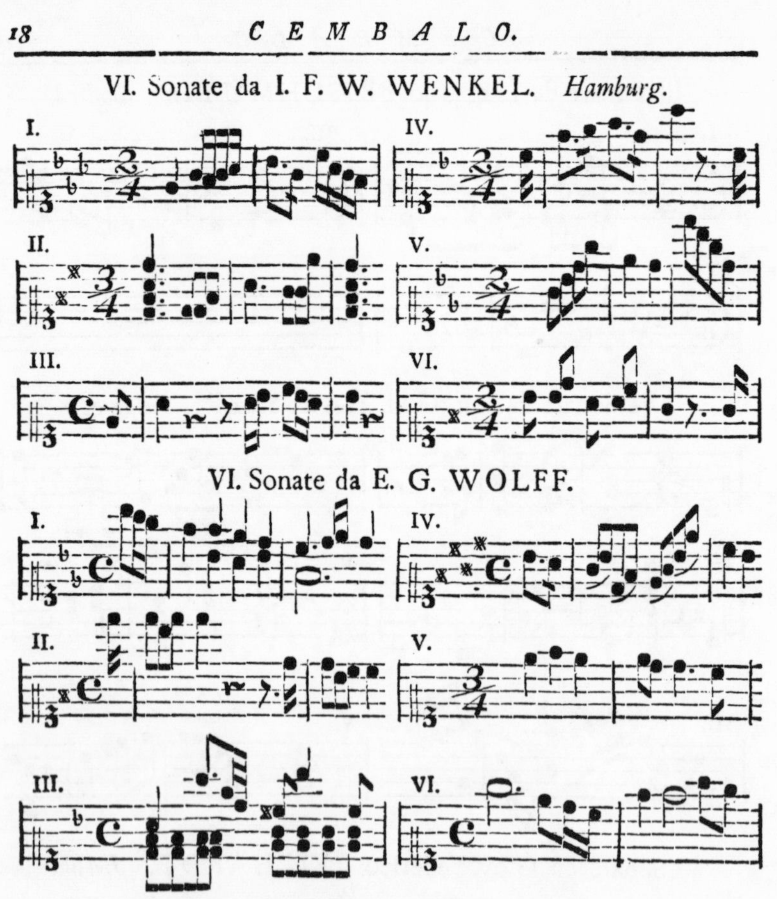

VI. Sonate da E. G. WOLFF.

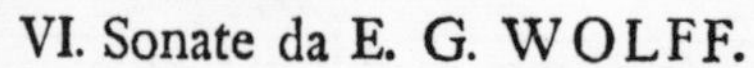

I. Duetto da I. Gottfr. MÜTHEL, *a 2 Clavicembali. Riga.*

TRII e TERZETTI.

I. Sonata da WIRBACH, *a Cembalo c. Violoncello obligato.*

I. Sonata da Benjam. UBER, *a Cembalo Viol. e B.*

QUATTRI e DIVERTIMENTI.

II. Sonate da Benj. UBER.

I. *a Cemb. 2 Cor. Violino e Violoncello.* II. *a Cemb. 2 Cor. 2 Fl. 2 Viol. e B.*

QUATTRI intagliati.

III. Quattri da I. BAUER, *a Cemb. Fl. Viol. e B. Op. IV*
Francf. sur le Main.

VI. Quattri da Giov. Giorg. LANG, *a Cemb. Fl. Viol. Violcl. ó Viola. Opera III. Offenbach.*

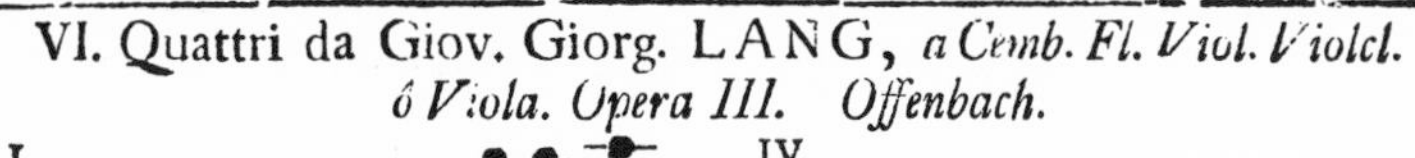

CONCERTI, *a Cemb. con più Stromenti.*

I. Conc. da BIRK, *a Cemb. conc. 2 Viol. V. e B.*

II. Concerti da LANGE.

I. *a Cemb. conc. 2 Viol. V. e B.* II. *a Cemb. conc. 2 C. 2 Viol. V. e B.*

I. Conc. da RICHTER, *a Cemb. conc. 2 Viol. V. e B.*

I. Conc. da RIEPEL, *a Cemb. conc. Viol. conc. 2 C. Ob. 2 Viol. V. e B.*

I. Conc. da SALES, *a Cemb. conc. 2 C. 2 Viol. V. e B.*

I. Conc. da SCHAFFRATH, *a Cemb. conc. 2 Viol. V. e B.*

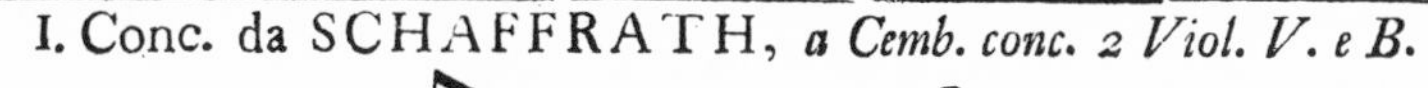

I. Conc. da SCHWANENBERG, *a Cemb. conc. 2 Viol. V. e B.*

I. Conc. da SENFFT, *a Cemb. conc. 2 Viol. e B.*

II. Concerti da Ignatio UMLAUFF.

I. *a Cemb. conc. 2 C. 2 Ob. 2 Cl. Tymp. 2 Viol. V. e B.* II. *a Cemb. conc. 2 C. 2 Ob. 2 Fl. Fag. 2 Viol. V. e B.*

I. Conc. da WILLFURTH, *a Cemb. conc. 2 C. 2 Ob. 2 Fl. 2 Viol. e B.*

I. Conc. da WOLFF, *a Cemb. conc. 2 Viol. V. e B.*

II. Concerti da ZACH.

I. *a Cemb. conc. 2 C. 2 Viol. V. e B.* II. *a Cemb. conc. 2 C. 2 O. 2 Viol. V. e B.*

CONCERTI *intagliati.*

I. Conc. da Ern. EICHNER, *a Cemb. conc. 2 C. 2 Viol. V. e. B. Op. VI. Francf. sur le Main.*

III. Conc. da LELEIN, *a Cemb. conc. 2 C. 2 Ob. o Fl. 2 Viol. V. e B. Opera V. Leipzig.*

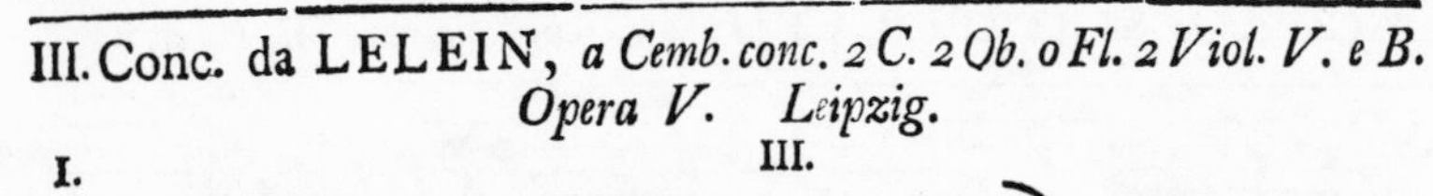

II. Conc. da PALSCHAU, *a Cemb. conc. 2 Viol. V. e B. Riga.*

H A R P A.

IX. Menuets con Trio da Conrad LEISS, *a Harpa.*

Marche des Janiſſaires avec Variation. par SIEBER, *a Harpa. Parigi.*

Premier Recueil de petits Airs choiſis, par SIEBER, *a Harpa. Parigi.*

II. Sonate *pour la Harpe con Violino* da SCHOBERT. *intagliate in Parigi Op. XIX.*

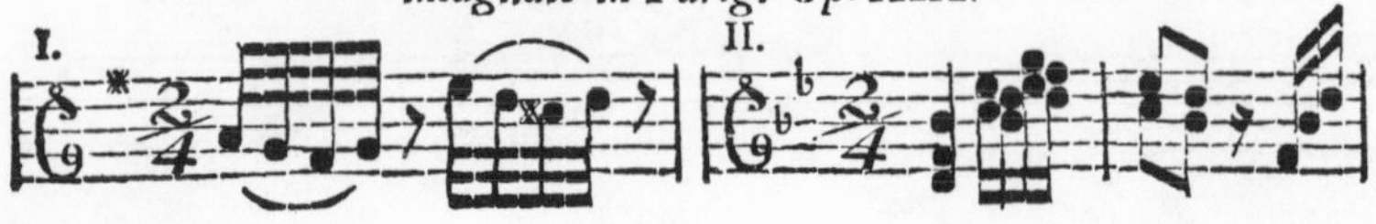

VI. Sonate *pour la Harpe con Viol. e B.* da SCHENCKER. *Parigi.*

ARIE e CANTATE con più Stromenti.

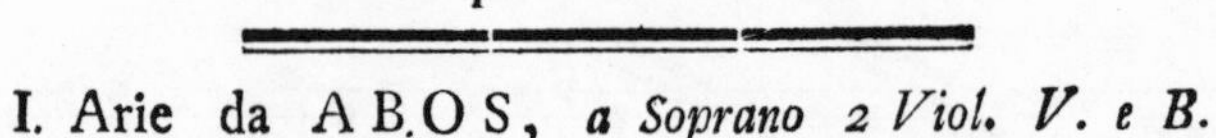

I. Arie da ABOS, *a Soprano 2 Viol. V. e B.*

I. Arie da Amadeo NAUMANN, *a Soprano 2 C. 2 Ob. Violino obl. 2 Viol. V. e B.*

IV. Arie da Giuſeppe SARTI.

I. *a Soprano 2 Viol. V. e B.* III. *a Soprano 2 Viol. V. e B.*

II. *a Sopr. O. obl. Violcl. obl. 2 Vi. V. e B.* IV. *a Soprano 2 Fag. 2 Viol. V. e B.*

I. Duetto da Giuſ. SARTI, *a 2 Soprani, 2 Viol. 2 Viole e B.*

Amynts Klagen über die Flucht der Lalage.

da Georg. BENDA.

a Soprano, 2 C. 2 Fl. 2 Viol. V. e B. Leipzig.

Aria 1.

Aria 2.

OPERA.

Der Kaufmann von Smirna.

da Sigr. STEGMANN.

OPERA.

Die Dorfgala.

da Sigr. SCHWEITZER.

DRAMMA ELISIUM.

da Sigr. SCHWEITZER.

1. Aria. *a 2 C. 2 Fl. 2 Viol. 2 Viole Sopr. e B.*

2. Aria. *a Fl. obl. 2 Viol. V. Sopr. e B.*

3. Aria. *a Ob. 2 Viol. V. Soprano e B.*

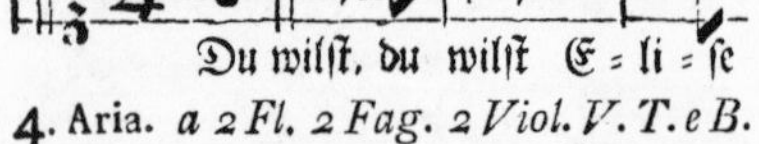

4. Aria. *a 2 Fl. 2 Fag. 2 Viol. V. T. e B.*

5. Duetto. *a 2 Ob. Fag. 2 Viol. V. Sopr. Tenore e B.*

6. Aria. *a 2 C. 2 Fl. 2 Viol. 2 Viole Soprano e B.*

7. Finale. *a 2 C. 2 Fl. 2 Viol. V. Soprani Bassi e B.*

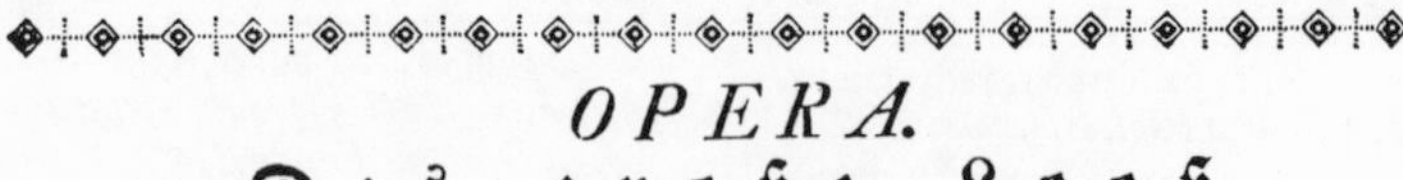

OPERA.

Das große Looß.

da Sigr. WOLFF.

Atto primo.

1. Aria. *a 2 C. 2 O. 2 Fl. 2 Viol. V. T. e B.*

2. Aria. *a 2 C. 2 Ob. 2 Fl. 2 Fag. 2 Viol. V. Tenore e B.*

3. Duetto. *a 2 Ob. 2 Fag. 2 Viol. V. Ten. Basso e B.*

4. Aria. *a 2 C. 2 O. 2 Viol. V. Basso e B.*

5. Duetto. *a 2 C. 2 Ob. 2 Viol. V. Soprano Basso e B.*

6. Duetto. *a 2 Ob. 2 Fl. 2 Viol. V. Soprano Tenore e B.*

7. Duetto. *a 2 Ob. 2. Viol. V. Soprano Tenore e B.*

8. Aria. *a 2 C. 2 Ob. 2 Fl. 2 Fag. 2 Viol. V. Tenore e. B.*

9. Aria. *a 2 C. 2 Ob. 2 Viol. V. Sopr. e B.*

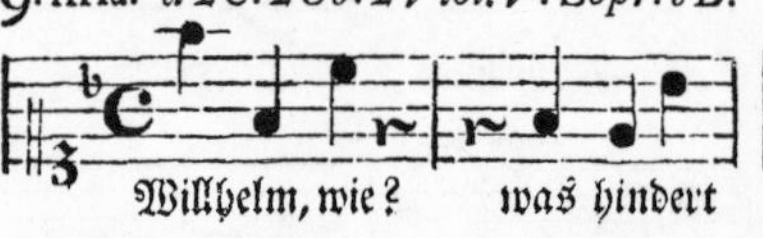

10. Terzetto. *a 2 C. 2 Ob. 2 Viol. V. 3 Soprani e B.*

11. Aria. *a 2 C. 2 Ob. 2 Fl. 2 Viol. Soprano e B.*

Atto secondo.

12. Duetto. *a 2 C. 2 Ob. 2 Fl. 2 Viol. V. Soprano Tenore e B.*

13. Aria. *a 2 Ob. 2 Fl. 2 Viol. V. Sopr. e B.*

14. Aria. *a 2 Fl. 2 Fag. 2 Viol. V. T. e B.*

15. Aria. *a 2 C. 2 Ob. 2 Fag. 2 Viol. V. Soprano e B.*

16. Terzetto. *a 2 C. 2 Ob. 2 Fl. 2 Fag. 2 Viol. V. Sopr. Ten. Basso e B.*

17. Duetto. *a 2 Ob. 2 Viol. V. Sopr. T. e B.*

18. Aria. *a 2 C. 2 Ob. 2 Fl. 2 Fag. 2 Viol. V. Tenore e B.*

19. Coro. *a 2 C. 2 Ob. 2 Fl. 1 Fag. 2 Viol. V. 2 Soprani 2 Bassi e B.*

Folgende Stücke sind theils in Partitur und in Stimmen theils aufs Clavier zu haben.

1. Operetten.

André Erwin und Elmire ein Schauspiel mit Gesang aufs Clavier und in Stimmen.

— — Leonore aufs Clavier.

Bach Americanerin in Partitur.

Benda Dorfjahrmarkt aufs Clavier.

Hillers Muse in Partitur

Holly Kaufmann von Smirna aufs Clavier.

Stegmann redendes Gemählde aufs Clavier.

2. Geistliche Gedichte.

Homilius Paßionscantate in Partitur.

Pergolesi Stabat mater mit der Klopstockischen Parodie von Hiller in Partitur.

Rolle Tod Abels aufs Clavier und in Partitur.

— Saul oder die Gewalt der Music aufs Clavier.

— Davids Sieg im Eichthale aufs Clavier.

Westenholtz Hirten bey der Krippe zu Bethlehem in Partitur.

SUPPLEMENTO XI.

DEI

CATALOGI

DELLE

SINFONIE, PARTITE, OVERTURE, SOLI, DUETTI, TRII, QUATTRI E CONCERTI

PER IL

VIOLINO, FLAUTO TRAVERSO, CEMBALO

ED ALTRI STROMENTI,

CHE

SI TROVANO IN MANOSCRITTO

NELLA OFFICINA MUSICA DI BREITKOPF

IN LIPSIA.

1776 ed 1777.

SINFONIE.

VI. Sinf. da ARDINA.
I. a 2 Cor. 2 Ob. 2 Viol. V. e B.
IV. a 2 Cor. 2 Ob. 2 Viol. V. e B.
II. a 2 C. Ob. ó Clar. 2 Fl. 2 Viol. V. e B.
V. a 2 Cor. 2 Ob. 2 Viol. V. e B.
III. a 2 Cor. 2 Ob. 2 Viol. V. e. B.
VI. a 2 Cor. 2 Ob. 2 Fl. 2 Viol. V. e B.
III. Sinf. da BARTA.
I. a 2 Cor. 2 Fl. 2 Viol. V. e. B.
III. a 2 Cor. 2 Ob. 2 Viol. V. e B.
II. a 2 Cor. 2 Ob. 2 Viol. V. e B.
VI. Sinf. da Carlo DITTERS.
I. a 2 Cor. 2 Ob. 2 Viol. V. e B.
IV. a 2 Cor. 2 Ob. 2 Viol. V. e B.
II. a 2 Cor. 2 Ob. 2 Viol. V. e B.
V. a 2 Cor. 2 Ob. 2 Viol. V. e B.
III. a 2 Cor. 2 Ob. 2 Viol. V. e B.
VI. a 2 C. 2 Ob. Tymp. 2 Viol. V. e B.
II. Sinf. da Carlo DITTERS.
I. a 2 Cor. 2 Ob. 2 Viol. V. e B.
II. a 2 Cor. 2 Ob. 2 Viol. V. e B.

III. Sinf. da Franc. DUSCHEK.
I. a 2 Cor. 2 Fl. 2. Viol. V. e B.
III. a 2 Cor. 2 Ob. 2 Viol. V. e B.
II. a 2 Cor. 2 Ob. 2 Viol. V. e B.
IV. Sinf. da Baron v. GEMMINGEN.
I. a 2 Cor. 2 Fl. 2 Viol. V. e B.
III. a 2 Cor. 2 Ob. 2 Fl. 2 Viol. V. e B.
II. a 2 Cor. 2 Ob. 2 Fl. 2 Viol. V. e B.
IV. a 2 Cor. 2 Fl. 2 Viol. V. e B.
II. Sinf. da F. I. GOSSEK.
I. a 2 Cor. 2 Fl. 2 Viol. V. e B.
II. a 2 Cor. 2 Ob. 2 Viol. V. e B.
VI. Sinf. da Giuf. HAYDEN.
I. a 2 Cor. 2 Ob. 2 Viol. V. e B.
IV. a 2 Cor. 2 Ob. 4 Viol. Violonc. e B.
II. a 2 Cor. 2 Ob. 2 Viol. V. e B.
V. a 2 C. ó Cl. Tymp. 2 O. 2 Fag. 2 Vi. V. e B.
III. a 2 C. 2 O. 2 Clar. Tymp. 2 Vi. V. e B.
VI. a 2 Cor. 2 Ob. 2 Viol. V. e B.

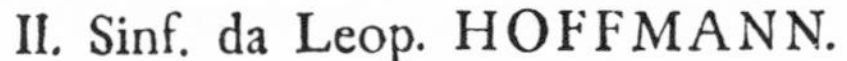

II. Sinf. da Leop. HOFFMANN.

I. *a 2 Cor. 2 Ob. 2 Viol. V. e B.* II. *a 2 Ob. 2 Viol. V. e B.*

I. Sinf. da HERSCHEL. *a 2 Cor. 2 Ob. 2 Viol. V. e B.*

I. Sinf. da KLUG. *a 2 Cor. 2 Ob. Fag. obl. Violonc. obl. 2 Viol. V. e B.*

VI. Sinf. da Giuf. MISLEWECZECK.

I. *a 2 Cor. 2 Ob. 2 Viol. V. e B.* IV. *a 2 Cor. 2 Ob. 2 Viol. V. e B.*

II. *a 2 Cor. 2 Ob. 2 Viol. V. e B.* V. *a 2 Cor. 2 Ob. 2 Viol. V. e B.*

III. *a 2 Cor. 2 Ob. 2 Viol. V. e B.* VI. *a 2 Cor. 2 Ob. 2 Viol. V. e B.*

III. Sinf. da MICZA.

I. *a 2 Cor. 2 Ob. 2 Viol. 2 Viole e B.* III. *a 2 Cor. 2 Ob. 2 Viol. V. e B.*

II. *a 2 C. 2 Ob. 2 Viol. V. Violonc. e B.*

VIII. Sinf. da Amadeo NAUMANN.

I. *a 2 O. 2 Fl. 2 Clar. Tymp. 2 Viol. V. e B.* V. *a 2 Cor. 2 Ob. 2 Fl. 2 Viol. V. e B.*

II. *a 2 C. 2 Ob. 2 Fl. Fag. 2 Clar. Tymp. 2 Viol. V. e B.* VI. *a 2 Cor. 2 Ob. 2 Fl. 2 Viol. V. e B.*

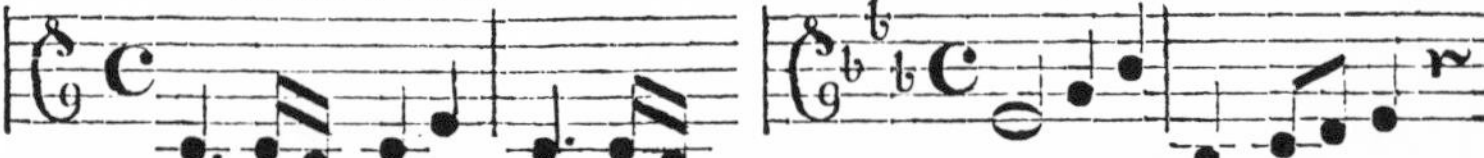

III. *a 2 C. 2 Ob. 2 Fl. Fag. 2 Viol. V. e B.* VII. *a 2 Cor. 2 Ob. 2 Fl. 2 Viol. V. e B.*

IV. *a 2 Cor. 2 Ob. 2 Fl. 2 Viol. 2 V. e B.* VIII. *a 2 Cor. 2 Ob. 2 Fl. 2 Viol. V. e B.*

I. Sinf. da PICHL. *a Viol. princ. 2 Clar. 2 Ob. 2. Viol. V. e B.*

V. Sinf. da Antonio ROSETTI.

I. *a 2 Cor. 2 Fl. Fag. 2 Viol. V. e B.* IV. *a 2 Cor. 2 Ob. 2 Viol. 2 Viole e B.*

II. *a 2 C. 2 O. 2 Viol. 2 Viole Violonc. e B.* V. *a 2 C. 2 Ob. 2 Fl. 2 Viol. 2 Viole e B.*

III. *a 2 Cor. 2 Ob. 2 Viol. V. e B.*

I. Sinf. da RUGIETZ. *a 2 Cor. 2 Ob. 2 Fag. 2 Viol. V. e B.*

I. Sinf. da SCHWEITZER. *a 2 Cor. 2 Fl. 2 Tromp. 2 Viol. V. e B.*

I. Sinf. da SPERLING. *a 2 Cor. 2 Ob. 2 Viol. V. e B.*

III. Sinf. da SPILLER.

I. *a 2 Cor. 2 Ob. 2 Fl. 2 Viol. V. e B.* III. *a 2 Cor. 2 Fl. 2 Viol. V. e B.*

II. *a 2 Cor. 2 Fl. 2 Viol. V. e B.*

II. Sinf. da Carlo STAMITZ.

I. *a 2 Cor. 2 Ob. 2 Viol. V. e B.* II. *a 2 Cor. 2 Ob. 2 Viol. V. e B.*

I. Sinf. da STARZER. *a 2 C. 2 Ob. 2 Clarin. 2 Clar. Tymp. Alto, Ten. e Basso Tromboni, Fag. 2 Viol. 2 Viole e B.*

II. Sinf. van SWIETEN.

I. *a 2 Cor. 2 Ob. 2 Viol. V. e B.* II. *a 2 Cor. 2 Ob. 2 Viol. V. e B.*

I. Sinf. da TOESCHI. *a 2 C. 2 Fl. 2 Clarin. 2 Fag. 2 Viol. V. e B.*

III. Sinf. da TOMASINI.

I. *a 2 Cor. 2 Ob. 2 Viol. V. e B.* III. *a 2 C. 2 Ob. Tymp. 2 Viol. V. Fag. in Trio e B.*

II. *a 2 Cor. 2 Ob. Fag. 2 Viol. V. e B.*

IV. Sinf. da Giov. VANHALL.

I. *a 2 Cor. 2 Ob. 2 Fl. 2 Viol. V. e B.* III. *a 2 C. 2 O. 2 Clar. Tymp. 2 Vi. V. e B.*

II. *a 2 C. 2 Ob. 1 Clar. Tymp. 2 Vi. V. e B.* IV. *a 2 C. in A. 2 C. in F. 2 O. 2 Vi. V. e B.*

I. Sinf. da WAGENSEIL. *a 2 Cor. 2 Ob. 2 Viol. V. e B.*

I. Sinf. da WALDEK. *a 2 Cor. 2 Fl. 2 Viol. V. e B.*

SINFONIE intagliate e stampate.

VI. Sinf. da Ferd. FISCHER. *a 2 Cor. 2 Ob. 6 Fl. 2 Viol. V. e B. Brunsvic.*

I. IV. II. V. III. VI.

VI. Overtures da Ant. KAMMEL. *a 2 C. 2 Ob. 6 Fl. 2 Viol. V. e B. Op. X. London.*

I. IV. II. V. III. VI.

VI. Sinf. da Giorg. Ant. KREUSSER. *a 2 Cor. 2 Ob. ó Fl. 2 Viol. V. e B. Op. I. Offenbach.*

III. Sinf. da SCHMITTBAUR. *a 2 Cor. 2 Ob. ó Fl. 2 Viol. V. e B. Op. II. Offenbach.*

SINFONIES PERIODIQUES.

I. Sinf. da I. F. REICHARDT. *a 2 Cor. 2 Ob. 2 Fl. 2 Viol. V. B. e Violono. Offenbach. No. VI.*

I. Sinf. da H. L. VETTER. *a 2 Cor. 2 Ob. 2 Viol. V. e B. Offenbach. No. III.*

V I O L I N O.

SOLI *con* BASSO.

I. Solo da Gaetano BRUNETTI.

II. Soli da Giuſ. HAYDEN, *a Violino e Viola.*

I. Solo da PANNENBERG.

IV. Soli da C. A. PESCH.

IV. Soli da PUGNANI.

I. Solo da Giov. Federico REICHARDT.

SOLI intagliati.

VI. Soli da Felice DEIARDINO. *Op. VIII. Paris.*

DUETTI intagliati.

VI. Duetti da CAMPINI. *Op. II. Amst.*

I. IV.

II. V.

III. VI.

VI. Duetti da W. LEEDER. *Hildesheim.*

IV.

II. V.

III. VI.

VI. Duetti da ZIMMERMANN. *Op. I. Lyon.*

TRII intagliati.

VI. Trii da Guil. CRAMER, *a 2 Viol. e B. Op. III. Paris.*

QUATTRI.

VI. Quattri da Mr. de St. GEORGE, *a 2 Viol. V. e B.*

VI. Quattri da T. GIORDANI, *a 2 Viol. V. e B.*

II. Quattri da LOLLI, *a 2 Viol. V. e B.*

VI. Quattri da Bar. Sigismondo de SECKENDORFF, *a 2 Viol. V. e B.*

VI. Quattri da Giov. VANHALL, *a 2 Viol. V. e B.*

QUATTRI intagliati:

VI. Quattri da CAMBINI, *a 2 Viol. V. e B. Op. II. Paris.*

VI Quattri da CANNABICH, *a 2 Viol. V. e B. Op. V. Mannh.*

III. Quattri da Carlo STAMITZ, *a 2 Viol. V. e B.* *Op. XIII. Amst.*

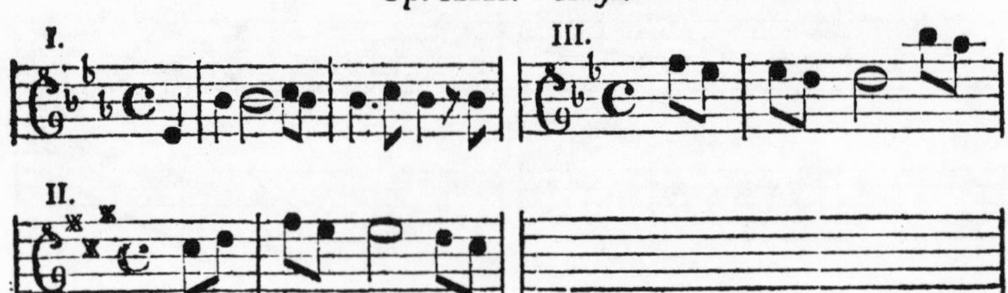

VI. Quattri da ZIMMERMANN, *a 2 Viol. V. e B.* *Op. III. Paris.*

QUINTETTI intagliati.

VI. Quint. da I. C. BACH, *a Fl. Ob. Viol. V. e B. Op. IX. Amst.*

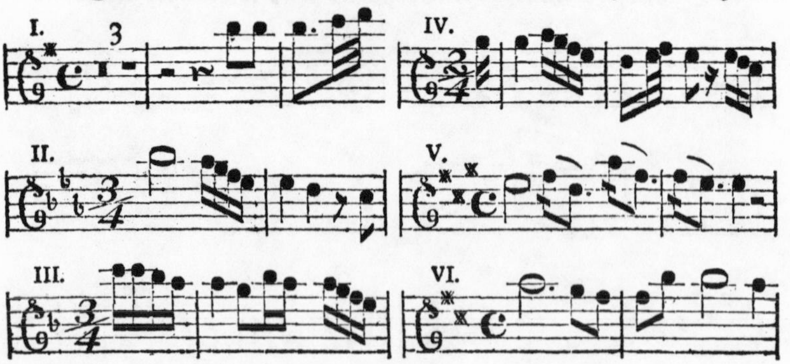

CONCERTI per il Violino concertato.

I. Conc. da CANNABICH, *a Viol. conc. 2 Cor. 2 Fl. 2 Viol. V. e B.*

I. Conc. da Carlo DITTERS, *a Viol. conc. 2 Cor. 2 Ob. 2 Viol. V. e B.*

II. Concerti da HERSCHEL.

I. *a Viol. conc. 2 C. 2 Ob. 2 Viol. V. e B.* II. *a Viol. conc. 2 C. 2 Ob. 2 Fl. 2 Viol. V. e B.*

II. Concerti da Ant. KAMMEL.

I. *a Viol. conc. 2 Cor. 2 Viol. V. e B.* II. *a Viol. conc. 2 Cor. 2 Viol. V. e B.*

II. Concerti da LEEDER.

I. *a Viol. conc. 2 C. 2 Clar. 2 Viol. V. e B.* II. *a Viol. conc. 2 C. 2 Ob. 2 Viol. V. e B.*

I. Concerto da LOLLI, *a Viol. conc. 2 Viol. Viola e Basso.*

I. Concerto da PICHL, *a Viol. conc. 2 Viol. Viola e Basso.*

I. Concerto da PUGNANI, *a Viol. conc. 2. Viol. V. e B.*

I. Conc. da G. F. REICHARDT, *a Viol. conc. 2 Viol. V. e B.*

III. Concerti da Carlo STAMITZ.

I. *a Viol. conc. 2 C. 2 Ob. 2 Viol. V e B.* III. *a Viol. conc. 2 C. 2 Fl. 2 Viol. V. e B.*

II. *a Viol. conc. 2 C. 2 Viol. 2 Viole e B.*

I. Concerto da TOESCHI, *a Viol. conc. 2 Viol. V. e B.*

CONCERTI *intagliati.*

III. Conc. da L. BORGHI, *a Viol. princ. 2 Cor. 2 Ob. 2 Viol. V. e B. Op. II. Amst.*

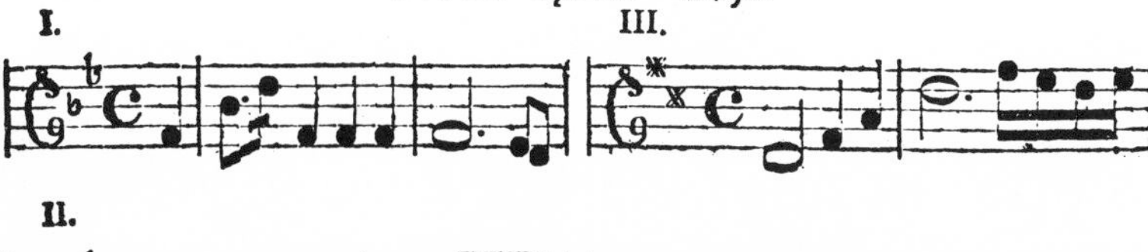

III. Conc. da L. BORGHI, *a Viol. princ. 2 Cor. 2 Ob. 2 Viol. V. e B. Op. III. Amst.*

I. Conc. da le DUC l'ainé, *a Viol. princ. 2 Cor. 2 Ob. 2 Viol. V. e B. Paris.*

II. Concerti da I. B. DUPONT, *a Viol. princ. 2 Viol. V. e B. Paris.*

I. Conc. da Adam VEICHTNER, *a Viol. conc. 2 Viol. V. e B. Riga.*

VIOLA.

III. Quintetti da Carlo STAMITZ, *a Corno, Viol. 2 Viole e B.*

III. Concerti da Carlo DITTERS.

I. *a Viola princ. 2 Cor. 2 Viol. V. e B.* III. *a Viola princ. 2 Cor. 2 Viol. V. e B.*

II. *a Viola princ. 2 Viol. V. e B.*

VIOLONCELLO.

SOLI *intagliati.*

VI. Sonate p. Mr. DUPORT, *pour Violoncelle ou Violon e Basse. Paris.*

TRII intagliati.

VI. Trii da L. BOCCHERINI, *a Viol. Viola e Violonc. obl.*
Op. XIV. Parigi.

CONCERTI per il Violoncello concertato.

I. Conc. da BODE, *a Violcl. conc. 2 Cor. 2 Viol. V. e B.*

I. Conc. da CRUSE, *a Violcl. conc. 2 Fl. 2 Viol. V. e B.*

I. Conc. da FILS, *a Violcl. conc. 2 Cor. 2 Viol. V. e B.*

II. Concerti da C. E. GRAAF.
I. *a Violcl. conc. 2 C. 2 Fl. 2 Viol. V. e B.* II. *a Viol. conc. 2 C. 2 Ob. 2 Viol. V. e B.*

I. Conc. da MAYLON, *a Violcl. conc. 2 C. 2 Ob. 2 Viole e B.*

I. Conc. da MEGELIN, *a Violcl. conc. 2 C. 2 Ob. Clar. Tymp. 2 Fag. obl. 2 Viol. V. e B.*

I. Conc. da Giuf. SCHMITT, *a Violcl. conc. 2 Cor. 2 Ob. 2 Viol. V. e B.*

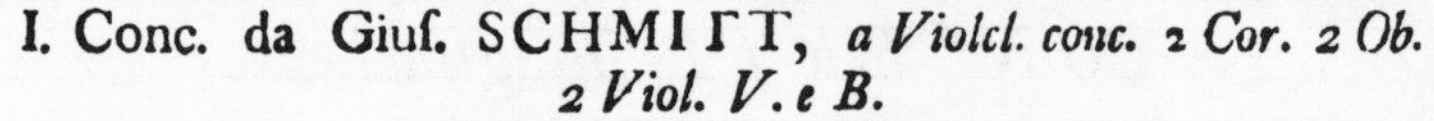

II. Concerti da Carlo STAMITZ.
I. *a Violcl. conc. 2 C. 2 O. 2 Vi. 2 Viole e B.* II. *a Violcl. conc. 2 C. 2 O. 2 Vi. 2 Viole e B.*

FLAUTO TRAVERSO.

DUETTI intagliati.

VI. Duetti da SCHETTKY, *a 2 Flauti. London.*

TRII.

VI. Trii da Felice BOSHTIETZKY, *a Fl. Viol. e Violcl.*

TRII intagliati.

VI. Trii da C. E. GRAAF, *a 2 Fl. e Basso. Op. III. Amst.*

CONCERTI,
A FLAUTO TRAVERSO CONCERTATO.

III. Concerti da C. E. GRAAF.

I. *a Fl. conc. 2 Cor. 2 Viol. V. e B.* III. *a Fl. conc. 2 Viol. V. e B.*

II. *a Fl. conc. 2 Viol. V. e B.*

II. Concerti da Giov. VANHALL.

I. *a Fl. conc. 2 Cor. 2 Viol. V. e. B.* II. *a Fl. conc. 2 C. 2 Ob. 2 Viol. V. e B.*

CONCERTI intagliati.

I. Conc. d'AME', *a Fl. conc. 2 Viol. V. e B. Parigi.*

I. Conc. da BAUERSCHMITT, *a Fl. conc. 2 C 2 Vi. V. e B. Op. II. Parigi.*

I. Conc. da Le BRUN, *a Fl. conc. 2 Viol. V. e B. Parigi.*

CEMBALO.

SOLI.

IV. Sonate da C. Ph. E. BACH.

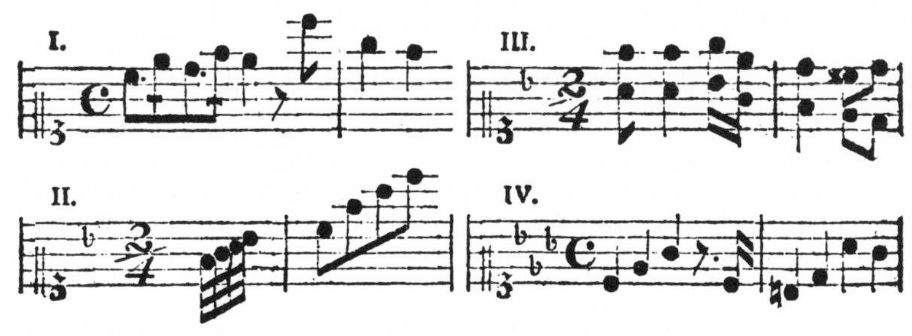

Fantàsia et Fuga da C. Ph. E. BACH.

VI. Sonate da C. S. BINDER.

VI. Sonate da Fr. Gugl. RUST.

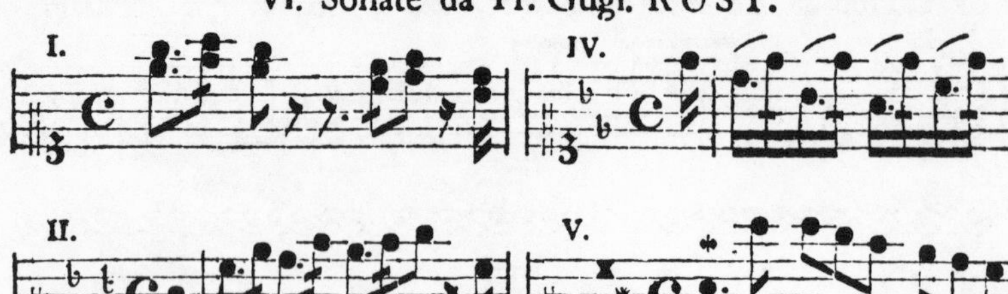

I. Serenate da Carlo DITTERS.

SONATE intagliate e ſtampate.

VI. Sonatines da Erneſt EICHNER. *Op. VII. Francf. ſur le Mein.*

VI. Sonate da Samuel SCHROETER. *Op. I. Amſt.*

VI. Sonate da D. G. TÜRK, *I. Samml. Leipzig und Halle.*

VI. Sonate da D. G. TÜRK, *II. Sámml. Leipzig und Halle.*

TRII.

A CEMBALO OBLIGATO CON VIOLINO O FLAUTO.

VI. Sonate da G. A. NAUMANN, *a Cemb. e Violino.*

TRII intagliati.

VI. Sonate da C. F. ABEL, *a Cemb. e Violino. Op. XV. Lond.*

VI. Sonate da I. C. F. BACH, *a Cemb. e Fl. ô Violino. Riga.*

III. Sonate da EDELMANN, *a Cembalo e Violino. Op. II. Offenbach.*

VI. Sonate da C. G. NEEFE, *a Cembalo e Violino. Glogau.*

VI. Sonate da C. Benj. UBER, *a Cemb. e Violino. Breslau.*

III. Sonate da C. Benj. UBER, *a Cembalo e Violino. Amst.*

VI. Sonate da W O L F F in Stettin, *a Cembalo e Violino, ó Fl. o Violetta.*

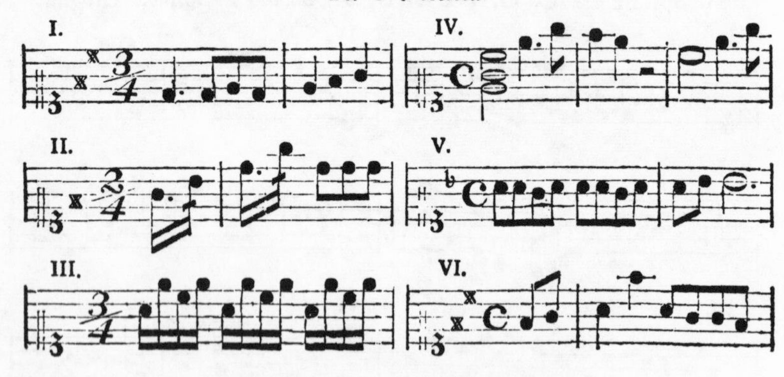

TERZETTI intagliati.

VI. Sonate da C. F. ABEL, *a Cembalo Violino ou Flauto e Violonc. Op. V. Amst.*

III. Sonate da C. P. E. BACH, *a Cembalo, Viol. e Violonc. I. Samml. Leipzig.*

IV. Sonate da C. P. E. BACH, *a Cembalo, Viol. e Violonc. II. Samml. Leipzig.*

VI. Sonate da C. P. E. BACH, *a Cembalo, Viol. e Violonc. London.*

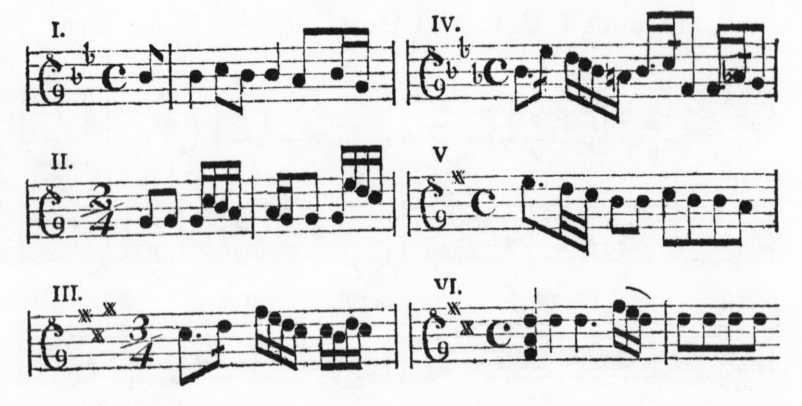

VI. Sonate da Ern. EICHNER, *a Cemb. Viol. e Violcl. Op. I. Amst.*

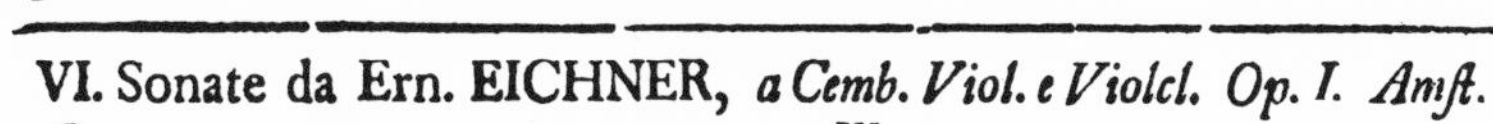

VI. Sonate da Ant. KAMMEL, *a Cembalo e Viol. e Violonc. Op. X. Amst.*

VI. Sonate da G. S. LOEHLEIN, *a Cemb. trois avec Violino e Violoncello. Op. VI. Leipsic.*

QUINTETTI e DIVERTIMENTI.

I. Sonata da Georg BENDA, *a Cembalo, 2 Viol. Viola e Basso.*

QUINTETTI e DIVERTIMENTI intagliati.

I. Sinf. da EDELMANN, *a Cemb. obl. 2 Cor. 2 Viol. e B. Opera I. Offenbach.*

III. Quintetti da T. GIORDANI, *a Cemb. 2 Viol. V. e B. Op I. Francf sur le Mein.*

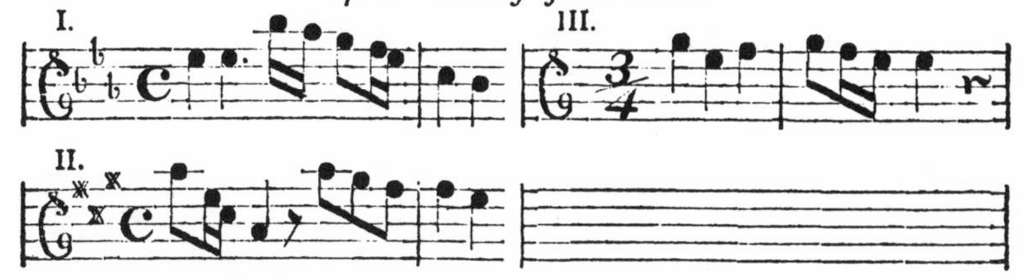

III. Quintetti da T. GIORDANI, *a Cmb. 2 Viol. V. e B. Op. II. Francf. sur le Mein.*

I. Divertim. da C. B. UBER, *a Cemb. 2 C. 2 Fl. 2 Viol. V. e B. Bresl.*

CONCERTI, a Cemb. con più Stromenti.

I. Concerto da I. HERSCHEL, *a Cemb. conc. 2 Viol. V. e B.*

I. Conc. da Leop. HOFFMANN, *a Cemb. conc. 2 Ob. 2 Viol. V. e B.*

I. Conc. da LANG, *a Cemb. conc. 2 Fl. 2 Viol. V. e B.*

I. Conc. da Giov. VANHALL, *a Cemb. conc. Viol. princ. 2 V. e B.*

I. Conc. da WAGENSEIL, *a Cemb. conc. 2 Viol. e B.*

CONCERTI intagliati.

II. Conc. da G. C. BACH, *a Cemb. conc. 2 Viol. V. e B. Riga.*

I. II.

I. Conc. da G. F. REICHARDT, *a Cemb. conc. 2 Fl. 2 Vi. V. e B. Leipſ.*

II. Conc. da C. G. RICHTER, *a Cemb. conc. 2 Viol. V. e B. Riga.*

I. II.

II. Concerti da Ern. Gugl. WOLFF. *Riga.*

I. *a Cemb. conc. 2 Ob. 2 Viol. V. e B.* II. *a Cemb. conc. 2 Viol. V. e B.*

HARPA.

I. Andantino c. Var. da I. B. KRUMPHOLTZ, *pour la Harpe a Pedal.*

I. Sonata da I. B. KRUMPHOLTZ, *pour la Harpe a Pedal.*

I. Sonata da E. G. B. LANG, *per L'Arpa con Violino. Norimb.*

ARIE e CANTATE con più Stromenti.

I. Arie da ANONYMO, *a Soprano, 2 Viol. V. e B.*

Oh Di-o man-car man-car mi ſen - to

I. Recit. ed Arie da Pasquale ANFASSI, *a Sopr. 2 C 2 Fl. 2 Viol. V. e B.*

Ah non par-ti-re a- Gia di ven-to fred-do

I. Recit. ed Arie da Giov. CAVI, *a Sopr. 2 C. 2 Ob. 2 Viol. V. e B.*

Ah ſe ſa-peſ-ſi quanto S'ho da per-dere un te-

I. Recit. ed Arie da C. GLUCK, *a Sopr. 2 C. 2 O. 2 Viol. V. Violcl. e B.*

Be-re-ni-ce che fai Per - che ſe tan-ti

ARIE e CANTATE.
II. Cantate da GRAUN.
I. a Soprano 2 Viol. V. e B.
An - tri pro-fon-di e
II. a Soprano 2 Viol. V. e B.
Ferma Dafne cru-del. A-pol-lo
I. Recit. ed Arie da P. GUGLIELMI, a Sopr. 2 C. 2 O. 2 Vi. 2 Viole e B.
Nu-mi cru-de-li ch'im-
Da mil-le ſmarie oh
I. Arie da HOLTZBAUR, a Soprano, 2 Viol. V. e B.
Par-to par-to oh Di-o a te con
VI. Arie da Giov. Amadeo NAUMANN.
I. a Soprano, 2 Cor. 2 Viol. V. e B.
Si t'in-ten-do ombra di-
IV. a Soprano, 2 Fl. 2 Viol. V. e B.
Cre-di pu-re al
II. a Sopr. 2 C. 2 Ob. 2 Fl. 2 Fag. 2 Vi. V. e B.
I-do-lo mio non
V. a Sopr. 2 Ob. 2 Fag. 2 Vi. 2 Viole e B.
Ve-di cu-ra in
III. a Soprano, 2 Viol. V. e B.
Bel-le lu-ci vez-zo
VI. a Sopr. 2 C. 2 O. 2 Fl. 2 Fag. 2 Vi. V. e B.
Se ve-der tu
I. Recit. ed Arie da A. SACCHINI, a Sopr. 2 C. 2 Ob. 2 Viol. V. e B.
Lo-de agli De-i
Nel fat-ta-le eſtremo ad-
II. Arie da Giov. SCHWANENBERG.
I. a Soprano, 2 Viol. V. e B.
Va lu-fin-gan-do a-
II. a Soprano, 2 Viol. V. e B.
Vo-i leg-ge-te in
I. Arie da T. TRAIETTA, a Ten. Viol. obl. 2 C. 2 Ob. 2 Viol. V. e B.
Il Pa-ſtor ſe tor-na a-pri-le.

33
Arie dell' Opera Romeo e Giulia.
dal Sign. Giov. SCHWANBERGER.
Atto primo.
Atto ſecondo.
1. Arie. a 2 C. 2 Ob. 2 Vi. V. Sopr. e Fond.
Non pa-ven-to a-
7. Arie. a 2 Viol. V. Tenore e Fond.
Al mi-ra-re il
2. Duetto. a 2 C. 2 O. 2 Vi. V. 2 Sopr. e Fond.
Pen-ſa ſe foſ-ſe
8. Arie. a 2 C. 2 Fl. 2 Vi. V. Sopr. e Fond.
Son pur-tu-o bell'
3. Arie. a 2 C. 2 Ob. 2 Viol. V. Ten. e Fond.
Con-dot-tier
9. Arie. a 2 Viol. Viola, Ten. e Fond.
Tanto all' u-ſa-to af-
4. Arie. a 2 Viol. V. Sopr. e Fond.
Ah ſe con-que-ſte
10. Arie. a 2 Fl. 2 Vi. 2 Viole Sopr. e Fond.
Ro-me-o — — cru-
5. Duetto. a 2 Fl. 2 Viol. V. 2 Sopr. e Fond.
Per quell, — ch'or
11 Duetto. a 2 C. 2 O. 2 Vi. V. 2 Sopr. e Fond.
So-gno? o tor-nar da
6. Arie. a 2 C. 2 Fl. 2 Viol. V. Sopr. e Fond.
Cu-re ad-o-ra-bi-li
12. Arie. a 2 C. 2 Ob. 2 Vi. V. Sopr. e Fond.
Se da tur-bi-ne
13. Terzetto. a 2 Cor. 2 Fl. 2 Ob. 2 Viol. V. 2 Soprani Ten. e Fond.
Ri-da il Ciel — fe-li-ci a-man-ti

OPERA.

Der Dorfjahrmarkt.

da Sigr. BENDA.

Atto primo.

1. Duetto. *a 2 Cor. 2 Fl. 2 Fag. 2 Viol. 2 Viole, Ten. B. et Fond.* — Trinkt, trinkt, trinkt,

2. Aria. *a 2 C. 2 Fl. 2 Fag. 2 Viol. 2 Viole Tenore e Fond.* — Hier steh ich vom Ge-

3. Aria. *a 2 Viol. V. Soprano e Fond.* — Schö-ne Her-ren

4. Aria. *a Fl. Ob. Fag. 2 Vi. V. Sopr. e Fond.* — Ja Lu-cas die-ser

5 Aria. *a Ob. Fag. 2 Vi. V. Sopr. e Fond.* — In un-serm gan-zen

6. Aria. *a 2 C. 2 Ob. 2 Viol. V. Ten. e Fond.* — Bald soll der Hoch-zeit-

7. Aria. *a 2 C. 2 Fl. Fag. 2 Vi. V. Sopr. e F.* — Schlaf im-mer-hin — am

8 Duetto. *a Fl. Fag. 2 Vi. V. Sopr. T. e F.* — Glaubest du mit Schmeiche-

9. Aria. *a 2 C. 2 Fl. 2 Viol. V. B. e Fond.* — Las-sen sie mich immer

10. Aria. *a 2 Violini, V. Basso e Fond.* — Auf e-wig, o

Atto secondo.

11. Aria. *a 2 Clar. Tymp. 2 C. 2 Fl. 2 Viol. V. Basso e Fond.* — Anfangs wird das Herzchen dir

12. Aria. *a Ob. Fag. 2 Viol. V. Ten. e Fond.* — Ach ich lieb-te sie so

13. Terz. *a 2 C. 2 Fag. 2 Vi. V. Sopr. T. B. e F.* — Pflicht und Eh-re

14. Aria. *a 2 Fag. 2 Viol. V. Sopr. e Fond.* — Mich willst du o Ge-

15. Aria. *a 2 Cl. 2 C. 2 Fl. 2 Fag. 2 Vi. V. T. e F.* — Schon lock-te mich der

16. Aria. *a 2 Fl. 2 Fag. 2 Vi. V. Sopr. e F.* — Ach Va-ter, die Wer-ber,

17. Aria. *a 2 C. 2 Fl. 2 Vi. V. Basso e Fond.* — Was für Ge-sper-re

18. Duetto. *a 2 C. 2 Fag. 2 Viol. V. Sopr. Basso e Fond.* — Fort mit ihm,

19 Aria. *a 2 Fl. 2 O. 2 Fag. 2 Vi V. T. e Fond.* — In an-drer Glück sein

20. Aria. *a 2 Fl. 2 Viol. V. Sopr. e Fond.* — Mein Ret-ter, mein Be-

21. Terzetto. *a 2 C. 2 Fl. 2 Fag. 2 Viol. V. Sopr. Ten. B. e Fond.* — Mu-sier gu-ter Her-ren

Piramus und Tisbe

von Herrn J. A. Hasse,

mit einer teutschen Parodie versehen

von M. Bernh. Theod. Breitkopf.

Atto primo.

1. Aria. *a 2 Ob. 2 Fl. 2 Vi. V. Sopr. e Fond.* — Ver-ge-bens fließt die

2. Duetto. *a 2 Ob. 2 Fl. 2 Vi. V. Sopr. T. e F.* — Seh ich dich end-lich

3. Aria. *a 2 C. 2 Ob. 2 Vi. V. Sopr. e Fond.* — Mit al-len ih-ren

4. Aria. *a 2 C. 2 Ob. 2 Vi. V. Sopr. e Fond.* — Den Ge-lieb-ten mir ent-

5. Aria. *a 2 C. 2 Ob. 2 Viol. V. Ten. e Fond.* — Beym An-blick dei-ner Schmer-

6. Duetto *a 2 C. 2 O. 2 Fl. 2 Vi. V. Sopr. T. e F.* — Ach — ver-zie-he, o

7. Aria. *a 2 C. 2 Fl. 2 Fag. 2 Vi. V. Ten. e F.* — O, komm in die Ge-

8. Duetto. *a 2 C. 2 Ob. 2 Vi. V. Sopr. T. e F.* — Wo-vor sollt ich er-

Folgende Stücke sind theils in Partitur und in Stimmen theils aufs Clavier zu haben.

1. Operetten.

Baumgarten, Andromeda aufs Clavier.
Benda, Walder aufs Clavier.
Neefe, Heinrich und Lyda aufs Clavier.
Schweitzers Alceste aufs Clavier.
— — Dorfgala aufs Clavier.
— — Lustiger Schuster in Partitur und aufs Clavier.
Stegmanns Erwin und Elmire aufs Clavier.
Wolfs Polyxena in Partitur.
— Seraphina in Partitur.

2. Geistliche Gedichte.

Homilius, Freude der Hirten über die Geburt Jesu, in Partitur.
Rolle, Abraham auf Moria aufs Clavier.

SUPPLEMENTO XII.

DEI

CATALOGI

DELLE

SINFONIE, PARTITE, OVERTURE, SOLI, DUETTI, TRII, QUATTRI E CONCERTI

PER IL

VIOLINO, FLAUTO TRAVERSO,

CEMBALO

ED ALTRI STROMENTI,

CHE

SI TROVANO IN MANOSCRITTO
NELLA OFFICINA MUSICA DI BREITKOPF
IN LIPSIA.

1778.

SINFONIE.

I. Sinf. da G. BENDA. *a Viol. princ. 2 C. 2 Ob. 2 Viol. V. e B.*

VI. Sinf. da Carlo de DITTERSDORF.

I. *a 2 C. 2 Ob. 2 Clar. Tymp. Fl. Fag. o Violcl. 2 Viol. V. e B.* IV. *a 2 C. 2 Ob. 2 Clar. Tymp. Fl. Fag. o Violcl. 2 Viol. V. e B.*

II. *a 2 C. 2 Ob. 2 Viol. V. e B.* V. *a 2 C. 2 Ob. 2 Viol. V. e B.*

III. *a 2 C. 2 Ob. 2 Viol. V. e B.* VI. *a 2 C. 2 Ob. 2 Viol. V. e B.*

I. Sinf. da FOERSTER. *a 2 C. 2 O. 2 Vi. Violino Solo in And. V. e B.*

IV. Sinf. da Giuf. HAYDEN.

I. *a 2 C. o Clar. 2 Ob. Tymp. 2 Viol. Fag. obl. e B.* III. *a 2 C. 2 Ob. 2 Viol. 2 Viole e B.*

II. *a 2 C. 2 Ob. 2 Viol. V. e B.* IV. *a 2 C. 2 Ob. 2 Viol. V. e B.*

II. Sinf. da KIRCHNER.

I. *a 2 C. 2 Ob. Tymp. 2 Viol. V. e B.* II. *a 2 C. 2 Ob. 2 Fag. 2 Viol. V. e B.*

I. Sinf. da MISCHA. *a 2 C. o Clar. 2 Ob. o Fl. Tymp. 2 Viol. V. e B.*

III. Sinf. da Antonio ROSETTI.

I. *a 2 C. 2 Ob. Fag. obl. 2 Viol. V. e B.* III. *a 2 C. 2 Ob. 2 Viol. 2 Viole e B.*

II. *a 2 C. 2 Fl. 2 Viol. V. e B.*

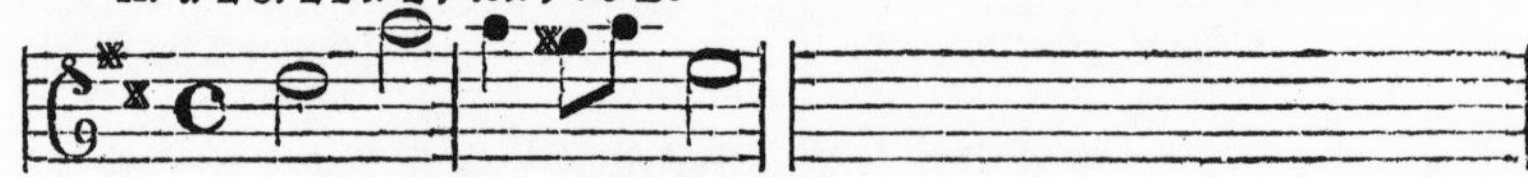

II. Sinf. da SCHUSTER.

I. *a 2 C. 2 Ob. 2 Viol. V. e B.* II. *a 2 C. 2 Ob. 2 Viol. 2 Viole e B.*

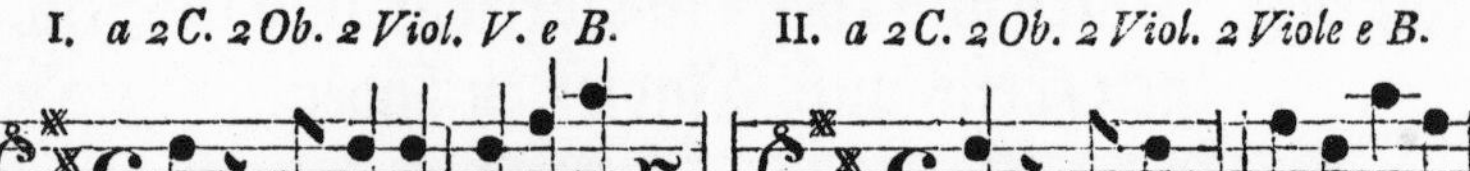

I. Sinf. da D. G. TÜRK. *a 2 C. 2 Ob. 2 Fl. 2 Viol. V. e B.*

V. Sinf. da Giov. VANHALL.

I. *a 2 C. 2 Ob. 2 Viol. Oboe e Fag. Solo in And. V. e B.* IV. *a 2 C. 2 Ob. 2 Clar. Tymp. 2 Viol. V. e B.*

II. *a 2 C. 2 O. 2 Viol. Viol. princ. Violcl. obl. 2 Viole e B.* V. *a 2 C. in D. 2 C. in F. Corno Solo in A. 2 O. 2 Viol. V. e B*

III. *a 3 C. 2 Ob. 2 Viol. V. e B.*

MINUETTI.

XII. *Dresdner Redout. Menuetten* da SIMON. 1779. XII. *Dresd. Redout. Men.* da RICHTER. 1779.

VI. *Dresdn. Polonoiſen* da DITTRICH. 1779.

XXIV. *Dresdn. Redout. Angloiſen e Quatrillen.* 1779.

SINFONIE *intagliate e ſtampate.*

IV. Sinf. da Giuſ. HAYDEN. *a 2 C. 2 Ob. 2 Viol. V. e B. Op. XXIV. Parigi.*

I. *a 2 Clar. Tymp. ad libit* III. *a 4 Viol. vid. Suppl. XI. No. IV.*

II. *vid. Suppl. VIII. No. VI.* IV.

III. Sinf. da Franc. HOFFMEISTER. *a 2 C. 2 Ob. 2 Viol. V. e B. Op. III. Lyon.*

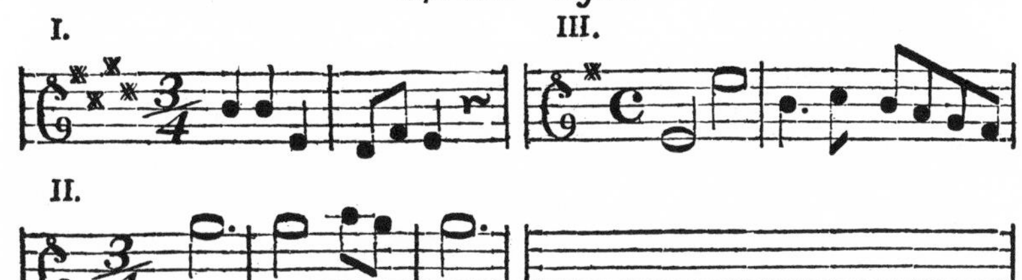

VI. Sinf. da C. STAMITZ fils ainé. *a 2 Cor. 2 Ob. o Fl. 2 Viol. V. e B. Op. XIII. Amſt.*

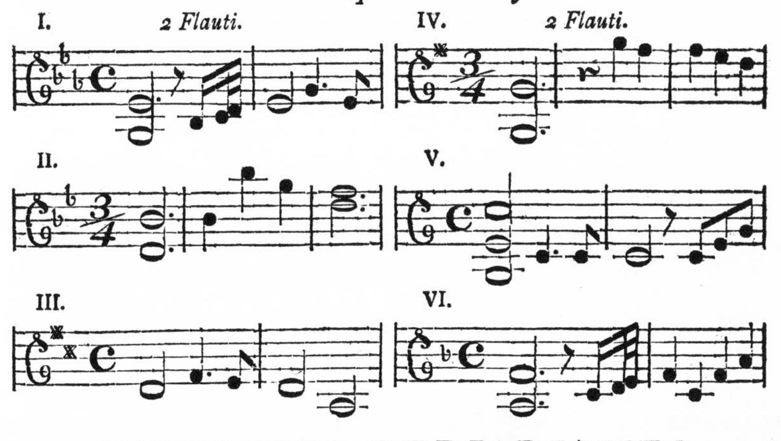

SINFONIES PERIODIQUES.

I. Sinf. concert. da Proſpero CAUCIELLO. *a 2 C. obl. 2 Fl. 2 Viol. e B. Lyon. No. I.*

I. Sinf. concert. da Proſpero CAUCIELLO. *a 2 C. obl. 2 Fl. 2 Viol. e B. Lyon. No. II.*

I. Sinf. concert. da Proſpero CAUCIELLO. *a 2 C. obl. 2 Fl. 2 Viol. e B. Lyon. No. III.*

I. Sinf. conc. da Ioſ. DEMACHI. *a 2 C. 2 O. 2 Viol. Violcl. concert. 2 Viol. V. e B. Op. X. Lyon.*

I. Sinf. conc. da Ios. DEMACHI. *a 2 C. 2 O. 2 Viol. e Viola concert. 2 Viol. V. e B. Op. XI. Lyon.*

I. Sinf. da Franc. HOFFMEISTER. *a 2 Cor. 2 Ob. 2 Clar. Tymp. Fl. obl. 2 Viol. V. e B. Lyon. No. II.*

I. Sinf. da Franc. HOFFMEISTER. *a 2 Cor. 2 Ob. 2 Viol. V. e B. Lyon. No. III.*

I. Sinf. da Franc. HOFFMEISTER. *a 2 Cor. 2 Ob. 2 Viol. V. e B. Lyon. No. V.*

I. Sinf. conc. da C. LOCHON. *a 2 Viol. princ. 2 C. 2 Ob. 2 Viol. V. e B. Op. II. Lyon.*

I. Sinf. da ORDONIZ. *a 2 C. 2 Ob. 2 Clar. Tymp. 2 Viol. V. e B. Lyon. No. I.*

DIVERTIMENTI, CONCERTINI etc.

I. Serenade da Louis BOCHERINI. *a 2 Cor. 2 Ob. 2 Viol. e B. Lyon.*

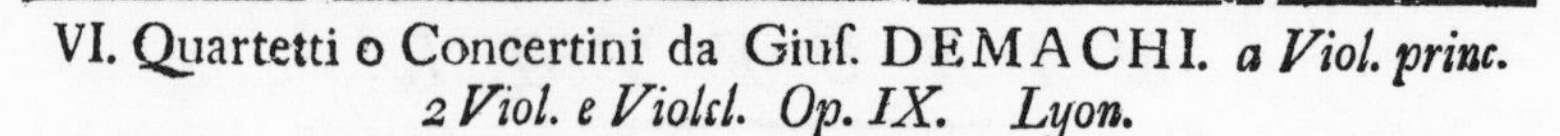

VI. Quartetti o Concertini da Gius. DEMACHI. *a Viol. princ. 2 Viol. e Violcl. Op. IX. Lyon.*

I. Divert. da C. LOCHON. *a 2 C. 2 Ob. 2 Viol. V. Fag. e B. Lyon. No. IV.*

V I O L I N O.

SOLI con BASSO intagliati.

VI. Soli da Le DUC. *Opera IV. Parigi.*

VI. Soli da Luc. GARNIER. *Op. I. Lyon.*

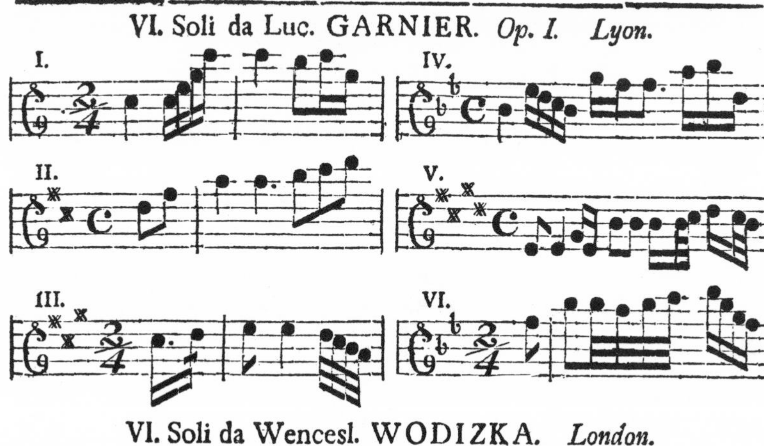

VI. Soli da Wencesl. WODIZKA. *London.*

DUETTI intagliati.

VI. Duetti da Prosp. CAUCIELLO. *Op. II. Lyon.*

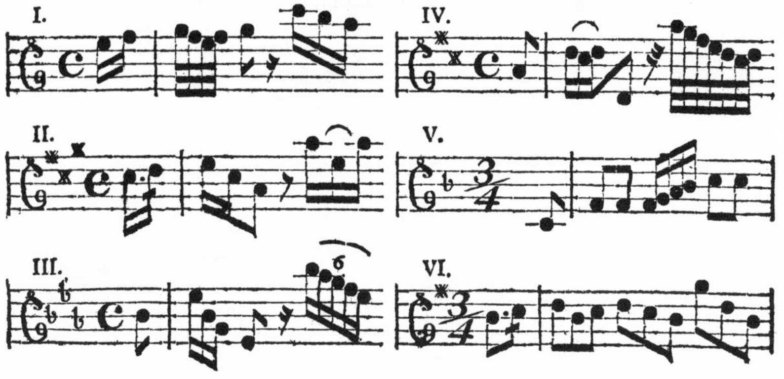

VI. Duetti da Prosp. CAUCIELLO. *Op. III. Lyon.*

VI. Duetti da Le DUC. l'ainé. *Op. III. Parigi.*

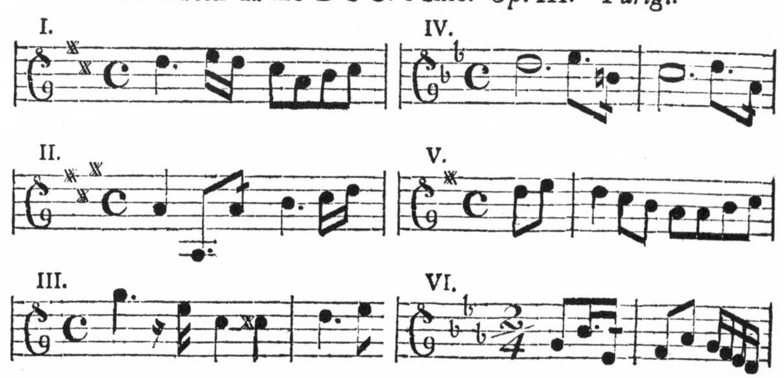

VI. Duetti da Ern. EICHNER. *a Violino e Viola. Op. VIII.*
Francf. sur le Mein.

VI. Duetti da Ant. KAMMEL. *Op. XI. Amst.*

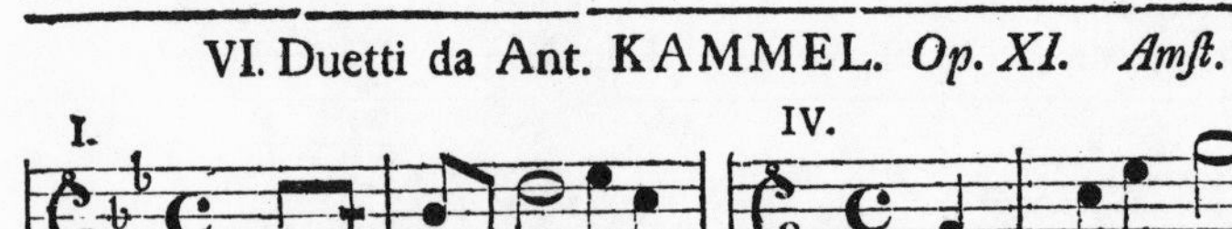

VI. Duetti da C. LOCHON. *Op. I. Lyon.*

VI. Duetti da STAMITZ le Fils. *Amst.*

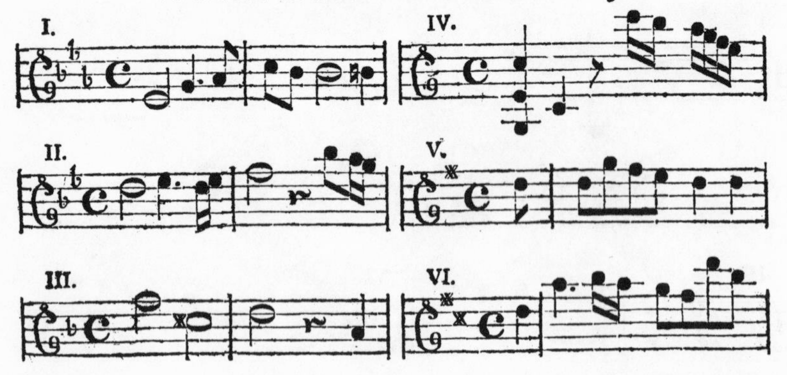

TRII *intagliati.*

A DUE VIOLINI CON BASSO.

VI. Trii da BACH, ABEL e KAMMEL. *Francf. sur le Mein.*

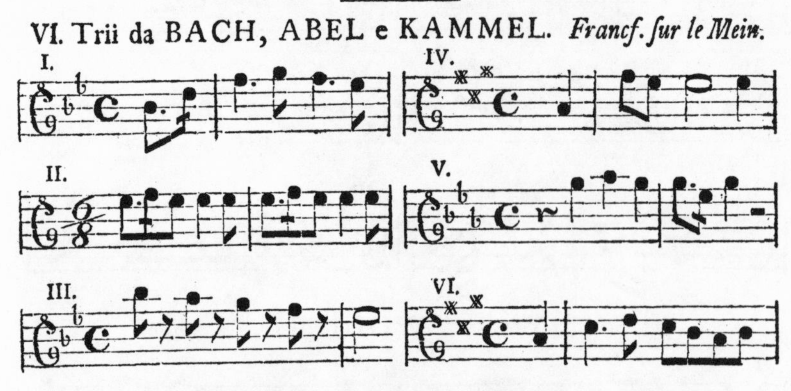

VI. Trii da BALDENECKER. *a Viol. Viola e B. concert. Op. I. Francf. sur le Mein.*

VI. Trii concert da CAUCIELLO. *Op. IV. Lyon.*

VI. Trii da Giov. Feder. REICHARDT. *Op. I. Offenbach.*

VI. Trii da Giov. VANHALL. *Op. XXII. Parigi.*

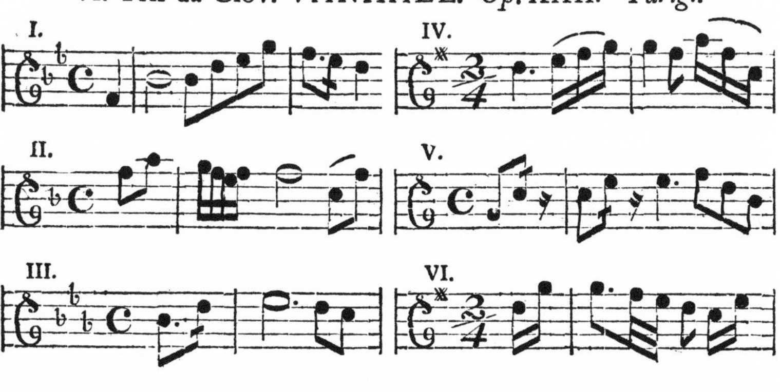

QUATTRI intagliati.

VI. Quattri da Giuſ. BARTTA. *a 2 Viol. V. e B. Op. I. Lyon.*

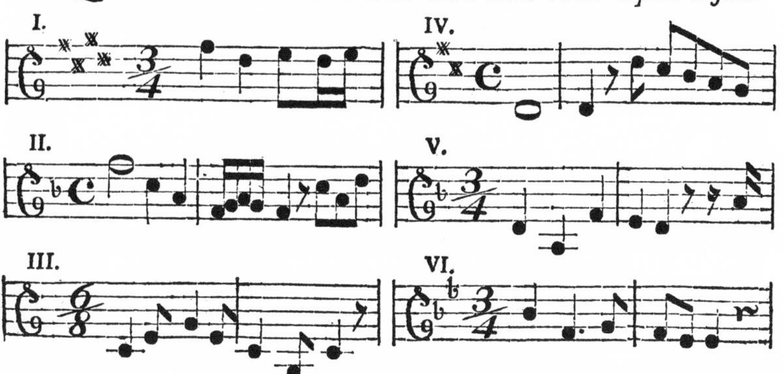

VI. Quattri da Giuſ. CAMBINI. *a 2 Viol. V. e B. Op. IV. Francſ. ſur le Mein.*

VI. Quattri da Giuſ. CAMBINI. *a 2 Viol. V. e B. Op. VII. Offenbach.*

VI. Quattri da Gian Batt. CIRRI. *a 2 Viol. V. e B. Op. XIII. London.*

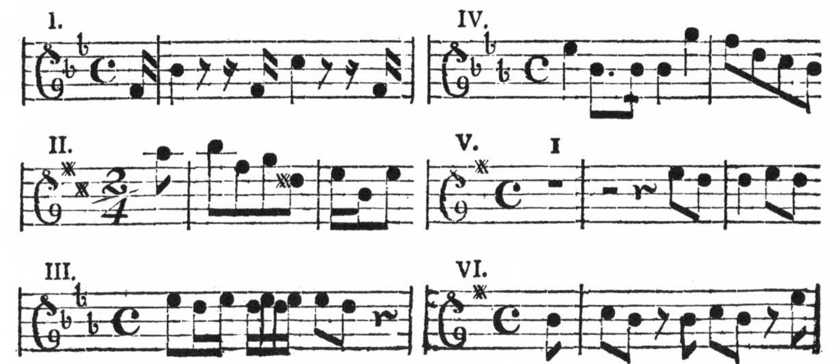

VI. Quattri da Mr. FIALA. *a 2 Viol. V. e B. Opera I.*
Francf. sur le Mein.

I. Quattro da GUILLON. *a 2 Viol. V. e Violoncello. Op. II.*
Lyon.

VI. Quattri da G. HAYDEN. *a 2 Viol. V. e B. Op. XX.*
Parigi.

VI. Quattri da MISLIWEZEK. *a 2 Viol. V. e B. Op. I.*
Offenbach.

VI. Quattri da ORDONNIZ. *a 2 Viol. V. e B. Op. I. Lyon.*

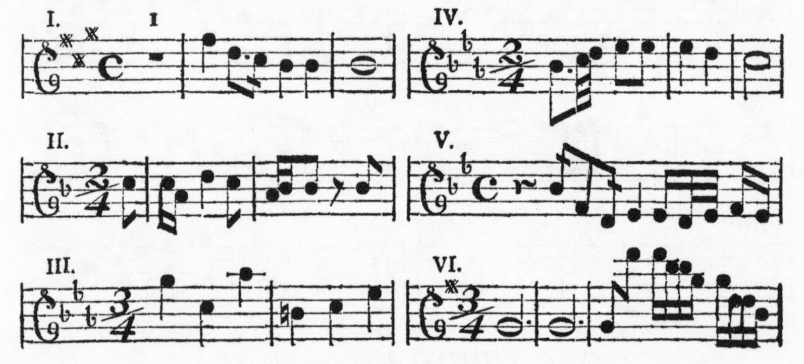

VI. Quattri da Giov. VANHALL. *a 2 Viol. V. e B.*
Op. XXI. Parigi.

QUINTETTI intagliati.

III. Quintetti da Profp. CAUCIELLO. *a 2 Viol. 2 Fl. Trav. e Violcl. Op. I. Lyon.*

VI. Quintetti da Luigi BOCCHERINI, *a 2 Viol. Viola e 2 Violcl. concert. Op. XIII. Parigi.*

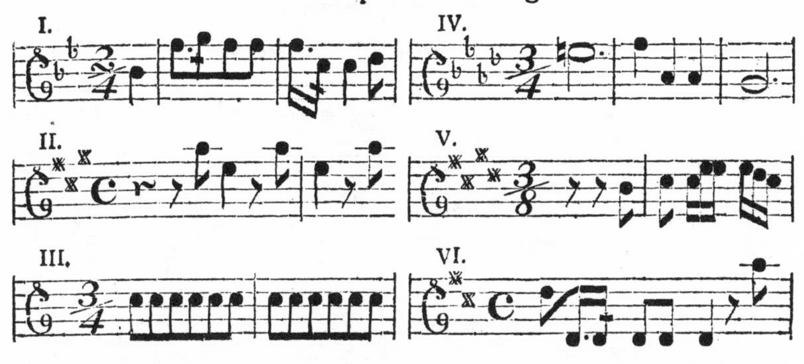

I. Seftetto da G. B. CIRRI. *a 2 Viol. Flauto, Viola, Violoncello e Baffo.*

CONCERTI per il Violino concertato.

I. Concerto da JARNOVIK. *a Viol. conc. 2 Cor. 2 Ob. 2 Viol. V. e B.*

III. Concerti da W. LEEDER.

I. *a Viol. conc. 2 C. 2 Ob. 2 Viol. V. e B.* III. *a Viol. conc. 2 C. 2 Fl. 2 Viol. V. e B.*

II. *a Viol. conc. 2 Clar. Tymp. 2 C. 2 Fl. 2 Viol. V. e B.*

I. Concerto da Ant. ROSETTI. *a Viol. conc. 2 Cor. 2 Ob. 2 Viol. V. e B.*

III. Concerti da Carlo STAMITZ.

I. *a Viol. conc. 2 C. 2 Ob. 2 Viol. 2 Viole in And. e B.* III. *a Viol. conc. 2 Cor. 2 Ob. 2 Viol. 2 Viole e B.*

II. *a Viol. conc. 2 C. 2 Ob. 2 Viol. V. e B.*

I. Concerto da VACHON. *a Viol. conc. 2 Cor. 2 Ob. 2 Viol. 2 Viole e B.*

CONCERTI intagliati.

I. Concerto da Alex. ROBINEAU. *a Viol. conc. 2 C. 2 Ob. 2 Viol. 2 Viole e B. Parigi.*

I. Concerto da Iof. SCHMITT. *a 2 Viol. conc. Violcl. e Viola obl. 2 Viol. 2 C. 2 Ob. e Baffo. Amft.*

II. Concerti da Giov. VIELHE. *a Viol. princ. 2 C. 2 Ob. 2 Viol. V. e B. Op. I. Lyon.*

VIOLA.

III. Duetti da C. STAMITZ fils aîné. *a Violino e Viola. Op. XII. Amft.*

CONCERTI a VIOLA.

II. Concerti da G. BENDA.

I. *a Viola conc. 2 C. 2 Viol. V. e B.* II. *a Viola conc. 2 C. 2 Viol. V. e B.*

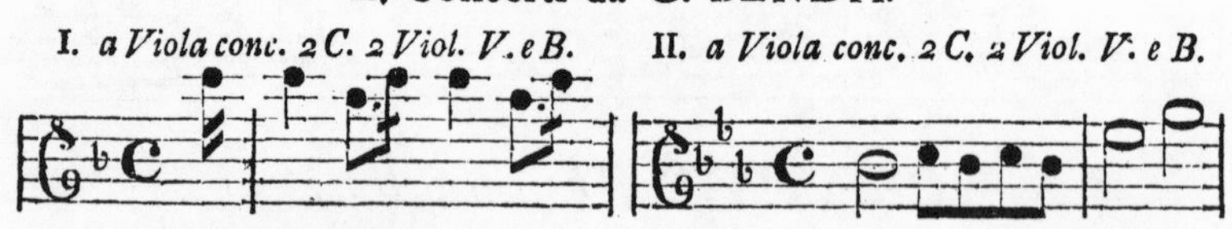

I. Concerto da C. E. GRAF. *a Viola conc. 2 Viol. e B.*

I. Concerto da WOLFF. *a Viola concert. 2 Ob. 2 Viol. V. e B.*

VIOLONCELLO.

I. Solo da SCHETTKY. *a Violonc. e B.*

Vetter Michel *con Variaz.*

I. Solo da Fr. WOSCHITKA. *a Violonc. e B.*

SOLI intagliati.

VI. Soli da F. GUERINI. *a Violcl. e B. Op. IX. London.*

DUETTI.

I. Duetto da MARA. *a Violino e Violoncello.*

I. Duetto da MEGELIN. *a Violino e Violoncello.*

VI. Duetti da I. B. BREVAL. *a 2 Violoncelli. Op. II. Parigi.*

III. Duetti da TILLIER. *a 2 Violoncelle. Parigi.*

CONCERTI, per il Violoncello concertato.

I. Conc. da MARA. *a Violcl. conc. 2 Viol. V e B.*

I. Conc. da MATTERN. *a Violcl. conc. 2 Viol. V. e B.*

II. Concerti da MEGELIN.

I. *a Violcl. conc. 2 C. 2 Ob. 2 Fag. 2 Viol. V. e B.* II. *2 Violcl. conc. 2 C. 2 Ob. 2 Fag. 2 Viol. V. e B.*

I. Concerto da WOSCHITKA. *a Violcl. conc. 2 Viol. V. e B.*

I. Concerto da L. BOCCHERINI. *a Violcl. conc. 2 C. 2 Viol. V. e B. Parigi.*

FLAUTO TRAVERSO.

SOLI intagliati.

VI. Soli da W. REINARDS. *a Fl. con Basso. Op. V. Amst.*

VI. Sonate da H. H. ZIELCHE. *a Fl. con Basso. Op. I. Amst.*

DUETTI intagliati.

VI. Duetti da W. HIMMELPAUER. *a Fl. o Viol. e Violcl. Op. I. Lyon.*

VI. Duetti da ROSINE. *a 2 Flauti. Op. I. Lyon.*

VI. Duetti da Giov. SIXT. *a 2 Flauti. Op. III. Lyon.*

TRII.

V. Trii da DOTHEL. *a Flauto, Violino e Basso.*

QUATTRI

A FLAUTO, VIOLINO, VIOLA e BASSO.

II. Quattri da DOTHEL.

II. Quattri da F. H. GRAAF.

QUATTRI intagliati.

VI. Quattri da Franc. HOFFMEISTER. *a Fl. Viol. V. e B. Op. II. Lyon.*

IV. Quattri da HUBER. *a Flauto, Viol. V. e B. Lyon.*

Quartetto periodique da C. STAMITZ. *a Flauto, Viol. V. e B. Amst. No. I.*

QUINTETTI.

III. Quint. da CAMBINI. *a Fl. 2 Vi. V. e B. Op. VIII. Frcf. sur le Mein.*

III. Quintetti da CAMBINI. *a Fl. 2 Viol. V. e B. Op. IX Offenb.*

CONCERTI

A FLAUTO TRAVERSO CONCERTATO.

III. Concerti. da F. H. GRAAF.

II. *a Fl. conc. 2 C. 2 Viol. V. e B.*

I. Conc. da F. KLEINKNECHT. *a Fl. conc. 2 C. 2 Viol. V. e B.*

VI. Concerti da Ant. ROSETTI.

I. *a Fl. conc. 2 C. 2 O. 2 Viol. 2 Viole e B.* IV. *a Fl. conc. 2 C. 2 Ob. 2 Viol. V. e B.*

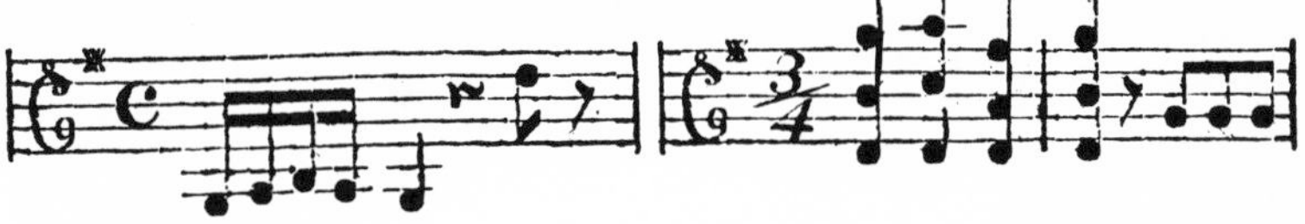

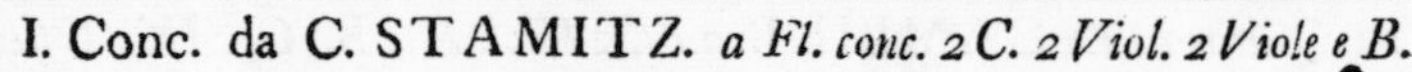

I. Conc. da C. STAMITZ. *a Fl. conc. 2 C. 2 Viol. 2 Viole e B.*

I. Conc. da G. TOESCHI. *a Fl. conc. 2 Viol. V. e B.*

V. Concerti da WIEFEL.

I. *a Fl. conc. 2 Viol. V. e B.* IV. *a Fl. conc. 2 C. 2 Viol. V. e B.*

II. *a Fl. conc. 2 C. 2 Viol. V. e B.* V. *a Fl. conc. 2 C. 2 Viol. V. e B.*

III. *a Fl. conc. 2 Viol. V. e B.*

CONCERTI intagliati.

I. Conc. d'AME'. *a Fl. conc. 2 Viol. V, e B. Parigi.*

VI. Serenade da F. ASPELMAYER. *a Fl. 2 C. Violcl. e Fag. Op. I. Lyon.*

I. IV.

II. V.

III. VI.

OBOE.

III. Partite da UNGELENK.

I. *a 2 Cor. 2 Ob. 2 Fag.* III. *a 2 Cor. 2 Ob. 2 Fag.*

II. *a 2 Clar. 2 Ob. 2 Fag.*

CORNO.

I. Solo da PUNTO. *a Corno e Basso.*

I. Trio da PUNTO. *a Corno obl. Violino e B.*

III. Quattri da LANDMANN. *a Corno, Violino, V. e B.*

I. III.

II.

Recueil de Duos et Ariettes da D. CHIAPPARELLI.

a 2 Cor. Op. I. Lyon.

FAGOTTO.

I. Conc. da EICHNER. *a Fag. conc. 2 C. 2 Fl. 2 Viol. V. e B.*

I. Conc. da GRENSER. *a Fag. conc. 2 C. 2 Fl. 2 Viol. V. e B.*

I. Conc. da SCHMITTBAUR. *a Fag. conc. 2 C. 2 Ob. 2 Viol. 2 Viole e B.*

II. Concerti da STAMITZ.

I. *a Fag. conc. 2 C. 2 Fl. 2 Viol. V. e B.* II. *a Fag. conc. 2 C. 2 Fl. 2 Viol. 2 V. e B.*

CEMBALO.

SOLI.

I. Sonata da BENDA.

Andante da G. HAYDEN. *con Variaz. per dui in uno Clavicemb.*

La parte del Maestro. La parte dello Scolare.

Arietta da LANDMANN. *con XV. Variaz. a Cembalo.*

II. Sonate da Ant. SCHWEITZER. *a Cembalo Solo.*

VI. Sonate da SEYDELMANN.

I. Divertimento da G. VANHALL. *a Cembalo.*

SONATE intagliate e ſtampate.

VI. Sonate da G. BARTTA. *Op. II. Lyon.*

II. Sonate da I. G. ECKARD. *Op. II. London.*

VI. Sonate da I. N. FORKEL. *Leipzig.*

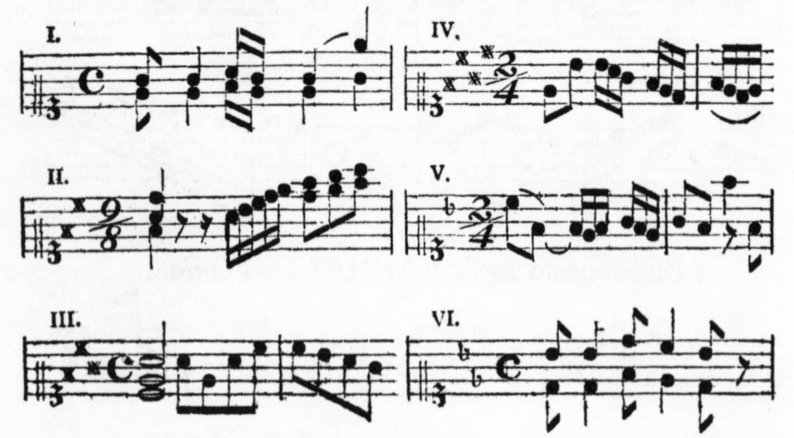

VI. Sonate da I. G. HAESSLER. *Leipzig.*

VI. Sonate da G. HAYDEN. *Op. XIV. Amſt.*

VI. Sonate da E. W. WOLFF. *Leipzig.*

TRII
A CEMBALO OBLIGATO CON VIOLINO O FLAUTO.

I. Sonata da I. C. BACH. *a Cembalo e Violino.*

V. Sonate da BEECKE. *a Cembalo e Violino.*

VI. Divertimenti da SCHUSTER. *a Cembalo e Violino.*

VI. Sonate da SEYDELMANN. *a Cemb. e Flauto.*

I. Sonata da C. B. UBER. *a Cemb. e Violino.*

VI. Sonatines da C. B. UBER. *a Cemb. e Violino.*

TRII intagliati.

VI. Sonate da L. BOCHERINI. *a Cemb. e Viol. oblig. Parigi*

VI. Sonate da I. A. JUST. *a Cemb. e Viol. oblig. Op. VII. Amst.*

VI. Sonate da I. F. REICHARDT. *a Cemb. e Viol. Op. II. Amst*

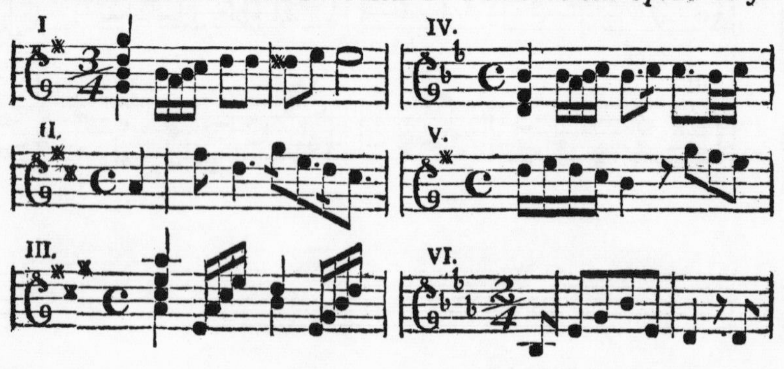

II. Sonate *a Cemb. e Violino, et una Sonata a 2 Cembali.* da G. SIXT. *Op. I. Lyon.*

III. Sonate da I. F. X. STERKEL. *a Cemb. e Violino. Op. IV. Francf. sur le Mein.*

VI. Sonate da Ant. ZIMMERMANN. *a Cemb. e Violino. Op. II. Lyon.*

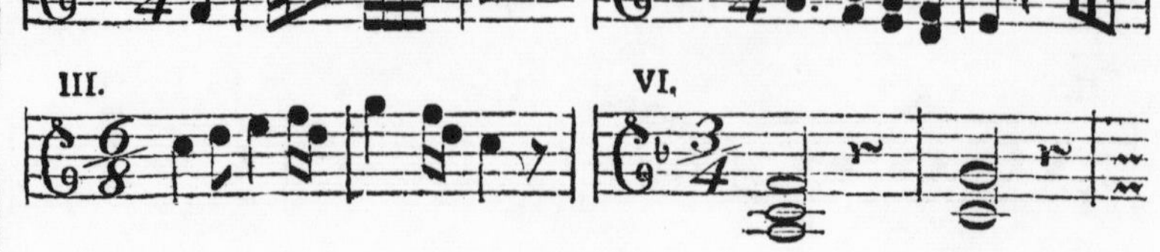

TERZETTI.

VI. Sonate da G. A. NAUMANN. *a Cembalo, Oboe o Fl. Fagotto o B.*

I. Sonata da SCHWEITZER. *a Cembalo, Viol. e B.*

TERZETTI *intagliati.*

VI. Sonate da J. C. BACH. *quatre a Cemb. Viol. e B. Cinquieme a quatre mains. Sixieme a deux Clavecins. Op. XV. Amst.*

VI. Sonate da Jos. DIETZ. *a Cemb. Viol. e Violonc. Op. III. Parigi.*

III. Sonate da J. F. X. STERKEL. *a Cemb. Viol. e B. Op. III. Francf. sur le Mein.*

III. Sonate da G. G. TROMLITZ. *a Cemb. Flauto o V. e B. Leipsic.*

VI. Sonate da E. W. WOLFF. *a Cemb. Viol. e Violoncello. Lyon.*

QUATTRI e DIVERTIMENTI.

I. Partita da BIRNBACH. *a Cemb. Flauto o Viol.*

I. Quattro da SCHMITTBAUR. *a Cemb. Flauto, Violino e Violoncello.*

QUATTRI intagliati.

III. Quattri da J. BAUER. *a Cemb. Flauto, Viol. e B. Op. V. Francf. sur le Mein.*

III. Quartetti da GIORDANI. *a Cemb. Flauto, Violino e B. Op. III. Francf. sur le Mein.*

III. Quattri da GRUNER. *a Cemb. Flauto, Viol. e Violoncello. Op. IV. Lyon.*

I. Quattro da G. S. LOEHLEIN. *a Cemb. Viol. V. e B. Op. VI. Lyon.*

III. Quattri da C. PREUS. *a Cemb. 2 Viol. e B. Cassel.* 1ster Th.

III. Quattri da J. SCHMITT. *a Cemb. Flauto, Viol. e Violonc. Op. IX. Amst.*

III. Quattri da J. C. WAGENSEIL. *a Cemb. 2 Viol. e Basso.*
Op. X. Parigi.

I. III. II.

CONCERTI, a Cemb. con più Stromenti.

III. Concerti da BEECKE.

I. *a Cemb. conc. 2 Viol. V. e B.* III. *a Cemb. conc. 2 Viol. V. e B.*

II. *a Cemb. conc. 2 Viol. V. e B.*

I. Concerto da G. BENDA. *a Cemb. conc. 2 Viol. V. e B.*

I. Conc. da A. BUCHAMMER. *a Cemb. conc. 2 Cor. 2 Viol. e B.*

I. Concerto da DEGEN. *a Cemb. conc. 2 Viol. V. e B.*

I. Concerto da F. DUSCHEK. *a Cemb. conc. 2 Cor. 2 Viol. V. e B.*

I. Concerto da St. GEORGE. *a Cemb. conc. Viol. princ. 2 Viol. V. e B.*

II. Concerti da I. H. ROLLE.

I. *a Cemb. conc. 2 Viol. V. e B.* II. *a Cemb. conc. 2 C. 2 Viol. V. e B.*

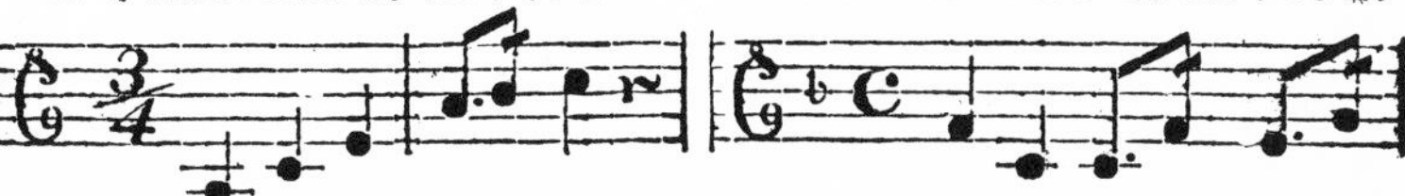

I. Conc. da SCHUSTER. *a Cemb. conc. 2 C. 2 Ob. 2 Viol. V. e B.*

I. Conc. da I. G. VIERLING. *a Cemb. conc. 2 Viol. V. e B.*

I. Conc. da E. G. WOLFF. *a Cemb. conc. 2 C. 2 Ob. 2 Viol. V. e B.*

CONCERTI intagliati.

II. Concerti da G. BENDA. *a Cemb. conc. 2 Viol. V. e B. Leipsic.*

I. II.

I. Conc. da GRUNER. *a Cemb. conc. 2 Cor. 2 Viol. e B.*
Op. III. Lyon.

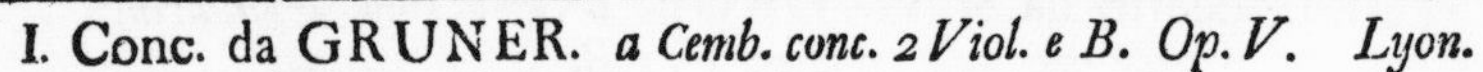
I. Conc. da GRUNER. *a Cemb. conc. 2 Viol. e B. Op. V. Lyon.*

I. Conc. da F. HOFFMEISTER. *a Cemb. conc 2 Viol. V. e B. Op. I. Lyon.*

III. Concerti da I. C. KELLNER. *a Cemb. conc. 2 Violini e B. Op. V. Francf. sur le Mein.*

I. Conc. da G. G. LANG. *a Cemb. conc. 2 C. 2 Ob. 2 Viol. V. e B. Offenbach.*

II. Concerti da C. G. RICHTER. *a Cemb. conc. 2 Viol. V. e B. Regiomonte.*

I. Divertiss. da GRUNER. *a Cemb. conc. 2 C. Fl. Viol. V. e B. Op. I. Lyon.*

I. Divert. da GRUNER. *a Cemb. conc. 2 C. Fl. Vi. Violcl. obl. e B. Op. II. Lyon.*

HARPA.

I. Duo da S. HARTMANN. *pour deux Harpes. Op. I. Lyon.*

III. Quattri da C. F. D. HOFFMANN. *a Harpa, Fl. Viol. e B. Op. I. Francf. sur le Mein.*

IV. Sonate da KRUMPHOLTZ. *a Harpa con Viol. Basso e 2 Cor. Op. III. Parigi.*

I. Concerto da M***. *a Harpa, 2 Cor. o Tromba, 2 Ob. o Fl. 2 Viol. V. e B. Parigi.*

Folgende Stücke sind in Partitur und in Stimmen zu haben.

1. Operetten.

Benda, Ariadne auf Naxos.
— — Medea.
— — Holzhauer.
— — Romeo und Julie.
Weimar, Schadenfreude.

2. Geistliche Gedichte.

Haendel, Oratorium The Messiah.
Rolle, Saul, oder die Gewalt der Musik.
— — Davids Sieg im Eichthale.
— — Abraham auf Moria.

Italiänische.

Ditters, David e Gionathan, *Oratorio.*
— — Pancrazio, *Opera buffa.*
— — *Cantata*, Clori e Nice, a 2 Soprani, 2 Cor. 2 Ob. 2 Viol. Fag. Viola e B.
— — *Cantata*, Silenzio o Muse, a Sopr. 2 Cor. 2 Ob. 2 Viol. V. e B.
Schwanberger, Romeo e Giulia, *Opera seria.*
Ubers Musik zum Prolog der Volontaire, a Soprano, Alto, Ten. Basso, 2 Cor. 2 Ob. 2 Fl. 2 Clar. Tymp. 2 Viol. V. e B.

SUPPLEMENTO XIII.

DEI

CATALOGI

DELLE

SINFONIE, PARTITE, OVERTURE, SOLI, DUETTI, TRII, QUATTRI

E

CONCERTI

PER IL

VIOLINO, FLAUTO TRAVERSO, CEMBALO

ED ALTRI STROMENTI,

CHE

SI TROVANO IN MANOSCRITTO NELLA OFFICINA MUSICA DI BREITKOPF IN LIPSIA.

1779 ed 1780.

SINFONIE.

II. Sinf. da Carlo DITTERS.

I. *a 2 C. 2 Ob. 2 Viol. V. Violcl. obl. e B.* II. *a 2 C. 2 Ob. 2. Viol. V. Violcl. e B.*

I. Sinf. de la DUCHESSA di Sax Gotha. *a 2 C. 2 Fl. 2 Viol. 2 Viole, Fag. V. e B.*

I. Sinf. da GRETRY. *(der Deserteur) a 2 C. 2 Ob. 2 Viol. 2 Fag. V. e B.*

VII. Sinf. da Giuf. HAYDEN.

I. *a 4 C. 2 Ob. 2 Viol. in And. V. solo Fl. V. Violcl. obl. e B.* V. *a 2 Clar. Tymp. 2 Cor. 2 Ob. 2 Viol. 2 Fag. V. e B.*

II. *a 2 C. 2 O. 2 Vi. Fl. 2 Fag. V. Violcl. e B.* VI. *a 2 C. 2 Ob. 2 Viol. 2 Fag. V. e B.*

IV. *a 2 C. 2 Ob. Fl. 2 Viol. 2 Fag. V. e B.*

I. Sinf. da Ant. ROSETTI. *a 2 C. 2 Ob. 2 Viol. V. e B.*

II. Sinf. da SCHUSTER.

I. *a 2 C. 2 Ob. 2 Fl. 2 Viol. V. Fag. e B.* II. *a 2 C. 2 Ob. 2 Fl. 2 Viol. V. e B.*

I. Sinf. da SCHWEITZER. *2 Clar. 2 C. 2 Fl. Fag. 2 Viol. 2 Viole, Violonc. e B.*

I. Sinf. da I. F. X. STERKEL. *a 2 Clar. Tymp. 2 C. 2 Ob. 2 Viol. 2 Viole e B.*

IX. Sinf. da Giov. VANHALL.

I. *a 2 Viol. princ. 2 C. 2 O. 2 Viol. V. e B.* VI. *a 2 C. 2 Ob. 2 Viol. V. e B.*

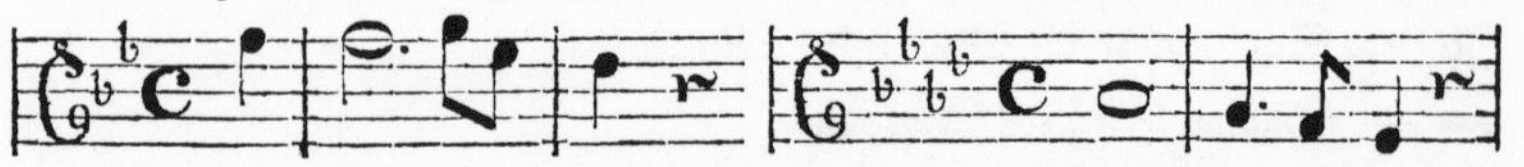

II. *a 2 Violcl. princ. 2 C. 2 Ob. 2 Viol. V. e B.* VII. *a 2 C. 2 Ob. in And. Fl. solo 2 Viol. V. e B.*

III. *a 2 C. 2 Ob. 2 Viol. V. e B.* VIII. *a 2 C. 2 Ob. 2 Viol. V. e B.*

IV. *a 2 C. 2 Ob. 2 Viol. V. e B.* IX. *a 2 C. 2 Ob. 2 Viol. V. e B.*

V. *a 2 C. 2 O. in And. 2 Fl. 2 Viol. V. e B.*

MINUETTI.

XII. *Hannover Redout. Menuetten* da PANNENBERG. *1780.*

I. *Hannov. Redout. Angloise 1780. a 2 Viol. 2 Fl. terz. 2 Fl. milit. 2 C. 2 Tr. Tymp. Triang. Türk. Tromm. Schellen in C. G. F. Becken in C. e Basso.*

IV. *Hannov. Redout. Angloisen. 1780.* VIII. *Hannov. Redout. Angloisen. 1780.*

IX. *Hannover Redout. Angloisen. 1780.*

IV. *Hannover Redout. Cottillon. 1780.*

SINFONIE *intagliate e stampate.*

IV. Orchest. Sinf. da C. P. E. BACH. *a 2 C. 2 Fl. 2 Ob. 2 Viol. V. Violonc. Fag. Flügel e Violon. Leipzig.*

II. Sinf. da L. BOCHERINI. *a 2 C. 2 Ob. 2 Viol. 2 Violoc. V. e B. Op. XVI. London.*

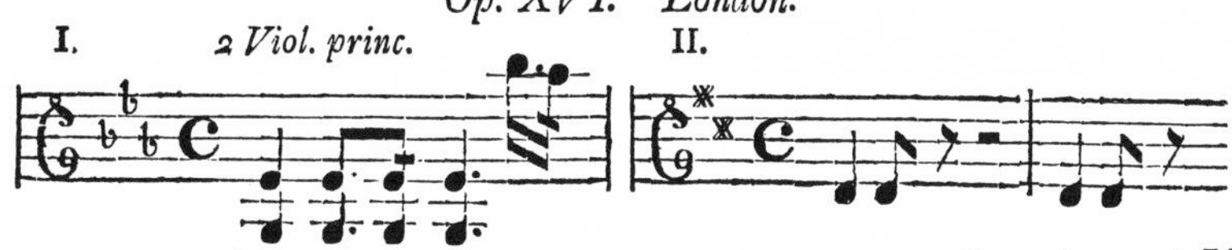

III. Sinf. da le DUC et GOSSECK. *a 2 C. 2 Ob. ó Fl. 2 Viol. V. e B. Op. I. Amst.*

VI. Sinf. da W. PICHL. *a 2 C. 2 Ob. 2 Viol. V. e B. Op. I. Berlin.*

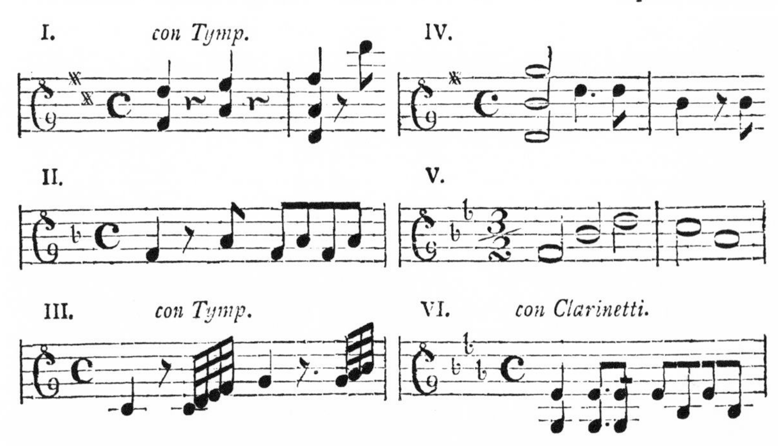

VI. Sinf. da STAMITZ. *a 2 C. 2 Ob. ó Fl. 2 Viol. V. e B. Amst.*

VIII. Sinf. da G. B. ZINGONI. *a 2 C. 2 Ob. 2 Viol. V. e B. Op. I. Amst.*

SINFONIES PERIODIQVES.

I. Sinf. da LACHNITH. *a 2 C. 2 Ob. 2 Viol. V. e B. No. I. Amst.*

I. Sinf. da LACHNITH. *a 2 C. 2 Ob. 2 Viol. V. e B. No. II. Amst.*

I. Sinf. da LACHNITH. *a 2 C. 2 Ob. 2 Viol. V. e B. No. III. Amst.*

I. Sinf. da LACHNITH. *a 2 C. 2 Fl. 2 Viol. V. e B. Op. V. Amst.*

I. Sinf. da LACHNITH. *a 2 C. 2 Fl. 2 Viol. V. e B. Op. VI. Amst.*

I. Sinf. la chaſſe da C. STAMITZ. *a 2 C. 2 Ob. 2 Viol. 2 Viole, ó 2 Fag. e B. Amst.*

DIVERTIMENTI, CONCERTINI etc.

I. Conc. da HOFFMEISTER. *a 2 Viol. ſoli, 2 C. 2 Ob. Fl. 2 Viol. 2 Viole, Violonc. e B.*

I. Conc. da HOFFMEISTER. *a 2 C. 2 Viol. Ob. ſolo, Fl. ſolo, Viola e B.*

II. Divert. da Giov. VANHALL.

I. *a Viol. princ. Viol. ſec. 2 C. 2 Fl. V. e B.* II. *a Viol. Flaut. 2 C. V. e B.*

VIOLINO.

SOLI con BASSO intagliati.

VI. Sonate da Giov. Fed. REICHARDT. *Berlin.*

DUETTI.

VI. Duetti da Maddalene Lombardini SYRMEN.

DUETTI intagliati.

VI. Duetti da I. BOULAY. *Mannheim.*

VI. Duetti da Giov. VANHALL. *Op. XXVIII. Vienna.*

10 VIOLINO.
TRII.
I. Trio da LAUSMEYER. a Viol. Violonc. e B.
I. Trio da Giov. VANHALL. a 2 Viol. e B.
TRII intagliati.
A DUE VIOLINI CON BASSO.
VI. Trii da P. BONAGA. a Viol. I. ó Fl. Viol. II. e B. Op. I. Vienna.
I.
II.
III.
IV.
V.
VI.
VI. Trii da Giuf. DEMACHI. Op. XV. Lyon.
I.
II.
III.
IV.
V.
VI.
VIOLINO. 11
VI. Trii da DOLPHIN. Op. I. Offenbach.
I.
II.
III.
IV.
V.
VI.
VI. Trii da KOSPOTH. a Viol. Viola e B. Op. I. Offenbach.
I.
II.
III.
IV.
V.
VI.
VI. Trii da MISLIWECECK. Op. II. Offenbach.
I.
II.
III.
IV.
V.
VI.

I. Quartetto da ASPELMAYER. *a 2 Viol. V. e B.*

QUATTRI *intagliati.*

VI. Quattri da Paul GEBHARD. *a 2 Viol. V. e B. Op. 1. Lyon.*

I. IV.

II. V.

III. VI.

SESTETTI.

V. Sestetti da HOFFMEISTER.

I. *a C. Ob. Fl. Viol. V. e Violonc.* IV. *a Cor. Ob. 2 Viol. V. e Violonc.*

II. *a C. Ob. Fl. Viol. V. e Violonc.* V. *a Viol. 2 Viole, 2 C. e Violonc.*

III. *a 2 C. 2 Viol. V. e Violonc.*

CONCERTI *per il Violino concertato.*

i. Conc. da G. BENDA. *a Viol. princ. 2 Viol. V. e Basso.*

I. Conc. da CRAMER. *a Viol. conc. 2 C. 2 Ob. 2 Fag. 2 Viol. V. e B.*

I. Conc. da ROSETTI. *a Viol. conc. 2 C. 2 Ob. 2 Viol. 2 Viole e B.*

I. Conc. da A. STAMITZ. *a Viol. conc. 2 C. 2 O. 2 Viol. 2 Viole e B.*

CONCERTI *intagliati.*

Conc. I. da Gius. DEMACHI. *a Viol. princ. 2 Cor. 2 Ob. 2 Viol. 2 Viole e B. Op. XII. Lyon.*

Conc. II. da Gius. DEMACHI. *a Viol. princ. 2 Cor. 2 Ob. 2 Viol. 2 Viole e B. Op. XVI. Lyon.*

VIOLA.

I. Conc. da Giov. Fed. KRANZ. *a Viola conc. 2 C. 2 Clar. 2 Viol. V. e B. Op. I. Weimar.*

VIOLONCELLO.

CONCERTI *per il Violoncello concertato.*

II. Concerti da SCHLICK.

I. *a Violcl. conc. 2 C. 2 Viol. 2 Viole e B.* II. *a Violcl. conc. 2 C. 2 Viol. V. e B.*

II. Conc. da TRICKLER.

I. *a Violcl. conc. 2 C. 2 O. 2 Viol. V. e B.* II. *a Violcl. conc. 2 Fl. 2 Viol. V. e B.*

Conc. IV. da L. BOCHERINI. *a Violcl. conc. 2 Viol. V. e B. Paris.*

FLAUTO TRAVERSO.

S O L I intagliati.

VI. Soli da I. F. GRONEMANN and others. *a Fl. con Basso. London.*

I. da GRONEMANN. IV. da GRONEMANN.

II. da DALL' OGLIO. V. da DALL' OGLIO.

III. da MARTINI. VI. da GRONEMANN.

D U E T T I intagliati.

VI. Sonate da Mr. GOSSEI. *a 2 Flauti. Libr. I. Paris.*

VI. Duetti da MÜLLER. *a 2 Flauti. Op. VIII. Lyon.*

T R I I intagliati.

III. Trios dialogues da Giuſ. DEMACHI. *a 3 Fl. ó Viol. Op. XIV.*

Q U A T T R I intagliati.

VI. Quattri da H. H. ZIELCHE. *a Fl. Viol. V. e B. Op. II. Leipſic.*

CONCERTI
A FLAUTO TRAVERSO CONCERTATO.

V. Concerti da F. H. GRAAF.

I. *a Fl. conc. 2 C. 2 Viol. V. e B.*   IV. *a Fl. conc. 2 C. 2 Viol. V. e B.*

II. *a Fl. conc. 2 C. 2 Viol. V. e B.*   V. *a Fl. conc. 2 C. 2 Viol. V. e B.*

III. *a Fl. conc. 2 C. 2 Viol. V. e B.*

I. Conc. da HOFFMEISTER. *a Fl. conc. 2 C. 2 Ob. 2 Viol. 2 Viole e B.*

I. Conc. da ROSETTI. *a Fl. conc. 2 C. 2 Ob. 2 Viol. V. e B.*

I. Conc. da WENDLING. *a Fl. conc. 2 C. 2 Viol. V. e B.*

CONCERTI *intagliati.*

I. Conc. da I. F. KLEINKNECHT. *a 2 Fl. conc. 2 Viol. 2 O. 2 Fag. Violcl. obl. 2 Viol. rip. 2 C. V. B. e Contra Baſſo.*

I. Conc. da METZGER. *a Fl. conc. 2 C. 2 Viol. V. e B. Op. II. Mannh.*

I. Conc. da METZGER. *a Fl. conc. 2 C. 2 Viol. V. e B. Op. III. Mannh.*

I. Conc. da METZGER. *a Fl. conc. 2 C. 2 Ob. 2 Viol. 2 Viole e B. Op. IV. Mannheim.*

I. Conc. da F. de STENGEL. *a Fl. conc. 2 C. 2 Viol. V. e B. Mannh.*

O B O E.

I. Partita da UNGELENCK. *a 2 C. 2 Ob. 2 Fag.*

I. Conc. da EICHNER. *a Ob. conc. 2 C. 2 Viol. V. e B.*

I. Conc. da FISCHER. *a Ob. conc. 2 C. 2 Viol. V. e B.*

FAGOTTO.

I. Conc. da EICHNER. *a Fag. conc. 2 C. 2 Viol. V. e B.*

I. Conc. da F. W. GRAF. *a Fag. conc. 2 Viol. V. e B.*

CEMBALO.

SOLI.

Andante et Marche da KOZELUCH. *a Cembalo.*

II. Sinf. da Giov. VANHALL. *accommodate per il Cemb. solo.*

SONATE intagliate e ſtampate.

VI. Son. da C. P. E. BACH. *für Kenner u. Liebhaber. Leipz. 1. Samml.*

VI. Sonate da I. C. BACH. *Op. XVII. Amſt.*

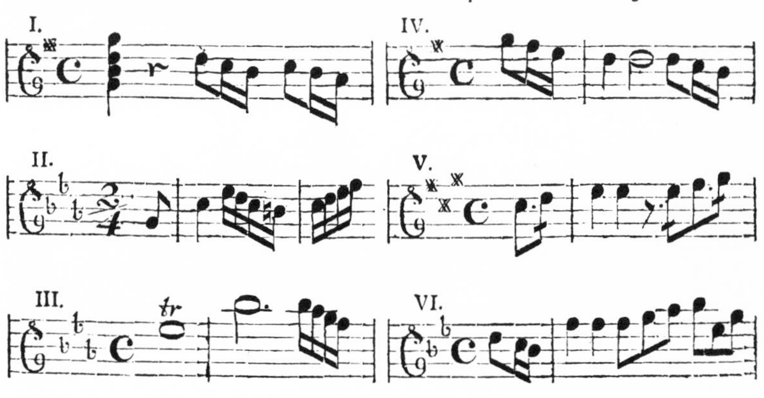

Douze Polonoiſes avec trois Pieces a la facon des Contredanſes
da B. BOHDANOWICZ. *Vienna.*

VI. Sonate da I. N. FORKEL. *con Viol. e Violonc. der zweyt. u. viert. Sonate, 2 Samml. Göttingen.*

VI. Sonate da Giuſ. HAYDEN. *Op. XXX.* *Vienna.*

III. Sonate da Leop. KOZELUCH. *Op. I.* *Vienna.*

III. Sonate da Leop. KOZELUCH. *Op. II.* *Vienna.*

VI. Sonate da C. W. PODBIELSKY. *Riga.*

XII. Pieces da STERCKEL. *Op. X.* *Vienna.*

VI. kleine Sonaten da E. W. WOLFF. *Leipzig.*

24 CEMBALO.
TRII
A CEMBALO OBLIGATO CON VIOLINO O FLAUTO.
VI. Sonate da I. C. BACH. a Cemb. e Viol. ò Fl. Op. XVI. Amst.
III. Sonate da F. A. de DALBERG. a Cemb. e Viol. Op. I. Mannh.
III. Sonate da EDELMANN. a Cemb. e Viol. Op. VI. Mannheim.
III. Sonate da EDELMANN. a Cemb. e Viol. Op. VIII. Mannh.
II. da Mlle. EDELMANN, soeur de l'Auteur.

CEMBALO. 25
III. Sonate da HULLMANDEL. a Cemb. e Viol. Op. III. Mannh.
III. Sonate da H. T. B. de KERPEN. a Cemb. e Viol. Op. I. Mannh.
III. Sonate da RASETTI. a Cemb. e Viol. Op. I. Mannheim.
VI. Sonate da C. STAMITZ. a Cemb. e Viol. la sixieme a deux Clavecins. Op. XX. Amst.

26 CEMBALO.

Sonata da L. TANTZ. *a Cemb. e Viol. Mannheim.*

III. Sonate da ZIMMERMANN. *a Cemb. e Viol. Op. I. Vienna.*

I. III.

II.

TERZETTI.

VI. Sonate da STAD. *a Cemb. Viol. e B.*

I. IV.

II. V.

III. VI.

VI. Sonate da C. STAMITZ l'aine. *a Cemb. Viol. e B.*

I. IV.

II. V.

III. VI.

CEMBALO. 27

VI. Sonate da F. A. BAUMBACH. *a Cemb. Viol. obl. e Basso. Leipsic.*

I. IV.

II. V.

III VI.

III. Sonate da GRUNER. *a Cemb. Viol. e Violel. Op. VI. Lyon.*

I. III.

II.

III. Sonate da GRUNER. *a Cemb. Viol. e Violel. Op. VII. Lyon.*

IV. VI.

V.

III. Sonate da I. F. X. STERKEL. *a Cemb. Viol. e B. Op. V. Francf. sur le Mein.*

I. III.

II.

III. Sonate da I. F. X. STERKEL. *a Cemb. Viol. e B. Op. VI. Francf. sur le Mein.*

I. III. II.

III. Sonate da L. TANZ. *a Cemb. Viol. e B. Op. II. Mannheim.*

I. III. II.

VI. Sonate da G. VOGLER. *a Cemb. e Viol. e B. Op. I. Mannh.*

I. IV. II. V. III. VI.

QUATTRI e DIVERTIMENTI.

III. Concertini da F. DUSCHECK. *a Cemb. Viol. e B.*

I. III. II.

I. Divert. da Giov. VANHALL. *a Cemb. Viol. conc. e Violcl.*

QUATTRI e QUINTETTI *intagliati.*

III. Quattri da PIOZZI. *a Cemb. 2 Viol. e Violcl. Op. I. Mannh.*

I. III. II.

III. Quattri da PIOZZI. *a Cemb. 2 Viol. e Violcl. Op. II. Mannh.*

I. III. II.

III. Quattri da A. RIGEL. *a Cemb. 2 Viol. e Violcl. Op. III. Mannh.*

I. III. II.

III. Quint. deux da SCHROETER et un da PUGNANI. *a Cemb. Fl. Viol. V. e Basso. Op. I. Francf. sur le Mein.*

I. III. II.

I. Sinf. da I. E. L. SIEVERS. *a Cemb. 2 C. 2 Fl. 2 Viol. e B. Francf. sur le Mein.*

CONCERTI, *a Cemb. con più Stromenti.*

CONCERTI *intagliati.*

III. Conc. da I. C. BACH. *a Cemb. conc. 2 C. 2 Ob. ou Fl. 2 Viol. e B. Op. XIII. Amst.*

III. Conc. da I. C. BACH. *a Cemb. conc. 2 C. 2 Ob. ou Fl. 2 Viol. e B. Op. XIV. Amst.*

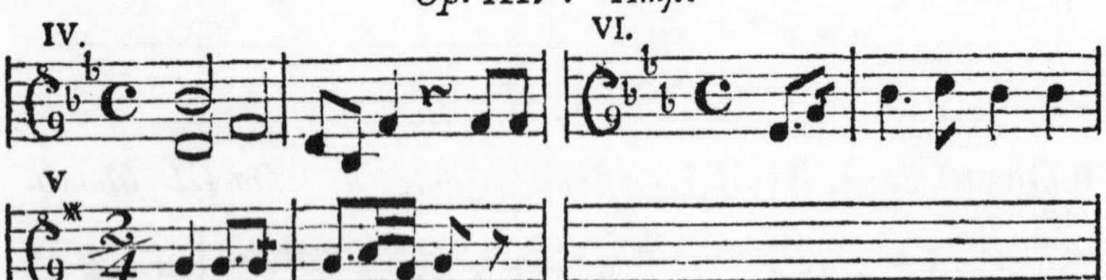

VI. Conc. da GIORDANI. *a Cemb. conc. 2 Viol. e B. Op. XX. Lyon.*

III. Conc. da I. C. KELLNER. *a Cemb. conc. 2 C. 2 Fl. 2 Viol. e B. Op. VIII. Francf. sur le Mein.*

I. Conc. da M. E. W. WOLFF. *a Cemb. conc. 2 Ob. 2 Viol. V. e B. Op. VII. Lyon.*

H A R P A.

III. Divertiss. da HARTMANN. *a Harpa con Viol. Op. III. Lyon.*

ARIE e CANTATE *con più Stromenti.*

II. Arie da Giov. Amadeo NAUMANN.

Cantata, Apollo und die Musen, da C. G. TAG. *a 2 C. 2 Fl. 2 Fag. 2 V. V. Soprano e B.*

Cantata, der Alte und der Jüngling, da C. G. TAG. *a 2 C. 2 Ob. 6 Fl. 2 V. V. Tenore e Basso, Violcl. e Fag. con Violono.*

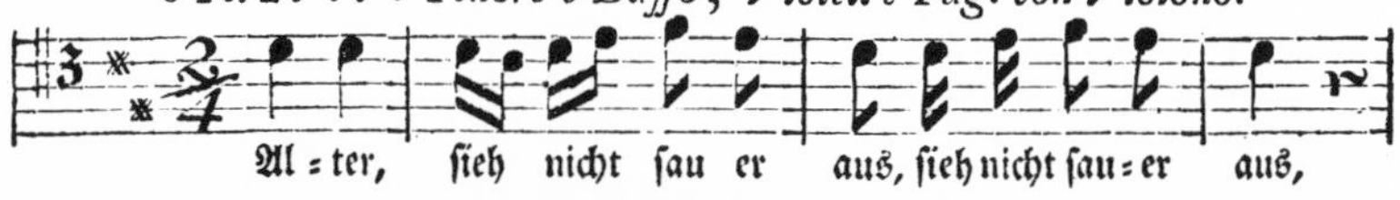

Folgende Stücke sind in Partitur und in Stimmen zu haben.

Operetten. Deutsche

Agosti, das Herbstabentheuer.
Benda, der Barbier von Sevilla.
— — der Dorfjahrmarkt.
— — der Holzhauer.
— — Romeo und Julie.
— — Walder.
Gretry, das Milchmädchen.
— — das redende Gemälde.
Guglielmi, Robert und Kalliste.
Holly, die Verwechslung.
Naumann, Armide.
Piccini, die Sclavin.
Schuster, der Alchimist.
— — die wüste Insel.
Seydelmann, Arsene.
— — der lahme Husar.
Stegmann, der Kaufmann von Smirna.
Wolf, Ehrlichkeit und Liebe.
Zanetti, das Wäschermädchen.
N. N. Mutter Natur.

Französische.

Gretry, La Rosiere de Salency.

Italiänische.

Benda, Hindo riconnosciuto.

SVPPLEMENTO XIV.

DEI

CATALOGI

DELLE

SINFONIE, PARTITE, OVERTURE, SOLI, DUETTI, TRII, QUATTRI

E

CONCERTI

PER IL

VIOLINO, FLAUTO TRAVERSO,

CEMBALO

ED ALTRI STROMENTI,

CHE

SI TROVANO IN MANOSCRITTO
NELLA OFFICINA MUSICA DI BREITKOPF
IN LIPSIA.

1781.

SINFONIE.

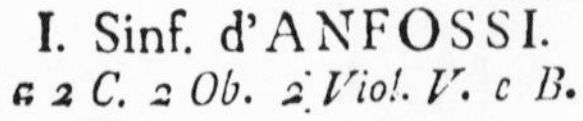

I. Sinf. d'ANFOSSI.
a 2 C. 2 Ob. 2 Viol. V. e B.

I. Sinf. d'ALEXANDRI.
a 2 C. 2 Ob. 2 Viol. V. e B.

I. Sinf. da I. C. BACH. *a 2 C. 2 Ob. 2 Fl. Fag. obl. 2 Viol. V. e B.*

I. Sinf. da BAISIELLO.
a 2 C. 2 Ob. 2 Viol. V. e B.

I. Sinf. da BEECKE.
a 2 C. 2 Ob. Fag. 2 Viol. V. e B.

I. Sinf. da F. C. BENDA. *a 2 C. 2 Fl. 2 Viol. V. e B.*

VI. Sinf. concert. da Gius. CAMBINI.

I. *a 2 Viol. obl. 2 C. 2 Ob. 2 Viol. V. e B.*

IV. *a 2 Viol. obl. Violcl. obl. 2 C. 2 Ob. 2 Viol. V. e B.*

II. *a 2 Viol. obl. 2 C. 2 Fl. 2 Viol. V. e B.*

V. *a Ob. pr. Fag. pr. 2 C. 2 Ob. 2 Viol. V. e B.*

III. *a 2 Viol. obl. 2 C. 2 Ob. 2 Viol. V. obl. e B.*

VI. *a Ob. pr. Fag. pr. 2 C. 2 Viol. 2 Viole e B.*

II. Sinf. concert. da Gius. CAMBINI.

I. *a 2 Viol. pr. 2 C. 2 Ob. 2 Viol. V. e B.* II. *a 2 Viol. pr. 2 C. 2 Ob. 2 Viol. V. e B.*

III. Sinfonie da Carlo de DITTERSDORFF.

I. *a 2 C. 2 Ob. 2 Viol. V. e B.* III. *a 2 Cor. 2 Ob. 2 Viol. V. e B.*

II. *a 2 C. 2 Ob. 2 Viol. V. e B.*

II. Sinfon. da Le DVC l'ainè.

I. *a 2 C. 2 Fl. 2 Ob. 2 Viol. 2 Viole e B.* II. *2 C. 2 Fl. 2 Ob. 2 Viol. V. e B.*

II. Sinf. da Giuseppe GAZANIGA.

I. *a 2 C. 2 Ob. 2 Viol. V. e B.* II. *a 2 C. 2 Ob. 2 Viol. V. e B.*

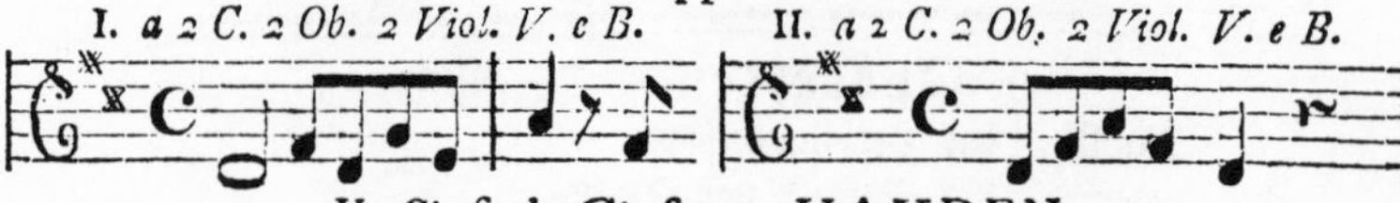

II. Sinf. da Giuseppe HAYDEN.

I. *2 C. 2 Ob. in And. 2 Fag. 2 Viol. V. e B.*

II. *a 4 Cor. 2 Ob. Viol. obl. Fl. obl. 2 Viol. Viola, Violcl. e Fag. e B.*

I. Sinf. da LAUSMAYER.
a 2 C. 2 Ob. 2 Viol. V. e B.

I. Sinf. d'Amad. NAUMANN.
a 2 C. 2 Ob. 2 Fl. 2 Viol. V. e B.

I. Sinf. da G. F. REICHARDT. *a 2 C. 2 Ob. 2 Viol. V. e B.*

III. Sinf. da Anton. ROSETTI.

I. *2 C. 2 Ob. 2 Viol. 2 Viole, Fagotto e B.* III. *a 2 C. 2 Ob. 2 Viol. 2 Viole, Fag. e B.*

II. *a 2 C. 2 Ob. 2 Fl. 2 Viol. 2 Viole, Fag. e B.*

4 SINFONIE.
II. Sinf. da SARTI.
I. a 2 C. 2 Fl. 2 Viol. V. Fag. Violcl. e B.
II. 2 Clar. Tymp. 2 C. 2 Ob. 2 Viol. V. e B.
VI. Sinf. da SCHMIDT.
I. 2 Clar. Tymp. 2 Ob. 2 Fl. 2 Viol. V. e B.
IV. a 2 Cor. 2 Clarinetti, 2 Viol. V. e B.
tr.
II. a 2 Cor. 2 Clarinetti, 2 Viol. V. e B.
V. a 2 C. 2 Fl. 2 Viol. V. e B.
III. a 2 C. 2 Ob. 2 Viol. V. e B.
VI. a 2 Clar. Tymp. 2 Ob. 2 Fl. 2 Vi. V. e B.
IV. Sinf. da SCHWEITZER.
I. a 2 C. 2 Ob. 2 Viol. V. e B.
III. 2 C. 2 Clar. 2 Ob. 2 Fl. 2 Viol. 2 Viole, Violcl. e B.
II. a 2 C. 2 Fl. 2 Viol. V. e B.
IV. a 2 C. 2 Ob. 2 Fl. 2 Viol. 2 Viole, Fag. Violcl. e B.
IV. Sinf. da Carlo STAMITZ.
I. 2 C. 2 Clarinet. 2 Viol. 2 Viole e B.
III. a Ob. pr. Fag. pr. 2 C. 2 Viol. 2 V. e B.
II. a Fl. pr. Viola pr. Violcl. pr. 2 C. 2 Clarinetti, 2 Viol. V. e B.
IV. a Ob. pr. Fag. pr. 2 Ob. 2 Viol. 2 Viole e B.

SINFONIE. 5
I. Sinf. da I. F. X. STERCKEL. a 2 C. 2 Fl. ó Ob. 2 Viol. V. e B.
I. Sinf. da TOZZI. a 2 C. 2 Ob. 2 Viol. V. e B.
II. Sinf. da Giov. VANHALL.
I. 2 C. 2 Ob. 2 Viol. V. Violcl. e B.
II. 2 C. 2 Ob. Flauto obl. 2 Viol. V. Violcl. e B.
p
I. Sinf. da Ant. WAGNER. a 2 C. 2 Ob. 2 Fl. 2 Viol. V. e B.
MINUETTI.
XII. Hannover Redout. Menuetten. da F. PANNENBERG. 1781.
XXVII. Hannover Redout. Angloisen. 1781.
VI. Hannover Redout. Cottillon. 1781.
VIII. Marcia da Em. Lud. GERBER. a 2 Clarinetten oü Trompe, Tymp. 2 Cor. 2 Viol. e B.

XXXII. *Neue Menuetten von Böhmischen Tonkünstlern. a 2 Viol. e B. Rotenburg an der Fulda.*

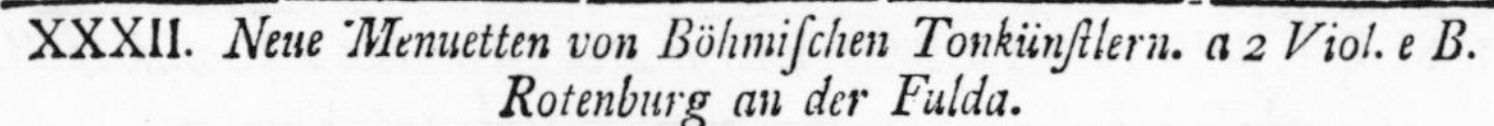

XII. *Contredances avec les Figures a Violon seul.* da HASLBOECK. *Vienna.*

SINFONIE intagliate e stampate.

VI. Sinf. da D. Angelo BALDAN. *a 2 C. 2 Ob. 2 Viol. V. e B. in Venezia.*

II. Sinf. conc. da DAVAUX. *a 2 Viol. pr. 2 C. 2 Ob. 2 Viol. V. e B. Op. III. a la Haye.*

II. Sinf. conc. da DAVAUX. *a 2 Viol. princ. 2 C. 2 Ob. 2 Viol. V. e B. Op. IV. a la Haye.*

II. Sinf. conc. da St. GEORGE. *Op. X. Parigi.*

I. *a 2 Viol. pr. Viola pr. 2 Viol. e. B.* II. *a 2 Viol. pr. Viola pr. 2 C. 2 Ob. 2 Viol. V. e B.*

III. Sinf. da GOSSEC et RIGEL. *a 2 Clarini, Tymp. 2 Cor. 2 Oboi, 2 Fag. 2 Viol. V. e B. Mannheim.*

VI. Sinf. da G. A. KREUSSER. *a 2 C. 2 Ob. 2 Viol. V. e B. Op. XVIII. à Mayence.*

Sinf. IIde concert. da Charles LOCHON. *a 2 Viol. pr. 2 C. 2 Ob. 2 V. V. e B. Op. IV. Lyon.*

SINFONIES PERIODIQUES.

I. Sinf. periodique da I. FRAENZL. *a 2 C. 2 Ob. 2 Viol. V. e B. No. VII. Mannheim.*

I. Sinf. period. da I. FRAENZL. *a 2 C. 2 Fl. 2 Viol. V. e B. No. VIII. Mannheim.*

I. Sinf. concert. da C. STAMITZ. *a Viol. obl. Violcl. obl. 2 C. 2 Ob. 2 Viol. 2 Viole e B. No. II. Paris.*

I. Sinf. concert. da C. STAMITZ. *a Viol. obl. 2 Cor. 2 Ob. 2 Viol. 2 Viole e B. No. III. Paris.*

I. Sinf. conc. da C. STAMITZ. *a Viol. obl. Violcl. obl. 2 C. 2 Clarinetti, 2 Viol. 2 Viole e B. No. IV. Paris.*

I. Sinf. conc. da C. STAMITZ. *a 2 Viol pr. Viola obl. 2 C. 2 Ob. 2 Viol V. e B. No. VII. Paris.*

I. Sinf. conc. da C. STAMITZ. *a Viol. obl. Violcl. obl. 2 C. 2 Ob. 2 Viol. 2 Viole e B. No. VIII. Paris.*

I. Sinf. conc. da C. STAMITZ. *a Viol. obl. Violcl. obl. 2 C. 2 Clarinetti, 2 Viol. 2 Viole e B. No. XII. Paris.*

I. Sinf. conc. da C. STAMITZ. *a 2 Viol. obl. Violcl. obl. 2 C. 2 Clarinetti, 2 Viol. 2 Viole e B. No. XV. Paris.*

I. Sinf. conc. da C. STAMITZ. *a 2 Viol. pr. 2 C. 2 Ob. ó Clarinetti, 2 Viol. 2 Viole e B. No. XVII. Paris.*

I. Sinf. conc. da C. STAMITZ. *a Viol. obl. Oboe ó Viol. II. obl. Viola obl. Fag. ó Violcl. obl. 2 C. 2 Viol. V. e B. Op. XIV. Paris.*

II. Sinf. concert. da C. STAMITZ. *Op. XVIII. Paris.*
I. a 2 Viol. pr. Viol. obl. 2 C. 2 O. 2 Viol. V. e B. II. 2 Viol. pr. 2 C. 2 Ob. 2 Viol. V. e B.

DIVERTIMENTI, CONCERTINI etc.

I. Concertino da ABEL. *a 2 C. Clarinetti, 2 Viole, Fagotto e B.*

I. Ouverture de l'Opera, le Tableau parlant, da GRETRY. *a 2 C. 2 Fl. 2 Viol. V. Fag. e B.*

I. Ouverture de l'Opera, les deux Avares, da GRETRY. *a 2 C. 2 Ob. 2 Viol. V. Fag. e B.*

I. Ouverture de l'Opera, les Femmes vengées, da D. PHILIDOR. *a. 2 C. 2 Ob. 2 Fag. 2 Viol. V. Violcl. e B.*

I. Partita da REICHARDT. *a 2 C. 2 Ob. 2 Flauti, 2 Fag. 2 Viol. V. e B.*

I. Concertino da Ant. ROSETTI. *a Clarinetto ó Oboe obl. Corno obl. 2 C. 2 Ob. 2 Viol. 2 Viole e B.*

I. Ouverture de l'Opera, la FRASCATANA. *a 2 C. 2 Ob. 2 Viol. V. e B. Paris.*

Entr' Acte de l'Opera, HENRI IV, ou la Bataille d'iury. *a 2 C. 2 Ob. oû Fl. 2 Viol. 2 Viole e B. a la Haye.*

VI. Divertiſſements da Ioſeph HAYDEN. *a 2 Cor. Flauto, 2 Viol. V. Violcello e B. Op. XXXI. Vienna.*

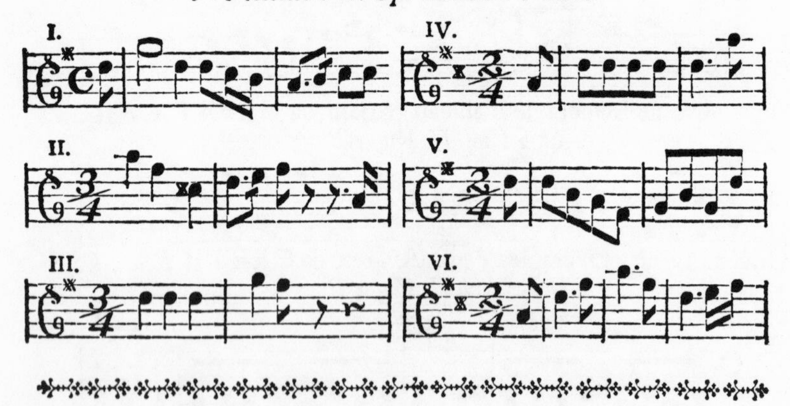

VIOLINO.

SOLI con BASSO.

III. Sonate da Franc. DAVILLO.

VI. Sonate da Pietro NARDINI.

DUETTI.

III. Duetti da Giov. PUNTO.

DUETTI intagliati.

VI. Duetti da I. B. CIRRI. *a Viol. e Violoncello. Op. XIII. Francſ. ſur le Mein.*

VI. Duetti da Pietro FIDANZA. *a 2 Violini. Firenze.*

VI. Duetti da A. GUENIN. *a 2 Violini. Op. III. Mannheim.*

VI. Duetti da Mich. KERZELL. *a 2 Violini. Op. II. Vienna.*

VI. Duetti da A. LIDEL. *a Violino e Viola. Op. III. Paris.*

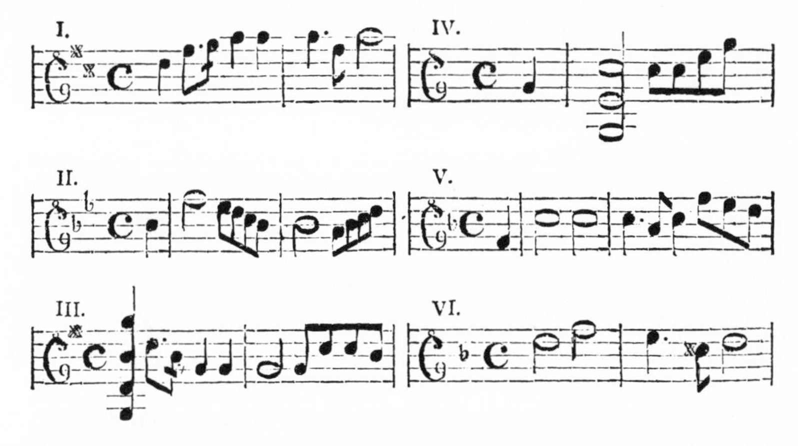

III. Duetti da M. LORENZITY. *a Violino e Viola. Op. III. Francf. sur le Mein.*

VI. Duetti da MAHONY. *a Violino e Viola. Op. IV. Paris.*

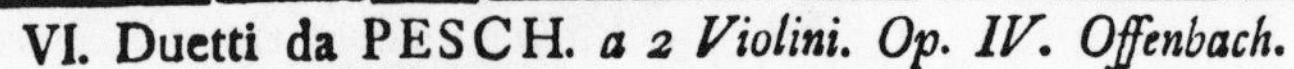

VI. Duetti da PESCH. *a 2 Violini. Op. IV. Offenbach.*

VI. Duetti da PICHL. *a 2 Violini. Op. IV. Francfort sur le Mein.*

VI. Duetti da Ant. STAMITZ. *a Violino e Viola. Op. X. Paris.*

VI. Duetti da Giov. VANHALL. *a 2 Violini. Paris.*

TRII.

VI. Trii da KLEINKNECHT. *a 2 Viol. e B.*

VI. Trii da WÜRTIG. *a 2 Viol. ó Fl. e B.*

TRII intagliati.

A DUE VIOLINI CON BASSO.

III. Trii concertans da Felice GIARDINI. *a Viol. Viola e B. Op. XIII. Francfort sur le Mein.*

VI. Trii da Ant. KAMMEL. *Op. XVII. Paris.*

VI. Trii da C. F. KERNTL. *Op. V. Lyon.*

VI. Trii da Ioseph SCHMITT. *Op. XI. Amst.*

I. *a Viol. Viola e Violcl.* IV. *a 2 V. e Violcl.*

II. *a 2 V. e Violcl.* V. *a Viol. Viola e Violcl.*

III. *a Viol. Viola e Violcl.* VI. *a 2 V. e Violcl.*

QUATTRI intagliati.

VI. Quattri concertans da BARRIERE. *a 2 Viol. V. e B. Op. I. Paris.*

I. IV. II. V. III. VI.

III. Quattri concertans a Giuseppe CAMPINI. *a 2 Viol. V. e B. Op. XII. Offenbach.*

I. III. II.

VI. Quattri da CAPUZZI. *a 2 Viol. V. e B. Vienna.*

VI. Quattri concertans da DAVAUX. *a 2 Viol. V. e B. Op. VI. a la Haye.*

VI. Quattri da Rom. HOFFSTETTER. *a 2 Viol. V. e B. Op. II. Mannheim.*

VI. Quattri da Vincenzo MANFREDINI. *a 2 Viol. V. e Violoncello. Firenze.*

VI. Quattri da PAISIBLE. *a 2 Viol. V. e B. Op. III. Paris.*

VI. Quattri da Wenceslao PICHL. *a 2 Viol. V. e Violoncello. Op. II. Berlin.*

VI. Quattri da Ferd. TITZ. *a 2 Viol. V. e B. Vienna.*

SESTETTI.

I. Seſtetto da HOFFMEISTER. *a C. Ob. Flauto, Viol. V. e B.*

I. Seſtetto da Ant. ROSETTI. *a C. Flauto, Violino, 2 Viole e B.*

CONCERTI per il Violino concertato.

I. Conc. da G. CRAMER. *a Viol. princ. 2 C. 2 Ob. 2 Viol. V. e B.*

I. Conc. da DAVAUX. *a Viol. princ. 2 Cor. 2 Viol. V. e B.*

II. Concerti da le DUC l'ainè.

I. *a Viol. princ. 2 C. 2 Ob. 2 Viol. V. e B.* II. *a Viol. pr. 2 C. 2 Ob. 2 Viol. V. e B.*

I. Conc. da HEMBEL. *a Viol. princ. 2 C. 2 Ob. 2 Viol. V. e B.*

II. Concerti da la MOTTE.

I. *a Viol. pr. 2 C. 2 Fl. 2 Viol. V. e B.* II. *a Viol. pr. 2 C. 2 Fl. 2 Viol. V. e B.*

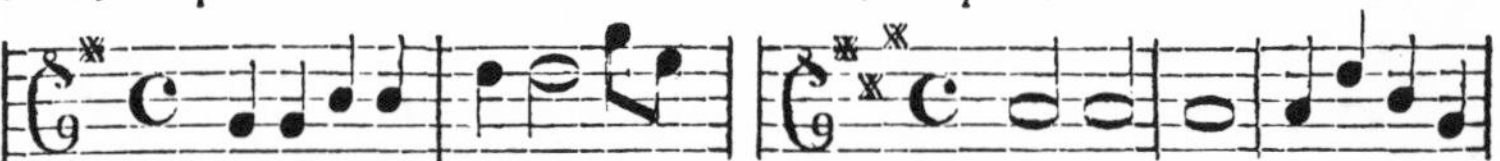

I. Conc. da Ant. ROSETTI. *a Viol. pr. 2 C. 2 Ob. 2 Viol. V. e B.*

I. Conc. da SCHMITTBAUER. *a Viol. princ. 2 C. 2 Ob. 2 Viol. V. e B.*

II. Concerti da Mr. STAD.

I. *a Viol. pr. 2 C. 2 Viol. V. e B.* II. *a Viol. princ. 2 Viol. V. e B.*

IV. Concerti da Ant. STAMITZ.

I. *a Viol. pr. 2 C. 2 Ob. 2 Viol. V. e B.* III. *a Viol. princ. 2 Ob. 2 Viol. V. e B.*

II. *a Viol. pr. 2 C. 2 Ob. 2 Viol. 2 Viole e B.* IV. *a Viol. pr. 2 C. 2 Ob. 2 Viol. 2 Viole e B.*

CONCERTI intagliati.

I. Conc. da DAVAUX. *a Viol. princ. 2 Viol. V. e B. III. Paris.*

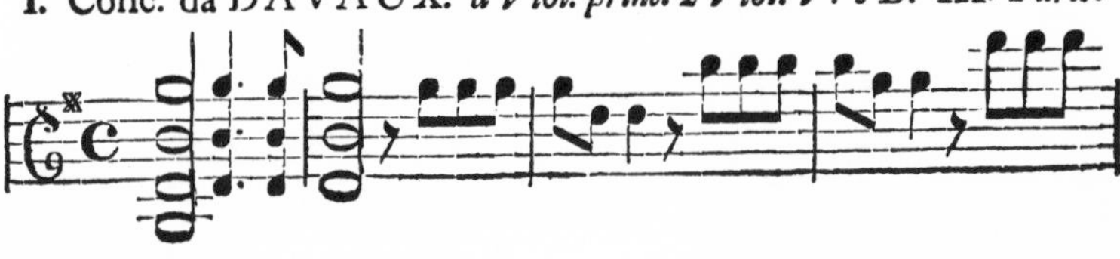

I. Conc. da GIORNOVICHI. *a Viol. princ. 2 C. 2 Ob. 2 Viol. V. e B. Libro I. Berlin.*

I. Concerto da PESCH. *a Viol. princ. 2 C. 2 Ob. ó Fl. 2 Viol. V. e B. Libro. I. Offenbach.*

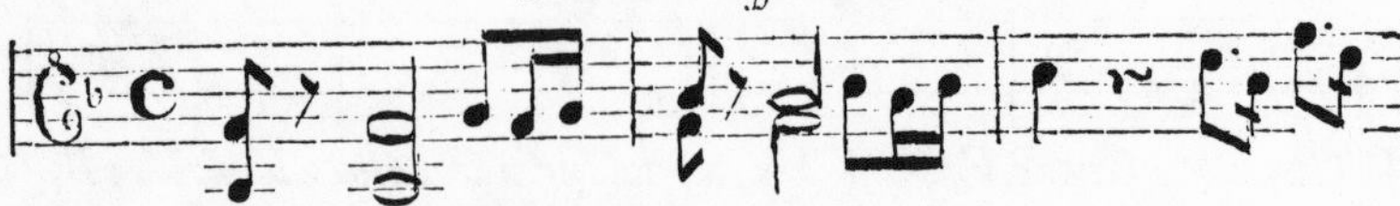

III. Concerti da Ignace RAIMONDI. *a Viol. pr. 2 C. 2 Ob. 2 Viol. V. e B. Op. VIII. Berlin.*

I. Concerto da VIOTTI. *a Viol. princ. 2 C. 2 Ob. 2 Viol. V. e B. Libro I. Berlin.*

VIOLONCELLO.

I. Solo da LUDWIG. *a Violoncello e B.*

I. Solo da MARA. *a Violonc. e B.*

VI. Soli da SCHLICK. *a Violonc. e B.*

I. Solo da SCHWACHOFFER. *a Violonc. e B.*

I. Solo da WOSCHITKA. *a Violoncello e B.*

QUATTRI.

I. Quattro da SCHLICK. *a Violcl. obl. Violino obl. Viola obl. e Basso.*

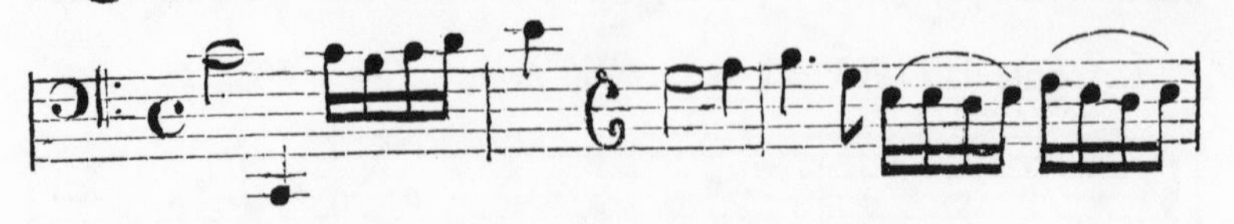

CONCERTI per il Violoncello concertato.

I. Conc. da GRAAF. *a Violcl. conc. 2 C. 2 Ob. 2 Viol. V. e B.*

I. Conc. da MEGELIN. *a Violc. conc. 2 C. 2 Ob. 2 Fag. 2 Viol. V. e B.*

IV. Concerti da Giuſeppe REICHA.

I. *a Violcl. conc. 2 C. 2 Ob. 2 Viol. V. e. B.* III. *a Violcl. conc. 2 C. 2 Ob. 2 Fl. 2 Viol. 2 Viole e B.*

II. *a Violc. conc. 2 C. 2 Ob. 2 Viol. 2 Viole e B.* IV. *a Violcl. conc. 2 C. 2 Fl. 2 Viol. V. e B.*

I. Conc. da Carlo STAMITZ. *a Violcl. conc. 2 C. 2 Viol. V. e B.*

FLAUTO. TRAVERSO.

III. Soli da H. O. C. ZINCK. *a Flauto con Baſſo.*

SOLI intagliati.

VI. Soli da I. G. NICOLAI. *a Fl. con Baſſo. Op. VI. Francf. ſur le Mein.*

VI. Soli da C. WEISS. *a Flauto con Baſſo. Op. III. Offenbach.*

DUETTI intagliati.

VI. Sonate da CAMBINI. *a 2 Flauti. Op. V. Berlin.*

VI. Duetti da WENDLING. *a 2 Flauti. Op. IX. Mannheim.*

VI. Duetti da WOLFF *a Stettin. a 2 Flauti. Op. I. Berlin.*

T R I I.

I. Trio da Giuſeppe FIEDLER. *a 3 Flauti.*

I. Trio da VANHALL. *a Flauto, Violino e B. Op. III. Offenbach.*

QUATTRI e QUINTETTI intagliati.

III. Quattri concert. da I. B. WENDLING. *a Flauto, Violino, V. e B. Op. X. Mannheim.*

I. Quintetto da VANHALL. *a Flauto, 2 Violini, V. e B. a Spire.*

C O N C E R T I

A FLAUTO TRAVERSO CONCERTATO.

I. Conc. da G. BENDA. *a Fl. conc. 2 Viol. V. e B.*

I. Conc. da le BRUN. *a Fl. conc. 2 C. 2 Viol. V. e B.*

II. Concerti da GRAAF.

I. *a Fl. conc. 2 Viol. V. e B.* II. *a Fl. conc. 2 C. 2 Viol. V. e B.*

II. Concerti da Leop. HOFFMANN.

I. *a Fl. conc. 2 Viol. V. e B.* II. *a Fl. conc. 2 Viol. V. e B.*

I. Conc. da KLEINKNECHT. *a Fl. conc. 2 Cor. 2 Viol. V. e B.*

I. Conc. da Ant. ROSETTI. *a Fl. conc. 2 C. 2 Ob. 2 Viol. V. e B.*

I. Conc. da Ant. STAMITZ. *a Fl. conc. 2 C. 2 Ob. 2 Viol. V. e B.*

II. Concerti da Carlo STAMITZ.

I. *a Fl. conc. 2 C. 2 Ob. 2 Viol. V. e B.* II. *a Fl. conc. 2 Viol. V. e B.*

III. Concerti da G. TOESCHI.

I. *a Fl. conc. 2 C. 2 Ob. 2 Viol. V. Violc. e B.* III. *a Fl. conc. 2 Cor. 2 Viol. V. e B.*

II. *a Fl. conc. 2 Viol. V. e B.*

I. Conc. da WENDLING. *a Fl. conc. 2 C. 2 Viol. V. e B.*

I. Conc. da le BRUN. *a Fl. conc. 2 Cor. 2 Viol. V. e B. Paris.*

OBOE.

VI. Soli da EICHNER. *a Oboe solo con Basso.*

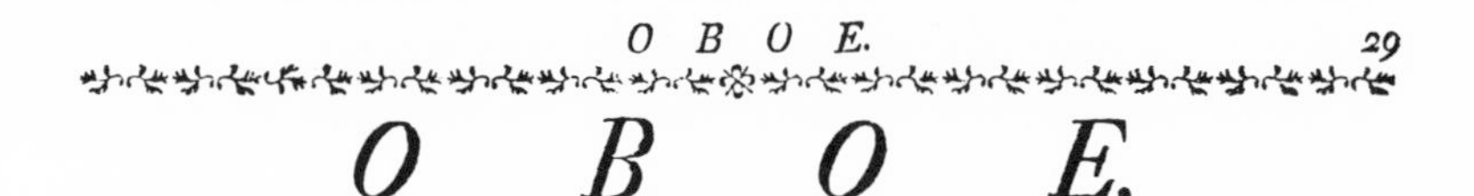

III. Soli da FISCHER. *a Oboe solo con Basso.*

I. Trio da SCHMITTBAUR. *a Oboe, Violino e Basso.*

CONCERTI, a OBOE concertato.

I. Conc. da BESOZZI. *a Ob. conc. 2 C. 2 Viol. V. e B.*

I. Conc. da BRAUN *a Ob. conc. 2 C. 2 Viol. V. e B.*

I. Conc. da EICHNER. *a Ob. conc. 2 C. 2 Fl. 2 Viol. V. e B.*

I. Conc. da FISCHER. *a Ob. conc. 2 C. 2 Viol. V. e B.*

IV. Concerti da GRAAF.

I. *a Ob. conc. 2 C. 2 V. V. e B.* III. *a Ob. conc. Fag. obl. 2 C. 2 Viol. V. e B.*

II. *a Ob. conc. 2 C. 2 Viol. V. e B.* IV. *a Ob. conc. 2 C. 2 Viol. V. e B.*

II. Concerti da I. C. KELLNER.

I. *a Ob. conc. 2 C. 2 Viol. V. e B.* II. *a Ob. conc. 2 C. 2 Viol. V. e B.*

I. Conc. da SCHMIDTBAUER. *a Ob. conc. 2 Cor. 2 Viol. V. e B.*

I. Conc. da Ant. STAMITZ. *a Ob. conc. 2 C. 2 Fl. 2 Viol. 2 Viole e B.*

I. Conc. da C. STAMITZ. *a Ob. princ. Fag. princ. 2 C. 2 Fl. 2 Viol. 2 Viole e B.*

CLARINETTO.

III. Trii da HAYDN. *a Clarinetto, Violino e B.*

III. Concerti da Carlo STAMITZ.

I. *a Clar. pr. 2 C. 2 Ob. 2 Viol. V. e B.* III. *a Clar. pr. 2 C. 2 Viol. V. e B.*

II. *a Clar. pr. 2 C. 2 Ob. 2 Viol. 2 Viole e B.*

CORNO.

I. Trio da MISLIWEZECK. *a Corno, Viol. e B.* I. Trio da PUNTO. *a Corno, Viol. e B.*

III. Quattri da Carlo STAMITZ.

I. *a Corno, Oboe, Violino e Fagotto.* III. *a Corno Oboe, Viola e Fagotto.*

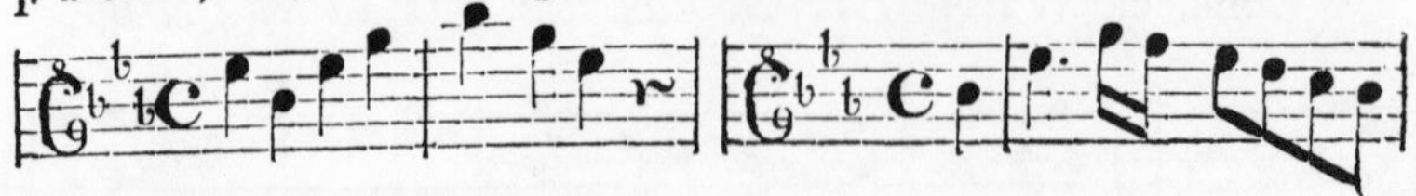

II. *a Corno, Oboe, Violino e Fagotto.*

I. Serenata da Giov. PUNTO. *a Corno obl. Violino, V. e B.*

I. Concerto da Ant. FILS. *a Corno princ. 2 Viol. V. e B.*

I. Concerto da G. C FISCHER. *a Corno princ. 2 Viol. V. e B.*

I. Concerti da ROSETTI. *a Corno pr. 2 C. 2 Ob. 2 Viol. V. Violc. e B.*

I. Concerto da HAYDEN. *a Corno princ. 2 Viol. V. e B.*

FAGOTTO.

I. Concerto da EICHNER. *a Fagotto princ. 2 C. 2 Fl. 2 Viol. V. e B.*

I. Concerto da FISCHER. *a Fag. princ. 2 C. 2 Fl. 2 Viol. V. e B.*

I Concerto da KÜGLER. *a Fagotto princ. 2 C. 2 Fl. 2 Viol. V. e B.*

I. Concerto da NICOLAI. *a Fag. princ. 2 C. 2 Fl. 2 Viol. 2 Viole e B.*

I. Concerto da RITTER. *a Fagotto princ. 2 Viol. V. e B.*

I. Concerto da Ant. ROSETTI. *a Fag. pr. 2 C. 2 Ob. 2 Viol. V. e B.*

II. Concerti da Carlo STAMITZ.

I. *a Fag. pr. 2 C. 2 Ob. 2 Viol. V. e B.* II. *a Fag. pr. 2 C. 2 Fl. 2 Viol. V. e B.*

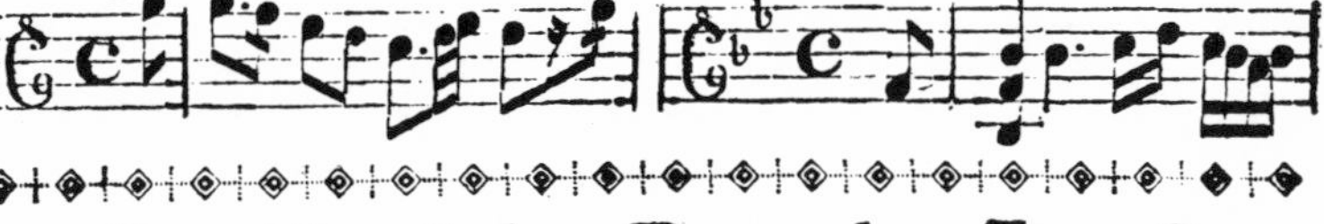

CEMBALO.

SOLI.

VI. Sonate da Giov. Ernesto ALTENBURG.

IV. Sonate da BEECKE.

I. Sonatina de la DUCHESSA *di Sax-Gotha.*

Sonata da Leop. KOZELUCH. *a quatro mani.*

Parte sinistra. *Parte dextra.*

IV. Sonate da Leop. KOZELUCH.

VI. Sonate da KÜFNER.

VI. Sonate da Fred. Theod. SCHUMANN.

I. Sonata da STERCKEL. *a quatro mani.*

La Parte del Maestro. *La Parte della Scolare.*

I. Sonatina da SCHWANENBERG.

March aus dem Trauerspiel Clavigo da SCHWEITZER.

I. Sonata da F. C. TODT. *a quatro mani.*

La Parte del Maestro. *La Parte della Scolare.*

SONATE intagliate e ſtampate.

XII. Fugues da I. G. ALBRECHTSBERGER. *Op. 1. Berlin.*

III. Rondo et III. Sonate da C. P. E. BACH. *für Kenner und Liebhaber. Leipzig. 2 Samml.*

III. Rondo et III. Sonate da C. P. E. BACH. *für Kenner und Liebhaber. Leipzig. 3 Samml.*

XII. Sonate da Arcangelo CORELLI. *Op. V. Firenze.*

III. Sonate da F. H. Baron de DALBERG. *Op. II. Mannheim.*

Ouverture d'Alceſte da EDELMANN. *Mannheim.*

38
C E M B A L O.
II. Sonate da EDELMANN. Op. VI. Offenbach.
I.
II.
III. MARCH. da FRAENZL. Mannheim.
I. aus dem König LEAR.
II. aus der AGNES BERNAUERIN.
III. aus dem Sturm von BOXBERG.
XII. Sonate da Giov. Battista GRAZIOLI. in Venezia.
I.
VII.
II.
VIII.
III.
IX.
IV.
X.
V.
XI.
VI.
XII.
C E M B A L O.
39
VI. Sonate da Nath. God. GRUNER. Leipzig.
I.
IV.
II.
V.
III.
VI.
VI. Sonate da I. W. HAESLER. Erfurth.
I.
IV.
II.
V.
III.
VI.
VI. Sonate da A. Baron de KNIGGE. Francfort sur le Mein.
I.
IV.
II.
V.
III.
VI.

La Chasse a Cembalo da Leop. KOZELUCH. *Op. V. Vienne.*

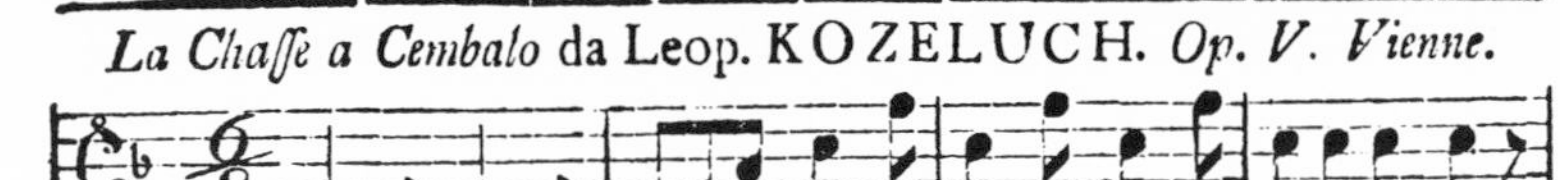

II. Divertimenti da Pietro MORANDI.

VI. Sonate da Gio. Marco RUTINI. *Op. XII. Firenze.*

VI. Sonate da Franz SEYDELMANN. ***per dui in uno Cembalo. Leipzig.***

III. Sonate da T. SMITH *per dui in uno Clavicemb. Op. I. Berlin.*

III. Sonate da T. SMITH *per dui in uno Clavicemb. Op. II. Berlin.*

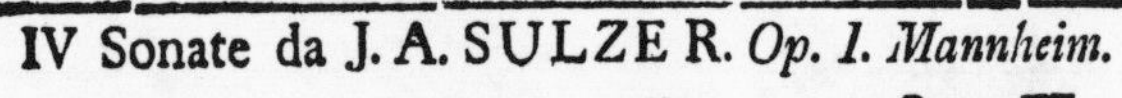

IV Sonate da J. A. SULZER R. *Op. I. Mannheim.*

VI Sonate da Ferd. TURRINI.

VI. Sonate da J. G. VIERLING. *Leipzig.*

VI. Sonate da Ernst. Willh. WOLF. *Leipzig.*

TRII.

A CEMBALO OBLIGATO CON VIOLINO O FLAUTO.

VI. Sonate da BARTHELMON. *a Cembalo e Violino.*

I. Sonata da BREUL. *a Cembalo e Violino.*

VI. Sonate da CLEMENTI. *a Cembalo e Violino.*

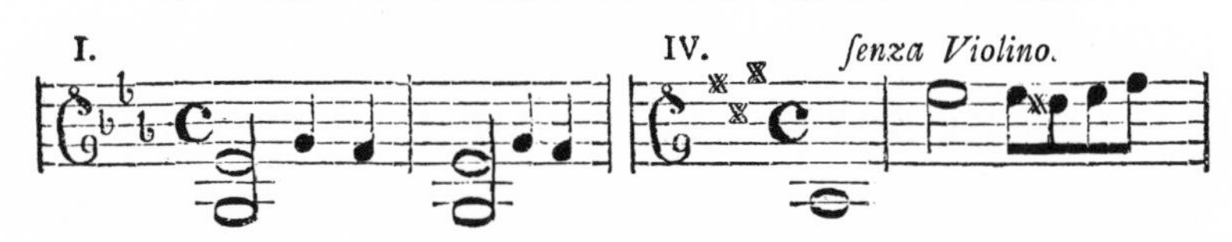

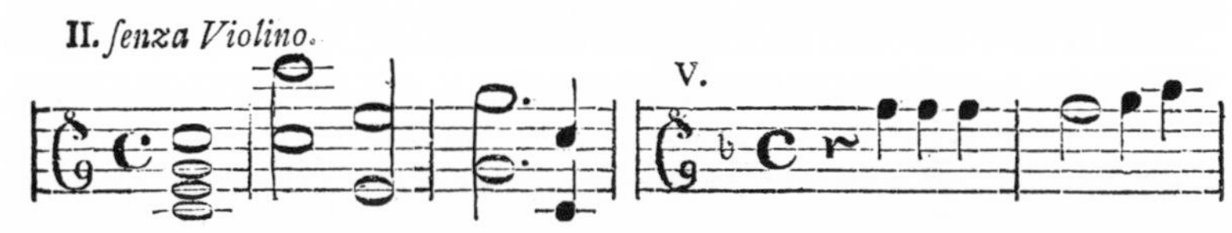

I. Sinfonia da KREUSSER. *a Cembalo e Violino.*

VI. Sonate da C. G. NEEFE. *a Cembalo e Violino.*

VI. Sonate da Ant. SACCHINI. *a Cembalo e Violino.*

VI. Sonate da SCHROETER. *a Cembalo e Violino o Flauto.*

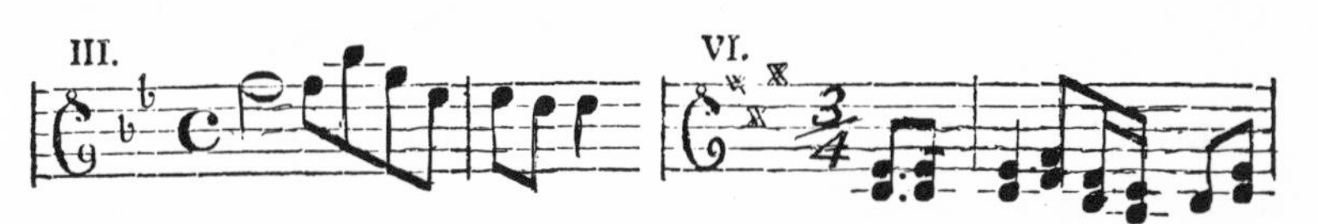

III. Sonate da Giov. P. SCHULTESSIUS. *a Cembalo e Violino.*

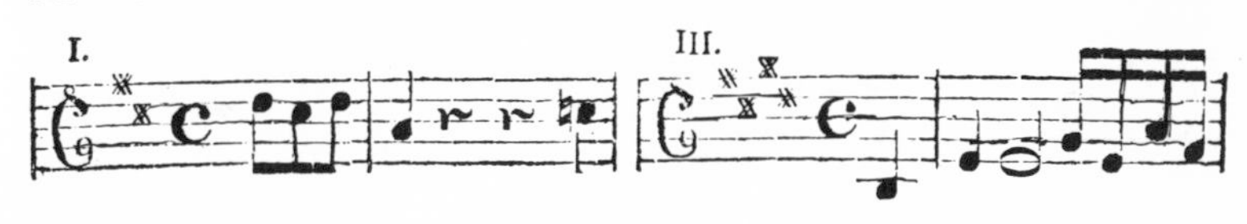

VI. Sonate da G. C. TODT. *a Cembalo e Violino.*

I. IV.

II. V.

III. VI.

I. Sonata da G. C. TODT. *a Cembalo e Violino.*

VI. Sonate da Giov. Guil. WIEFEL. *a Cembalo con diversi voci.*

I. *con Violino.* IV. *con Fagotto o Violoncello.*

II. *con Flauto o Violino.* V. *con Fagotto o Violoncello.*

III. *con Flauto o Violino.* VI. *con Violino.*

I. Sonata da Giov. Guil. WIEFEL. *a Cembalo con Violino.*

T R I I intagliati.

SONATES tirées des meilleues Operas français et arrangéer *pour le Clavecin, con Violino.*

I. *de la belle Arsene.* II. *de Zemire et Azor.*

III. Sonate da J. B. BIANCHI. *a Cemb. e Violino. Offenbach.*

I. III. II.

III. Sonate da L. CERRO. *a Cemb. e Violino. Firenze.*

I. III. II.

III. Sonate da EDELMANN. *a Cemb. e Violino. Op. III. Offenbach.*

I. III. II.

II. Sonate da EDELMANN. *a Cemb. e Violino. Op. VII. Mannheim.*

I. II.

III. Sonate da J. A. EINBERGER. *a Cemb. e Violino. Op. I. Mannheim.*

III. Sonate da A. GUENIN. *a Cemb. e Violino. Op. V. Mannheim.*

VI. Sonate da Amede RASETTI. *a Cemb. e Violino. Op. I. Offenbach.*

III Sonate da Amede RASETTI. *a Cemb. e Violino. Op. II. Mannheim.*

VI. Sonate da Ant. RIEGEL. *a Cemb. e Violino. Op V. Spire.*

VI. Sonate da Giov. Marco RUTINI. *a Cemb. e Violino. Op. X. Firenze.*

VI. Sonate da Giov. Marco RUTINI. *a Cemb. e Violino. Op. XI. Firenze.*

TERZETTI.

VI. Sonate da G. C. TODT. *a Cembalo, Viol. e Violoncello.*

IV. Sonate da G. C. TODT. *a Cembalo, Viol. e Violoncello.*

TERZETTI *intagliati.*

III. Sonate da L. BOCCHERINI. *a Cembalo, Viol. e Violonc. Op. XII. Mannheim.*

III. Sonate da L. BOCCHERINI. *a Cembalo, Viol. e Violonc. Op. XIII. Mannheim.*

VI. Sonate da J. F. HOBEIN. *a Cembalo, Viol. ou Fl. e Basso. Cassel.*

III. Sonate da J. C. KELLNER. *a Cemb. Viol. e Basso. 1ster Theil. Cassel.*

III. Sonate da J. C. KELLNER. *a Cemb. Viol. e Basso. 2ter Theil. Cassel.*

III. Sonate da Leop. KOZELUCH. *a Cemb. Viol. e Basso. Op. II. Vienna.*

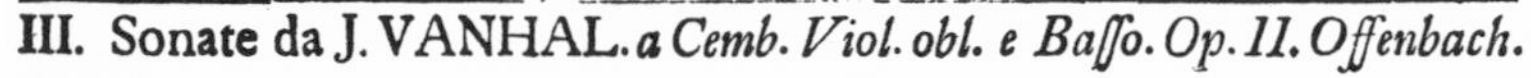

III. Sonate da J. VANHAL. *a Cemb. Viol. obl. e Basso. Op. II. Offenbach.*

IV. Sonate da VANHALL. *a Cemb. Viola ou Violino obl. e Basso. Op. V. Offenbach.*

QUATTRI intagliati.

III. Quattri da Men. RAUZZINI. *a Cemb. 2 Viol. e B. Op. I. Offenbach.*

III. Quattri da SCHMITTBAUR. *a Cemb. Viol. Flauto e B. Op. I. Spire*

CONCERTI a Cembalo con più Stromenti.

I. Concerto da J. C. BACH. *a Cemb. conc. 2 Cor. 2 Viol. V. e B.*

I. Conc. da Ch. S. BINDER. *a Cemb. conc. 2 C. 2 Ob. 2 Fl. 2 Fag. 2 Viol. V. e B.*

I. Conc. da F. BRODSKY. *a Cemb. conc. 2 Viol. Viol. obl. e B.*

I. Conc. da Franc. DUSCHECK. *a Cemb. conc. 2 Viol. V. e B.*

I. Concerto da FOERSTER. *a Cemb. conc. 2 Viol. V. e. B.*

II. Conc. da C. E. GIRBERT. *a Cemb. conc. 2 C. 2 Fl. 2 Viol. V. e B.*

I. Conc. da Franc. KLEIN. *a Cemb. conc. 2 Fl. 2 Viol. Viola obl. e B.*

I. Concerto da Vincenzo MASCHEK. *a Cemb. conc. Viol. pr. 2 C. 2 Clarinetti, 2 Viol. V. e B.*

VIII. Concerti da G. C. TODT.

I. *a Cemb. conc. 2 Viol. V. e B.* — V. *a Cemb. conc. 2 Viol. V. e B.*

II. *a Cemb. conc. 2 C. 2 Viol. V. e B.* — VI. *a Cemb. conc. 2 C. 2 Fl. 2 Viol. V. e B.*

III. *a Cemb. conc. 2 C. 2 Fl. 2 Viol. V. e B.* — VII. *a Cemb. conc. Viol. pr. 2 C. 2 Viol. V. e B.*

IV. *a Cemb. conc. 2 Viol. V. e B.* — VIII. *a Cemb. conc. 2 C. 2 Fl. 2 Viol. V. e B.*

I. Conc. da E. W. WOLFF. *a Cemb. conc. 2 C. 2 Ob. 2 Viol. 2 Viole e B.*

CONCERTI *intagliati.*

I. Concerto da Ern. EICHNER. *a Cemb. ou Harpe conc. 2 C. 2 Fl. 2 Viol. V. e B. Op. IX. Mannheim.*

II. Conc. da J. A. JUST. *a Cemb. conc. 2 C. 2 Ob. ò Fl. 2 Viol. e B. London.*

I. Concerto Pastorale da G. G. LANG. *a Cemb. conc. 2 C. 2 Fl. 2 Viol. V. e B. Op. V. Offenbach.*

I. Concerto da LOEHLEIN. *a Cemb. conc. 2 C. 2 Fl. 2 Viol. V. e B. Op. VIII. N. I.*

III. Conc. da G. S. LOEHLEIN. *a Cemb conc. 2 Viol. e B. Op. VII. Lyon.*

III. Concerti da J. S. SCHROETER. *a Cemb. conc. 2 Viol. V. e B. Op. VIII. Amsterdam.*

Concerto I. da Ern. Gugl. WOLF. *a Cemb. conc. 2 Viol. V. e B. Breslau.*

Concerto II. da E. G. WOLF. *a Cemb. conc. 2 C. 2 Ob. 2 Viol. V. e B. Breslau.*

HARPA.

I. Sonate da Anton STAMITZ. *a Harpe solo.*

VI. Sonate da HINNER. *a Harpe con Violino.*

ARIE e CANTATE
con più Stromenti.

I. Arie da ANFOSSI. *a Soprano, 2 Ob. 2 Viol. V. e B.*

I. Arie da Pietro GUGLIELMI. *a Soprano, 2 C. 2 Ob. 2 Viol. V. e B.*

I. Arie da Franc. di MAJO. *a Soprano, 2 Viol. V. e B.*

II. Arie da Ant. SALIERI.

I. *a Soprano, Viol. pr. 2 C. Ob. 2 Viol. Fagotto, V. e B.*

II. *a Soprano, Viol. pr. 2 Cor. 2 Ob. 2 Viol. V. e B.*

Folgende Stücke sind in Partitur und in Stimmen zu haben.

Operetten.

Andrä. Erwin und Elmine.
— — das tartarische Gesetz.
Audinot, der Faßbinder.
Desaides, die drey Pächter.
Girbert, Williams und Sulmuth.
— — die Bezauberten.
— — Philint und Lucinde, oder eins sucht das andere.
— — die Wilddiebe.
Gretry, die Freundschaft auf der Probe.
— — Erast und Lucinde.
Holly, der Kaufmann von Smyrna.
— — das Gespenst.
— — der Bassa von Tunis.
— — die Zigeuner.
Lorazi, der Kapellmeister.
Monsigny, der Deserteur.
Nicolai, der Geburtstag.
Philidor, der Hufschmidt.
— — Tom Jones.
— — Melide oder der Schiffer.
— — der zaubernde Soldat.
Piccini, Bastien und Bastienne.
— — der eifersüchtige Ehemann.
— — das gute Mädchen.
— — Mutter Natur.
Preu, Adrast und Isidore.
— — der Irrwisch.
Prudent, die Gärtner.
Reichardt, Ino.
Schweitzer, der lustige Schuster.

2. Geistliche Gedichte.

Forckel, die Hirten bey der Krippe zu Bethlehem, eine Cantate v. Raml
— — Hiskias, ein Oratorium von Blum.
Händel, Judas Maccabäus.
Hayden, Stabat mater.
Rolle, David und Jonathan.
— — Lazarus.
Schweitzer, die Auferstehung Christi, eine Cantate.
Seydelmann, Salve Regina.

Weltliche.

Krebs, der Abend, eine Cantate.
Rolle, die Götter und Musen, ein musicalisches Drama.

SVPPLEMENTO XV.
DEI
CATALOGHI
DELLE
SINFONIE, PARTITE, OVERTURE, SOLI, DUETTI, TRII, QUATTRI E CONCERTI

PER IL

VIOLINO, FLAUTO TRAVERSO,

C E M B A L O

ED ALTRI STROMENTI,

CHE

SI TROVANO IN MANOSCRITTO NELLA OFFICINA MUSICA DI BREITKOPF IN LIPSIA.

1782. 1783 ed 1784.

SINFONIE.

IV. Sinfon. da Pasq. AMFOSSI.

I. *a 2 Clar. Tymp. 2 C. 2 Ob. 2 Viol. V. e B.* III. *a 2 C. 2 Ob. 2 Viol. V. e B.*

II. *a 2 C. 2 Ob. 2 Viol. V. e B.* IV. *a 2 C. 2 Ob. 2 Viol. V. e B.*

II. Sinf. da BEECKE.

I. *a 2 C. 2 Ob. 2 Clarinetti. 2 Fl. 2 Fag. 2 Viol. V. e B.* II. *a 2 C. 2 Ob. 2 Fl. 2 Viol. 2 Viole Violcl. e B.*

III. Sinf. da BLEYL.

I. *a 2 C. 2 Ob. 2 Viol, V. e B.* III. *a 2 C. 2 Ob. 2 Viol. 2 Viole Violcl. e B.*

II. *a 2 C. 2 Ob. 2 Viol. 2 Viole e B.*

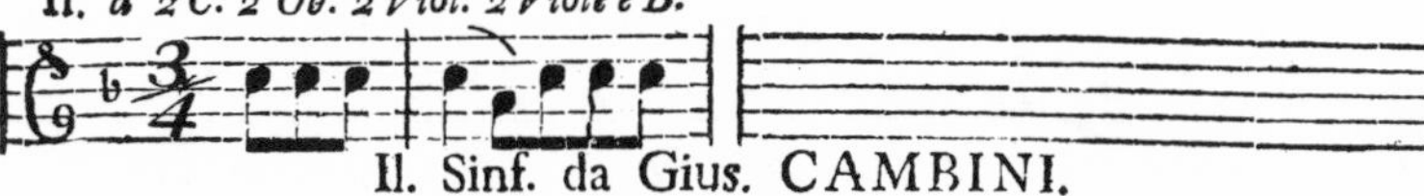

II. Sinf. da Gius. CAMBINI.

I. *a 2 C. 2 Ob. 2 Viol. V. e B.* II. *a 2 C. 2 Ob. 2 Viol. V. e B.*

I. Sinf. da Carlo de DITTERSDORFF.

a 2 C. 2 Ob. 2 Viol. Viola Violcl. e B.

II. Sinfon. da EISENMANN.

I. *a 2 C. 2 Fl. 2 Viol. V. e B.* II. *a 2 C. 2 Fl. 2 Viol. V. e B.*

I. Sinfon. la Chasse da GOSSECK.

a 2 Clar. Tymp. 2 C. 2 Ob. 2 Clarinetti. 2 Fag. 2 Viol. V. e B.

I. Sinf. da Gius. HAYDN.

a 2 C. 2 Ob. 2 Viol. V. Violcl. e B.

II. Sinfon. da Franc. HOFFMEISTER.

I. *a 2 C. 2 Ob. 2 Viol. V. e B.* II. *a 2 C. 2 Ob. 2 Viol. V. e B.*

I. Sinf. da HOPFFE.

a 2 Clar. Tymp. 2 C. 2 Ob. 2 Fl. 2 Viol. V. e B.

I. Sinf. da KLEINKNECHT.

a 2 C. 2 Ob. 2 Fl. 2 Fag. 2 Viol. 2 Viole Violcl. e B.

III. Sinf. da Vincenzo MASCHECK.

I. *a 2 C. 2 Ob. 2 Viol. V. e B.* III. *a 2 C. 2 Fl. 2 Viol. 2 Viole e B.*

II. *a 2 C. 2 Ob. 2 Viol. 2 Viole Fag. obl. e B.*

II. Sinfon. d'Amad. NAUMANN.

I. *Amphion. a 2 C. 2 Fl. 2 Ob. 2 Viol. V. e B.* II. *le Prolg. a 2 C. 2 Fl. 2 Ob. 2 Viol, V. e B.*

4 SINFONIE.
II. Sinfonie da Anton ROSETTI.
I. a 2 C. 2. Ob. 2 Viol. 2 Viole e B.
II. a 2 C. 2 Ob. 2 Viol. 2 Viole e B.
I. Sinf. da SACCHINI. a 2 C. 2. Ob. 2 Viol. 2. Viole e B.
I. Sinf. da Ant. SALIERI.
a 2 C. 2 Ob. 2 Fl. 2 Fag. 2 Viol. V. e B.
I. Sinf. da SARTI.
a 2 C. 2 Ob. 2 Viol. V. e B.
I. Sinf. Hypochondr. da SCHMITTBAUR. a Tromba Solo.
2 C. 2 Ob. 2 Fl. 2 Fag. 2 Viol. 2 Viole e B.
II. Sinf. da Gius. SCHUSTER.
I. a 2 C. 2 Clarinetti. 2 Ob. 2 Fag. 2 Viol. 2 Viole e B.
II. a 2 Clar. Tymp. 2 C. 2 Ob. 2 Fl. 2 Fag. 2 Viol. V. e B.
II. Sinf. da Carlo STAMITZ.
I. a Ob. pr. Fag. pr. 2 C. 2 Viol. V. e B.
II. a 2 Clar. Tymp. 2 C. 2 Ob. 2 Fl. 2 Viol. 2 Viole Violcl. e B.
IV. Sinf. da I. F. X. STERCKEL.
I. a 2 C. 2 Ob. 2 Viol. V. e B.
III. a 2 C. 2 Fl. 2 Viol. 2 Viole e B.
II. a 2 C. 2 Ob. 2 Viol. V. e B.
IV. a 2 C. 2 Ob. 2 Viol. V. e B.

SINFONIE. 5
III. Sinf. da Barone van SUITEN.
I. a 2 C. 2 Ob. 2 Viol. V. e B.
III. a 2 C. 2 Ob. 2 Viol. V. e B.
II. a 2. C. 2 Ob. 2 Viol. V. e B.
V. Sinf. da Giuseppe TOUCHEMOLIN.
I. a 2 C. 2 Ob. 2 Fl. 2 Viol. V. e B.
IV. a 2 Clar. Tymp. 2 C. 2 Ob. 2 Fl. 2 Viol. 2 Viole e B.
II. a 2 C. 2 Ob. 2 Fl. 2 Viol. V. e B.
V. a 2 C. 2. Ob. 2 Fl. 2 Fag. 2 Viol. 2 Viole e B.
III. a 2 C. 2 Ob. 2 Fl. 2 Fag. 2 Viol. V. e B.
I. Sinf. da Giov. VANNHALL. a 2 C. 2 Ob. Fl. in And. 2 Viol. V. e B.
I. Sinf. da WINTER. a 2 Clar. Tymp. 2 C. 2 Ob. 2 Fl. 2 Fag. 2 Viol. 2 Viole e B.
I. Sinf. da WISTEIN. a 2 C. 2 Fl. 2 Viole. V. e B.
II. Sinf. da ZIMMERMANN.
I. a 2 Clar. Tymp. 2 C. 2 Ob. 2 Viol. V. e B.
II. a 2 C. 2 Ob. 2 Fag. 2 Viol. V. e B.

MINUETTI.

X. Minuetti da MASCHECK *a 2 C. 2 Ob. 2 Viol. e B.*

VI. Minuetti da ROSETTI. *a 2 C. 2 Ob. e Clarinetti. 2 Viol. e B.*

XII. *Hannover Redout. Menuetten.* da PANNENBERG. *1782.*

VI. *Hannover Redout. Angloiſen.* 1782.

XII. *Hannover Redout. Angloiſen.* 1782.

VI. *Hannover Redout. Cottillon.* 1782.

XII. *Hannover Redout. Menuetten.* da PANNENBERG. 1783.

XII. *Hannover Redout. Angloiſen.* 1783.

XII. *Hannover Redout. Angloiſen.* 1783.

VI. *Hannover Redout. Cottillon.* 1783.

VI. Menuetti con Trios. VI. Tedeski. VI. Contradances da F. A. HOFFMEISTER. *a 2 C. 2 Ob. 2 Viol. e B.*

XII. Menuetti con Trios. XX. Tedeski da Jos. STADLER de WOLFERSGRÜN. *Vienna.*

VIII. Contradances da HUBER. *Vienna.*

SINFONIE intagliate e ſtampate.

III. Sinf. da Jos. HAYDN. *a 2 C. 2. Ob. 1 Fag. 1 Fl. 2 Viol. V. e B. Vienna.*

II. Sinf. da Gius. HAYDN. Libro I. *Op. XVIII. Berlin.*
I. *a 2 Tromp. o C. Tymp. Fl. obl. 2 Ob. 2 Viol. V. Violcl. e B.*
II. *a 2 C. 2 Ob. Fl. obl. Fag. 2 Viol. V. Violcl. e B.*

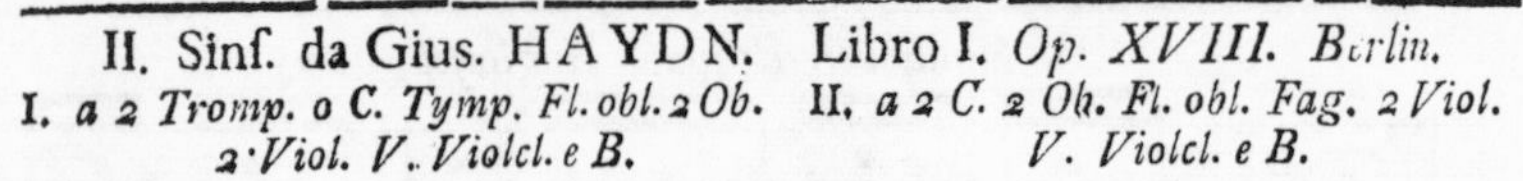

II. Sinf. da Gius. HAYDN. *a 2 C. 2. Ob. Fl. obl. 2 Viol. V. Violcl. e B. Libro II. Op. XVIII. Berlin.*

II. Sinf. da Gius. HAYDN. *a 2 C. 2 Ob. Fl. 2 Viol. V. Violcl. e B. Libro III. Op. XVIII. Berlin.*

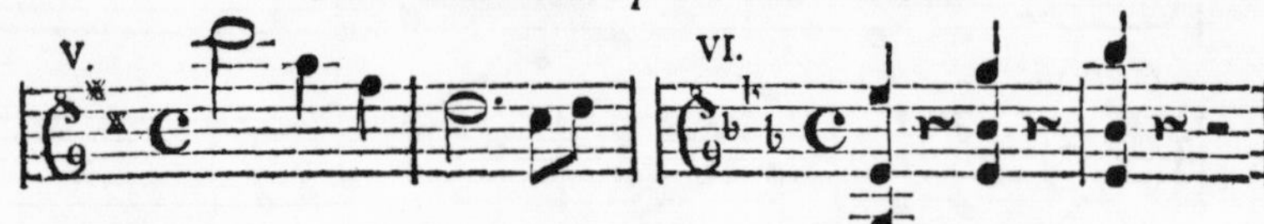

VI. Sinf. da Gius. HAYDN. *a 2 C. 2 Ob. 2 Viol. V. e B. Op. XXXV. Vienna.*

I. la Chasse grand Sinf. da Jos. HAYDN. *a 2 C. 2 Ob. 2 Fag. Flauto. 2 Viol. V. e B. Op. XXXIV. Vienna.*

III. Sinf. da G. VANHALL. *a 2 C. 2 Ob. ou Fl. 2 Viol. V. e B. Op. VIII. a la Haye.*

III. Sinf. da G. VANHALL. *a 2 C. 2 Ob. ou Fl. 2 Viol. V. e B. Op. IX. a la Haye.*

SINFONIES PERIODIQVES.

I. Sinf. Periodique da I. C. BACH. *a 2 C. 2 Clarinetti. 2 Fl. 2 Ob. 2 Fag. 2 Viol. V. e B. No. IX. Amst.*

I. Sinf. periodique da I. SCHMITT. *a 2 Clar. Tymp. 2 C. 2 Ob. 2 Viol. V. e B. Op. XII. Amst.*

DIVERTIMENTI, CONCERTINI CASSATIONES etc.

I. Ouverture da Gaet. ANDREOZZI. *a 2 Clar. Tymp. 2 C. 2 Ob. 2 Viol. V. e B.*

I. Ouverture da BAISIELLO. *a 2 C. 2 Ob. 2 Viol. V. Fag. e B.*

I. Concertino da CARCANI. *a 2 C 2 Fl. 2 Violini e B.*

I. Caſſatio da Gius. HAYDN. *a 2 C. 2 Viol. V. e B.*

I. Notturno da I. P. HEINEL. *a 2 Viol. Corno, Flauto, Fagotto e B.*

I. Concertino da HEMBEL. *a 2 C. Oboe. Fagotto. 2 Viol. V. e B.*

I. Divert. da HOLLER. *a Viol. obl. Clarinetto obl. Fag. obl. 2 Cor. 2 Viole e Violono.*

I. Caſſatio da Theod. LOTZ. *a 2 C. 2 Clarinetti. 2 Viol. V. Fag. e B.*

I. Serenata da Gius. MICHL. *a 2 C. 2 Ob. 2 Fl. Fag. 2 Viol. V. e B.*

I. Divert. da Gius. MICHL. *a 2 Cor. Violino. Oboe. Viola. Fagotto e B.*

I. Concertino da G. F. REICHARDT. *a Flauto. Oboe. Fag. conc. 2 C. 2 Fl. 2 Viol. V. e B.*

I. Ouverture da Ant. SALIERI. *a 2 C. 2 Ob. 2 Viol. V. e B.*

I. Divert. da SPAETH. *a 2 C. 2 Fl. 2 Ob. 2 Fag. 2 Viol. e B.*

I. Concertino da C. STAMITZ. *a Corno obl. Viol. obl. 2 C. 2 Fl. 2 Viol. V. e B.*

I. Partita da TOESCHI. *a Flauto. Oboe. Violino. Viola. Fagotto e B.*

I. Divert. da WEND. *a Violino obl. Viola obl. Clarinetto obl. Fagotto obl. e Violono.*

VIOLINO.

SOLI con BASSO.

I. Sonate da Giov. VANHALL.

VI. Sonate. da Giorgio DRUZECKI. *Op. I. Linz.*

XXXVII. Variationes da Franc. STAD. *Vienna.*

DUETTI.

VI. Duetti da L. BORGHI.

VI. Duetti d'Amad. NAUMANN.

DUETTI intagliati.

VI. Sonate da F. A. BAUMBACH. *a 2 Viol. e B. Dessau.*

VI. Divertim. d'Ant. KAMMEL. *a 2 Viol. ou Viol. et Viola. Op. XVII. Amst.*

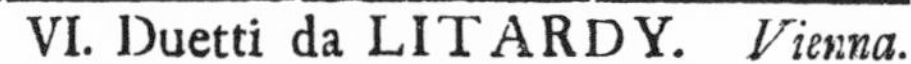

VI. Duetti da LITARDY. *Vienna.*

VI. Duetti da MÜLLER. *a Violino e Viola. Op. II. Francf. sur le Mein.*

VI. Duetti da RAIMONDI. *Op. V. Lyon.*

VI. Duetti d'Antonio ROSETTI. *Vienna.*

III. Duetti da Ferdinand TITZ. *Vienna.*

TRII.

II. Notturni da Giov. VANHALL. *a 2 Viol. e B.*

TRII intagliati.

A DUE VIOLINI CON BASSO.

III. Trii concertans da CAMBINI. *a 2 Violini e Viola. Op. I. Mannheim.*

III. Trii concertans da CAMBINI. *a Violino, Viola e Violcello. Op. II. Mannheim.*

VI. Trii concertans da G. CAMBINI. *a Violino, Viola e Violcello. Op. XVII. Offenbach.*

VI. Trii da HEMBERGER. *Op. VIII. Lyon.*

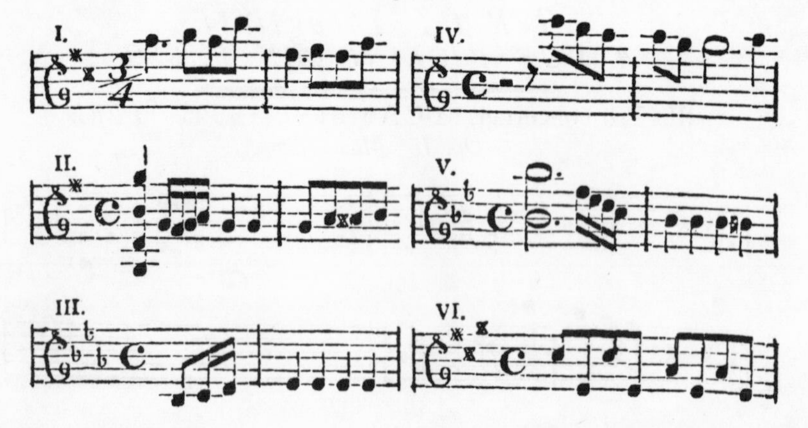

VI. Trii d' Anton. KAMMEL. *Op. XXIII. Mannheim.*

III. Trii da C. L. MAUCOURT. *Op. I. Offenbach.*

VI. Trii da J. VANNHALL. *Op. XIX. Paris.*

Q U A T T R I.

I. Quartetto da GASMANN. *a 2 Viol. V. e B.*

I. Quatuor da HAYDN. *a 2 Viol. V. e B.*

VI. Quattri concert. d' Ant. Franc. HOFFMEISTER. *a 2 Viol. V. e B.*

VI. Quattri da HOFFMEISTER. *a 2 Viol. V. e B.*

VI. Quattri da Guglielmo KÜFFNER. *a 2 Viol. V. e Violoncello.*

I. Quartetto da Gius. MICHL. *a Violino, Oboe, Viola e Fagotto.*

IV. Quattri da VANNHALL. *a 2 Viol. V. e B.*

VI. Quattri da I. C. VOGEL et PUNTO. *a Viol. obl. Alto ou Corno obl. Violoncello obl. e B.*

QUATTRI *intagliati.*

VI. Quattri da BOCCHERINI. *a 2 Viol. V. e B.*
Op. XXXII. Vienna.

VI. Quattri da BOCCHERINI. *a 2 Viol. V. e B.*
Op. XXXIII. Vienna.

III. Quattri concertans da G. CAMBINI. *a 2 Viol. V. e B.*
Op. III. Mannheim.

VI. Quattri da G. CAMBINI. *a 2 Viol. V. e B.*
Op. XV. Offenbach.

VI. Quattri d' Ant. CAPUZZI. *a 2 Viol. V. e B.*
Op. II. Vienna.

III. Quattri da I. M. DREYER. *a 2 Viol. V. e B.*
Op. I. Mannheim.

VI. Quattri ou Divertiſſements da Ioſeph HAYDN. *a 2 Viol. V. e B. Op. XIX. Berlin.*

VI. Quattri da Ioſeph HAYDN. *a 2 Viol. V. e B. Op. XXXIII. Vienna.*

VI. Quattri da Franc. HOFFMEISTER. *a 2 Viol. V. e B. Op. VII. Vienna.*

VI. Quattri concertans da Fr. Ant. HOFFMEISTER. *a 2 Viol. V. e B. Op. IX. Vienna.*

VI. Quattri concertans da I. F. LOISEL. *a 2 Viol. V. e B. Offenbach.*

VI. Quattri da I. PAISIELLO. *a 2 Viol. V. e Violoncello. Op. I. Offenbach.*

Quartetto da Ant. ROSETTI *a 2 Viol. V. e B.*
No. II. Amst.

VI. Quattri da VANNHALL. *a 2 Viol. V. e B.*
Op. XXVI. Paris.

QUINTETTI.

VI. Quintetti da Carlo MARATSECK. *a Violino,*
Oboe, 2 Viole e Violoncello.

VI. Quintetti da Gius. MISLIWECECK. *a Oboe e Fl. 2 Viol. V. e B.*

I. Sestetto da HAYDN. *a Cor. Oboe, Fag. Violino, Viola e B.*

CONCERTI per il Violino concertato.

I. Concerto da HAACKE. *a Viol. princ. 2 C.*
2 Ob. 2 Viol. V. e B.

I. Conc. da HUTTI. *a Viol. princ. 2 C. 2 Viol. V. e B.* I. Conc. da la MOTTE. *a Viol. princ. 2 C. 2 Fl. 2 Viol. V. e B.*

II. Concerti da Anton STAMITZ.
I. a Viol. princ. 2 C. 2 Ob. 2 Viol. V. e B. II. a Viol. pr. 2C. 2 Ob. 2 Viol. 2 Viole e B.

I. Conc. da ZARTH. *a Viol princ. 2 C. 2 Fl. 2 Viol. V. e B.*

CONCERTI intagliati.

I. Conc. da BARRIER. *a Viol. princ. 2 C. 2 Ob. 2 Viol. V. e B. Op. V. Paris.*

Concerto I. da BORRA. *a Viol. princ. 2 C. 2 Ob. 2 Viol. V. e B. Lyon.*

Concerto II. da BORRA. *a Viol. princ. 2 C. 2 Ob. 2 Viol. V. e B. Lyon.*

I. Conc. da CAMBINI. *a Viol. princ. 2 C. 2 Ob. 2 Viol. V. e B. Paris.*

II. Conc. da St. GEORGES. *Op. V. Paris.*

I. *a Viol. princ. 2 C. 2 Ob ou Clarinetti. 2 Viol. V. e B.* II. *a Viol. princ. 2 Viol. V. e B.*

Conc. VI. da GARNOVIK. *a Viol. princ. 2 C. 2 Ob. 2 Viol. V. e B. Paris.*

Conc. VIII. da JARNOVICK. *a Viol. princ. 2 C. 2 Ob. 2 Viol. V. e B. Lyon.*

I. Concerto da Ant. LOLLI. *a Viol. princ. 2 C. 2 Viol. V. e B. Paris.*

II. Concerti da Ant. LOLLI. *Op. V. Paris.*

I. *a Viol. princ. 2 Viol. V. e B.* II. *a Viol. princ. 2 Viol. e B.*

I. Concerto da I. G. NICOLAI. *a Viol. princ. Violcl. obl. 2 C. 2 Fl. 2 Viol. V. e B. Op. VII. Offenbach.*

Concerto VI. da Ant. STAMITZ. *a Viol. princ. 2 C. 2 Ob. 2 Viol. 2 Viole e B. Paris.*

VIOLA.

VI. Duetti da Chrift. STUMPFF. *a 2 Viole. Op. XV. Francf. fur le Mein.*

CONCERTI a VIOLA.

I. Concerto da GRENZER. *a Viola princ. 2 C. 2 Viol. V. e B.*

I. Concerto da Gius. MICHL. *a Viola conc. 2 C. 2 Viol. V. e B.*

VIOLONCELLO.

I. Solo da SCHETTKY. *a Violoncello e B.*

I. Duetto da SCHLICK. *a 2 Violoncelli.*

TRII.

VI. Trii da SCHWACHHOFFER. *a Violoncello. Violino e B.*

QUATTRI.

VI. Quattri da MICHL. *a Violoncello obl. Violino. V. e B.*

I. Quattro da SCHLICK. *a Violoncello, Violino, V. e B.*

CONCERTI per il Violoncello concertato.

II. Concerti da Giuseppe FIALA.

I. *a Violcl. conc 2 C. 2 Ob. 2 Viol. 2 Viole e B.* II. *a Violcl. conc. 2 C. 2 Viol. 2 Viole e B.*

I. Conc. da GERAUL. *a Violcl. conc. 2 Viol. V. e B.*

I. Conc. da HAMMER. *a Violcl. conc. 2 C. 2 Ob. 2 Viol. V. e B.*

II. Concerti da HOFFMEISTER.

I. *a Violcl. conc. 2 Clarini, Tymp. 2 C. 2 Ob. 2 Viol. V. e B* II. *a Violcl. conc. 2 C. 2 Ob. 2 Viol. V. e B.*

I. Conc. da MEGELIN. *a Violcl. conc. 2 C. 2 Ob. 2 Viol. V. e B.*

II. Concerti da PLEYL.

I. *a Violcl. conc. 2 C. 2 Ob. 2 Viol. V. e B.* II. *a Violcl. conc. 2 C. 2 Ob. 2 Viol. 2 Viole e B.*

II. Concerti da Giuſeppe REICHA.

I. *a Violcl. conc. 2 C. 2 Ob. 2 Viol. 2 Viole e B.* II. *a Violcl. conc. 2 C. 2 Ob. 2 Viol. 2 Viole e B.*

I. Conc. da Franc. SCHLECHT. *a Violcl. conc. 2 C. 2 Fl. 2 Viol. V. e B.*

VI. Concerti da SCHLIK.

I. *a Violcl. conc. 2 C. 2 Ob. Fag. obl. 2 Viol. V. e B.* IV. *a Violcl. conc. 2 C. 2 Viol. V. e B.*

II. *a Violcl. conc. 2 Viol. V. e B.* V. *a Violcl. conc. 2 C. 2 Viol. V. e B.*

III. *a Violcl. conc. 2 C. 2 Viol. V. e B.* VI. *a Violcl. conc. Viol. conc. 2 C. 2 Viol. V. e B.*

I Conc. da TRIKLIR. *a Violcl. conc. 2 C. 2 Ob. 2 Viol. V. e B.*

I Concerto da L. BOCCHERINI. *a Violcl. obl. 2 Viol. conc. 2 C. 2 Ob. 2 Viol. rip. Viola, Contra Baſſo e B. rip. Vienna.*

FLAUTO TRAVERSO.

I. Allegro con 3 Var. da POYDE. *a Flauto ſolo.*

Aria. Ich ſchlief, da träumte mir. con 28 Var. da QUANZ. *a Fláuto con Baſſo.*

SOLI intagliati.

VI. Soli da A. I. STEINFELDT. *a Flauto con Baſſo. Op. I. Berlin.*

DUETTI.

IV. Duetti da GROSE. *a 2 Flauti.*

VI. Duetti da REINARDS. *a 2 Flauti.*

VI. Duetti da VANHALL. *a 2 Flauti.*

DUETTI *intagliati.*

VI. Duetti da G. CAMBINI. *a Flauto e Violino. Op. XVI. Offenbach.*

I. IV.

II. V.

III. VI.

VI. Duetti concertant da L. DEMACHI. *a 2 Flauti. Op. I. Lyon.*

I. IV.

II. V.

III. VI.

TRII *intagliati.*

VI. Trii da Gius. CAMBINI. *a Flauto, Violino e B. Op. III. Francfort sur le Mein.*

III. Trios dialogués da Gius. DEMACHI. *a 3 Flauti o Viol. Op. XVII. Lyon.*

VI. Trii da MEZGER. *a Flauto, Violino e B. Op. I. Mannheim.*

VI. Trii da Ios. SCHMITT. *a Flauto, Violino e B. Op. XIII. Amst.*

QUATTRI.

A FLAUTO, VIOLINO, VIOLA e BASSO.

VI. Quattri da ADAM.

VI. Quattri da Franc. HOFFMEISTER.

III. Quattri da RAIMONDI.

QUATTRI intagliati.

III. Quattri da PINTO. *a Flauto, Violino, Viola e Basso.*

VI. Quattri da C. WEISS. *a Flauto, Violino, V. e B. Op. IV. Offenbach.*

QUINTETTI.

II. Quintetti da FORSTMEYER. *a Corno obl. 2 Flauti obl. Fag. obl. e Violoncello.*

QUINTETTI intagliati.

VI. Quintetti da CAMBINI. *a Flauto, Violino, 2 Viole e B. Op. XIII. Offenbach.*

CONCERTI

A FLAUTO TRAVERSO CONCERTATO.

III. Concerti da Giuseppe FIALA.

I. *a Fl. conc. 2 C. 2 Ob. 2 Viol. V. e B.* III. *a Fl. conc. 2 C. 2 Fl. 2 Viol. V. e B.*

II. *a Fl. conc. 2 C. 2 Ob. 2 Viol. V. e B.*

I. Conc. da Giov. GLOESCH. *a Fl. conc. 2 Viol. V. e B.*

I. Conc. da GROOSE. *a Fl. conc. 2 Viol. V. e B.*

I Conc. da Franc. HOFFMEISTER. *a Fl. conc. 2 C. 2 Ob. 2 Viol. V. e B.*

I. Conc. da PICHL. *a Fl. conc. 2 Viol. V. e B.*

III. Concerti da Ant. ROSETTI.

I. *a Fl. conc. 2 C. 2 Ob. 2 Viol. 2 Viole e B.*

III. *a Fl. conc. 2 C. 2 Ob. 2 Viol. 2 Viole e B.*

II. *a Fl. conc. 2 C. 2 Ob. 2 Viol. 2 Viole e B.*

I Concerto da C. STAMITZ. *a Fl. conc. 2 C. 2 Ob. 2 Viol. 2 Viole e B.*

I Concerto da Giov. VANHALL. *a Fl. conc. 2 C. 2 Viol. V. e B.*

I Concerto da Thomas GIORDANI. *a Fl. conc. 2 Viol. e B. Paris.*

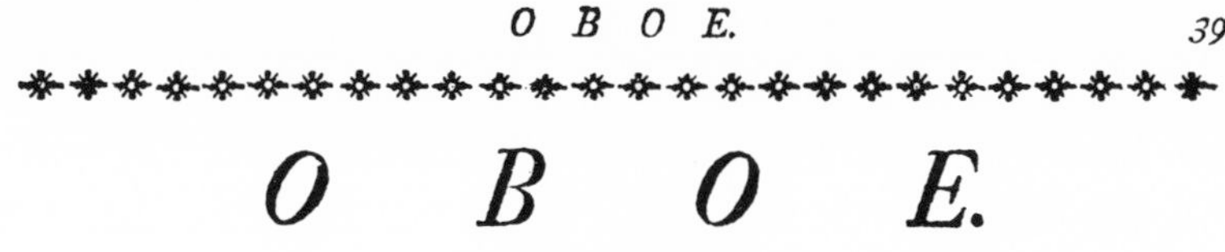

O B O E.

I Sonata da I. C. KELLNER. *a Oboe e Basso.*

I Partita da UNGELENK. *a 2 C. 2 Ob. 2 Fag.*

VI. Divertimenti da Gius. HAYDN.

I. *a 2 C. 2 Ob. 3 Fag. e Serpent.*

IV. *a 2 C. 2 Ob. 3 Fag. e Serpent.*

II. *a 2 C. 2 Ob. 2 Clarinetti. 2 Fag.*

V. *a 2 Clarini. 2 Ob. 2 Clarinetti. 2 Fag.*

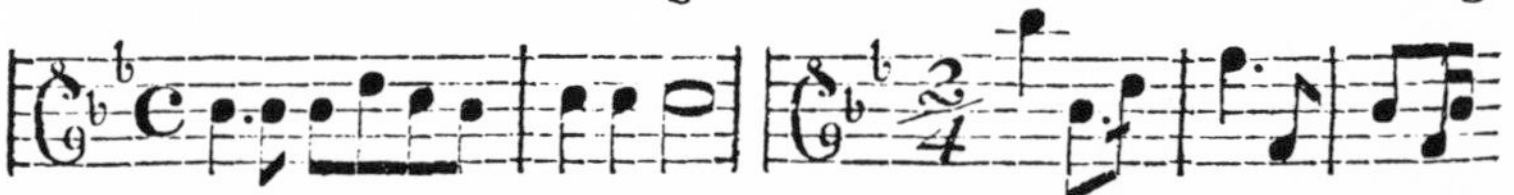

III. *2 C. o Clarini. 2 Ob. 2 Clarinet. 2 Fag.*

VI. *a 2 C. 2 Ob. 3 Fag. e Serpent.*

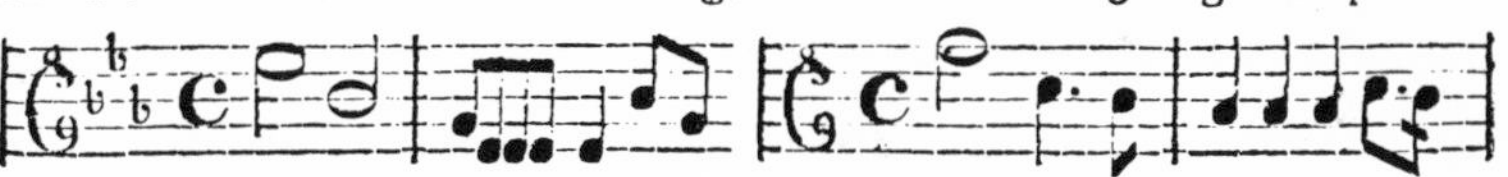

CONCERTI, a OBOE concertato.

I Conc. da le BRUN. *a Ob. conc. 2 C. 2 Viol. V. e B.*

I Conc. da DRUSCHETZKY. *a Ob. conc. 2 C. 2 Fl. 2 Viol. V. e B.*

I Conc. da GEYER. *a Ob. conc. 2 C. 2 Ob. 2 Viol. V. e B.*

I Conc. da GRAFF. *a Ob. conc. 2 C. 2 Viol. V. e B.*

III Concerti da Ant. ROSETTI.

I. *a Ob. conc. 2 C. 2 Fl. 2 Viol. 2 Viole. Violcl. e B.* III. *a Ob. conc. 2 C. 2 Fl. 2 Viol. V. Violcl. e B.*

II. *a Ob. conc. 2 C. 2 Fl. 2 Viol. 2 Viole. Violcl. e B.*

I Concerto da WOLFF. *a Ob. conc. 2 C. 2 Viol. V. e B.*

CLARINETTO.

III Quartetti da F. BLASIUS. *a Clarinetto, Violino, Viola e Violcello.*

I Quintetto da ROSETTI. *a Oboe, Flauto, Clarinetto, Taille e Fagotto.*

CONCERTI a CLARINETTO concertato.

I Conc. da EICHNER. *a Clarinet. pr. 2 C. 2 Fl. 2 Viol. V. e B.*

I Conc. da HOFFMEISTER. *a Clarinetto pr. 2 C. 2 Ob. 2 Viol. V. e B.*

I Conc. da IUST. *a Clarinetto pr. 2 Viol. V. e B.*

I Conc. da MICHL. *a Clarinetto pr. 2 C. 2 Ob. 2 Viol. V. e B.*

I Conc. da ROSETTI. *a Clarinetto pr. 2 C. 2 Ob. 2 Viol. 2 Viole e B.*

I Conc. da SCHREIER. *a Clarinetto pr. 2 C. 2 Ob. 2 Viol. V. e B.*

I Conc. da VOGEL. *a Clarinetto pr. 2 C. 2 Ob. 2 Viol. V. e B.*

I Rondeau c. V. Variaz. *a Clarinetto pr. 2 Viol. V. e B.*

CORNO.

III Duetti da PUNTO. *a Corno e Fagotto.*

XXIV. Duos e Airs da CAPARELLI. *a 2 Cors de Chaſſe. Op. VI. Lyon.*

I Trio da HOLTZBOGEN. *a Corno obl. Oboe obl. e Fagotto obl.*

I Trio da PUNTO. *a Corno obl. Viola obl. Violcello obl.*

II Trii da SPANDAU.

I. *a Cor. obl. Oboe obl. e B.* II. *a Corno obl. Violino e B.*

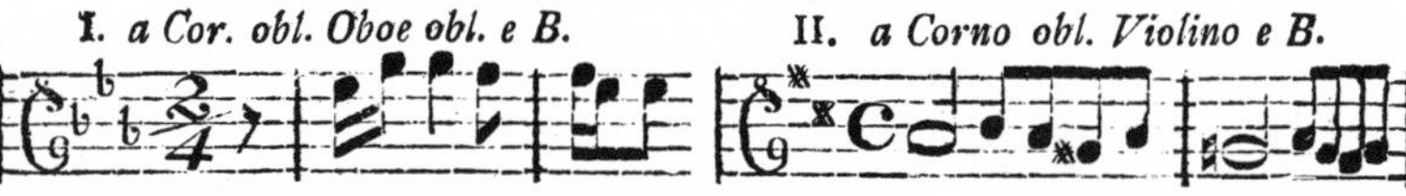

I Quattro da PUNTO. *a Corno obl. Violino. V. e B.*

I Quattro da SPANDAU. *a Corno obl. 2 Viol. e B.*

CONCERTI.

I Conc. da HEMBEL. *a Corno princ. Cor. 2do. 2 Ob. 2 Viol. V. e B.*

I Conc. da I. A. KELLNER. *a Corno princ. 2 Fl. 2 Viol. V. e B.*

II Concerti da KOERBER. *a Corno pr. 2 C. 2 Ob. 2 Viol. V. e B.*

I Concerto da KREUSSER. *a Corno pr. 2 C. 2 Fl. 2 Viol. V. e B.*

II Concerti da Gius. MICHL.

I. *a Cor. pr. Fag. pr. 2 C. 2 Ob. 2 Viol. V. e B.* II. *a Cor. pr. 2 C. 2 Ob. 2 Viol. V. e B.*

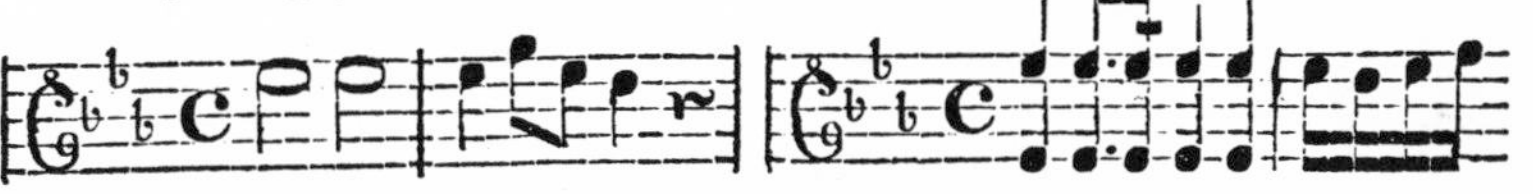

IV Concerti da PUNTO.

I. *a Cor. pr. 2 C. 2 Ob. 2 Viol. V. e B.* III. *a Cor. pr. 2 C. 2 Viol. V. e B.*

II. *a Cor. pr. 2 C. 2 Fl. 2 Viol. V. e B.* IV. *a Corno pr. 2 C. 2 Ob. 2 Viol. V. e B.*

II Concerti da ROSETTI.

I. II. *a Cor. pr. 2 C. 2 Fl. 2 Viol. V. e B.*

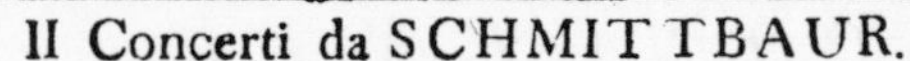

II Concerti da SCHMITTBAUR.

I. *a Cor. pr. 2 C. 2 Fl. 2 Viol. V. e B.* II. *a Cor. pr. 2 C. 2 Fl. 2 Viol. V. e B.*

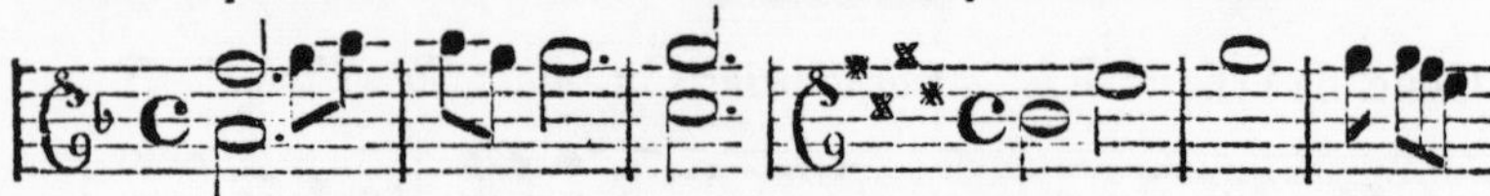

III Concerti da Carlo STAMITZ.

I. *a Cor. pr. 2 C. 2 Fl. 2 Viol. V. e B.* III. *a Cor. pr. 2 C. 2 Fl. 2 Viol. V. e B.*

II. *a Cor. pr. 2 C. 2 Fl. 2 Viol. V. e B.*

Premier Concerto da A. F. HOFFMEISTER. *a Corno pr. 2 C. 2 Ob. 2 V. V. e B. Op. IV. Lyon.*

FAGOTTO.

I Solo da Gius. SCHUSTER.

VI Quattri da RITTER. *a Fag. obl. Violino. V. e B.*

CONCERTI.

II. Concerti da BACH.

I. *a Fag. conc. 2 Ob. 2 Viol. V. e B.* II. *a Fag. conc. 2 Ob. 2 Viol. 2 Viole e B.*

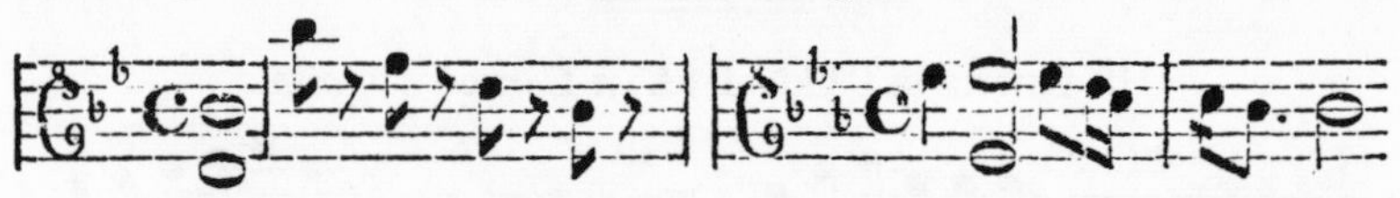

I Concerto da EICHNER. *a Fag. conc. 2 C. 2 Viol. V. e B.*

I Concerto da FERRERE. *a Fag. conc. 2 C. 2 Ob. 2 Viol. V. e B.*

I Concerto da GRENSER. *a Fag. conc. 2 C. 2 Ob. 2 Viol. V. e B.*

I. Concerto da HENNIG. *a Fag. conc. 2 C. 2 Ob. 2 Viol. V. e B.*

I Concerto da KÜFFNER. *a Fag. conc. 2 C. 2 Ob. 2 Viol. V. e B.*

I Concerto da LEEDER. *a Fag. conc. 2 Cor. 2. Viol. V. e B.*

I Concerto da MALZART. *a Fag. conc. 2 Ob. 2 Viol. 2 Viole e B.*

I Concerto da Agostino POLI. *a Fag. conc. 2 C. 2 Ob. 2 Viol. V. e B.*

I Concerto da REICHARDT. *a Fag. conc. 2 C. 2 Fl. 2 Viol. V. e B.*

III Concerti da Ant. ROSETTI.

I. *a Fag. conc. 2 C. 2 Ob. 2 Viol. V e B.* III. *a Fag. conc. 2 C. 2 Fl. 2 Viol. 2 Viole e B.*

II. *a Fag. conc. 2 C. 2 Fl. terz. 2 Viol. V. e B.*

I Concerto da SCHMITTBAUR. *a Fag. conc. 2 C. 2 Ob. 2 Viol. V. e B.*

I Concerto da SCHUSTER. *a Fag. conc. 2 C. 2 Ob. 2 Viol. V. e B.*

I Concerto da SIRET. *a Fag. conc. 2 C. 2 Fl. 2 Viol. V. e B.*

III Concerti da STAMITZ.

II. *a Fag. conc. Ob. conc. 2 C. 2 Viol. V. e B.* III. *a Fag. conc. 2 C. 2 Ob. 2 Viol. 2 Viole e B.*

II. *a Fag. conc. 2 C. 2 Ob. 2 Viol. V. e B.*

I Concerto da ULLINGER. *a Fag. conc. 2 C. 2 Ob. 2 Viol. V. e B.*

I Concerto da Giov. VANHALL. *a Fag. conc. 2 C. 2 Ob. 2 Viol. V. e B.*

I Concerto da E. G. WOLFF. *a Oboe e Fag. conc. 2 C. 2 Viol. 2 Viole e B.*

TROMMEL.

I Trommel Solo da G. W. PFINGSTEN.

I Duetto da I. M. F. PFINGSTEN. *a 1 Octav Flöte u. Trommel in D.*

II Trii da I. M. F. PFINGSTEN. *a 2 Octav Flöten e 1 Trommel in G.*

I. II.

II Quattri da I. M. F. PFINGSTEN. *a 2 Octav Flöten e 2 Trommeln in D.*

I. II.

48 CEMBALO.
CEMBALO.
SOLI.
I Sonata da C.Ph.E.BACH.
March de deux Avares con Variaz. da IUST.
VI Sonate da Fried. Christ. RUDORF.
I.
IV.
II.
V.
III.
VI.
II Sonate da RUST.
I.
II.
I Allegro da I.C.SCHUKNECHT.
III Sonate da I.C.SCHUKNECHT.
I.
III.
II.

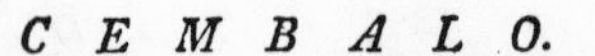
CEMBALO.

49
I Fantasia da STERCKEL.
SONATE intagliate e stampate.
Kleine Clavierstücke. 1te Sammlung.
Kleine Clavierstücke. 2te Sammlung.
I Sonata da Marianna d'AUENBRUGG, con Ode d'Ant. SALIERI. Vienna.
III Rondo e II Sonate e Fantasie da C.P.E.BACH.
Für Kenner und Liebhaber. Leipzig. 4te Samml.
I. Rondo.
I. Sonata.
II.
II.
III.
Fantasia.
III Divertissements da Ios. BENGRAF. Recueil. I. Vienna.
I.
III.
II.

Variations da Louis van BETTHOVEN, age de dix ans. *Mannheim.*

III Sonate da I. Lud. Theodor BLUM. *Leipzig.*

III Sonate da Mutius CLEMENTI. *Op. VII. Vienna.*

III Sonate da M. CLEMENTI. *Op. IX. Vienna.*

I Sonata et I Arietta c. XVIII Var. da I. N. FORKEL. *Göttingen.*

Petits Airs connus varies da C. FODOR. *Op. III. Offenbach.*

I Sonata a quatro mani da FODOR le jeune. *Op. I. Offenbach.*

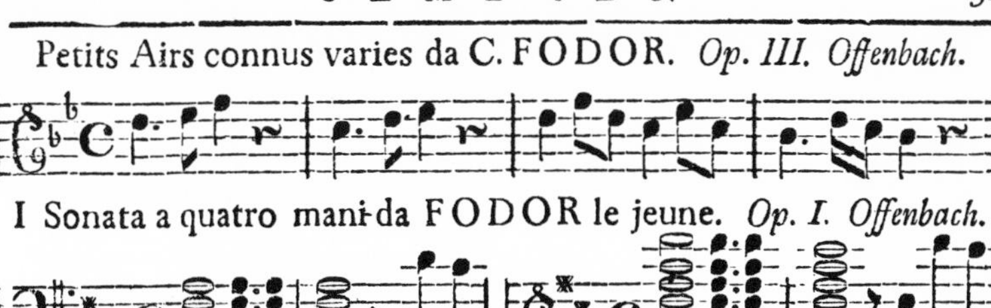

Ouverture d'Iphigenie da Chev. GLUCK. *Vienna.*

VI. Sonate da Nath. God. GRUNER. *2ter Theil. Leipzig.*

I. IV. II. V. III. VI.

VI. Sonate da G. N. IAHN. *Leipzig.*

III Sonate da Leop. KOZELUCH, dont la troisieme est à 4 mains. Op. VIII. *Vienna.*

VI. Sonate da Giov. Ant. MATIELLI. *Vienna.*

III Sonate da W. A. MOZARD. *Mannheim.*

II Sonate da Franc. RAUCH *Vienna.*

II. Sonate da Franc. Xav. RIGLER, *Op. I. Libr. I. Vienna.*

II Sonate da Fr. Xav. RIGLER. *Op. I. Libr. II. Vienna.*

VI leichte Clav. Sonaten da D. G. TÜRK. *1ter Theil. Leipzig.*

VI. leichte Clav. Sonaten da D. G. TÜRK. *2ter Theil. Leipzig.*

I Sinfonia da VANHALL. *Op. IV. Offenbach.*

Arietta con XII. Var. da Giov. VANHALL. *Op. XXXI. Vienna.*

III Sonate da Giov. VANHALL. *Op. XXX. Vienna.*

I. III. II.

III Caprifes da VANHALL. *Op. XXXI. Vienna.*

I. III. II.

II Sonate da I. G. VIERLING. *Leipzig.*

I. II.

T R I I.

A CEMBALO obligato con VIOLINO ó FLAUTO.

I Sonata da I. C. KELLNER, *a Cemb. e Flauto ou Violino.*

VI Sonate da I. W. LEEDER, *a Cembalo e Violino.*

I. IV. II. *con Flauto.* V. III. VI.

IV. Sonate da C. F. RUPPE. *a Cembalo e Violino.*

I. III. II. IV.

II Sonate da STERCKEL. *a Cembalo e Violino.*

I. II.

T R I I intagliati.

SONATES tirées des meilleurs Operas français et arrangées pour le Clavecin, con Violino. *No. III. Offenbach.*

III Sonate da I. L. ADAM, *a Cemb. e Violino. Op. III. Offenbach.*

I. III. II.

56 CEMBALO.
III Sonate da I. B. BIANCHI, a Cemb. e Violino. Offenbach.
I.
III.
II.
III Sonate da L. BOCCHERINI, a Cemb. e Violino. Op. II. Offenbach.
I.
III.
II.
VI Trii da L. BOCCHERINI, a Cemb. e Violino obl. Vienna.
I.
IV.
II.
V.
III.
VI.
III Sonate da le BRUN, a Cembalo e Violino. Op. I. Offenbach.
I.
III.
II.
CEMBALO. 57
IV. Sonate da C. FODOR, a Cemb. e Violino. Op. II. Offenbach.
I.
III.
II.
IV.
VI Sonate da KOSPOTH, a Cembalo e Violino. Op. II. Berlin.
I.
IV.
II.
V.
III.
VI.
III Sonate da KUHN, a Cemb. e Violino. Op. I. Mannheim.
I.
III.
II.
VI Sonate da W. Amad. MOZART, a Cemb. e Violino. Op. II. Vienna.
I.
IV.
II.
V.
III.
VI.

Ouverture de Farnace da I. F. STERCKEL, *a Cembalo e Violino obl. Francf. sur le Mein.*

III Sonate da F. STUBENVOLL. *a Cemb. e Violino. Op. I. Mannheim.*

III Sonate da THUBE, *a Cemb. e Violino. Op. I. Paris.*

III Sonate da I. VERAZI, *a Cemb. e Violino. Op. I. Mannheim.*

TERZETTI.

III Sonate da HEMMERLEIN, *a Cembalo Viol. e Violoncello.*

III Sonate da I. C. KELLNER, *a Cembalo, Viol. ou Ob. ou Fl. e Violoncello.*

III Sonate da I. C. KELLNER, *a Cembalo, Viol. ou Ob. ou Fl. e Violoncello.*

I Sonata da KLÖFFLER, *a Cembalo, Viol. e Basso.*

II Sonate da LANGE, *a Cembalo, Viol. e Basso.*

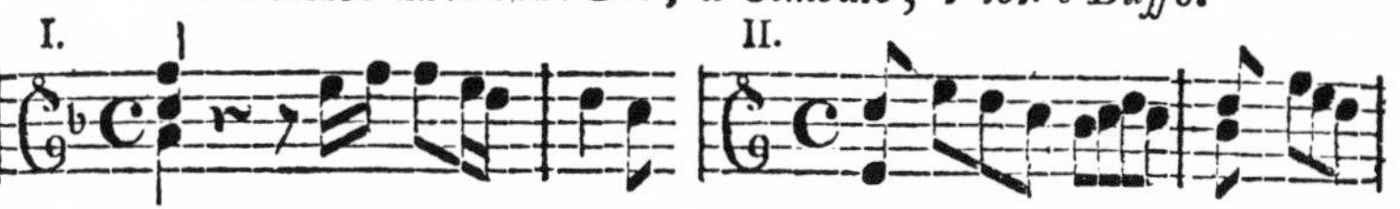

VI Sonate da NICOLAI, *a Cembalo, Viol. e Basso.*

VI. Sonate da C. F. RUPPE, *a Cembalo, Viol. e Basso.*

I Sonata da I. F. STERCKEL, *a Cembalo, Viol. e Violoncello.*

IV Sonate da G. C. TODT, *a Cembalo, Viol. e Basso.*

I Sonata da I. G. VIERLING, *a Cembalo, Viol. e Violoncello.*

TERZETTI intagliati.

Ouverture des Evenemens imprévus da BENAUT, *a Cembalo, Viol. e Violoncello. Paris.*

III Sonate da I. M. DREYER, *a Cemb. Viol. e Violoncello. obl. Op. I. Mannheim.*

III Sonate da C. KALKBRENNER, *a Cemb. Viol. e Basso. Op. II. Cassel.*

III Sonate da L. KOZELUCH, *a Cemb. Viol. e Violoncello. Op. VI. Vienna.*

IV Grandes Sonates da I. G. LANG, *a Cembalo, dont l'une est à quatre mains, avec Viol. e Violoncello. Op. VII. Offenbach.*

III Divertissements da A. ROSETTI, *a Cemb. Viol. e Violoncello obl. Op. I. Francfort sur le Mein.*

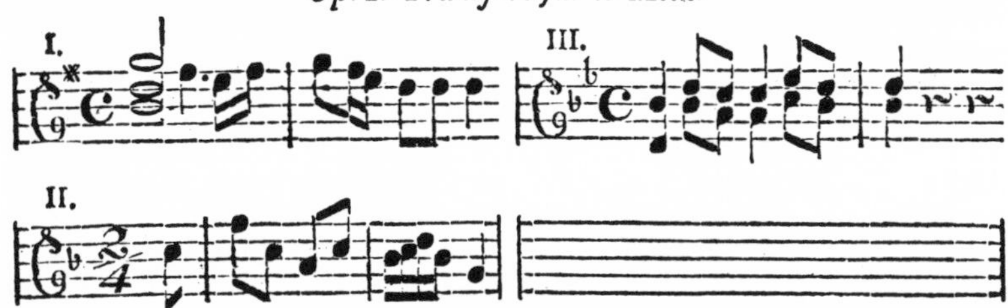

III Sonate da I. F. X. STERCKEL, *a Cemb. Viol. e B. Op. VII. Francfurt sur le Mein.*

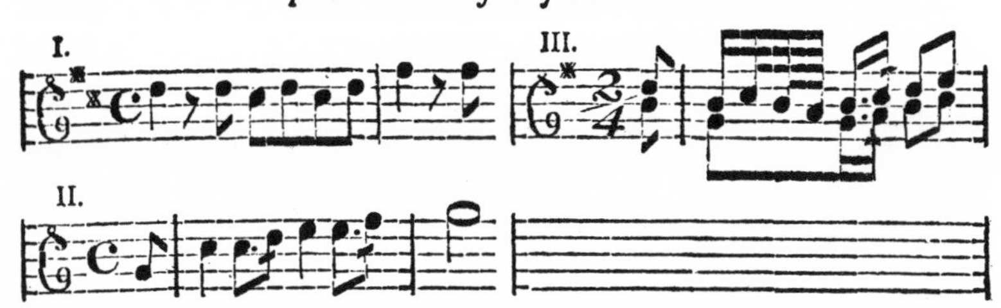

III Sonate da STERCKEL, *a Cemb. Viol. e Basso. Op. IX. Mannheim.*

III Sonate da L. TANTZ, *a Cembalo, Viol. obl. e Basso. Op. III. Mannheim.*

III Sonate da I. C. TODT, *a Cembalo, Viol. e Violoncello. Op. I. Mannheim.*

III Sonate da VANHALL, *2 con Viol. et Violcl. et la 3 con Viol. Alto et Violcl. Op. XXIX. Vienna.*

II Sonate da I. G. VIERLING, *a Cemb. Viol. e Violoncello. Op. I. Mayence.*

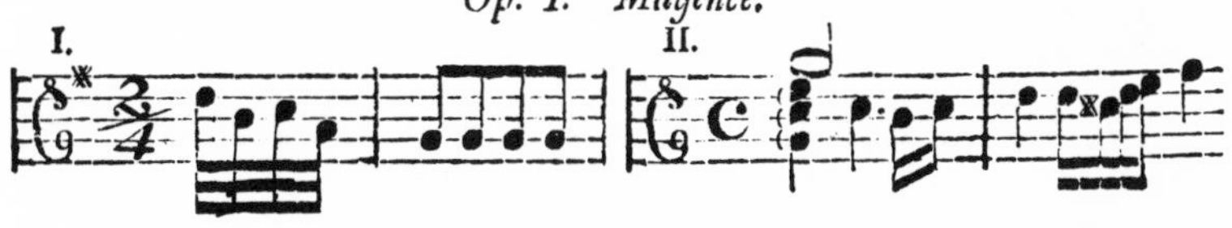

QUATTRI e DIVERTIMENTI.

I Quartetto da I. C. BACH, *a Cemb. 2 Viol. e Violoncello.*

I Quintetto da I. C. BACH, *a Cemb. Flauto, Oboe, Viol. e Violoncello.*

I Concertino da DUSCHECK, *a Cemb. Violino solo e Basso.*

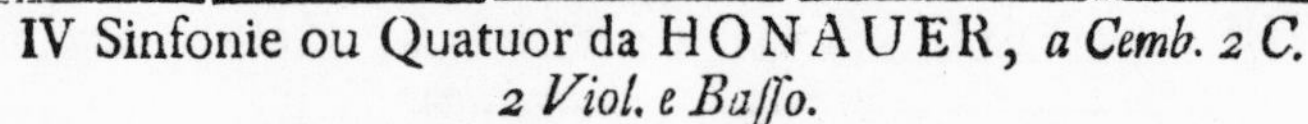

IV Sinfonie ou Quatuor da HONAUER, *a Cemb. 2 C. 2 Viol. e Baſſo.*

II. *ſenza Corni.* IV.

II Quattri da C. KELLNER, *a Cemb. Flauto ou Oboe, Viol. e Violoncello.*

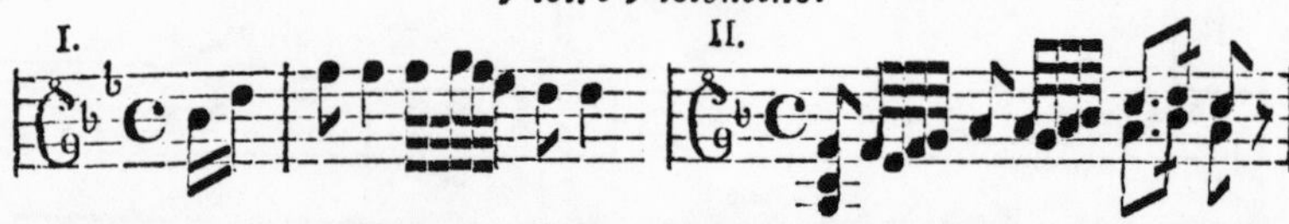

I Divertimento da Ant. ZIMMERMANN, *a Cemb. Viol. e Viola.*

SESTETTI et CONCERTINI intagliati.

I Seſtetto da I. C. BACH, *a Cemb. 2 C. Oboe, Viol. e Violoncello. Op. III. Offenbach.*

I Concertino da Fr. DUSCHECK, *a Cemb. 2 Viol. V. e B. Linz.*

III Simphonies da HEMBERGER, *a Cemb. 2 Viol. e B. Op. IX. Lyon.*

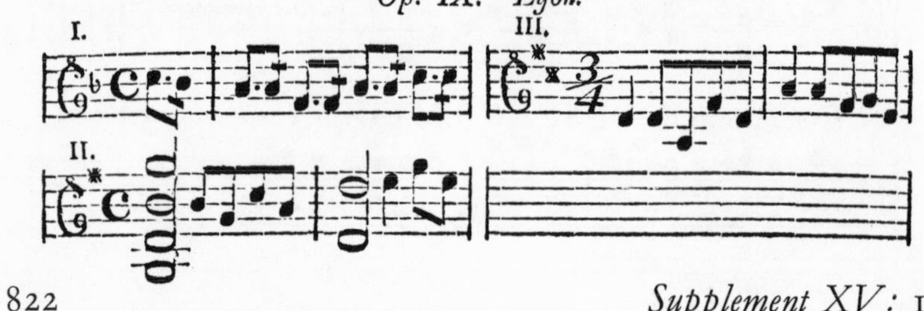

CONCERTI a Cembalo con più Stromenti.

I Concerto da M. DEMLER, *a Cemb. conc. 2 C. 2 Viol. V. e B.*

I Conc. da C. E. GIRBERT, *a Cemb. conc. 2 Clarin. Tymp. 2 C. 2 Fl. 2 Viol. V. e B.*

I Concerto da GREINER, *a Cemb. conc. 2 Viol. V. e B.*

II Concerti da Gius. HAYDN.

I. *a Cemb. conc. 2 C. 2 Ob. 2 Viol. V. e B.* II. *a Cemb. conc. 2 Viol. V. e B.*

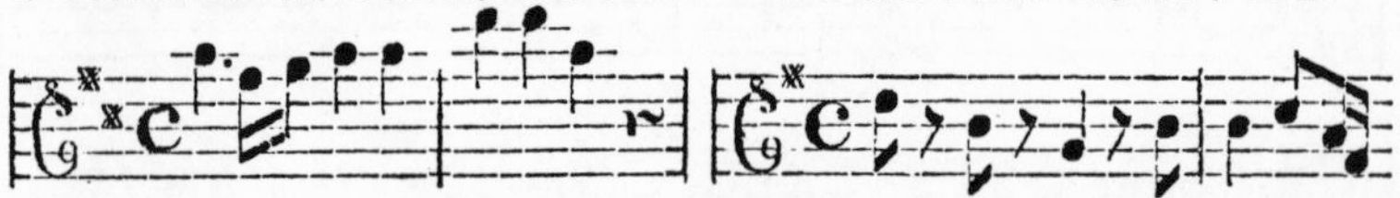

I Conc. da Leop. HOFFMANN, *a Cemb. conc. 2 Violini. V. e B.*

VI Concerti da I. C. KELLNER.

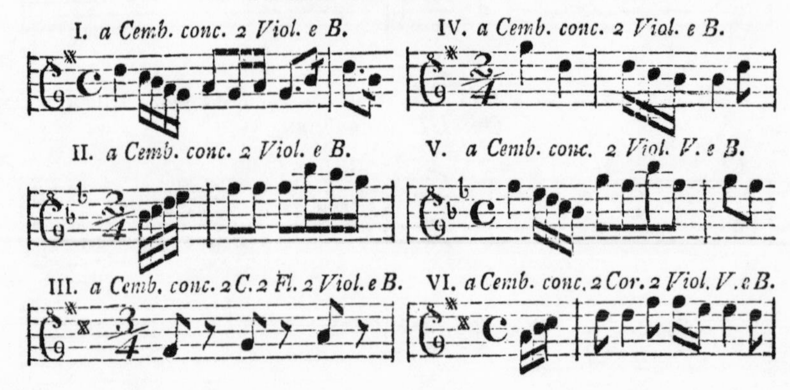

IV Concerti da LANG.

I. *a Cemb. conc. 2 C. 2 Fl. 2 Viol. V. e B.* III. *a Cemb. conc. 2 Viol. V. e B.*

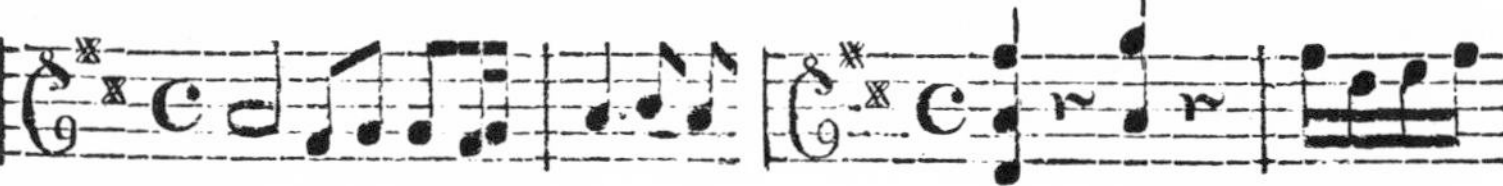

II. *a Cemb. conc. 2 C. 2 Fl. 2 Viol. V. e B.* IV. *a Cemb. conc. 2 Viol. V. e B.*

I Conc. da Ignatio UMLAUF, *a Cemb. conc. 2 C. 2 Ob. 2 Viol. 2 Viole e B.*

II Concerti da I. G. VIERLING.

I. *a Cemb. conc. 2 C. 2 Fl. 2 Viol. V. e B.* II. *a Cemb. conc. 2C. 2Ob. 2Viol. V. e B.*

I Conc. da E. W. WOLFF, *a Cemb. conc. 2 Violini Fagotto e B.*

CONCERTI *intagliati.*

II Conc. da I. A. K. COLIZZI, *a Cemb. conc. 2 Ob. ou Fl. 2 Viol. V. e B. Op. VI. A la Haye.*

I. II.

I Conc. da I. L. DUSSIK, *a Cemb. conc. 2 C. 2 Ob. 2 Viol. V. e B. Op. I. Libro II. A la Haye.*

I Conc. da EDELMANN, *a Cemb. conc. 2 C. 2 Ob. 2 Viol. e B. Op. VII. Offenbach.*

I Conc. da Fr. Ant. HOFFMEISTER, *a Cemb. conc. 2 C. 2 Ob. 2 Viol. V. e B. Vienna.*

I Conc. da Charles Louis IUNKER, *a Cemb. conc. 2 C. 2 Viol. V. e B. Winterthur.*

I Conc. da I. C. KELLNER, *a Cemb. conc. 2 C. 2 Ob. 2 Viol. V. e B. Op. XI. Francf. sur le Mein.*

I Conc. da C. G. NEEFE, *a Cemb. conc. 2 C. 2 Ob. 2 Viol. V. e B. Mannheim.*

I Conc. da Ant. ROSETTI, *a Cemb. conc. 2 C. 2 Fl. 2 Viol. V. e B. Op. III. Francf. sur le Mein.*

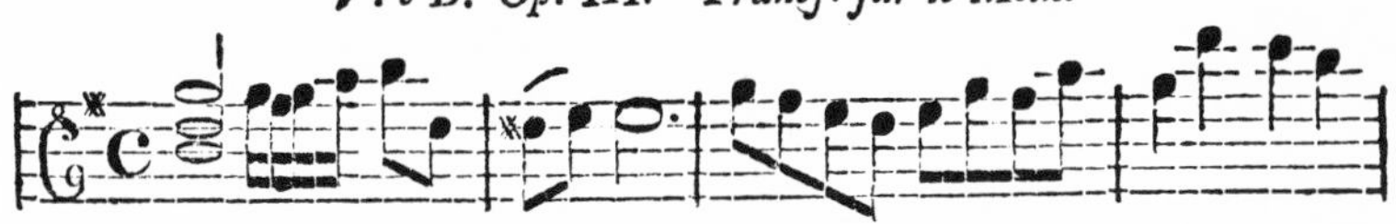

Concerto I. da F. S. SANDER, *a Cemb. conc. 2 C. 2 Ob. 2 Viol. V. e B. Livre I. Breslau.*

Concerto II. da F. S. SANDER, *a Cemb. conc. 2 C. 2 Ob. 2 Viol. V. e B. Livre II. Breslau.*

VI Conc. da W. SMETHERGELL, *a Cemb. conc. 2 Viol. et Violoncello. London.*

Concerto fecond. da E. W. WOLFF, *a Cemb. conc. 2 C. 2 Ob. 2 Viol. V. e B. Op. VIII. Lyon.*

Conc. III. da E. G. WOLFF, *a Cemb. conc. 2 Viol. V. e B. Breslau.*

Conc. IV. da E. G. WOLFF, *a Cemb. conc. 2 C. 2 Ob. 2 Viol. V. e B. Breslau.*

I Grand Concert da Ant. ZIMMERMANN, *a Cemb. conc. 2 C. 2 Ob. 2 Viol. V. e B. Op. III. Vienna.*

HARPA.

I Sonata da M. EHRENBERG, *a Harpa con 2 Cor. Violino ó Viola d'Amore obl.*

VI Sonate da E. I. G. PAESSLER, *a Harpa. Bernburg.*

III Sonate da C. A. SIBIN, *a Harpa con Flauto e Viola. Op. I. Francf. fur le Mein.*

ARIE e CANTATE
con più Stromenti.

I Duetto da ANFOSSI, *a Soprano et Tenore, 2 C. 2 Fl. 2 Viol. V. e B.*

I Coro da ANFOSSI, dell Opera: Il Curiofo indifcreto. *a Cembalo e Voci.*

I Arie da Chr. BACH, *a Soprano. Corno obl. 2 Viol. V. e B.*

La Pergola Minuè da BIANCHI, *a Soprano, 2 C. 2 Fl. 2 Viol. V. e B.*

I Aria da Gius. HAYDN, la ſcuola de Geloſi, *a Baſſo. 2 C. 2 Viol. V. e B.*

I Aria da MISLEWECECK, *a Soprano, 2 C. 2 Ob. 2 Viol. V. e B.*

I Recitat. ed Arie da Carlo MONZA, *a Soprano, 2 C. 2 Ob. 2 Viol. V. e B.*

I Rondo da PRATI, *a Soprano, 2 C. 2 Fl. 2 Viol. V. e B.*

I Aria da SCHUSTER, *a Soprano, 2 C. 2 Ob. 2 Viol. V. e B.*

I Aria alla Polacca da SCHUSTER, *a Soprano, 2 Viol. V. e B.*

I Duetto da SEYDELMANN, *a 2 Soprani, 2 C. 2 Ob. 2 Viol. V. e B.*

I Duetto da SEYDELMANN, *a 2 Soprani, 2 C. 2 Viol. V. e B.*

I Cavatina da SEYDELMANN, *a Soprano, 2 C. 2 Fl. 2 Viol. V. e B.*

I Coro da SEYDELMANN, *a Sopr. Alto, Ten. Baſſo. 2 C. 2 Fl. 2 Ob. 2 Viol. V. e B.*

III Arie da Anton SCHWEITZER.

I. *a Soprano, 2 Fl. 2 Fag. 2 Viol. 2 Viole e B.*

II. *a Soprano, 2 C. 2 Fl. 2 Viol. 2 Viole. e B.*

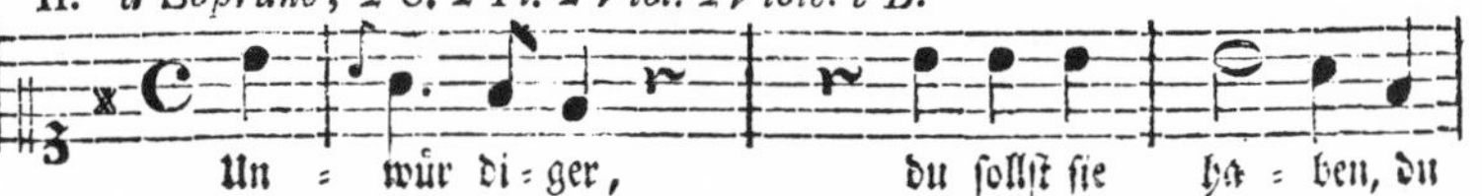

III. *a Soprano, Trompe, Corno, 2 Ob. 2 Fl. 2 Viol. 2 Viole e B.*

O P E R A.

Der Glückswechsel, oder die Mutter-Natur in ihren Kindern. Da Sign. PICCINI.

Operette. Ehrlichkeit und Liebe. Da Sign. WOLFF.

74

9. Aria. 2 *Viol. V. Basso e B.*

Ihr die durch gü-ti-

11. Aria. *2 C. 2 Fl. 2 Viol. V. Sopr. e B.*

Und die Hoffnung hebt in

10. Romanze. *2 Viol. V. Sopr. e B.*

Einst lieb-te treu und

12. Coro. *2 C. 2 Ob. 2 Fl. 2 Viol. V. 2 Soprani Tenore Basso e B.*

Steigt durch die Wol-ken fro-

Opera. **Das Rosenfest.** Da Sign. WOLFF.

ATTO I.

1 Aria. *2 C. 2 Ob. 2 Fl. 2 Viol. V. Soprano e B.*

Knap-pen setzt die

2. Aria. *2 Ob. 2 Viol. V. Sopr. e B.*

Hann-chen siehst du

3. Aria. *2 Viol. V. Soprano e B.*

Ja lie-ber Gu-stel

4. Duetto. *2 Ob. 2 Viol. V. 2 Bassi e B.*

Be-glück-tes

5. Coro. *2 C. 2 Ob. 2 Viol. V. 2 Tenore. 2 Bassi e B.*

Herr Amt-mann sie

ATTO II.

6 Aria. *2 Viol. V. Soprano e B.*

Scherzt und schäckert, laßt euch

7. Aria. *2 Viol. V. Soprano e B.*

Wir rei-sen seit dem

8. Aria. *2 Fl. 2 Viol. V. Sopr. e B.*

Singt doch, singt ihr kleinen

9. Aria. *2 Ob. 2 Viol. V. Sopr. e B.*

Die Mut-ter schmält ohn

10. Duetto. *2 C. 2 Ob. 2 Fl. 2 Viol. V. 2 Soprani e B.*

Un-ge-rath-nes bö-ses

75

ATTO III.

11. Aria. *2 Fl. 2 Viol. V. Sopr. e B.*

Kann man ei-ner

15. Aria. *2 Ob. 2 Viol. V. Sopr. e B.*

Oh-ne Schwerd-streich

12. Duetto. *2 Viol. V. 2 Soprani e B.*

Lott-chen gieb dein Herz

16. Coro. *2 C. 2 Ob. 2 Fl. 2 Viol. V. 2 Soprani Tenore Basso e B.*

Hört al-le zu ich

13. Aria. *2 C. 2 Ob. 2 Fl. 2 Viol. V. Basso e B.*

Schenkt mir Hannchen

17. Vaudeville. *2 C. 2 Ob. 2 Fl. 2 Viol. V. 2 Sopr. Tenore Basso e B.*

Ihr Mäd-chen wollt ihr

14. Duetto. *2 C. 2 Fl. 2 Viol. V. 2 Sopr. e B.*

Bli-cke mich voll Mit-

18. Romanze. *2 C. 2 Viol. V. Sopr. e B.*

Ein Rit-ter wie die

Opera. **Das Gärtner Mädchen.**

Da Sign. WOLFF.

ATTO I.

1. Aria. *2 Fl. 2 Viol. V. Soprano e B.*

Noch liegt er in

3. Duetto. *2 C. 2 Viol. V. Sopr. Basso e B.*

Schön ist mein Mädchen,

2. Aria. *2 Ob. 2 Fl. 2 Viol. V. Sopr. e B.*

Welch verdrieß-li-ches —

4. Duetto. *2 C. 2 Ob. 2 Viol. V. 2 Bassi e B.*

Mein Lie-bes-Schiff

76

5. Aria. *2 Viol. V. Soprano e B.*

Wenn ich ei = ne

12. Duetto. *2 Ob. 2 Viol. V. Sopr. Basso e B.*

Kein Glücksfall kein

ATTO III.

6 Terzetto. *2 C. 2 Fl. 2 Viol. V. 2 Soprani Basso e B.*

Wer meinen Grafen sieht der

13. Aria. *2 C. 2 Ob. 2 Fl. 2 Viol. V. Soprano e B.*

Gleich und gleich ge = sel=

ATTO II.

7. Aria. *2 Ob. 2 Viol. V. Sopr. e B.*

Das Glück hebt dich hoch

14. Duetto. *2 Viol. V. Sopr. Basso e B.*

Wie froh bin ich, daß mei=

8. Aria. *2 Fl. 2 Viol. V. Soprano e B.*

Im Ge füh = le, im Ge=

15. Canzonnetta. *2 Viol. V. Sopr. e B.*

Wer mich ein = mal hin = ter =

9. Aria. *2 Viol. V. Soprano e B.*

Wer wird sich um ein

16. Canzonnetta. *Fl. Fagotto, 2 Viol. V. Soprano e B.*

Des Le = bens Freu =

10. Canzonnetta. *2 Viol. V. Sopr. e B.*

Es ist der Lie = be

17. Duetto. *2 Viol. V. 2 Sopr. e B.*

Mit dir — ver =

11. Duetto. *2 Ob. 2 Fl. 2 Viol. V. Soprano Basso e B.*

Wenn ich die Lie = be

18. Rondello. *2 C. 2 Ob. 2 Fl. 2 Viol. V. Sopr. Alto. Ten. Basso e B.*

Der Lie = be sanft Ge

77

Opera. Die Sklavinn. Da Sign. PICCINI.

ATTO I.

1. Quartetto. *2 C. 2 Ob. 2 Viol. V. 2 Soprani. 2 Bassi e B.*

Werden sie denn nicht mehr

8. Aria. *2 Viol. V. Soprano e B.*

Von der Lie = be mit

2. Aria. *2 Viol. V. Sopr. e B.*

Mich kann nichts so

9. Aria. *2 C. 2 Ob. 2 Viol. V. Basso e B.*

Wenn ich zur Frau dich

3. Aria. *2 Viol. V. Tenore e B.*

Was man schö = ners je ge=

10. Duetto. *2 Viol. V. Sopr. Basso e B.*

Nein ge = wiß, das ist zum

ATTO III.

4. Aria. *2 C. 2 Ob. 2 Viol. V. Tenore e B.*

O wie will ich sie strei =

11. Aria. *2 Viol. V. Soprano e B.*

Blaue Au = gen schwar =

5. Aria. *2 C. 2 Ob. 2 Viol. V. Basso e B.*

Kund sey heut, sey heut

12. Aria. *2 C. 2 Viol. V. Tenore e B.*

Wel = che Pla = gen,

ATTO II.

6. Aria. *2 C. 2 Ob. 2 Viol. 2 Viole. Soprano. e B.*

Oh = ne Schutz voll

13. Duetto. *2 C. 2 Ob. 2 Viol. V. Soprano Tenore e B.*

Es ist ent = schie = den,

7. Aria. *2 Viol. V. Soprano e B.*

Man spricht doch im = mer,

14. Coro. *2 C. 2 Ob. 2 Viol. V. 2 Sopr. Tenore Basso e B.*

Kein Un = fall muß uns

Opera. Die wüste Insel.

Da Sign. SCHUSTER.

1. Aria. 2 C. 2 Fl. 2 Viol. V. Sopr. e B.

Ich ver=las=sen! ich vom

4. Aria. 2 C. 2 Fl. 2 Fag. 2 Viol. V. Tenore e B.

Bey den To=den ist mein

2. Aria. 2 Viol. V. Tenore. e B.

Hei=li = ger als tau=send

5. Aria. 2 C. 2 Ob. 2 Viol. V. Sopr. e B.

Ist dies Jammer? ist dies

3. Aria. 2 C. 2 Ob. 2 Viol. 2 Viole. Soprano e B.

Der O=den stockt, die

6. Coro. 2 C. 2 Ob. e Fl. 2 Fag. 2 Viol. V. 2 Soprani 2 Tenore e B.

Wenn in grausen Unge=

Die Muse. Da Sign. HILLER.

1. Aria. Oboe solo. 2 Viol. V. Soprano. e B.

Schau Jüng=ling schau U=

4. Duetto. 2 Ob. 2 Fag. 2 Viol V. Soprano Basso e B.

Vor dei=ner Rei=tze

2. Aria. 2 Ob. 2 Viol. V. Soprano e B.

Willst du mein gan=

5. Aria. 2 C. 2 Viol. V. Soprano e B.

Sonst gieng der Lenz mir

3. Aria. 2 Fag. 2 Viol. V. Sopr. e B.

O see = lig wem

6. Coro. 2 Trompe. Tymp. 2 Ob. 2 Viol. V. Sopr. Alto. Ten. Basso e B.

Nicht Pa = phos nur, nicht

Opera. Die Verwechselung.

Da Sign. HOLLY.

13. Aria. 2 C. 2 Fl. 2 Viol. V. Basso e B.

Frisch, frisch, frisch ihr

14. Aria, 2 Fl. 2 Fag. 2 Viol. V. Soprano e B.

Ha! nun bin ich

15. Terzetto. 2 C. 2 Fag. 2 Viol. V. 2 Soprani Tenore e B.

Al = les wird sie dort ver =

16. Aria. 2 C. 2 Fl. 2 Fag. 2 Viol. V. Soprano e B.

Ich tra = ge kein Be =

17. Finale. 2 C. 2 Ob. eine Trommel. 2 Viol. V. Alto. Ten. 2 Bassi e B.

Beym Henker, beym Teufel,

Opera. **Die Einsprüche.** Da Sign. NEEFE.

ATTO I.

1. Duetto. 2 Viol. V. Sopr. Basso e B.

Ein = spruch hin und Ein =

2. Aria, 2 Ob. 2 Viol. V. Soprano e B.

Wird die Lie = be lau =

3. Aria. 2 Viol. V. Tenore e B.

Vox haesit fau -

4. Aria. 2 Violini V. Soprano e B.

Ich will sie bey = de

5. Terzetto. 2 C. 2 Ob. 2 Viol. V. 2 Soprani Tenore e B.

Gut ge = trof = fen

6. Aria. 2 Viol. V. Soprano e B.

Herr, nehm er mich den

7. Duetto. 2 Fl. 2 Fag. 2 Viol. Sopr. Tenore e B.

Quid fe - ci quid com -

8. Aria. 2 Clarin. Tymp. 2 Ob. 2 Viol. V. Tenore e B.

Ver = brannt muß er werden,

9. Duetto. 2 C. 2 Ob. 2 Viol. V. Tenore Basso e B.

Wenn er nun nicht her =

13. Terzetto. 2 Viol. V. Sopr. Tenore Basso e B.

Zehn, zehn, Her =

14. Aria. 2 Fl. 2 Viol. V. Sopr. e B.

Wohl = an, so eil ich

15. Aria. 2 Ob. 2 Viol. V. Tenore e B.

Ich lie = be sie

ATTO II.

10. Duetto. a 2 Fl. 2 Viol. V. Soprano Basso e B.

Kei = ne See = le läßt sich

11. Aria. 2 Ob. 2 Viol. V. Sopr. e B.

Wie sie schwillt, hy, wie sie

12. Aria. 2 C. 2 Viol. V. Basso e B.

Kutsch und Pferde,

16. Coro. 2 C. 2 Ob. 2 Viol. V. Soprano, Alto, Tenore, Basso e B.

Es ge = be der Himmel

17. Divertissement. 2 C. 2 Ob. 2 Fl. 2 Viol. V. 2 Sopr. Ten. Basso e B.

Mei = ne Tochter, wie ich

Folgende Stücke sind in Partitur und in Stimmen zu haben.

Deutsche Operetten.

Achilles in Sciro.

Gestewitz, Die Liebe ist sinnreich.

Holzbauer, Günther von Schwarzburg.

Italiänische.

Sarti, Giulio Sabino.

Seydelmann, il Capricio corretto.

Italiänische Oratoria.

Ditters, l' Ester.

Deutsche Oratoria.

Rolle, Thirza und ihre Söhne.

Türck, die Hirten bey der Krippe.

Kozeluch, Joseph der Menschen Segen, eine Kantate.

SVPPLEMENTO XVI.

DEI

CATALOGHI

DELLE

SINFONIE, PARTITE, OVERTURE, SOLI, DUETTI, TRII, QUATTRI

E

CONCERTI

PER IL

VIOLINO, FLAUTO TRAVERSO, CEMBALO

ED ALTRI STROMENTI,

CHE

SI TROVANO IN MANOSCRITTO NELLA OFFICINA MUSICA DI BREITKOPF IN LIPSIA.

1785. 1786 ed 1787.

SINFONIE.

I. Sinf. da Gius. CAMBINI *a Oboe pr. Fag. pr. 2 C. 2 Fl. 2 Viol. V. e B.*

I. Sinf. da ENGEL. *a 2 Clar. Tymp. 2 Ob. 2 Viol. V. e B.*

I. Sinf. da GRAAF. *a 2 C. 2 Ob. 2 Fag. in And. Fl. Solo. 2 Viol. 2 Viole e B.*

I. Sinf. da Franc. HOFFMEISTER. *a 2 C. 2 Clarinetti. 2 Viol. V. e B.*

VI. Sinf. da KAFFKA.

I. *a 2 C. 2 Ob. 2 Fag. Flauto. Violino solo, in Adag. 2 Viol. V. e B.*

IV. *a 2 C. 2 Ob. 2 Fag. Violino solo. in Adag. 2 Viol. 2 Viole e B.*

II. *a 2 C. 2 Ob. 2 Viol. V. e B.*

V. *a 2 C. in C. 2 C. in Es. 2 Ob. 2 Fl. 2 Viol. V. e B.*

III. *a 2 C. 2 Ob. 2 Fag. 2 Viol. 2 Viole e B.*

VI. *a 2 C. 2 Ob. 2 Fag. Violino e Viola obl. in Adag. 2 Viol. V. e B.*

I. Sinf. da MAINTZER. *a 2 C. 2 Clarinetti, in And. Fag. solo. 2 Viol. V. e B.*

I. Sinf. da MILLER. *a 2 C. 2 Viol. V. e B.*

II. Sinf. da PICHL.

I. *a 2 C. 2 Ob. 2 Viol. V. e B.*

II. *a 2 Clar. Tymp. 2 Ob. 2 Viol. V. e B.*

IV. Sinfon. da Anton. ROSETTI.

I. *a 2 C. 2 Ob. 2 Viol. 2 Viole. Violclo. Fag. e B.*

III. *a 2 Clar. Tymp. 2 Clarin. 2 C. 2 Ob. 2 Fl. 2 Fag. 2 Viol. 2 Viole. Violcl. e B.*

II. *a 2 C. 2 Ob. 2 Viol. 2 Viole Violcl. Fag. e B.*

IV. *a 2 C. 2 Ob. Flauto solo 2 Viol. 2 Viole. Violcl. Fag. e B.*

I. Sinf. da Gius. SARTI. *a 2 Tromb. 2 Ob. 2 Viol. V. e B.*

I. Sinf. da SCHMIDT. *a 2 C. 2 Flauti. 2 Viol. V. e B.*

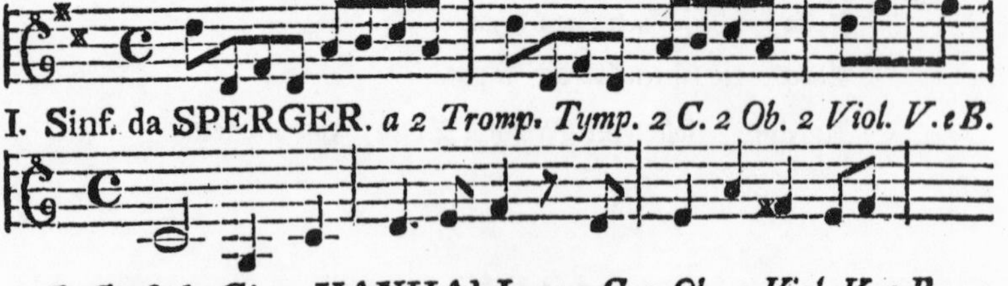

I. Sinf. da SPERGER. *a 2 Tromp. Tymp. 2 C. 2 Ob. 2 Viol. V. e B.*

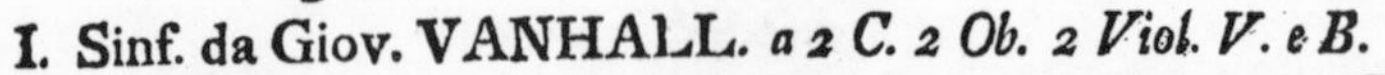

I. Sinf. da Giov. VANHALL. *a 2 C. 2 Ob. 2 Viol. V. e B.*

I. Sinf. concert. da Pietro WINTER. *a C. conc. Clarinetto conc. Fag. conc. Violino conc. 2 Viol. V. e B.*

MINUETTI.

Hannover Redout. Menuetten da PANNENBERG. *1784.*

XII. Angloiſen da MASCHECK.

XII. Menuetti da Ign. PLEYL. *Vienna.*

XII. Minuetti da Giov. VANHALL. *a 2 Viol. e Baſſo. Vienna.*

VI. Allemandes da Ioſ. HAYDEN. *Vienna.*

VI. Allemandes da VANHALL. *aplusieurs Inſtrumens. Vienna.*

XII. Deutſche Tänze, da VANHALL. *a 2 Viol. e Baſſo. Vienna.*

XII. Ländleriſch deutſche Tänze für zwo *Violini. Vienna.*

XII. Ländleriſch deutſche Tänze für eine *Violine. Vienna.*

SINFONIE *intagliate e ſtampate.*

III. Sinfonies da Carl DITTERS de DITTERSDORF, ex primant trois Metamorphoſes d'Ovide. Part. I. *Vienna.*

I. *a 2 Clar. Tymp. 2 C. 2 Ob. 2 Fag. Flauto 2 Viol. V. e B.* III. *a 2 C. 2 Ob. Flauto. Violonc. 2 V. V. e B.*

II. *a 2 Clar. Tymp. 2 C. 2 Ob. 2 Fag. Flauto. 2 V. V. B.*

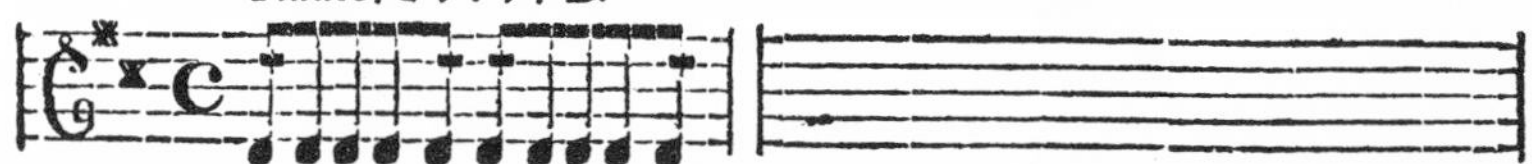

III. Sinf. da Michele HAYDEN. *Vienna.*

I. *a 2 C. 2 Ob. 2 Fag. 2 Viol. V. e Violoncello.* III. *a 2 Cl. Tymp. 2 C. 2 Ob. 2 Fag. 2 Viol. V. Violcello. e B.*

II. *a 2 Clarini 2 C. 2 Ob. 2 Fag. 2 Viol. V. Violoncello e B.*

III. Sinf. da L. KOZELUCH. *a 2 C. 2 Ob. 2 Viol. V. Fag. Baſſo. e Violcello. Vol. I. Vienna.*

III. Sinf. da L. KOZELUCH. *a 2 C. 2 Ob. 2 Viol. V. Fag. Baſſo. e. Violcello. Vol. II. Vienna.*

III. Sinf. da Ant. ROSETTI. *a 2 C. 2 Ob. 2 Viol. 2 Viole Violcello Fagotto e Violono Op. V. Vienna.*

SINFONIES PERIODIQVES.

I. Grande Sinfonie da Iof. HAYDN. *a 2 C. 2 Ob. 2 Fag. Flauto. 2 V. V. e B. Op. 38. Vienna.*

II. Grande Sinf. da I. HAYDN. *a 2 C. 2 Ob. 2 Fag. Flauto. 2 V. V. e B. Op. 39. Vienna.*

III. Grande Sinfonie da I. HAYDN. *a 2 C. 2 Ob. 2 Fag. Flauto. 2 V. V. e B. Op. 40. Vienna.*

I. Grande Sinfonie periodique da W. A. MOZART. *a 2 Clar. Tymp. 2 C. 2 Ob. 2 Fag. 2 Viol. V. e B. Op. 8. Vienna.*

II. Grande Sinf. period. da W. A. MOZART. *a 2 C. 2 Ob. 2 Fag. 2 V. V. Violcello obl. e Violono. Op. 9. Vienna.*

I. Sinf. periodique da I. PLEYL. *a 2 C. 2 Ob. 2 Viol. V. e B. Op. III. N. I. Mannheim.*

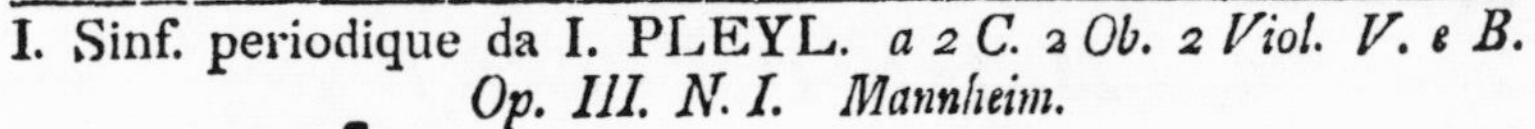

II. Sinf. periodique da I. PLEYL. *a 2 C. 2 Ob. 2 Viol. V. e B. Op. III. N. II. Mannheim.*

DIVERTIMENTI, CONCERTINI etc.

I. Notturno da MASHECK. *a 2 C. 2 Clarinetti. 2 Fag. 2 Viole.*

VIOLINO.

SOLI con BASSO.

I. Sonata da L. SIRMEN. *a Violino e Baſſo. Vienna.*

DUETTI intagliati.

VI. Duetti da G. CAMBINI. *a Violino e Viola. Op. 18. Offenbach ſur le main.*

TRII intagliati.

A DUE VIOLINI CON BASSO.

VI. Trii da L. BOCCHERINI. *Op. XXXV. Vienna.*

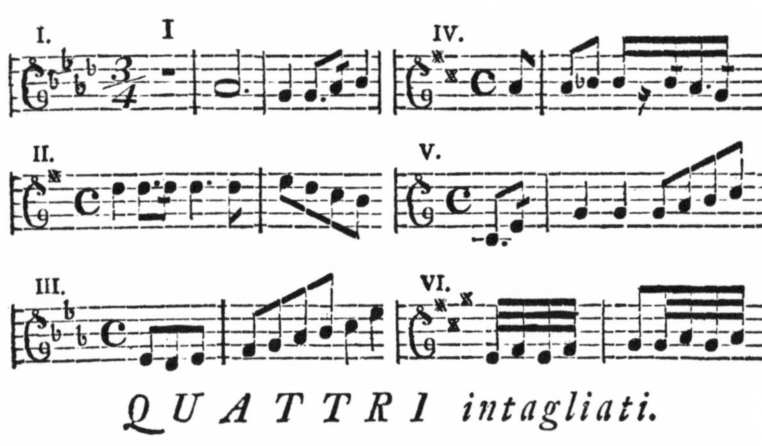

QUATTRI intagliati.

III. Quattri da Iofeph FIALA. *a 2 Viol. V. e B. Op. 3. Vienna.*

III. Quattri da Iofeph FIALA. *a 2 Viol. V. e B. Op. 4. Vienna.*

VI. Quattri da W. A. MOZART. *a 2 Viol. V. e B. Op. X. Vienna.*

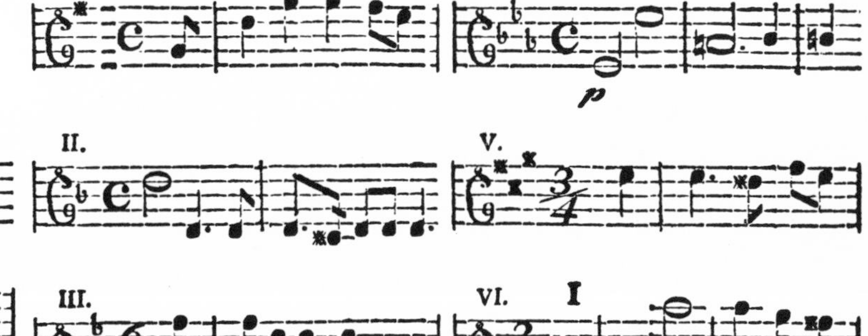

VI. Quattri da Silvere MÜLLER. *a 2 Viol. V. e B. Vienna.*

III. Quattri da Franc. NEUBAUR. *a 2 Viol. V. e B. Spire.*

10
VIOLINO.
VI. Quattri da Ignaz. PLEYL. a 2 Viol. V. e B. Op. I. Vienna.
VI. Quattri da Ign. PLEYL. a 2 Viol. V. e B. Op. 2. Vienna.
VI. Quattri da Ign. PLEYL. a 2 Viol. V. e B. Op. 3. Vienna.

VIOLINO.
11
VI. Quattri da Ign. PLEYL. a 2 Viol. V. e B. Op. 6. Vienna.
III. Quattri da Ign. PLEYL. a 2 Viol. V. e B. Op. 7. Vienna.
III. Quattri da Ign. PLEYL. a 2 Viol. V. e B. Op. 8. Vienna.
III. Quattri da Ign. PLEYL. a 2 Viol. V. e B. Op. 9. Vienna.

III. Quattri da Ign. PLEYL. *a 2 Viol. V. e B. Op. 10. Vienna.*

III. Quattri da Ign. PLEYL. *a 2 Viol. V. e B. Op. 11. Vienna.*

III. Quattri da A. ROSETTI. *a 2 Viol. V. e B. Op. IV. Offenbach.*

QUINTETTI intagliati.

III. Quintetti da L. BOCCHERINI. *a 2 V. V. 2 Violoncelli. Op. 36. Vienna.*

VI. Quintetti da F. PITICCHIO. *a 2 Viol. 2 Viole e Violoncello. Offenbach sur le main.*

III. Quintetti da H. L. VETTER. *a 2 Viol. 2 Flauti e B. Spire.*

CONCERTI per il Violino concertato.

II. Concerti da BENDA.

I. *a Viol. pr. 2 C. 2 Ob. 2 Fl. 2 Viol. Violcl. e B.*

II. *a Viol. pr. 2 C. 2 Ob. 2 Viol. V. Violcl. e B.*

I. Concerto da Franc. HOFFMEISTER. *a Viol. pr. 2 C. 2 Ob. 2 Viol. V. e B.*

II. CONCERTI da HUTTI.

I. *a Viol. pr. 2 C. 2 Ob. 2 Viol. Viole e B.* II. *a Viol. pr. 2 C. 2 Ob. 2 Viol. 2 Viole e B.*

I. Conc. da Ign. PLEYL. *a Viol. princ. 2 Tromboni, 2 Clar. Tymp. 2 C. 2 Ob. 2 Viol. V. e B.*

I. Conc. da Ant. ROSETTI. *a Viol. pr. 2 C. 2 Ob. in And. 2 Fag. 2 Viol. V. e B.*

CONCERTI *intagliati.*

I. Conc. da Pierre LEM. *a 2 Viol. pr. 2 C. 2 Ob. 2 Fl. 2 Viol. V. Violcello e B. Vienna.*

VIOLA.

CONCERTI a VIOLA.

I. Conc. da Romanus HOFFSTETTER. *a Viola pr. 2 C. 2 Fl. 2 Viol. V. e B.*

I. Conc. da Rom. HOFFSTETTER. *a Viola pr. Violcello obl. 2 C. 2 Fl. 2 Viol. e B.*

I. Conc. da PREUS. *a Viola pr. 2 C. 2 Ob. 2 Viol. V. e B.*

I. Conc. da PREUS. *a Viola pr. 2 C. 2 Ob. 2 Viol. V. e B.*

I. Conc. da G. F. ZELTER. *a Viola pr. 2 C. 2 Viol. V. e B.*

VIOLONCELLO.

CONCERTI *per il Violoncello concertato.*

I. Conc. da EICNER. *a Violc. conc. 2 C. 2 Fl. 2 Viol. 2 Viole e B.*

II. Conc. da IANSON. *a Violc conc. 2 C. 2 Ob. 2 Viol. V. e B.*

I. Conc da KREUSER. *a Violcl. conc. 2 C. 2 Fl. 2 Viol. 2 Viole e B.*

II. Concerti da Giuseppe REICHA.

I. *a Violc. conc. 2 C. 2 Fl. 2 Viol. V. e B.* II. *a Violcl. conc. 2 C. 2 Ob. 2 Viol. 2 Viole e B.*

I. Conc. da SHLICK. *a Violcl. conc. 2 C. 2 Ob. 2 Viol. V. e B.*

I. Conc. da Giov. VANHALL. *a Violcl. conc. 2 Clar. Tymp. 2 Ob. 2 Viol. V. e B.*

I. Conc. da ZAPPA. *a Viocl. conc. 2 C. 2 Ob. 2 Viol. V. e B.*

I. Conc. *a Violcl. conc. 2 C. 2 Ob. 2 Viol. V. e B.*

FLAUTO TRAVERSO.

DUETTI.

VI. Duetti da I. C. VOGEL. *a 2 Flauti.*

TRII.

VI. Trii da G. F. KLEINKNECHT. *a Flauto Violino e B.*

III. Trii da Giuſ. Aloyſ. SCHMITTBAUR. *a 2 Flauti e B. Spire.*

I. Sextetto da A. ROSETTI. *a Violino. Flauto. 2 Corni. V. e B. Op. I. Spire.*

QUATTRI intagliati.

III. Quattri da SCHMITTBAUR. *Op. III. Vienna.*

I. *a Flauto Viol. V. e B.* III. *a Flauto. 2 Violini e B.*

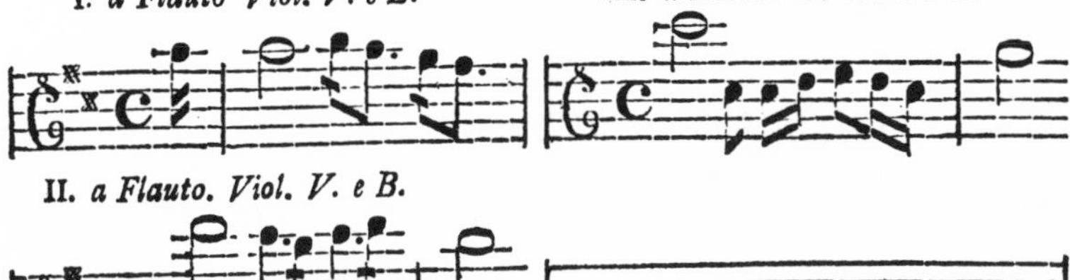

II. *a Flauto. Viol. V. e B.*

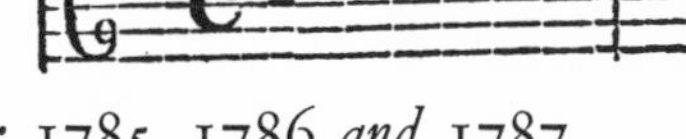

CONCERTI
A FLAUTO TRAVERSO CONCERTATO.

I. Conc. da Franc. HOFFMEISTER. *a Fl. con. 2 C. 2 Ob. 2 Viol. 2 Viole e B.*

I. Conc. da Giuſ. MICHL. *a Fl. conc. 2 C. 2 Ob. 2 Viol. V. e B.*

I. Conc. da Ant. SALIERI. *a Flauto conc. Oboe conc. 2 C. 2 Ob. 2 Viol. 2 Viole Fag. e B.*

I. Conc. da STAMITZ. *a 2 Flauti conc. 2 C. 2 Ob. 2 Viol. 2 Viole e B.*

II. Concerti da VOGEL.

I. *a Flauto conc. 2 C. 2 Ob. 2 Viol. V. e B.*

II. *a Flauto conc.. 2 C. 2 Ob. 2 Viol. V. e B.*

OBOE.

CONCERTI, a OBOE concertato.

I. Conc. da DRUSCHETZKY. *a Oboe conc. 2 C. 2 Fl. 2 Viol. V. e B.*

I. Conc. da Franc. HOFFMEISTER. *a Oboe conc. 2 C. 2 Fl. 2 Viol. V. e B.*

CLARINETTO.

XII. Quattri da MAINZER. *a Clarinetto. Violino. V. e B.*

VI. Partite da STEPHANI. *a 2 Clarinetti. 2 Cor. 2 Oboi 2 Fagotti.*

Adagio da STÖTZER. *a Clarinetto princ. 2 Viol. V. e B.*

CONCERTI a CLARINETTO concertato.

I. Conc. da AHNERT. *a Clarinetto pr. Fag. pr. 2 C. 2 Ob. 2 Viol. V. e B.*

II. Concerti da BÄR.

I. *a Clarinetto pr. 2 C. 2 Ob. 2 Viol. V. e B.* II. *a Clarinetto pr. 2 C. 2 Ob. 2 Viol. V. e B.*

I. Conc. da HOFFMEISTER. *a Clarinetto pr. 2 C. Flauto. Oboe. in And. Fagotto ſolo. 2 V. V. e B.*

I. Conc. da ROSETTI. *a Clarinetto pr. 2 C. 2 Fl. 2 Viol. 2 Viole e B.*

I. Conc. da STOETZER. *a Clarinetto pr. 2 C. 2 Ob. 2 Viol. 2 Viole e B.*

FAGOTTO.

VI. Quattri da MICHL. *a Fagotto obl. 2 Viol. e Baſſo.*

CONCERTI.

II. Concerti da Giuſ. MICHL.

I. *a Fag. conc. 2 C. 2 Viol. V. e B.* II. *a Fag. conc. 2 C. 2 Ob. 2 Viol. V. e B.*

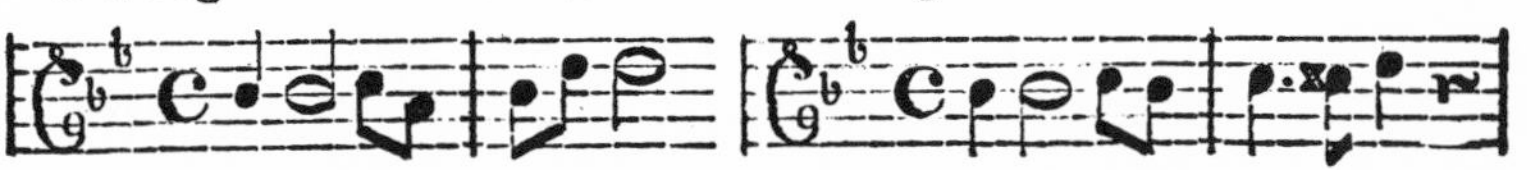

I. Concerto da RITTER. *a Fag. conc. 2 C. 2 Viol. V. e B.*

I. Concerto da ROSETTI. *a Fag. conc. 2 C. 2 Ob. 2 Viol. V. e B.*

CONCERTI intagliati.

Concerto I. da M. OZI. *a Fag. pr. 2 C. 2 Ob. 2 Viol. V. e B.* *Op. 3. Paris.*

Concerto II. da M. OZI. *a Fag. pr. 2 C. 2 Ob. 2 Viol. V. e B.* *Op. 4. Paris.*

Concerto III. da M. OZI. *a Fag. pr. 2 C. 2 Ob. 2 Viol. V. e B.* *Op. 6. Paris.*

Concerto I. da C. STUMPF. *a Fag pr. 2 C. 2 Fl. 2 Viol. V. e B. Paris.*

Concerto II. da C. STUMPF. *a Fag. pr. 2 C. 2 Viol. V. e B. Paris.*

CEMBALO.

SOLI.

Das Kosackenlager oder der verunglückte Stutzer. Ballo da Vincenz MASCHECK. *a Cembalo.*

Der Spatziergang in die Alee, ein komisch pantomimisches Ballet. da MASCHECK.

SONATE intagliate e stampate.

Arietta con Variaz. da Frederic FLEISCMANN. *Vienna.*

II. Sonate. II. Rondo. II. Fantasie da C. P. E. BACH. *Für Kenner und Liebhaber. Leipzig. 5te Samml.*

II. Rondo. II. Sonate. II. Fantasie. da C. P. E. BACH.
Für Kenner und Liebhaber. Leipzig. 6te Sammlung.

Rondo. *Rondo.*

Sonata. *Sonata.*

Fantasia. *Fantasia.*

XII. Minuetti da F. HAYDEN. *Vienna.*

I. Sonata da HAYDEN. *Op. 42. Offenbach.*

II. Sonate da F. A. HOFFMEISTER. *Mannheim.*

I. II.

Differentes petites Pieces da I. HAYDEN. *Op. 46. Vienna.*

Fantasia da KAUER. *Vienna.*

III. Sonate da Leop. KOZELUCH. *Op. XIII. Vienna.*

I. III. II.

I. Sonata da Leop. KOZELUCH a quattro mani.
Op. X. Vienna.

parte sinistra. *parte dextra.*

III. Sonate da KOZELUCH.
Part. I. Vienna.

I. II. III.

III. Sonate da KOZELUCH.
Part. II. Vienna.

I. II. III.

III. Sonate da Leop. KOZELUCH. *Part. III. Vienna.*

I. III. II.

Air de Malborouck avec 20. Variaz. da Ioseph LAQUETTA.
Mannheim.

Overtura dell' Opera una Cosa rara da V. MARTIN. *Vienna.*

Overtura dell' Opera l'en levement du Serail da W. A. MOZART. *Vienna.*

Fantasie et Sonate da W. A. MOZART. *Op. XI. Vienna.*

III. Sonate da W. A. MOZART. *Op. VI. Vienna.*

III. Sonate da W. A. MOZART. *la troisieme c. Viol. obl. Op. VII. Vienna.*

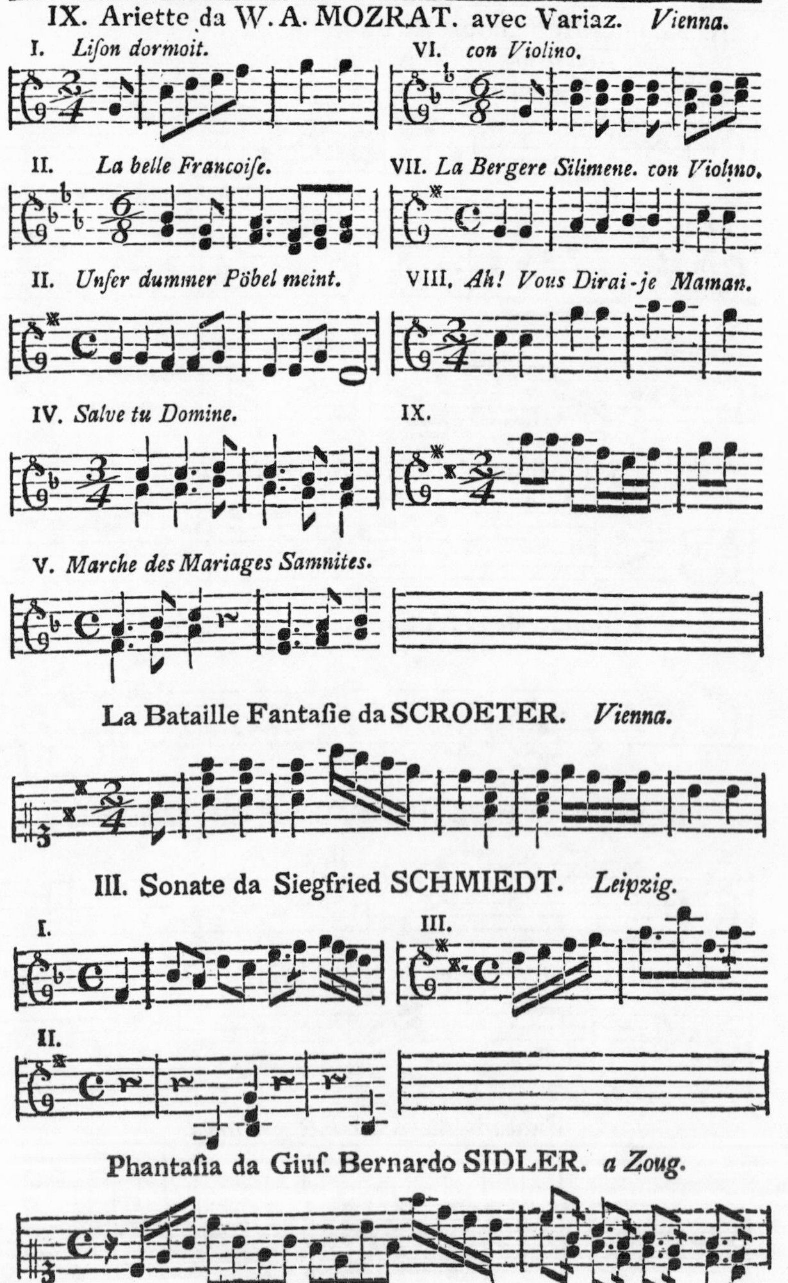

Phantaſia da Mr. le Capitain SIDLER. *a Zoug.*

Phantaſia da Mr. le Capitain SIDLER. *a Zoug.*

Air favori varie pour le Clavecin et un Rondeau da I. VANHALL. *Op. 33. Vienna*

XII. Minuetti da I. VANHALL. *Vienna.*

XII. Deutſche Tänze, da I. VANHALL. *Vienna.*

TRII.

A CEMBALO obligato con VIOLINO intagliati.

III. Sonate da Franc. HASCHCKE. *a Cemb. e Violino. Vienna.*

III. Sonate da I. HAYDN. *a Cembalo la premiere et la troiſieme ſont avec de Violon. Op. 41. Offenbach.*

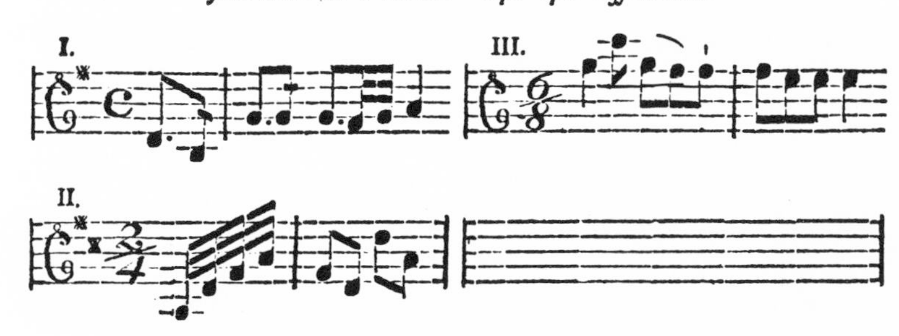

Divertimento da Niccola PICCINI. *a Cemb. con Violino. Venezia.*

Sonata caratteriſtica da Giuſ. SARDI. *a Cemb. c. Violino obl. Op. I. Vienna.*

Variazioni del Minuetto Lara-del Opera la Grotta di Trifonio. da SARDI. *a Cemb. c. Violino obl. Vienna.*

Sonata da Niccola ZINGARELLI. *a Cemb. con Violino. Venezia.*

TERZETTI.

II. Sonate da MASCHECK. *a Cembalo, Viol. e Violoncello.*

TERZETTI intagliati.

III. Sonate da Leop. KOZELUCH. *a Cembalo, Viol. e Violoncello. Part. IV. Vienna.*

III. Sonate da Leop. KOZELUCH. *a Cembalo Viol. e Violoncello. Part. V. Vienna..*

VI. Sonate da I. F. STERCKEL. *a Cembalo, Viol. et Basso obl. Op. XVII. Vienna.*

QUATTRI e DIVERTIMENTI.

I. Quartetto da MASCHEK. *a Cemb. 2 Viol. e Basso.*

Variaziones da MASCHEK. *a Cemb. 2 Viol. e Basso.*

QUATTRII intagliati.

III. Quattri da PLEYL. *a Cemb. Violino, Viola e Violoncello. Offenbach.*

CONCERTI a Cembalo con più Stromenti.

I. Conc. da Franc. DUSCHECK. *a Cemb. conc. 2 C. 2 Fl. 2 Viol. V. Violoncello e B.*

I. Conc. da Leop. KOZELUCH. *a Cemb. conc. a 4 main. 2 C. 2 Ob. 2 Viol. V. e B.*

I. Conc. da SCHUSTER. *a Cemb. conc. 2 C. 2 Ob. 2 Fl. in And. 2 Viol. V. e B.*

CONCERTI *intagliati.*

II. Concerti da KOZELUCH. *a Cemb. conc. 2 C. 2 Ob. 2 Viol. V. e B. Vol. I. Vienna.*

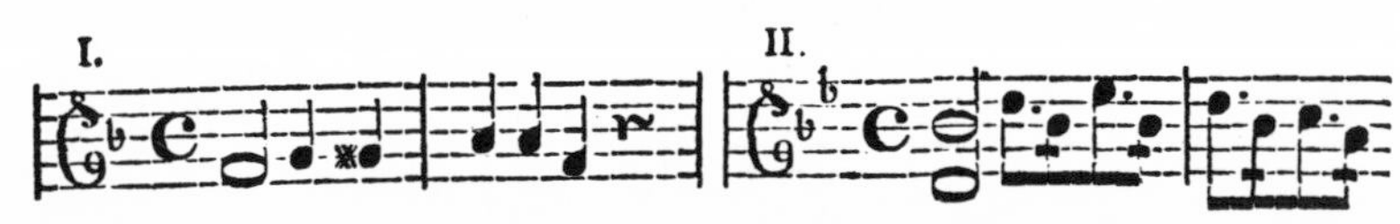

II. Conc. da L. KOZELUCH. *a Cemb. conc. 2 C. 2 Ob. 2 Viol. V. e B. Vol. I Vienna.*

II. Concerto da Leop. KOZELUCH. *a Cemb. conc. 2 C. 2 Ob. 2 Viol. V. e B. No. V. Vienna.*

I. Grand Concert da W. A. MOZART. *a Cemb. 2 C. 2 Ob. 2 V. V. e B. Oeuvre IV. Livre I. Vienna.*

II. Grand Conc. da W. A. MOZART. *a Cemb. 2 C. 2 Ob. 2 Viol. V. e B. Oeuvre IV. Livre II. Vienna.*

III. Grand Conc. da W. A. MOZART. *a Cemb. 2 C. 2 Ob. 2 Viol. V. e B. Oeuvre IV. Livre III. Vienna.*

I. Concerto da E. G. WOLF. *a Cemb. conc. 2 C. 2 Ob. 2 Viol. V. e B. Lipsia.*

ARIE e CANTATE con più Stromenti.

I. Cantate da I. HAYDN. *a Soprano. 2 C. 2 Ob. Flauto, Fagotto. 2 V. V. e B. Vienna.*

Ah come il co-re mi pal-pi-ta nel se-no.

I. Aria da Giov. Amadeo NAUMANN. *a Soprano. 2 C. 2 Flauti ed Oboi 2 Violini V. e B.*

Deutsche Arien *und* Duette *von verschiedenen Componisten, herausgegeben von* Ioh. Adam HILLER. *1ster Theil.*

I. Aria da GASMANN. *a Soprano. 2 Ob. 2 Viol. V. e B.*

II. Aria da HASSE. *a Soprano. 2 Viol. V. e B.*

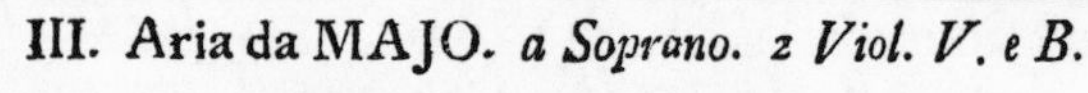

III. Aria da MAJO. *a Soprano. 2 Viol. V. e B.*

IV. Aria da SARTI. *a Soprano. 2 C. 2 Ob. 2 Violini. 2 Viole e B.*

V. Aria da HILLER. *a Soprano. 2 C. 2 Fl. 2 Viol. 2 Viole e B.*

VI. Aria da I. C. BACH. *a Soprano. 2 Viol. V. e B.*

VII. Aria da PRATI. *a Soprano 2 Viol. V. e B.*

VIII. Duetto. da ANFOSSI. *a 2 Soprani. 2 Viol. 2 Viole e B.*

O P E R A.

Der Abend im Walde. Da Sign. WOLFF.

ATTO I.

1. Terzetto. *2 Ob. 2 Viol. V. 2 Tenore. Basso e B.*

7. Aria. *2 C. 2 Ob. 2 Fl. Fag. 2 Viol. V. Soprano e B.*

2. Aria. *2 C. 2 Ob. 2 Viol. V. Basso e B.*

8. Aria. *2 Fl. 2 Viol. V. Soprano e B.*

3. Duetto. *2 C. 2 Ob. 2 Fl. 2 Viol. 2 Viole Soprano Tenore e B.*

9. Quartetto. *2 C. 2 Ob. 2 Fag. 2 Viol. V. Soprano 2 Ten. Basse e B.*

ATTO II.

4. Duetto. *2 C. 2 Ob. 2 Fl. 2 Fag. 2 Viol. V. Soprano Tenore e B.*

10. Aria. *2 C. 2 Ob. 2 Fl. 2 Viol. V. Basso e B.*

5. Aria. *2 Ob. 2 Viol. V. Soprano e B.*

11. Aria. *2 C. 2 Ob. 2 Fl. 2 Viol. V. Soprano e B.*

6. Aria. *2 Viol. V. Soprano e B.*

12. Aria. *2 C. 2 Ob. 2 Fl. Fag. 2 Viol. V. Tenore e B.*

36
13. Aria. 2 C. 2 Ob. 2 Viol. V. Tenore e B.
Von Sproße zu Sproße
16. Aria. 2 C. 2 Ob. 2 Viol. V. Tenore e B.
Daß dich die Gicht, daß
14. Aria. 2 Ob. 2 Fl. 2 Fag. 2 Viol. V. Basso e B.
Wie lieb, wie werth
17. Rundgesang. 2 Ob. 2 Fl. 2 Fag. 2 Viol. V. 2 Soprani. 2 Tenore Basso e B.
Sanft, wie im Schat=
15. Aria. 2 Ob. 2 Viol. V. Soprano e B.
Laß den Win=ter Eiß und
Opera. Die treuen Köhler. Dal Sign. WOLFF.
ATTO I.
1. Aria. 2 C. 2 Fl. 2 Fag. 2 Viol. V. Basso e B.
Du klei=nes Hauß
4. Aria. 2 C. 2 Ob. 2 Fl. 2 Viol. V. Basso e B.
Ein Wort an dich
2. Terzetto. 2 Viol. V. 2 Soprani Basso e B.
Ihr gu=ten Sachsen denkt
5. Aria. 2 C. 2 Ob. 2 Fag. 2 Viol. V. Basso e B.
Wenn die bunten Fah=nen
3. Aria. 2 C. 2 Fl. 2 Viol. V. Basso e B.
Die Für=sten sind die
6. Aria. 2 C. 2 Ob. 2 Fl. 2 Viol. V. Basso e B.
Mäd=chen laßt euch

37
7. Aria. 2 Viol. V. Soprano e B.
Es la=gen einst in
12. Aria. 2 Viol. V. Soprano e B.
Der gu= — te
8. Aria. 2 Viol. V. Soprano e B.
In die schö=ne Stadt nach
13. Aria. 2 Viol. V. Soprano e B.
An Treu, an Muth
9. Terzetto. 2 C. 2 Ob. 2 Viol. V. Tenore. 2 Bassi e B.
Das wäre zum Henken.
14. Aria. 2 C. 2 Ob. 2 Fl. 2 Viol. V. Soprano e B.
Schön ist der Pur=pur,
ATTO II.
10. Aria. 2 Fl. 2 Viol. V. Soprano e B.
Wer nicht be=ständig liebt,
15. Rundgesang. 2 C. 2 Ob. 2 Fl. 2 Viol. V. 2 Tenore Basso e B.
So wie zur frü=hen Mor=
11. Duetto. 2 C. 2 Ob. 2 Fl. 2 Viol. V. Soprano. Tenore e B.
Nimm hin der

Opera. Arsene. Da Sign. SEYDELMANN.

ATTO I. — *ATTO II.*

1. Aria. 2 *Fl.* 2 *Viol. V. Tenore e B.*

7. Aria. 2 *C.* 2 *Ob.* 2 *Fag.* 2 *Viol. V. Tenore e B.*

2. Aria. 2 *C.* 2 *Ob.* 2 *Viol. V. Basso e B.*

8. Aria. 2 *C.* 2 *Ob.* 2 *Viol. V. Soprano e B.*

ATTO III.

3. Aria. 2 *C.* 2 *Ob.* 2 *Fl.* 2 *Fag.* 2 *Viol. V. Soprano e B.*

9. Coro. 2 *C.* 2 *Ob.* 2 *Fl.* 2 *Viol. V.* 2 *Sopr.* 2 *Alto. e B.*

4. Aria. 2 *C.* 2 *Ob.* 2 *Viol. V. Soprano e B.*

10. Aria. 2 *C.* 2 *Ob.* 2 *Viol. V. Soprano e B.*

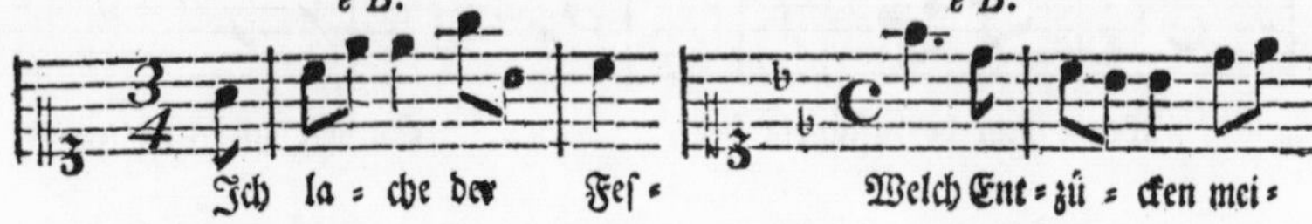

5. Coro. 2 *C.* 2 *Ob.* 2 *Fag.* 2 *Viol. V. Sopr. Alto. Ten. Basso e B.*

11. Rondo. 2 *C.* 2 *Fl.* 2 *Viol. V. Soprano e B.*

6. Duetto. 2 *C.* 2 *Ob.* 2 *Fl.* 2 *Viol. V. Soprano Tenore e B.*

12. Terzetto. 2 *C.* 2 *Ob.* 2 *Fl.* 2 *Viol. V.* 2 *Soprani. Tenore e B.*

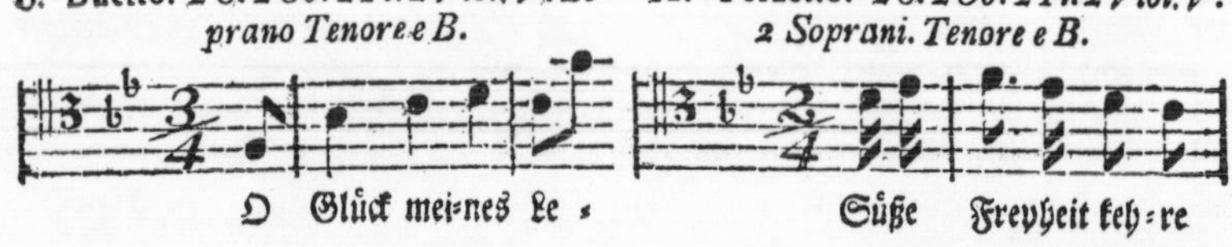

ATTO IV.

13. Aria. 2 *Ob.* 2 *Viol. V. Soprano e B.*

15. Aria. 2 *C.* 2 *Ob.* 2 *Viol. V. Tenore e B.*

14. Cavatina. 2 *C.* 2 *Ob.* 2 *Viol. V. Tenore e B.*

16. Coro. 2 *C.* 2 *Ob.* 2 *Viol. V. Soprano. Alto. Tenore e B.*

Opera. Der lahme Husar. Da Sign. SEYDELMANN.

ATTO I.

1. Duetto. 2 *Fl.* 2 *Viol. V.* 2 *Soprani e B.*

5. Duetto. 2 *C.* 2 *Fl.* 2 *Viol. V. Soprano. Tenore e B.*

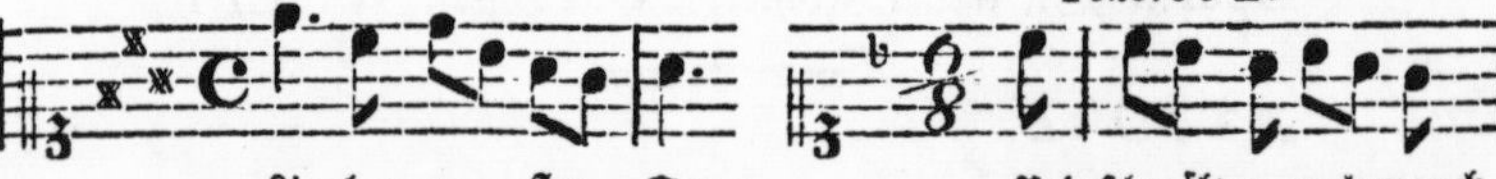

2. Cavatina. 2 *Ob.* 2 *Viol. V. Tenore e B.*

6. Terzetto. 2 *C.* 2 *Ob.* 2 *Viol. V. Soprano Tenore. Basso e B.*

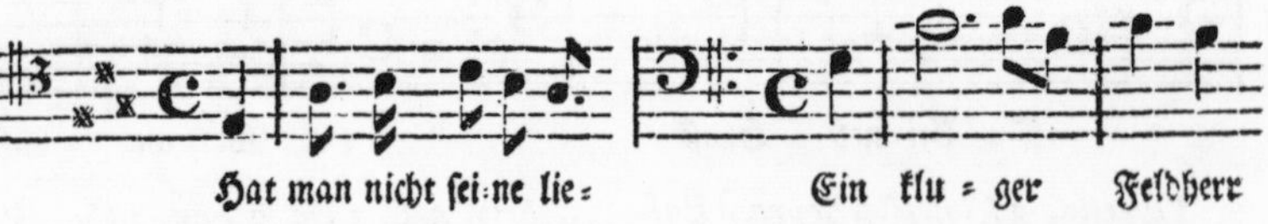

ATTO II.

3. Romanze. 2 *Fl.* 2 *Viol. V. Tenore e B.*

7. Aria. 2 *C.* 2 *Ob.* 2 *Viol. V. Soprano e B.*

4. Quartetto. 2 *C.* 2 *Ob.* 2 *Viol. V. Soprano.* 2 *Tenore e B.*

8. Aria. 2 *C.* 2 *Ob.* 2 *Viol. V. Tenore e B.*

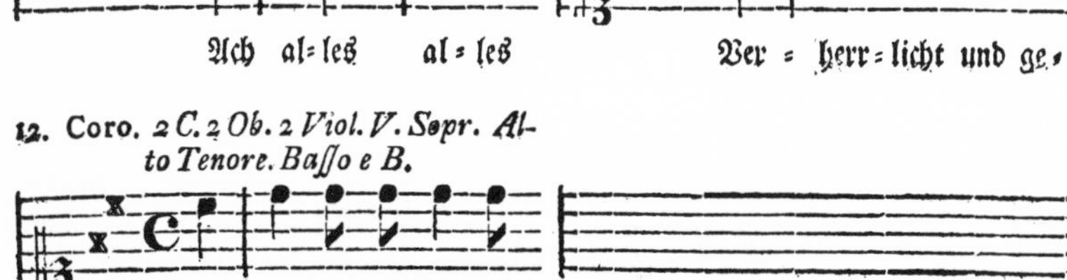

Opera. Das Herbstabentheur. Da Sign. AGOSTI.

ATTO I.

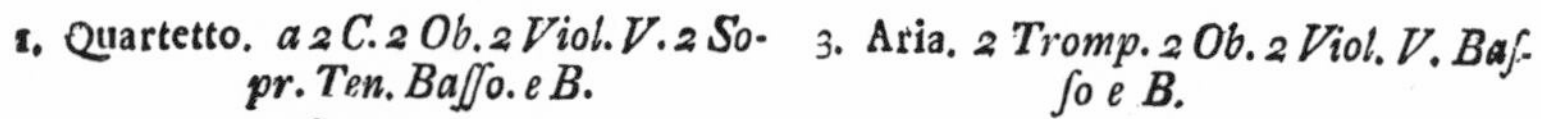

42
5. Aria. 2 C. 2 Fl. 2 Fag. 2 Viol. 2 Viole. Basso e B.
Da steh ich und er=
10. Terzetto. 2 Viol. V. Soprano. Tenore. Basso e B.
Was hilft denn das Quä=len
. Aria. 2 C. 2 Fl. 2 Fag. 2 Viol. V. Soprano e B.
Wams und Mie=der, Hut
11. Septuor. 2 Fl. 2 Viol. V. 3 Sopr. 2 Ten. 2 Bassi e B.
Könnt ihr bey ih=rer
7. Aria. 2 C. 2 Fl. 2 Fag. 2 Viol. V. Soprano e B.
Ge=hor=chen muß
12. Aria. 2 C. 2 Fl. 2 Fag. 2 Viol. V. Basso e B.
Frisch Va=len.
8. Aria. 2 Viol. V. Basso e B.
Man grüßt mich, küße
13. Quartetto. 2 C. 2 Fl. 2 Fag. 2 Viol. V. 2 Sopr. Ten. Basso e B.
Das Schicksal hat
9. Aria. Viol. conc. 2 Viol. V. Tenore e B.
O macht mich doch
43
Opera. Romeo und Julie. Da Sign. BENDA.
ATTO I.
1. Aria. 2 C. 2 Fl. 2 Fag. 2 Viol. V. Soprano e B.
Du die von brau=
8. Duetto. 2 Fl. 2 Viol. V. 2 Soprani e B.
Hat noch ein Paar
2. Aria. 2 Fl. 2 Viol. V. Soprani e B.
Ehr=lich=keit und
9. Aria. 2 C. 2 Fag. 2 Viol. V. Soprano e B.
Wo bist du Ro=
ATTO III.
3. Aria. Oboe. Fagotto. 2 Viol. V. Tenore e B.
Hoff und Lie=be
10. Quartetto. 2 Fl. 2 Fag. 2 Viol. V. 2 Soprani. Tenore. Basso e B.
Im Gra=be wohnt Ver=
4. Terzetto. 2 C. 2 Fl. 2 Fag. Viol. conc. 2 Viol. 2 Viole. Violcl. 2 Sopr. Tenore e B.
Ja, der Ler=che frü=
11. Aria. 2 Fl. 2 Viol. V. Tenore e B.
Ihr trenn=tet uns
ATTO II.
5. Aria. 2 C. 2 Fl. 2 Fag. Violino Solo 2 Viol. V. Soprano e B.
Laßt ihr Nach=ti=
12. Duetto. 2 C. 2 Fl. 2 Fag. 2 Viol. V. Soprano. Tenore e B.
Be=ste du le=best
6. Aria. 2 Fl. 2 Fag. 2 Viol. V. Soprano e B.
Fo=dre dei=ner Toch=
13. Coro. 2 C. 2 Fl. 2 Fag. 2 Clar. Tymp. 2 Viol. V. 2 Soprani. 2 Tenore Basso e B.
Auf un=ter Reu=e
7. Aria. 2 Viol. V. Tenore e B.
Ich dein Va ter? Nein,

Opera. Das Milmädchen. Da Sign. GRETRY.
1. Aria. 2 Fl. 2 Fag. 2 Viol. V. Tenore e B.
Ich bin er = fro = ren,
2. Aria. 2 C. 2 Ob. 2 Viol. 2 Viole Basso e B.
Weil ich noch im = mer
3. Duetto. 2 C. 2 Ob. 2 Fag. 2 Viol. V. Tenore Basso e B.
Wohl an Ni = klas,
4. Aria. 2 Viol. V. Basso e B.
Wenn der Stahl den Stein
5. Aria. 2 C. 2 Fl. 2 Viol. V. Fag. obl. Soprano e B.
Hier ist das klei = ne das klei =
6. Aria. Flauto. Oboe. 2 Viol. Basso e Fagotto.
Einstmal wollt mir ein
7. Duetto. 2 Fl. 2 Fag. 2 Viol. V. Soprano. Basso e B.
Find ich nur die Zeit.
8. Aria. 2 Viol. V. Soprano e B.
Dies ist mein Wunsch und
9. Aria. 2 C. 2 Fl. 2 Fag. 2 Viol. V. Basso e B.
Mädchen von so jun = gen
10. Aria. 2 C. 2 Fl. 2 Fag. 2 Viol. V. Soprano e B.
O weh! mein gan = zes
11. Terzetto. 2 C. 2 Ob. 2 Viol. V. Soprano. Tenore Basso e B.
Ich fal = le, ich fal =
12. Aria. Flauto Solo. 2 Viol. Soprano e B.
Du ver = sprichst mir Glück
13. Vaudeville. 2 C. 2 Ob. 2 Viol. V. Soprano. Tenore Basso e B.
Ich lag in lau ter Angst
Opera. Clariße. Da Sign. UBER.
ATTO I.
1. Duetto. 2 C. 2 Viol. V. 2 Tenore. e B.
Nar = ren den = ken wie
2. Aria. 2 C. 2 Viol. V. Tenore e B.
Der Landmann hat viel
3. Aria. 2 Fl. 2 Viol. V. Tenore e B.
Das Feu = er dei = ner
4. Duetto. 2 Fl. 2 Viol. V. 2 Soprani e B.
Wieder = sprich dem Her =
5. Duetto. 2 C. 2 Fl. 2 Viol. V. Soprano Tenore e B.
Was füh len zwey ver =
7. Aria. 2 C. 2 Viol. V. Soprano e B.
Kommt Schäfer kommt her =
8. Aria. 2 Fl. 2 Viol. V. Soprano e B.
Ihr Mädchen wüßt
9. Coro. 2 C. 2 Fl. 2 Viol. V. 2 Soprani 2 Tenore Basso e B.
Laß Mädchen laß dich doch
10. Aria. 2 Ob. 2 Viol. V. Tenore e B.
Hoch = muth Hoch = muth Hoch =
11. Coro. 2 C. 2 Ob. 2 Viol. V. 3 Soprani 2 Tenore. Basso e B.
Es ist ihr Sohn es
ATTO II.
6. Duetto. 2 Ob. 2 Viol. V. Soprano Tenore e B.
Da woll ten wir noch
ATTO III.
12. Aria. 2 Fl. 2 Viol. V. Tenore e B.
Es ist um mich ge =

44
13. Aria. 2 C. 2 Viol. V. Tenore e B.
Kaum läßt sich so ein
16. Duetto. 2 C. 2 Fl. 2 Viol. V. Soprano Tenore e B.
So flieht um uns
14. Aria. 2 Fag. 2 Viol. V. Soprano e B.
Hier ruht seit sechs ver=
17. Duetto. 2 Ob. 2 Viol. V. Soprano. Tenore e B.
Ende gut al = les gut
15. Duetto. 2 Fl. 2 Viol. V. Soprano. Tenore e B.
Ihr Blick in Thrä = nen
18. Coro. 2 C. 2 Ob. 2 Fl. 2 Viol. V. 2 Soprani. Tenore Basso e B.
Es geh euch al = len
Saul. Oder: Die Gewalt der Musik. Dal Sign. ROLLE.
1. Coro. 2 C. 2 Ob. 2 Viol. V. Soprano. Alto. Tenore Basso e B.
Ei = le Gott ihm
4. Aria. 2 Fl. 2 Viol. V. Tenore e B.
Die Heer=den schmü=
2. Aria. 2 Ob. 2 Viol. V. Tenore e B.
Ihr Stür=me schweigt
5. Coro. 2 Fl. 2 Viol. V. Soprano. Alto. Tenore. Basso e B.
Frie = den prei = set
3. Coro. 2 Clar. Tymp. 2 Ob. 2 Viol. V. Sopr. Alto. Ten. Basso e B.
Den, der euch ge = macht,
6. Duetto. 2 Ob. 2 Viol. V. Soprano. Tenore e B.
Wein' o Er = de ban=
45
7. Coro. 2 Clar. Tymp. 2 Ob. 2 Viol. V. Sopr. Alto. Ten. Basso e B.
Ge = hor=sam ist der O=ce=
12. Aria. 2 Ob. 2 Viol. V. Tenore e B.
Herr des Gnad uns
8. Coro. 2 Ob. 2 Viol. V. Soprano. Alto Tenore Basso e B.
Du hörst des tro=tzen=den
13. Coro. 2 Ob. 2 Viol. V. Soprano. Alto. Tenore Basso e B.
All = gü = ti = ger voll
9. Aria. 2 Fag. 2 Viol. V. Tenore e B.
Flie = ßet mil = der
14. Coro. 2 Fl. 2 Viol. V. Soprano Alto Tenore Basso e B.
Dank dem gü=
10. Coro. 2 Ob. 2 Viol. V. Soprano Alto Tenore Basso e B.
Barm=her=zig und von
15. Coro. 2 C. 2 Fl. 2 Viol. V. Sopr. Alto. Ten. Basso. e B.
Sanf = tes Lied, laß
11. Aria. 2 Fag. 2 Viol. V. Basso e B.
Au = gen wer = det

Folgende Stücke sind in Partitur und in Stimmen zu haben.

Italiänische Operetten.

Antonio Salieri. La Grotta di Trofonio.

Deutsche Oratoria.

Benedictus Kraus. Die Schöpfung, eine Kantate.

Rosetti Oratorium. Der sterbende Jesus.

Rolle Oratorium. Die am Creutz über Sünde, Tod, Teufel und Hölle triumphirende Liebe unsers Bräutigams und Erlösers Jesu Christi, aus Mattheo am 26 und 27. Capitel.

INDEX OF FIRST LINES

NOTE ON THE INDEX OF FIRST LINES

This index gives text underlays of vocal incipits in alphabetical order. The incipits appear principally in the sections of the Catalogue entitled *Arie* or *Cantate*. Each entry contains all words given by Breitkopf. When the final word in an underlay is incomplete, this is indicated in the index by the use of three dots: e.g., "Addio, addio per sem . . . 183."

Words in brackets represent attempts to clarify the immediately preceding word (in the case of "Io," the immediately following word) by indicating its more conventional spelling. This index is concerned with first lines only; for *titles* of operas, cantatas, arias, etc., see the General Index which follows. Both indexes are discussed further in the Introduction to this volume.

The page numbers given are those running consecutively through the entire volume.

INDEX OF FIRST LINES

A

B

C

D

G

H

I

J

K

L

M

N

O

P

Q

R

S

T

U

V

W

Z

GENERAL INDEX

NOTE ON THE GENERAL INDEX

Composers' last names are given in SMALL CAPITALS, with a full capital initial letter. First names and initials are given in ordinary (roman) type. All variant spellings of last and first names and initials appearing in the catalogue are included; the currently accepted best form of the name comes first.

Titles of works are given in *italics*.

Genres, such as Sonata, Duet, etc. are given in ordinary type both as separate entries and as subheadings within composer listings.

Material supplied by the editor, e.g., modern spellings, missing first names, etc. is enclosed in brackets. Where a first name is currently unknown or uncertain, such brackets enclose a space left blank for the eventual insertion of the name.

In cases where last-name entries appear both with and without first names, and in instances where similar names may or may not refer to the same individual, the indexing procedure is as follows: (a) If only one composer of that name is known to have existed, all works are indexed together; (b) if two or more composers of the same name are known to have existed, a separate entry is given for each major variant.

Further discussion of this index may be found in the Introduction to this volume.

The page numbers given are those running consecutively through the entire volume.

GENERAL INDEX

A

B

D

E

F

G

H

I

J

K

L

M

N

Q

R

S

T

U

V

W

X

Y

Z